Learning Resources Center
Carroll
1601 W
Westmi

WITHDRAWN

D0138690

INTRODUCTION TO
ANIMAL SCIENCE

WILSON G. POND
Cornell University

KEVIN R. POND
Texas Tech University

JOHN WILEY & SONS, INC.

New York ∎ Chichester ∎ Weinheim ∎ Brisbane ∎ Singapore ∎ Toronto

ACQUISITIONS EDITOR	Ellen Schatz
MARKETING MANAGER	Bonnie Cabot
FULL SERVICES MANAGER	Jeanine Furino
INTERIOR DESIGN	Lee Goldstein
COVER DESIGN	Sue Noli
SENIOR ILLUSTRATION EDITOR	Edward Starr
PHOTO EDITOR	Jilly Hilycord
PRODUCTION MANAGEMENT SERVICES	Suzanne Ingrao

This book was set in Adobe Garamond by Nesbitt Graphics and printed and bound by R.R. Donnelley & Sons. The cover was printed by Lehigh Press.

This book is printed on acid-free paper. ∞

Copyright © 2000 John Wiley & Sons, Inc. All rights reserved.

No part of this publication may be reproduced, stored in a retrieval system or transmitted in any form or by any means, electronic, mechanical, photocopying, recording, scanning or otherwise, except as permitted under Sections 107 or 108 of the 1976 United States Copyright Act, without either the prior written permission of the Publisher, or authorization through payment of the appropriate per-copy fee to the Copyright Clearance Center, 222 Rosewood Drive, Danvers, MA 01923, (978) 750-8400, fax (978) 750-4470. Requests to the Publisher for permission should be addressed to the Permissions Department, John Wiley & Sons, Inc., 605 Third Avenue, New York, NY 10158-0012, (212) 850-6011, fax (212) 850-6008, E-Mail: PERMREQ@WILEY.COM. To order books please call 1(800)-225-5945.

Library of Congress Cataloging in Publication Data:
Pond, Wilson G., 1930–
    Introduction to animal science / Wilson G. Pond, Kevin R. Pond.

        p.   cm.
    ISBN 0-471-17094-1 (cloth : alk. paper)
    1. Livestock.   2. Animal industry.   I. Pond, K. R.   II. Title.

    SF61.P65   1999
    636—dc21   99-29011
                                                                              CIP

Printed in the United States of America

10 9 8 7 6 5 4 3 2 1

PREFACE

This book is intended for use in introductory animal science courses for students interested in animal agriculture and biology. The subject is presented at a level appropriate for first or second year college students majoring in animal science or related areas of agriculture or biology and for those who have not yet selected a specific area of specialization at the undergraduate level. A strong background in high school chemistry and biology is desirable.

The first section (Chapter 1–3), "Animals in Society," addresses human population, food supply, interrelationships between crop and animal production, and the role of animal agriculture in the United States and worldwide in meeting human needs.

The second section (Chapters 4–8), "Biological Principles of Animal Production," addresses animal reproduction, lactation, genetics, growth, and nutrition and feeding within the context of life-cycle production for economic and biologic efficiency. The purpose of this section is to provide a solid foundation for the study of animal production practices and the animal industries.

The third section (Chapters 9–11), "Stewardship," describes the current knowledge and principles associated with animal husbandry and well-being (Chapters 9 and 10 authored by S. E. Curtis), and emerging issues related to the role of animals in environmental stability and sustainable agriculture in a world with a growing population and finite resources. Important issues include animal well-being, food safety, air and water quality, water availability, environmental stability, land use, soil fertility, waste management, and biotechnology. The importance of stewardship of natural resources associated with animal production so as to ensure an adequate food supply and abundant life for future generations is emphasized. We are indebted to D. E. Ullrey and D. G. Sisler for their contributions to indentifying and characterizing emerging issues.

In the fourth section (Chapters 12–21), "Animal Industries," individual chapters are devoted to the description and analysis of the various animal industries. The section includes animals used in the production of meat, fish and marine species, milk, poultry and eggs, animal fiber and other products, the production and uses of other animals; and the roles of companion animals, notably horses, dogs, and cats. The art and science of raising specific species and classes of animals and producing and marketing the meat, milk, eggs, and other products of each are addressed. We are indebted to the following authors whose expertise and knowledge of their respective topics are well recognized:

S. P. Jackson, L. E. Chase, A. D. Herring, R. Ernst, D. Topliff, R. T. Lovell, D. Laflamme, S. S. Hannah, D. E. Ullrey and J. Bernard.

The fifth section (Chapters 22–26), "Animal Products," contains chapters on the products of animal agriculture, including meat and milk products, milk and milk products, poultry and poultry products, aquaculture products, and wool, mohair, and other animal fibers. We are indebted to the following authors whose expertise and knowledge of their respective topics are well recognized: M. F. Miller, C. B. Ramsey, R. Bradley, A. Sams, R. T. Lovell, and D. E. Hogue.

The final chapter (Chapter 27), "Animals and Society in the 21st Century," addresses the future of animal agriculture, trends and prospects in technology, and opportunities for careers in animal agriculture.

We thank Dr. David Buchanan for his valuable contributions to Genetics (Chapter 6); Dr. Michael Thonney and Dr. Douglas Hogue for their valuable contributions to Sheep and Goats (Chapter 18); Dr. Alan Bell and the faculty and staff of the Department of Animal Science, Cornell University, for space and resources provided to one of us (WGP); and the editorial and production staffs of John Wiley & Sons, Inc., for their cooperation and support throughout the preparation of this textbook.

WILSON G. POND
Visiting Professor
Department of Animal Science
Cornell University
Ithaca, NY 14853

KEVIN R. POND
Professor and Chair
Department of Animal Science and Food Technology
Texas Tech University
Lubbock, TX 79409

CONTENTS

Preface

CHAPTER 16   HORSES AND THE HORSE INDUSTRY   400

CHAPTER 17   SWINE   441

CHAPTER 18   SHEEP AND GOATS   486

CHAPTER ONE
FOOD PRODUCTION

HISTORICAL PERSPECTIVE

HUMAN POPULATION GROWTH

ROLE OF RESEARCH AND OF LAND, WATER, SOIL, AND ENERGY
RESOURCES

FOOD CONSUMPTION

WHO PRODUCES THE FOOD?

SUMMARY

The purposes of this introductory chapter are to consider the history of food production, examine the present and future challenges to society in relation to food production, and characterize plant and animal products as contributors to food and nutrients for a rapidly growing human population. The production of crops and animals is closely interdependent in food production. The study of animal science, therefore, must embrace the concept of this interdependence as the basis for sustained food production.

HISTORICAL PERSPECTIVE

We live in a world with bountiful human and natural resources. All through recorded history, humanity has survived natural disasters that have disrupted food supplies and created famines. Evidence indicates that the mesolithic (middle stone age) period of 10,000 to 15,000 years ago was the prelude to the transition from food gathering to food production. The decline of glaciation brought with it a gradual forestation of the tundra, which had sustained the abundant animal life on which the early humans' food supply was based. Herbivorous animals such as the bison, horse, reindeer, elk, and deer ranged the tundra, but some species became extinct with the intrusion of forests, which sheltered carnivorous predators. Forest mammals, including pigs, wild cattle, the large cats, and many other species, became prevalent.

The period from 7000 B.C. to about 1750 A.D. coincides with the early stages of agriculture. Previous civilizations had been based on hunting and gathering. Biblical accounts record the importance of grain production, grazing of herds of livestock, fishing, and other organized methods of food production. Many important developments at that time set the stage for later major advances in food production. They included methods of cultivation of plants, methods of irrigation, primitive mechanization, invention of the wheel, and development of the ox-drawn plow. Fish, fowl, and wild game continued to be hunted, but domestication of livestock (5,000 to 15,000 years ago by most accounts) stabilized the food supply and had a major role in the progress toward more advanced civilizations.

The domesticated animals used for food production and as draft animals in ancient times have persisted through the centuries as important contributors to society. About 200 years ago, Robert Bakewell and other animal breeders introduced the concept of animal improvement through selection. Changes in animal mature size, body composition, and many other highly heritable traits (most traits are controlled both by environment and heredity) have been brought about through selection practices begun in those times. Modern population geneticists and biologists, using more sophisticated and advanced methods, continue to improve animals to meet current consumer and societal needs.

HUMAN POPULATION GROWTH

We live on a planet with about 58 million square miles of land area. Less than half of it is useful for crop and forage production as we know it today. This finite space accommodates a rapidly growing human population. It has been estimated that the human population in 8000 B.C. was about 5 million. From then to the year 1650 A.D., the population increased 100-fold to 500 million; and in the next 200 years (1850 A.D.), it doubled to 1 billion. It doubled again in the 80 years from 1850 to 1930 (2 billion) and again in the 45 years from 1930 to 1975 (4 billion). The curve continues upward (Figure 1-1) and projections indicate sustained growth in the twenty-first century, from the current 5.5 billion to 8 to 9 billion by 2030 (Brown, 1994).

The rate of population growth varies greatly among countries (Table 1-1). Among the slower growing countries, the United States is expected to increase from 250 million in 1990 to 345 million by 2030 (38%), whereas Japan and Western European countries are projected to hover at about the same number (Japan, Italy, Germany) or increase modestly (United Kingdom, France). Rapidly growing countries are projected to increase at much faster rates; for example, Nigeria, Ethiopia, Iran, Pakistan, Bangladesh, and Egypt are expected to more than double their populations from 1990 to 2030. Even more impressive is the projected increase during the same period of about 1.2 billion people in the three Asian countries of Indonesia, India, and China. If projections are accurate,

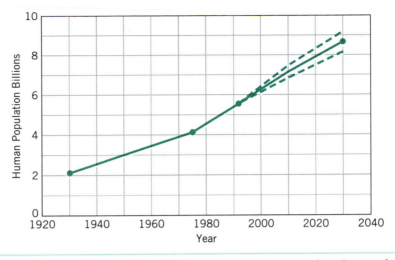

FIGURE 1-1

World human population from 1930–1990 with projections to 2030. Note the range of predictions for 2010 and 2030, reflecting uncertain birth rates and death rates.

TABLE 1-1

POPULATION GROWTH 1950–1990, WITH PROJECTIONS TO 2030, FOR THE MOST POPULOUS COUNTRIES

Country	1950	1990 (million)	2030
Slowly Growing Countries			
United States	152	250	345
Russia	114	148	161
Japan	84	124	123
United Kingdom	50	58	60
Germany	68	80	81
Italy	47	58	56
France	42	57	67
Rapidly Growing Countries			
Philippines	21	64	111
Nigeria	32	87	278
Ethiopia and Eritrea	21	51	157
Iran	16	57	183
Pakistan	40	118	260
Bangladesh	46	114	243
Egypt	21	54	111
Mexico	28	85	150
Turkey	21	57	104
Indonesia	83	189	307
India	369	853	1,443
Brazil	53	153	252
China	563	1,134	1,624

Source: U.S. Bureau of the Census, in Francis Urban and Ray Nightingale, *World Population by Country and Region, 1950–90 and Projections to 2050* (Washington, D.C.: U.S. Department of Agriculture, Economic Research Service, 1993).

within the working lifetimes of today's students, the world population will grow by approximately 3.5 billion (from 1990 to 2030) to a total of about 8 to 9 billion.

ROLE OF RESEARCH AND OF LAND, WATER, SOIL, AND ENERGY RESOURCES

One of the greatest challenges for the human intellect over the coming decades will be to increase food and fiber production at a rate sufficient to provide an adequate supply for all. This must be accomplished within the constraints of a finite land area. Therefore, efficiency of agricultural production must be increased dramatically, and the effort must be combined with diligent conservation of natural resources and the environment. To meet this challenge, it has been proposed (Avery, 1997) that: "What makes sense is high-yield conservation—producing the most food possible per acre, so we can leave the most land for the wildlife."

More than 200 years ago, Malthus (1798) proposed the theory that mankind multiplies geometrically while food supply does not. The ultimate result could be mass starvation and the demise of society. Since that dire prediction, population has indeed grown exponentially, but through dramatic advances in agriculture, food supplies have kept pace with food needs throughout the nineteenth and twentieth centuries. One can take the pessimistic view of Malthus or, alternatively, adopt the thesis that, through Divine guidance, continued advances in knowledge and its wise application and stewardship will preserve and enhance the quality of life for future generations.

Role of Research

Increases in food production have been the result of sustained investments in agricultural research by government, universities, foundations, and private industry, and the application by farmers and ranchers of that knowledge. The enormously successful and efficient food production system in the United States is based on the application of research done at publicly supported and private universities located in each of the 50 states and at private institutions and government laboratories. The dissemination of this knowledge to the food producer and consumer via the network of the federal, state, and county extension service is the pipeline through which the results from the laboratory have been put to use in the field. The marriage of the research efforts of the United States Department of Agriculture with the land-grant colleges was vastly improved by the Hatch Act of 1887 as a means of augmenting research capabilities of state experiment stations through federal support of land-grant college research. Increases in food production were brought about by the application by farmers of a combination of technologies growing out of this research. Improved plant varieties, particularly the development of hybrid-seed corn, improved animal genetics and feeding practices, disease control in plants and animals, and increased use of chemical fertilizers and of irrigation played a major role in increased output of agricultural production in the United States in the twentieth century.

Animal food production and crop production are intertwined in providing increased food supplies as the world population rises. During the latter half of the twentieth cen-

TABLE 1-2

MEMBERS OF THE CONSULTATIVE GROUP ON INTERNATIONAL AGRICULTURAL RESEARCH (CGIAR)

Research Center	Acronym	Location	Year of Initiation
International Center for Maize and Wheat	IMMYT	Mexico	1943
International Rice Institute	IRRI	Philippines	1959
International Institute of Tropical Agriculture	IITA	Nigeria	1967
Center for International Agriculture in the Tropics	CIAT	Colombia	1967
International Center for Potatoes	CIP	Peru	1971
West African Rice Development Association	WARDA	Liberia	1972
International Crops Research Institute for the Semi-Arid Tropics	ICRISAT	India	1972
International Livestock Center for Africa	ILCA[1]	Ethiopia	1974
International Laboratory for Research on Animal Diseases	ILRAD[1]	Kenya	1974
International Board for Plant Genetics Resources	IBPGR	Italy	1974
International Food Policy Research Institute	IFPRI	Washington, D.C.	1975
International Center for Agriculture Research in Dry Areas	ICARDA	Syria	1976
International Service for National Agricultural Research	ISNAR	The Netherlands	1979

[1]ILCA and ILRAD were combined in 1994 to form International Livestock Research Institute (ILRI) with headquarters in Kenya.

tury, several international research centers financed jointly by private foundations, governments, and other sources have had a major effect on crop and animal production around the world. The first of these centers was the International Center for Wheat and Maize (IMMYT), started in 1943 by the joint action of the Rockefeller Foundation and the Mexican Government. Its first director, Norman Borlaug, was awarded the Nobel Peace Prize in 1977 for his research leadership in development of new high-yielding varieties of wheat and maize (corn). This and other similar international centers for agricultural research (Table 1-2) have contributed to the "Green Revolution" of increased world food production. These 13 centers comprise the Consultative Group on International Agricultural Research (CGIAR). All are investing heavily in research efforts to improve yields of plant and animal crops in order to enhance food production capabilities in the developing countries. In accord with the consensus reached by CGIAR directors, more research will be directed toward increasing food production in ways conducive to environmental stability.

Land Area for Food Production

About 11% of the world's land area is used for crop production, and another 12% now in grassland and forests could be used. Productive agricultural land continues to be taken by urban expansion, highway construction, and energy production. Almost 1 million acres (of a total of 350 million acres of prime cropland in the United States) have been converted to nonfarm uses each year for the past 30 years and the trend continues. On a global basis, the amounts of irrigated land, cropland, rangeland and pasture, and forests totaled about 21 billion acres in 1990 (8.5 billion hectares, 1 ha = 2.47 acres) (Table 1-3; FAO, 1991). Irrigated land increased to 631 million acres in 1995 (FAO, 1996) and continuing modest increases in irrigated land, cropland, and rangeland and pastures have been projected for 2010 (Postel, 1994); but the growth of the human population over that same period will exceed these increases, resulting in a per-capita decline in land available for crops and grazing. Therefore, the increase in food production required to sustain the growing population must come from increased crop yields and improved efficiency of production of plants and animals. It follows from this conclusion that emphasis on increased food production should be focused on areas of the world with the most favorable land, climate, soils, and other resources for increased crop and animal production. The United States is one such area.

The number of acres used as cropland per person in the United States is large compared with that of most countries, and the favorable latitude of the United States provides the environment for a greater variety and higher yield of crops than in many other regions. Total U.S. land area is 2.265 billion acres (9 acres per person), of which 964 million acres is agricultural land. Cropland makes up 19.6% of total land area and 46.0% of agricultural land, whereas pasture and rangelands make up 42.5% of agricultural land. The four major crops (corn for grain, hay and silage, wheat for grain, and soybeans) used about 78% of the 304.1 million acres devoted to production of major crops in 1992 (CAST, 1995; Table 1-4). Orchard crops (citrus, grapes, apples, pecans and other nuts,

TABLE 1-3

POPULATION SIZE AND AVAILABILITY OF CROPLAND, RANGELAND AND PASTURE, AND FORESTS IN 1990, WITH PROJECTIONS FOR 2010

	1990	2010	Total Change (percent)
	(million)		
Population	5,290	7,030	+33
Irrigated Land (acres)[1]	585	668	+17
Cropland (acres)	3,567	3,744	+5
Rangeland and Pasture (acres)	8,403	8,744	+4
Forests (acres)	8,430	7,818	−7

[1]Irrigated land was 631 million acres in 1995 (FAO, 1996).
Sources: 1990 population figures from U.S. Bureau of the Census (1993); 2010 population projection from Postel (1994); 1990 land and forest figures from FAO *Production Yearbook* (1992); 2010 land and forest projections from Postel (1994).

TABLE 1-4

NUMBER OF ACRES OF ALL MAJOR CROPS HARVESTED IN 1992 IN THE UNITED STATES (U.S. DEPARTMENT OF COMMERCE, 1994)

Crop	Acres
Corn for grain	69,339,869
Hay (alfalfa, other tame, small grain, wild grass, silage, and others)	56,596,466
Wheat for grain	59,089,470
Soybeans	56,351,304
Cotton	10,961,720
Sorghum for grain	10,887,147
Barley for grain	6,818,065
Corn for silage	6,069,124
Orchards	4,770,778
Oats for grain	4,187,873
Vegetables	3,782,358
Rice	3,117,718
Sunflower seed	1,905,088
Field seed and grass seed	1,725,743
Peanuts	1,594,611
Dry edible beans	1,548,766
Sugar beet	1,441,815
Irish potato	1,351,084
Sugar cane	883,927
Tobacco	831,231
Sorghum for silage	493,589
Berries	171,999
Flax seed	156,630
Total	304,076,375

Source: CAST (1995).

plums, cherries, and other fruits) and vegetable crops (sweet corn, tomatoes, peas, beans, lettuce, watermelons, carrots, and a long list of others) were produced on 4.5 and 3.2 million acres, respectively (less than 2% of all cropland in the U.S.) in 1992 (CAST, 1995). The profile of cropland use has remained relatively stable during the past decade.

Water Resources and Soil Fertility

Available land area and fertile soils are of limited value for expanded food production without an adequate water supply. The importance of an adequate water supply for crop production has been recognized throughout the history of civilization. Two-thirds of the world's population lives in countries largely dependent on irrigation for their food. Irrigated lands contribute disproportionately to the world's food supply. The 585 million acres of irrigated land in 1990 made up only 16% of the total cropland, but supplied about 35% of the total production (Table 1-3; Postel, 1994). Cropland has been projected to increase to 3,744 billion acres by 2010 (5% above the 1990 level), whereas irrigated land has been projected to increase by 17% to 668 billion acres during the same period. A total of 631 billion acres was irrigated in 1995 (FAO, 1996).

The use of fertilizer to increase crop yields is more effective when water supply is not a limiting factor. This synergism between water and fertilizer use in increasing crop yields has been a major factor in explaining the dramatic increase in grain production as new varieties have been developed that are capable of responding to rising inputs of fertilizer. World fertilizer use increased steadily from 1950 to 1989, when it plateaued in response to high fertilizer cost in relation to value of the increased grain yield. The delicate balance between water supplies, soil fertility, and crop production must be recognized in the context of animal and crop production systems and sustainable agriculture. It was predicted (Homer-Dixon et al., 1993) that by 2025 severe water shortages may be widespread. The projection was that many nations, particularly in Africa and the Middle East, will fall below the minimum of 1000 cubic meters of water per person per year considered necessary for an industrialized nation. The validity of that projection remains unknown but, clearly, water is becoming an increasingly critical resource in food production in many parts of the world.

Soil Fertility and Intensive Agriculture

As pressure mounts to increase agricultural output, there is concern about the detrimental effects on soils resulting from intensive agricultural practices. Soil and crop scientists have been effective in their advocacy of greater reliance on soil-saving practices such as strip cropping, contour farming, greater use of pasture and cover crops, and no-till farming, in which corn and other row crops are planted without plowing or without otherwise preparing the soil in the traditional ways. New soil formed by natural processes is commonly 2 to 5 tons per acre annually, so the trend for excessive water and wind erosion of soils in the United States and around the world is a reversible process. It is important to continue efforts to curb soil erosion and losses in fertility worldwide to ensure sustainable agricultural production at a level sufficient to provide food needs of the future.

Pesticide Use in Crop Protection and Productivity

Crop yields are reduced by an array of plant diseases, insects, and competing weeds. The use of pesticides,[1] including both natural and synthetic chemicals and microbial agents (both naturally occurring organic and genetically engineered agents) for use as insecticides, herbicides, fungicides, and rodenticides has become important in order to maintain efficient crop yield and quality. With these technologies has come an increased concern for food safety and environmental pollution. Governmental regulations (including the Pesticide Use/Risk Reduction initiative of the U.S. Department of Agriculture, U.S. Food

---

[1]A pesticide is defined by the Federal Insecticide, Fungicide, and Rodenticide Act as "any substance or mixture of substances intended for preventing, destroying, repelling, or mitigating any insects, rodents, nematodes, fungi, or weeds or any other forms of life declared to be pests; and any substance or mixture of substances intended for use as a plant regulator, defoliant, or desiccant."

and Drug Administration, and Environmental Protection Agency) designed to protect water, soil, and the food supply from residues of some of these chemicals have provided good protection from the potential adverse effects of these well-established practices. Active research continues through both governmental and private funding to develop more effective and safer products for use in assuring an adequate and safe food supply while at the same time protecting the environment. Plant breeders and molecular biologists are developing plants with genetic resistance to some of the plant pests whose control in the past has been dependent on agricultural chemicals. These advances can be expected to continue to provide biological rather than chemical control measures in plant protection that will help to alleviate the concerns about pesticides and agricultural chemicals in the environment. In their efforts to introduce into crops genetic resistance to pathogens and insect pests, scientists are aware of the potential for the inadvertent introduction of these resistant genes into other plants, including weeds.

Energy Resources and Their Use in Agriculture

Food production depends on solar energy for photosynthesis, the first step in the food chain. Mechanized agriculture requires energy from other sources to provide fuel for tractors, irrigation, and fertilizer manufacture, and energy for an array of other uses. Tractor fuel use and fuel for irrigation and fertilizer manufacture have increased enormously in the past few decades.

Total energy use by agriculture continues to rise with increased mechanization, but fossil fuel use may be expected to be partially supplanted over time by the increased use of nuclear energy and energy from renewable resources (e.g., ethanol and methanol from corn and other crops and from fermentable materials, including animal wastes and industrial wastes).

FOOD CONSUMPTION

The human nutritional requirements (males and females, children and adults, infants and the elderly) have been studied extensively in many laboratories for many decades. Based on this information, dietary recommendations have evolved, the details of which are revised continuously as new knowledge becomes available. The "food pyramid" (Figure 1-2) now commonly displayed on retail packaged food containers in grocery stores in the United States depicts the basic food groups: bread at the base, vegetables and fruits on the next tier, meat and milk on the third tier, and fats, oils, and sweets at the peak. Sample diets for one day for people at three different calorie intake levels are shown in Table 1-5 (USDA, 1992). A daily intake of 1600 calories is adequate for many sedentary women and older adults; 2200 calories is adequate for most children, teenage girls, active women, and many sedentary men; 2800 calories is adequate for teenage boys, many active men, and some very active women. Obviously, the exact requirement for an individual will depend on genetic background, gender, body size, and physiological state (e.g., growth, pregnancy, lactation, and other factors), as well as on level of physical activity.

The Food Guide Pyramid

A Guide to Daily Food Choices

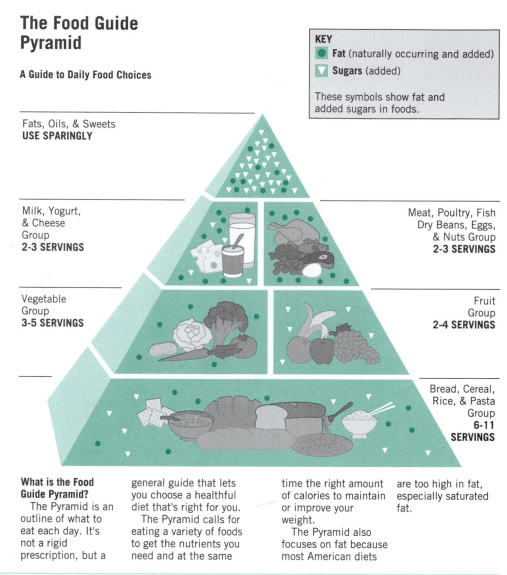

KEY
- ● **Fat** (naturally occurring and added)
- ▽ **Sugars** (added)

These symbols show fat and added sugars in foods.

Fats, Oils, & Sweets
USE SPARINGLY

Milk, Yogurt, & Cheese Group
2-3 SERVINGS

Meat, Poultry, Fish Dry Beans, Eggs, & Nuts Group
2-3 SERVINGS

Vegetable Group
3-5 SERVINGS

Fruit Group
2-4 SERVINGS

Bread, Cereal, Rice, & Pasta Group
6-11 SERVINGS

What is the Food Guide Pyramid?

The Pyramid is an outline of what to eat each day. It's not a rigid prescription, but a general guide that lets you choose a healthful diet that's right for you.

The Pyramid calls for eating a variety of foods to get the nutrients you need and at the same time the right amount of calories to maintain or improve your weight.

The Pyramid also focuses on fat because most American diets are too high in fat, especially saturated fat.

FIGURE 1-2

Food Guide Pyramid (USDA, 1992). The Food Guide Pyramid emphasizes foods from the five major food groups shown in the lower sections of the pyramid. Each food group provides some, but not all, of the required nutrients. All food groups are needed for good nutrition.

The amount and quality of dietary protein and the adequacy of minerals and vitamins in the diet are important in ensuring adequate nutrition. Meat, poultry, fish, milk, eggs, beans, and nuts contain the highest amount of protein. Animal products contain protein of higher nutritional value and also tend to be higher than plant protein products in the nutritional value of the mineral elements and vitamins they contain (higher biological availability).

TABLE 1-5

SAMPLE DIETS FOR A DAY AT THREE CALORIE LEVELS

	Lower 1,600	Moderate 2,200	Higher 2,800
Bread Group Servings[1]	6	9	11
Vegetable Group Servings[2]	4	4	5
Fruit Group Servings[3]	2	3	4
Milk Group Servings[4]	2–3	2–3	2–3
Meat Group (ounces)[5]	5	6	7
Total Fat (grams)	53	73	93
Total Added Sugars (teaspoons)	6	12	18

[1]One serving is 1 slice of bread, 1 ounce of dry ready-to-eat cereal or ½ cup of cooked cereal, rice, or pasta.

[2]One serving is 1 cup of raw leafy vegetables, ½ cup of other vegetables (cooked or chopped raw), or ¾ cup of vegetable juice.

[3]One serving is 1 medium apple, banana, or orange, ½ cup of chopped, cooked, or canned fruit, or ¾ cup of fruit juice.

[4]One serving is 1 cup of milk or yogurt, 1½ ounces of natural cheese, or 2 ounces of processed cheese.

[5]One serving is 2 to 3 ounces of cooked lean meat, poultry, or fish (½ cup of cooked dry beans, 1 egg, or 2 tablespoons of peanut butter count as 1 ounce of lean meat).

Source: USDA Human Nutrition Information Service (1992).

Animal products have been constituents of human diets in many cultures for centuries. The consumption of animal products historically increases as economic status improves. In the richest countries, per-capita consumption of total protein tends to plateau as family incomes rise (Figure 1-3), but animal protein consumption continues to rise (except among those who choose a vegetarian diet). Food products from animals enhance

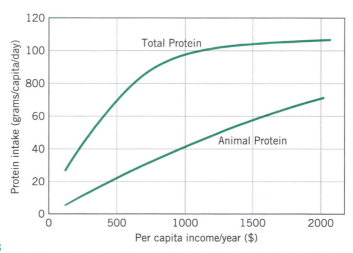

FIGURE 1-3

Per-capita consumption of total protein and animal protein in populations in relation to yearly income. Note that total protein consumption plateaus at higher income levels.

TABLE 1-6

CONTRIBUTIONS OF VARIOUS FOOD GROUPS TO THE WORLD FOOD SUPPLY

Food Group	Calories (%)	Protein (%)
Plant Products	84	66
Cereals	49	43
Roots, tubers, pulses	10	10
Nuts, oils, vegetable fats	8	4
Sugar and sugar products	9	2
Vegetables and fruits	8	7
Animal Products	16	34
Meat	7	15
Eggs	1	2
Fish	1	5
Milk	5	11
Other	2	1

Source: Adapted from FAO publications. Animal products tend to increase in developing countries as economic status improves. Therefore the values listed for each plant and animal product continue to change as the population demographics change.

TABLE 1-7

CHANGES IN PER-CAPITA CALORIE AND PROTEIN SUPPLY

Area	Year	Calories	Per-Capita Calorie Supply (calories per day) From Animal Products Calories	Percent	Total Protein (g)	Per-Capita Protein Supply From Animal Products Grams	Percent
Developed Market Economies							
	1961–63	3,031	825	27	95	63	66
	1988–90	3,404	1008	30	128	76	59
Developing Market Economies							
	1961–63	1,940	142	7	29	10	34
	1988–90	2,473	240	10	48	18	38
World							
	1961–63	2,287	359	16	63	20	32
	1988–90	2,697	424	16	71	25	35

Source: FAO Production Yearbook (1992).

TABLE 1-8

MAJOR FOODS: TRENDS IN U.S. PER-CAPITA CONSUMPTION IN THE PAST 30 YEARS

Food	1970	1980	1996
	Pounds		
Red meat[1]	131.7	126.4	112.0
Chicken and turkey[1]	33.8	40.8	64.3
Fish and shellfish[1]	11.7	12.4	14.7
Eggs	39.5	34.8	30.4
Cheese[2]	11.4	17.5	27.7
Ice cream	17.8	17.5	15.9
Fluid cream products	5.2	5.6	5.4
All dairy products[3]	563.8	543.2	574.6
Fats and oils	52.6	57.2	64.9
Animal	14.1	12.3	8.8
Vegetable	38.5	44.8	56.1
Peanuts and tree nuts[4]	7.2	6.6	7.8
Fruits and vegetables[5]	565.6	594.6	695.6
Fruits	230.0	258.1	283.2
Vegetables	335.6	336.6	412.4
Caloric sweeteners[6]	122.2	123.0	152.0
Refined sugar (sucrose)	101.8	83.6	66.2
Corn sweeteners	19.1	38.2	84.0
Honey and edible syrup	1.5	1.2	1.3
Flour and cereal products[7]	135.3	144.6	197.7
Wheat flour	110.9	116.9	148.1
Rice	6.7	9.4	18.8
Corn products	11.1	12.9	22.9
Oat products	4.4	3.7	6.6
Rye and barley	2.2	1.8	1.2
Cocoa (chocolate liquor equivalent)	3.1	2.7	3.6
	Gallons[8]		
Milk	31.3	27.6	24.9
Whole	25.5	17.0	9.4
Lowfat and skim	5.8	10.6	15.5
Coffee	33.4	26.7	26.0
Tea	6.8	7.3	7.1
Soft drinks	24.3	35.1	46.6
Fruit juices	NA	7.2	8.4

[1]Boneless, trimmed equivalent.

[2]Excludes full-skim American, cottage, pot, and baker's cheese.

[3]Milk equivalent, milkfat basis.

[4]Shelled basis.

[5]Farmgate weight.

[6]Dry basis.

[7]Consumption of items at the processing level (excludes quantities used in alcoholic beverages and corn sweeteners).

[8]1993 data for right-hand column.

Sources: USDA *Agriculture Fact Book* (1996), and USDA *Agricultural Statistics* (1998).

TABLE 1-9

PERCENTAGE OF TOTAL FOOD NUTRIENTS CONTRIBUTED BY MAJOR FOOD GROUPS IN THE U.S. HAS SHIFTED IN THE PAST 30 YEARS[1]

Nutrient	Meat, Poultry, Fish			Dairy Products			Eggs			Fats and Oils			Fruits		
	1970	1990	1995	1970	1990	1995	1970	1990	1995	1970	1990	1995	1970	1990	1995
Food energy	21.6	17.4	14.3	10.3	9.4	9.3	1.9	1.3	1.3	17.6	19.0	19.5	2.8	3.1	3.4
Carbohydrates	0.1	0.1	0.1	6.1	5.0	4.7	0.1	0.1	0.1	0.1	0.1	0.0	6.1	6.1	6.4
Protein	43.8	41.1	39.3	19.8	19.8	19.3	5.4	3.9	3.8	0.1	0.2	0.1	1.1	1.2	1.3
Total fat	36.9	30.3	24.5	12.3	11.8	12.3	2.7	2.0	2.1	41.2	47.6	52.2	0.3	0.4	0.5
Saturated fat	44.2	38.2	26.4	20.0	20.8	23.6	2.2	1.7	2.0	28.9	33.0	40.9	0.2	0.3	0.3
Monounsaturated fat	39.9	32.7	25.7	8.5	8.3	8.6	2.5	1.8	2.0	43.3	49.9	56.3	0.2	0.3	0.4
Polyunsaturated fat	21.7	17.2	14.9	2.6	2.0	2.1	2.2	1.4	1.5	62.0	67.9	68.9	0.4	0.4	0.5
Cholesterol	43.7	47.3	43.8	13.5	14.5	16.1	37.3	33.2	34.4	5.5	5.0	5.6	0	0	0
Vitamin A (retinol equivalent)	29.4	22.9	21.4	17.2	18.4	17.4	5.5	4.3	4.2	13.1	13.2	11.7	0	0	3.3
Carotene (retinol equivalent)	0	0	0	3.3	2.5	2.3	0	0	0	3.5	2.7	2.4	0	0	7.6
Vitamin E	7.4	6.0	4.8	3.9	3.0	2.8	6.6	4.3	2.1	57.0	62.5	67.8	4.0	3.8	3.8
Vitamin C	2.4	2.3	2.0	3.8	3.2	2.7	0	0	0	0	0	0	37.9	41.5	43.5
Thiamin (B1)	29.7	21.1	18.7	9.0	6.7	6.2	1.3	0.8	0.8	<0.1	<0.1	<0.1	4.4	4.1	4.4
Riboflavin (B2)	25.1	19.8	18.7	34.2	30.9	30.7	9.3	6.4	6.5	0.1	0.1	0.1	2.4	2.7	2.3
Niacin	47.7	40.1	38.2	1.9	1.5	1.4	0.1	0.1	0.1	<0.1	<0.1	<0.1	2.4	2.2	2.4
Vitamin B6	41.9	38.7	36.4	11.0	10.4	9.7	2.9	2.1	2.0	<0.1	<0.1	<0.1	8.5	10.4	11.0
Folate	10.9	8.5	7.4	8.2	8.1	7.3	7.2	5.1	4.8	0.1	0.1	0.1	9.5	10.2	12.4
Vitamin B12	77.3	74.8	72.9	17.1	19.7	21.0	4.1	3.7	4.1	0.1	0.1	0.1	0	0	0
Calcium	3.7	3.4	3.3	74.3	74.5	72.9	2.4	1.7	1.7	0.2	0.1	0.2	2.4	2.5	2.7
Phosphorus	29.9	26.5	24.8	34.6	33.7	32.8	5.2	3.6	3.6	0.1	<0.1	0.1	1.6	1.7	1.9
Magnesium	14.8	13.6	12.8	19.6	17.6	16.4	1.3	0.9	0.9	<0.1	<0.1	<0.1	5.8	6.2	6.6
Iron	25.8	18.5	16.3	2.2	2.1	2.1	4.0	2.4	2.3	0.1	0.1	0.1	3.0	2.9	2.8
Zinc	50.2	43.7	41.5	17.5	19.0	18.9	3.7	2.8	2.8	0.1	0.1	0.1	1.2	1.3	1.4
Copper	20.0	15.6	14.0	3.5	3.5	2.8	0.4	0.3	0.3	0.1	0.1	0.1	6.6	7.0	7.2
Potassium	18.9	17.9	16.7	21.0	19.7	18.5	1.5	1.1	1.1	0.1	<0.1	<0.1	9.0	10.6	11.6

Nutrient	Vegetables 1970	Vegetables 1990	Vegetables 1995	Legumes and Nuts 1970	Legumes and Nuts 1990	Legumes and Nuts 1995	Grain Products 1970	Grain Products 1990	Grain Products 1995	Sugars and Sweeteners 1970	Sugars and Sweeteners 1990	Sugars and Sweeteners 1995	Miscellaneous 1970	Miscellaneous 1990	Miscellaneous 1995
Food energy	5.2	4.6	2.6	2.8	2.8	2.9	19.0	23.0	25.1	17.9	17.9	18.3	1.1	1.1	1.1
Carbohydrates	10.2	8.3	8.2	2.2	1.8	2.0	34.6	39.5	40.5	39.8	38.2	37.3	0.9	0.9	0.9
Protein	5.6	5.2	5.3	5.1	5.2	6.0	18.0	22.3	23.7	<0.1	<0.1	0	1.1	1.3	1.2
Total fat	0.4	0.4	0.5	3.4	3.7	3.1	1.3	1.8	2.2	0	0	0	1.6	2.1	2.3
Saturated fat	0.2	0.2	0.1	1.6	1.9	2.1	0.6	0.8	1.1	0	0	0	2.3	3.0	3.4
Monounsaturated fat	0.1	0.1	0	3.6	4.2	4.1	0.5	0.8	1.0	0	0	0	1.4	1.9	1.9
Polyunsaturated fat	1.1	0.9	1.0	5.8	5.5	5.5	3.4	3.8	4.5	<0.1	0	0	0.8	0.9	1.0
Cholesterol	0	0	0	0	0	0	0	0	<0.1	0	0	0	0	0	0
Vitamin A (retinol equivalent)	27.1	36.4	35.3	0.1	<0.1	<0.1	0.2	0.5	0.5	0	0	0	4.6	1.2	6.1
Carotene (retinol equivalent)	81.1	83.9	80.7	0.1	0.1	0.1	0.6	0.9	1.4	0	0	0	2.7	2.8	5.7
Vitamin E	9.9	8.2	7.3	6.1	6.4	5.5	4.5	5.0	5.1	0	0	0	0.6	0.8	0.9
Vitamin C	51.5	52.2	47.2	<0.1	0.1	0.1	0	0	<0.1	<0.1	<0.1	<0.1	4.3	0.8	4.5
Thiamin (B1)	12.4	10.1	10.0	5.1	4.3	4.7	37.4	52.2	54.5	0.2	0.2	0.2	0.5	0.6	0.7
Riboflavin (B2)	6.2	5.8	6.1	1.5	1.6	1.7	19.0	30.2	31.0	1.2	1.3	1.4	1.0	1.2	1.4
Niacin	13.1	10.8	11.1	4.6	4.1	4.0	26.0	38.1	40.1	<0.1	<0.1	<0.1	4.1	3.3	2.7
Vitamin B6	22.9	22.3	22.5	3.4	3.4	3.8	8.5	11.5	12.8	0.2	0.3	0.2	0.7	1.0	1.5
Folate	29.0	26.4	24.0	20.0	18.5	20.1	12.4	21.2	21.8	<0.1	<0.1	<0.1	1.9	2.0	2.2
Vitamin B12	0	0	0	0	0	0	1.4	1.7	1.9	0	0	0	0	0	0
Calcium	6.9	6.2	6.4	3.8	3.7	4.4	3.5	4.4	4.9	0.7	0.8	0.8	2.0	2.6	2.9
Phosphorus	8.1	7.3	7.3	5.1	5.2	5.9	13.0	19.0	20.8	0.4	0.3	0.3	2.1	2.6	2.5
Magnesium	17.0	14.4	14.1	12.3	12.0	13.2	17.4	23.7	25.5	0.8	0.9	0.9	10.9	10.8	9.6
Iron	14.4	11.2	11.0	9.1	7.3	8.3	35.0	48.9	50.5	1.3	1.1	1.1	5.2	5.5	5.7
Zinc	7.4	7.0	7.2	5.7	5.8	6.3	11.5	16.9	18.4	0.5	0.5	0.5	2.2	3.0	3.0
Copper	24.2	20.6	19.8	15.8	16.6	20.1	16.7	22.7	23.3	4.3	4.4	4.2	8.5	9.4	8.4
Potassium	27.9	26.5	26.5	7.5	7.7	9.2	6.0	8.9	9.7	0.5	0.6	0.6	7.7	7.0	11.6

[1]Trends since 1990 indicate a slight reduction in the percentage of dietary protein and fat derived from animal products and an increase in fat intake from plant products.

Source: U.S. Department of Agriculture (1998) *Agricultural Statistics*, Washington, D.C.

the likelihood of adequate intakes of certain indispensable amino acids, vitamin B12, niacin, calcium, phosphorus, iron, and zinc in biologically available forms.

Data from surveys done by the Food and Agriculture Organization (FAO) of the United Nations indicate that cereals contribute about half the calories and more than two-fifths of the protein to the world food supply, whereas animal products provide one-sixth of the calories and one-third of the protein. Table 1-6 contains a more detailed breakdown of the contributions of plant and animal products to the total food supply. FAO data on per-capita calorie and protein supplies in economically developed and developing countries 30 years ago and in 1988–1990 (FAO, 1992; Table 1-7) indicate increases in calorie and in protein availability in each sector. It is significant that a large discrepancy remains in both calorie and protein availability in the economically developed compared with the economically developing sector.

The high incidence of obesity in the United States may be a reflection of the excess availability of calories relative to needs in our affluent society. An increasing proportion of adults in the United States is overweight (one in three in 1998). However, recent surveys indicate that Americans are changing eating patterns (USDA, 1996, 1998). Consumption of fat accounted for 40% of total calorie intake in the 1970s, but the value has decreased to about 33%. Despite the decline in the percentage of dietary calories supplied from fat, per-capita total fat and sweetener intake increased notably from 1970 to now (Table 1-8). Per-capita consumption of food fats from animals has steadily decreased, while that from vegetable sources has steadily increased over the past 30 years. Other notable changes in consumption patterns since 1970 are decreases in red meat, whole milk, and egg consumption, and increases in consumption of yogurt, poultry, fish, grain products, fruits, and vegetables, and a large increase in consumption of caloric sweeteners, comprised mainly of corn sweeteners (notably high-fructose corn syrup). About 20% of the added sugars are consumed in carbonated soft drinks and the remainder in an array of prepared foods. Sugars now provide nearly two-fifths of the carbohydrate calories in the average American diet; most of the remainder of the carbohydrate calories come from bread, cereal, pasta, and other foods high in starch.

The changes in the contributions of major food groups to total food nutrients consumed in the United States from 1970 to now shown in Table 1-9 illustrate the relationships between shifts in eating patterns and the percentages of various nutrients supplied by animal products versus plant products. It is important to recognize that animal products generally provide most nutrients in a biologically more available form than do plant products, so that the actual amounts of a particular nutrient available to the body from a given intake of a plant product may be less than the value listed in the table would suggest. This higher nutrient density of animal products is often overlooked in making comparisons of the nutritional value of foods of plant and animal origin.

WHO PRODUCES THE FOOD?

The structure of agriculture has changed dramatically in the economically developed countries. In the United States, about 20% of the population lived on farms in 1950; now, the figure is about 2.6%. (Over three-fourths of all agricultural products are provided by about one-fourth of the farms; many farm families derive some of their income from nonfarm jobs). This high efficiency of food production, including that of animal production, enables U.S. agriculture to provide most of the food needs of 270 million Americans plus the export of billions of dollars' worth of agricultural goods abroad to materially aid in the balance of trade with other countries. The sharp contrast among countries and regions of the world in the percentage of the workforce engaged in farming is shown dramatically in Table 1-10. Countries with 30% or more of their workforce in

TABLE 1-10

FARM POPULATION IN SELECTED COUNTRIES AND REGIONS (RANKED INVERSELY BY PERCENT OF POPULATION IN AGRICULTURE)

Country or Region	1996 Population (millions)	Percent of Population Economically Active in Agriculture
Country		
United Kingdom	58.3	2.1
Canada	29.7	2.3
United States	269.4	2.6[1]
Germany	79.4	2.8
Australia	18.1	4.4
Japan	125.4	5.3
USSR (former)[2]	293.0	12.0
Brazil	161.1	17.9
Mexico	92.7	31.9
Egypt	63.3	31.9
Nigeria	115.0	36.7
Turkey	61.8	50.5
Bangladesh	120.1	60.9
India	944.6	61.2
China	1232.1	71.1
Kenya	27.8	77.7
Malawi	98.5	86.3
Nepal	22.0	93.3
Regions		
North and Central America	461.2	9.6
Europe	728.8	10.4
Oceana	28.7	19.3
South America	32.3	19.4
Africa	738.7	59.5
Asia	3416.7	60.2
World Total	5767.8	47.1

[1]More than three-fourths of U.S. agricultural production is provided by less than one-fourth of the farms in the United States (many families living on small farms earn part of their income from nonfarm employment).

[2]Figures for former USSR are from the 1992 *FAO Production Yearbook.*

Source: FAO *Production Yearbook* (1996).

agriculture tend to be those at the lower end of economic development; they depend on subsistence agriculture for most of their food supply. Expenditures for food are now less than 12% of disposable income in the United States compared to more than 50% in China and India and even higher levels in the very poor countries. This imbalance signals the continued need for action to raise subsistence agriculture to a higher plane toward self-sufficiency in food production and economic growth. It also emphasizes the importance of continued increases in efficiency of food production in regions of high crop and animal productivity and of minimizing international trade barriers to the marketing of crop and animal products.

SUMMARY

This introductory chapter considers the partnership of animals and humans from early times and addresses the challenge of food production in a rapidly changing world. The human population is expected to increase from the current level of 5.8 billion to 8 to 9 billion by 2030 (within the working lifetime of today's students). Land available for food production is finite. The dramatic increases in food production brought about by agricultural research and technology have resulted in adequate food supplies, although not adequate food distribution, for a growing world population. A paramount challenge to society now is to continue to meet the growing demand for food and other products of agriculture within the constraints of a finite land area and limited natural resources. Cereal grains currently provide about half of the calories and two-fifths of the protein in the human diet, whereas animal products provide about one-sixth of the calories and one-third of the protein. Mounting pressure to increase food production and raise economic standards in many parts of the world to ensure adequate nutrition for future generations presents a major challenge to society.

REFERENCES

Avery , D. T. 1997. Saving the planet with high feed efficiency. *Proc. Cornell Nutrition Conference for Feed Manufacturers, Department of Animal Science and Division of Nutritional Sciences,* Cornell University, Ithaca, NY, pp. 77–87.

Brown, L. R. 1994. Facing food insecurity. In L. R. Brown (ed.), *State of the World 1994.* New York: Norton, pp. 177–197.

Council for Agricultural Science and Technology (CAST). 1995. Waste management and utilization in food production and processing. CAST Task Force Report No. 124, pp. 1–125.

Davidson S., Passmore, R., Broch, J. F., and Trusswell, G. S. 1979. *Human Nutrition and Dietetics.* New York: Churchill Livingstone, pp. 1–5.

Food and Agricultural Organization. 1991. *FAO Production Yearbook,* Rome, Italy.

Food and Agricultural Organization. 1992. *FAO Production Yearbook,* Rome, Italy.

Food and Agricultural Organization. 1996. *FAO Production Yearbook,* Rome, Italy.

Homer-Dixon, T. F., Boutwell, J. H., and Rathjens, G. W. 1993. Environmental change and violent conflict. *Scientific American,* February: 38–45.

Malthus, T. R. 1798. *An Essay on the Principles of Population as It Affects the Future Improvement of Society.* London: J. Johnson.

National Agricultural Lands Study. 1981. *National Agricultural Lands Study Final Report.* Washington, D.C.: U. S. Government Printing Office.

Plunknett, D. L. and Smith, N. J. H. 1982. Agricultural research and third world food production. *Science,* 217: 215–220.

Postel S. 1994. Carrying capacity: Earth's bottom line. In L. R. Brown (ed.), *State of the World, 1994.* New York: Norton, pp. 1–21.

USDA. 1992. *The Food Guide Pyramid.* Human Nutrition and Information Service, U. S. Department of Agriculture, *Home and Garden Bulletin* 252, pp. 1–20.

USDA. 1994. *Agriculture Fact Book 1994.* Office of Communication, U. S. Department of Agriculture. Washington, D.C.: U. S. Government Printing Office, pp. 1–216.

USDA. 1996. *Food and Nutrition Research Briefs.* Agriculture Research Service, U. S. Department of Agriculture. Washington, D.C., January 1996.

USDA. 1998. *Agricultural Statistics.* U. S. Department of Agriculture, Washington, D.C.

Voegtlin, W. L. 1975. *The Stone Age Diet.* New York: Vantage Press, Table II, p. 60.

CHAPTER TWO
DOMESTIC ANIMALS

Animals are an integral part of societies throughout the world. The many contributions by domestic animals to human welfare are often taken for granted or ignored and even challenged by some. The purposes of this chapter are to provide the basis for a better appreciation of the diverse contributions of domestic animals and to highlight the exciting reality and challenge of animal agriculture in a changing world.

AN OVERVIEW OF THE CONTRIBUTIONS OF DOMESTIC ANIMALS

Domestic animals contribute to society in several important ways. Some of these contributions are identified below.

Food, Fiber, and Other Products

Several species of mammals, birds, and fish contribute as major sources of food and fiber. Meat from cattle, swine, sheep, fish, poultry, and other animals, as well as eggs from chickens and other birds, and milk from cows, sheep, goats and other animals throughout the world contribute a major portion of food nutrients. Many nonfood products of the meat, poultry, and dairy industries are used in agricultural and industrial applications. Wool, leather, hair and pelts, and feathers are used for the manufacture of clothing, bedding, upholstery, carpets, and other products. Inedible animal fats are used for producing soaps, animal feeds, lubricants, pharmaceuticals, cosmetics, candles, food emulsifiers, plasticizers, floor waxes, paints and varnishes, printing inks, and other materials. New products of animal origin continue to be developed through advances in knowledge and technology.

Pleasure, Companionship, and Service

Horses, dogs, cats, and an array of other domestic animals have provided companionship and pleasure throughout civilization. Whereas humans must be good stewards of animals, in return, animals are faithful stewards in a variety of ways. Dogs are used as guides and guardians for the blind and handicapped, and in illegal drug search, herding livestock, guarding property, and trustworthy companionship. Dogs and cats are household pets everywhere and also are effective in rodent and pest control. Animals are used throughout the world for draft power and transportation and their excreta are used for fuel and fertilizer.

Nutrient Recycling and Ecological Stability

Animal wastes and food processing wastes are recycled through animals, resulting in enhanced utilization of valuable resources and reduced environmental pollution. Domestic animals as well as wild animals are needed for ecological stability and conservation of natural resources. Moreover, agriculture is unlikely to be sustainable without the use of domestic animals. The potential negative effects of domestic animal production on the environment must be recognized and appropriate actions must be continuously pursued by the animal industries and by all of agriculture and society to ensure sustained stability of the environment.

Animal Products and Pharmaceuticals for Human Health

Many life-saving pharmaceuticals and therapeutic agents are derived from animals. Heart valves from pigs are used to replace damaged human heart valves and animals are now being studied for use as donors of liver, heart, kidneys, and other organs and tissues in human medicine (xenotransplants). Biomedical research depends heavily on the use of animal models to provide fundamental knowledge for application in human health.

FOOD FROM ANIMALS

Globally, animal products contribute about 16% of total calories and 34% of total protein in the human diet. Of these totals, meat comprises nearly half of the calories and half of the protein provided by animal sources, whereas milk provides almost one-third of the calories and one-third of the protein from animal sources; eggs and fish contribute most of the remainder. In most industrialized countries, animal products constitute an even higher proportion of food energy and protein. For example, in the United States, about one-fourth of the total food energy and two-thirds of the protein in the diet comes from animal products (recall Table 1-9 in Chapter 1). Animal products are unique providers of several essential nutrients. They are the only reliable food source of vitamin B12; they contain higher biologically available levels of many vitamins and trace mineral elements than plant products. Dairy products are the major source of calcium in the diet; meat is a major source of iron of high biological availability, and is a good source of available zinc, selenium, and other trace elements. Although it is possible to meet all human nutrient requirements on a diet excluding animal products, oral supplements (often expensive) of vitamin B12 and several other vitamins and of calcium and several other mineral elements are needed to avoid inadequate nutrition among vegetarians. Animal agriculture is a multibillion-dollar enterprise, providing a livelihood not only for farmers, but for those associated with providing the many goods and services required by the farmer (feed, fertilizer, farm equipment, financial and banking institutions) and in the network from farmer to consumer (marketing, transportation, processing, advertising, distribution, retail sales). The agricultural industry in the United States employs more than 22 million workers (more than 20% of the workforce) and each year generates 900 billion dollars or more (about 14 to 15% of the gross national product, GNP). About half of this amount is generated by animal agriculture.

Animal products worldwide are provided by more than 1.2 billion cattle, 1.1 billion sheep, .5 billion goats, 11 billion chickens, 250 million turkeys, 550 million ducks, 860 million pigs, and millions of other animals, birds, and aquatic species. The approximate numbers of food animals comprising the animal industry in the United States are listed in Table 2-1. The number of individual species and types of animal enterprise vary from year to year, depending on economic and other factors. In 1998, the value of all cattle and their products (beef and dairy cattle) in the United States was about 60 billion dollars. Values for poultry, swine, sheep (meat and wool), and other livestock (including horses, goats, mink, and rabbits) were about 16, 5, 0.8, and 1.8 billion dollars in 1998, giving a total value of more than 83 billion dollars for animal agriculture, and representing more than half of the total combined value of animal and plant agricultural production in the United States. The total number of animals, their value, and that of their products varies from month to month and year to year, but the data in Table 2-1 provide a snapshot view of the enormity of animal production. The critical role of animal products, the complexity of domestic animal food production, and the economic and nutritional impact of food animal production on society are clear.

TABLE 2-1

THE SCOPE OF THE ANIMAL INDUSTRY IN THE UNITED STATES

Animals	Number of Animals
Poultry	
Chickens, 3 months and older, not laying	351,310,317
Pullets, younger than 3 months	49,843,029
Turkeys	87,612,131
Broilers	888,617,180
Total poultry	1,377,382,657
Cattle and Calves	
Beef cows	32,545,976
Milk cows	9,491,818
Heifers and heifer calves	26,201,587
Steers	27,896,444
Total cattle	96,135,825
Swine	
Barrows and gilts for market	50,641,504
Sows and boars for breeding	6,921,614
Total swine	57,563,118
Other Livestock	
Sheep and lambs	10,770,391
Horses and ponies	2,049,522
Goats	2,515,541
Mink	1,767,777
Rabbits	789,406
Total other livestock	17,892,637
Grand total, all animals	1,548,974,437[1]

[1]The actual number of animals produced per year exceeds the total shown, because several species (poultry, sheep, swine, mink, rabbits) have a reproduction interval of less than one year. For example, the number of barrows and gilts marketed in a given 12-month period would be approximately twice that shown in the table, because sows produce a litter twice per year. In 1997, 48.5 million barrows and gilts were marketed in the first half of the year and 50.5 million in the second half, giving a total of 99 million for the entire year. Similar adjustments would be needed to reflect annual production of poultry and other species that reproduce more frequently than once a year. The totals listed in this table represent census figures based on inventory taken at one time-point during the year.

Source: CAST (1995), and *Agricultural Statistics* (1998).

ANIMAL BYPRODUCTS

Animal byproducts are the substances or products remaining after those of greater value have been removed. Some byproducts are edible, others are inedible. A list of edible and inedible byproducts of meat animals is in Table 2-2.

The edible byproducts are sold as specialty foods in some markets. They are used also in pet foods and in diets for mink, foxes, and other fur-bearing animals. Organ meats

TABLE 2-2

EDIBLE AND INEDIBLE BYPRODUCTS FROM MEAT ANIMALS

Edible	Inedible
Brain	
Cheek meat	Bile (gall bladder contents)
Ears	Dried blood (80% protein)*
Feet	Gullet*
Head meat	Hides and skins
Heart	Lung*
Kidney	Manure
Lips	Meat and bone meal (50%)*
Liver	Rendered fat*
Salivary glands	
Snouts	
Spleen	
Stomach	
Sweetbread (thymus)	
Tail	
Tallow and lard	
Tongue	
Tripe (stomach compartment of ruminants)	
Weasand meat (muscular tissue surrounding esophagus)	

*Used in livestock feeds and/or pet foods.
Source: Taylor (1995) and McDowell (1991).

(brain, heart, kidney, liver, sweetbread, tongue, tripe) are referred to as variety meats. The edible byproducts from a typical 1000-pound market-weight steer would be expected to produce about 32 pounds of blood meal, 36 pounds of variety meats, 13 pounds of edible tallow, and 9 pounds of other edible products. In addition to the edible byproducts of cattle, sheep and goats, and swine slaughter, the commercial aquaculture industry produces large amounts of fishery wastes (offal, heads, tails, gills) that can be used in animal feeds and pet foods. A more detailed account of the uses of edible byproducts of each of the animal industries is included in later chapters dealing with individual animal species.

Inedible meat animal products noted with an asterisk in Table 2-2 are used mostly in animal feeds and pet foods. Animal feed and pet food manufacturers are themselves components of multibillion-dollar industries whose success depends heavily on the byproducts of the meat animal industry. Hides and skins from cattle (hides weigh at least 30 pounds; skins weigh less than 30 pounds), and skins from swine, sheep (usually called pelts), and goats represent a significant portion of the inedible portion of the carcass. The annual production of leather from cattle, sheep, and pigs in the United States is approximately 14 million cattle hides, 4 million sheepskins, and 10 million pigskins, representing a 1.5 billion-dollar industry. More than half of the hides from the more than 30 million cattle slaughtered annually in the United States are exported for tanning. Hides are preserved (cured) by covering the inner surface with salt, which penetrates the hide and allows it to be shipped without spoilage for further processing and tanning. Of the more than 80 million pigs slaughtered annually in the United States, skins are removed from less than 20% for leather; the remainder is sold on the wholesale carcass, which is processed for human food. Sheepskins may be tanned for leather or the pelt with wool retained may be used for lambskin coats and other sheepskin garments. Wool pulled from sheep pelts (excluding shorn wool from living sheep) is used for blankets, clothing, and lanolin isolation (the natural oil secreted from the skin of sheep). Hair from cattle and swine may be processed for use as insulation, padding for upholstery and carpets, or in brushes. Poultry feathers are used for pillow stuffing, decorations, brushes, and animal feed. Gelatin extracted from animal skins is used for capsules for administering medicinals. Blood is used as an adhesive for plywood, for fabric printing and dying, and as a sticking agent for insecticides, and for use in isolating pharmaceuticals. Bones may be used in animal feeds and for glue, buttons, and novelty items. More detailed information on inedible byproducts is included in later chapters dealing with individual animal species and their products.

PHARMACEUTICALS AND THERAPEUTIC AGENTS

Many hormones and other therapeutic agents used in human medicine are obtained from organs and tissues of animals at the time of slaughter for food. With the rapid growth of molecular biology and advances in biotechnology, some of these substances (for example, growth hormone or somatotropin) can be produced in mass quantities by recombinant DNA technology at a competitive cost. Others likely will follow. Some vaccines depend on animal tissues in their production. Table 2-3 lists many of the hormones and other metabolites that are obtained from food animals and used in human and veterinary medicine. Many advances in physiology and medicine would have been impossible without the availability of these products of animals. As science and technology continue to advance, even greater contributions to human and animal health can be expected from the use in clinical medicine of tissues and organs of food animals.

COMPANIONSHIP AND PLEASURE

Humans and their domesticated animals have lived in close harmony for centuries. Respect and reverence toward animals is recorded through paintings and sculptures on cave walls dating thousands of years ago. This apparent natural affinity to animals is reflected in the high ownership of family dogs and cats and the increasing popularity of family pleasure horses. It is estimated that there are more than 55 million dogs and at least as many cats in the homes of U.S. families. The emotionally therapeutic value of household pets for the elderly and ill is well documented. The importance of dogs and cats in society is underscored in Chapter 20.

It has been projected (Fountain and Thurman, 1998) that by 2003 companion ani-

TABLE 2-3

HORMONES AND OTHER METABOLITES FROM ANIMALS[1]

Substance	Source
Amfetin	Amnionic fluid
Cholesterol	Brain and spinal cord
Chymotrypsin	Pancreas
Chenodeoxycholic acid	Bile
Cholesystokinin	Brain, intestine
Cholic acid	Bile
Corticosteroids	Adrenal gland
Corticotropin	Pituitary gland
Epinephrine	Adrenal gland
Estrogens	Ovaries
Fibrinolysin	Blood
Gamma globulin	Blood
Gastrin	Stomach
Glucagon	Pancreas
Heparin	Lungs, intestine
Hyaluronidase	Testes
Insulin	Pancreas
Insulin-like growth factors (IGF)	Pancreas and other tissues
Lipase	Intestine
Liver extracts	Liver
Mucin	Stomach
Norepinephrine	Adrenal gland
Oxytocin	Pituitary gland
Parathyroid hormone	Parathyroid gland
Pepsin	Stomach
Plasmin	Blood
Progesterone	Ovaries
Rennin	Stomach
Somatotropin	Pituitary
Thrombin	Blood
Thyroxin	Thyroid gland
Thyrotropin (TSH)	Pituitary gland
Trypsin	Pancreas
Vasopressin	Pituitary gland

[1]This is only a partial list. Production by recombinant DNA technology will reduce demand for some because of the lower cost of production compared with the cost of their isolation and purification from animal tissues.

mals in the United States will represent over one-third of the animal health industry's total revenue (companion animals currently are second only to cattle in animal health revenues in the United States). According to their projection, many pet owners are willing to spend for the health and well-being of their pets at a level equal to what they would spend for themselves or their family. Companion animal health expenditures include not only veterinary care, but prepared dog, cat, horse, and other pet foods.

The number of pleasure horses, whose population in the United States was greatly exceeded by draft horses little more than a generation ago, continues to grow rapidly (see Chapter 16). The horse racing and dog racing industries are flourishing as spectator sports, and dog shows and cat shows are popular in every large city. State, county, and local fairs held everywhere in the United States include rodeos as well as livestock shows and exhibitions, in which youth (4-H and Future Farmers of America) and adult breeders enter their animals (from household pets to farm animals) in competition for prizes, and sometimes for advertising purposes. Animals such as the alpaca and llama are increasingly kept as pets by rural families in the United States. Even domestic livestock, including goats, sheep, and pigs, are often kept for recreation as well as a source of supplemental income or food. The contribution of animals to human pleasure represents a unique symbiotic relationship.

FAITHFUL STEWARDS

An impressive list of services is performed by animals in the everyday lives of people in all walks of life and in all cultures. We tend to take for granted the daily milk supplied by dairy cows, the woolen clothing and other woolen goods provided by sheep, the eggs produced by the hen, all as a part of their normal life cycle. The dog, "man's best friend," is not only a beloved and devoted family member in urban societies, but in the rural setting extends its service to farm chores such as rounding up cattle and sheep, controlling farm rodents and other pests, and guarding the farm premises when the rest of the family is away. Sporting men and women swear by the loyalty and work of their canine hunting partners. Seeing-eye dogs and dogs trained to assist people limited in physical mobility provide an invaluable daily service to people in all walks of life. Dogs, with their keen sense of smell, are effective in tracking escaped prisoners and in locating illegal drugs and other contraband at airports, in schools, and in international customs offices. Cats are ubiquitous in urban societies as family pets and are common on most farms and ranches. They also serve by satisfying their natural instinct to prey on rats and mice, whose presence as a nuisance and menace in barns and in stored grains on farms is virtually a certainty. Cats can be as effective as commonly used poisons in controlling rodents. Police mounted on horseback are still common in large cities and in crowd control at fairs and other large gatherings. Horses are an integral part of ranching operations throughout the world; on U.S. ranches, cattle could not be rounded up from rangeland grazing without the service of the horse to carry the rider over rough terrain. The calf-roping and cattle-sorting activities of trained quarter horses and their riders seen at rodeos are still very much a part of modern ranching practices in many areas of the United States and elsewhere. (It is noteworthy that the use of calf chutes and tables is more efficient and less stressful than roping, and is increasingly important in modern ranching practice.) These examples of the diverse ways in which animals serve us today reflect the partnership that began long ago.

DRAFT POWER AND TRANSPORTATION

Before tractors, U.S. agriculture depended on draft power from horses, donkeys, mules, and oxen. Plowing and cultivation of land, hauling of materials via carts and wagons and on the backs of these animals, persisted into the mid-twentieth century in North America and Europe. In more than 70 countries, power from animals is still vital to agriculture. Cattle, buffalo, yak, camel, horse, donkey, mule, and reindeer are the most prevalently used. There are more than 250 million oxen, buffalo, camels, horses, mules, and donkeys used for power in Asia. Africa and Latin America also depend heavily on draft animals in agriculture. Replacement of draft animals in Asia alone by mechanization would cost many billions of dollars of capital, and additional annual costs for fuel and repairs. Draft animals feed principally on crop residues and forages, resulting in little or no requirement of the farmer for cash outlay for power. Mountain peoples of Asia and Latin America and farmers in many developing countries are highly dependent on animals for transport of agricultural products to market. Also, in many urban areas of developing countries, animal transport is essential for moving goods and people. Although the importance of animal draft power in agriculture in the industrialized countries has been supplanted by mechanization, draft animals are still critical to food production and distribution in much of the world. Draft horses still are used as the main, and in some cases, the only source of power for field work on some family farms scattered in many areas of the United States.

MANURE, CROP RESIDUES, AND FOOD PROCESSING WASTES

Manure and Crop Residues

Manure (excretory products, including feces and urine) produced by animals throughout the world represents an enormous amount of organic matter and inorganic minerals. In the United States alone on any one day, about 1.4 billion poultry, 96 million cattle, 58 million swine, and 18 million other livestock, including sheep, horses, goats, mink, and rabbits are producing manure. (Poultry, swine, and smaller species such as mink and rabbits reach market age in less than one year, so the number of these animals produced per year is greater than the inventory numbers on a given day.) The quantity and use of animal manure and other organic wastes produced annually in the United States (CAST, 1995) illustrate the massive volume (Table 2-4). Animal manure and crop residues together contribute more than 75% of total organic wastes, municipal refuse contributes nearly 20%, and miscellaneous other sources contribute the remainder. The U.S. Department of Agriculture estimates that 90% of the manure, nearly 70% of the crop residues, and nearly 25% of sewage sludge and septage is applied to the land. The fertilizer value provided by recycling of organic matter and nutrients in this way is significant. Large amounts of nitrogen, phosphorus, and potassium, the three major ingredients in most commercial fertilizers, are returned to the soil by land application of manure, crop residues, and sewage

TABLE 2-4

QUANTITY AND USE OF ORGANIC WASTES IN THE UNITED STATES

Organic Waste	Annual Production (tons of dry matter)	Total Production (%)	Applied to Land (%)
Animal manure	158,500,000	22	90
Crop residue[1]	387,978,000	54	68
Sewage sludge and septage[2]	3,932,000	<1	23
Municipal refuse	130,500,000	18	1
Other	42,417,000	5	1

[1]Crop residues from grain include vegetative portions of the plant remaining in the field after harvest (corn stalks, grain straw, weeds). Crop residues from forages include unharvested clippings of hay, corn silage and clippings of weeds associated with effective pasture management, and wasted hay and silage from feedlots and livestock barns. These feedlot wastes usually become mixed with manure. Crop residues from fruits and vegetables include mostly nonharvested plant parts.

[2]Sewage sludges (also called biosolids) are products of wastewater treatment processes. Although they are organic in nature and contain useful plant nutrients, they may also contain potentially hazardous elements from the wastestream entering the treatment plant. Careful monitoring of these biosolids guards against soil and water pollution from sewage sludge. It is expected that in the future there will be continued increase in the use of sewage sludge in land applications.

Source: USDA.

sludge. In fact, there is growing concern over water and soil pollution by the land application of excessive amounts of these mineral elements (see Chapter 11).

Animal manure can be processed in several ways before land application. Common methods are composting, flush-lagoon systems, pit storage, and gravity drainage. Of course, grazing animals spread their own manure on the land. Much of the nitrogen excreted is lost to the atmosphere, but some nitrogen and all of the inorganic mineral elements are returned to the soil. Poultry and swine manure collected in confinement feeding facilities can be recovered for refeeding to beef cattle, dairy cattle, and sheep. This practice has been shown through research to be an effective system of recovering, processing, and refeeding such wastes as sources of energy, protein, and mineral nutrients in ruminant animal production. Pathogenic organisms in the manure are killed by anaerobic fermentation of the manure, rendering the processed material safe to be refed without danger to animal or human health. The product of the fermentation process not only provides valuable nutrients in animal feeds, but assists in animal waste management and disposal. Another alternative use of poultry and swine manure is the production of methane from anaerobic fermentation. This microbiological process by which methane is produced from animal wastes has been practiced in many parts of the world for decades as a means of providing fuel for cooking food, powering motor vehicles, and generating electricity.

Food Processing Wastes

Processing and recycling wastes from a variety of plant and animal sources are used effectively in animal production. Wastes have been characterized as "resources out of place." In a publication of the Council for Agricultural Science and Technology (CAST, 1995), the status of food processing waste has been described as follows:

". . . food processing waste generally is either a potential feed ingredient for farm animal or pet food or a potential nutrient source for crops. For example, in cereal processing, firms such as breweries, distilleries, and mills, by-products are not wasted but marketed as livestock feed ingredients. Similarly, in meat processing firms, poor-quality meat-by-products can be converted to better-quality human food-products by means of breakdown and recombination of by-product components. Other by-products such as stomachs, intestines, and fish wastes are converted to pet foods. Finally, poor-quality effluent may be used on cropland as a nutrient source."

Although a significant amount of food processing waste is recycled, it has been estimated that food wasted from the first stage of processing to the point of consumption may be approximately 25% of total food supply on an energy basis (CAST, 1995). Crop residues can be utilized in several ways—fuel, animal feed, bulking agents in manure and sewage sludge composting systems—so as to produce organic wastes that are safe, stable, and unobjectionable for land application as fertilizer. These and other approaches are under development to reduce crop processing losses.

Improved utilization of residues from animal waste processing is under development using several approaches. Potential advances include:

- Composting of manure, bedding, dead animals, hatchery wastes for land application
- Production of methane and other biogas fuels from manure, dead animals, and hatchery wastes by anaerobic fermentation
- Improved digestibility of nutrients in common feedstuffs so as to reduce levels of carbon, nitrogen, and phosphorus lost in manure (for example, supplementation of diets with the enzyme phytase improves the utilization of bound phosphorus in plant feedstuffs)
- Refeeding to animals of animal wastes and approved slaughterhouse wastes (restrictions have been imposed on the refeeding of some animal tissues)
- Developing methods for reducing water volume used in meat, poultry, fish, and dairy processing plants

The continued pursuit of innovative, safe, and cost-effective ways of utilizing food processing wastes in animal production can be expected to enhance sustainable agriculture through improved resource utilization. A legitimate and worthwhile goal for animal agriculture would be to reduce by half the food processing wastes (currently estimated to be 25%) that currently occur between harvest and delivery to the consumer.

BIOMEDICAL RESEARCH

Laboratory animals such as rats, mice, and guinea pigs have been used for many years as the primary animal models in biomedical research. Dogs, cats, and nonhuman primates (monkeys, baboons) have also made major contributions to our current knowledge of animal and human biology and have provided fundamental knowledge upon which many current practices in medicine are based. In more recent years, the larger farm animals have been used in increasing numbers. Sheep are commonly used in studies of fetal development and physiology. Cattle and sheep are used in developmental research in the use of artificial organs for humans. Pigs are the most commonly used farm animals for biomedical research. Many medical schools and biomedical research units in the United States now employ the pig instead of the dog in research directed toward solving human disease problems. Pigs resemble humans more closely than do common laboratory animals in many aspects of physiology and anatomy, including the heart and circulatory system, lipid and cholesterol metabolism, the digestive system, and the skin. Pig heart valves are used to replace defective or diseased heart valves in humans. Pig skin is used in burn therapy.

A major breakthrough may be approaching in animal organ replacements in other animals and humans (xenotransplantation). Human organs for transplantation are scarce. This limits the number of transplants performed annually in the United States to a small fraction of the number that would be done if organs were available for all potential recipients. For example, about 2400 heart transplants are performed annually in the United States but there are 40,000 potential recipients. The same problem exists for kidney, liver, lung, and pancreas transplants. Ongoing research in the immunological aspects of organ rejection by the host is providing favorable prospects for eventual success in long-term survival of recipients of xenotransplants. Genetic engineering of the donor to minimize organ rejection by the recipient of xenotransplants appears to be important to the feasibility of broad clinical application. Emphasis is on the pig as a suitable xenotransplant donor for several reasons. The pig is of an appropriate size, its organ physiology is like that of humans, there is limited risk of zoonotic disease (disease transmittable from pig to human), genetic engineering is feasible in the pig, and there is relatively good knowledge of the immune system (Platt, 1996). Some estimates indicate a pig-to-human heart transplant as early as 2000.

SUMMARY

Animals have been an integral part of society for centuries. Domestic farm animals are an important source of food nutrients in most cultures. In the United States, animal products provide about one-fourth of the energy (calories) and two-thirds of the protein, essentially all of the vitamin B12, and significant amounts of other vitamins and of mineral elements in the average diet. Although only about 2.6% of the population is engaged in farming, the agricultural industry in the United States employs more than 22 million workers and generates 900 billion dollars annually, of which more than half comes from animal agriculture. Edible and inedible byproducts of animal agriculture and pharmaceutical therapeutic agents derived from animals contribute significantly to society. Animals provide companionship and pleasure for urban and rural families alike. Animals serve people in diverse ways, including the production of milk, wool, and eggs; service as seeing-eye dogs; in rodent control; in herding livestock; guarding property; and giving trustworthy companionship. Animals are used throughout the world for draft power and transportation and their excreta are used for fertilizer, fuel, and feed. Laboratory and domestic farm animals are used as animal models in biomedical research and their organs are potentially valuable as replacement for diseased or damaged organs in humans (xenotransplantation). The contributions of animals to society outlined in this chapter provide the basis for the in-depth study of the broad field of animal science that unfolds in succeeding chapters.

REFERENCES

CAST. 1995. Waste management and utilization in food production and processing. Council for Agricultural Science and Technology Report No. 124. Ames IA: CAST, pp. 1–125.

Fountain, R. and Thurman, D. 1998. Animal health industry faces mixed times. *Feedstuffs*, 70: 1 (November 9).

Gonzalez-Stawinski, G. V., Lin, S. S., and Platt, J. L. 2000. Chapter 17 in W. G. Pond and H. J. Mersmann, (eds.), *Biology of the Domestic Pig*. Ithaca, New York: Cornell University Press.

McDowell, R. E. 1991. *A Partnership for Humans and Animals*. Raleigh, NC: Kinnic Publishers, pp. 1–91.

Platt, J. L. 1996. Xenotransplantation. *Science and Medicine,* July/August: 62–71.

Taylor, R. E. 1995. *Scientific Farm Animal Production*. Upper Saddle River, NJ: Prentice Hall, pp. 1–672.

USDA, 1980. *Appraisal, Soil and Water Resources Conservation Act, Part 1*. Washington, D.C.: U.S. Department of Agriculture.

USDA, 1998. *Agricultural Statistics*. Washington, D.C.: U.S. Department of Agriculture Economic Research Service.

CHAPTER THREE
ANIMAL AGRICULTURE IN THE UNITED STATES AND THE WORLD

HISTORICAL PERSPECTIVE
ANIMAL AND CROP PRODUCTION PROFILES IN THE WORLD
ANIMAL AND CROP PRODUCTION PROFILES IN THE UNITED STATES
THE PLACE OF THE UNITED STATES IN WORLD ANIMAL AGRICULTURE
SUMMARY

In this chapter we describe the development of animal agriculture; its dependence on crop production; its utilization of byproducts and wastes of food processing; its current profile in the United States and globally; and trends resulting from new advances in science and technology. The purpose is to provide the basis for developing concepts of stewardship and sustainability of animal agriculture and the principles of animal biology and the animal industries, subjects to be explored in depth in succeeding chapters of the book.

HISTORICAL PERSPECTIVE

Animals and their products were used for clothing, tools, and other purposes even before their domestication and animal products have been constituents of human diets in many cultures for centuries. The growth of agriculture has been accompanied by a steady increase in numbers of domestic farm animals for food and draft purposes as well as for companionship, transportation, and improved soil fertility. In addition, animals, as in the past, continue to provide a variety of nonedible products, including wool, hides, furs, and industrial, pharmaceutical, and medicinal products.

ANIMAL AND CROP PRODUCTION PROFILES IN THE WORLD

Animal and crop production are so closely linked that it is important to consider both components in describing the development and current profile of animal agriculture. Any change in world crop production has an impact on animal production. Therefore both are discussed briefly.

Crop Production in the World

World grain production (wheat, rye, rice, corn, oats, barley, and sorghum) has increased threefold since 1950 (from 631 million tons in 1950 to 1841 million tons in 1996) (Figure 3-1; Brown, et al., 1997; USDA World Grain Database, 1993). The use of grains for animal feed also has increased, but at a slower rate. Wheat, rye, and rice are used primarily for direct human consumption, but most of the corn, oats, barley, and sorghum (also called milo) is fed to animals. Although the growth in world grain production has been dramatic, the human population also has increased steadily; yet the amount available per capita has remained stable, due largely to a steady increase in grain yield per acre. World Bank (Crosson and Anderson, 1992) estimates that total world demand for cereal grains (this does not include corn) will double between 1992 and 2030 and that a major portion of this increase will be for food animal production, reflecting the continued increase in demand for animal products. Byproducts from processing of grains and seed

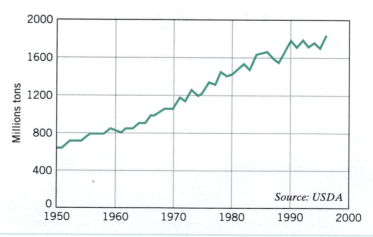

FIGURE 3-1

World grain production (barley, corn, oats, rice, rye, sorghum, and wheat) 1950–1996.

legumes (e.g., soybeans) for human consumption provide large amounts of animal feedstuffs. This outlet for such resources reduces costs of meat, milk, and egg production while providing a market for byproducts of grain and seed legume processing. World grain use, which includes consumption by humans as well as by animals, has risen steadily for centuries, and may be expected to continue, within the constraints of land availability and resources.

Crops used mostly for human consumption, but also for animals, include the cereal grains and corn, root crops, such as cassava (also known as tapioca, manioc, yuca), yams, sweet potatoes; grains such as pearl millet, amaranth; seed legumes such as an array of peas and beans; and other crops grown in small plots in many areas for local use. These plant resources represent major dietary constituents for families and communities, particularly in developing regions of the world. Many small farms that produce these crops also produce traditional crops to support modest livestock enterprises and for direct human consumption.

Animal Production in the World

World meat production trends from 1950 to 1997 are shown in Figure 3-2*a, b,* and *c* (adapted from Brown, et al., 1997). Per-capita meat consumption worldwide has doubled since 1950, from 17.2 kg (37.8 lb) then to 33.8 kg (74.4 lb) in 1996 (Brown, et al., 1997). Taking into consideration the expanded human population, the total meat produced during that same period increased about 4.5-fold (from 44 million tons in 1950 to 195 million tons in 1996). Pork and poultry production have increased more rapidly than beef and lamb, especially since the mid-1970s.

Worldwide, ruminant animals (beef cattle, dairy cattle, sheep, goats, water buffalo, and other species) and nonruminant herbivores (horses, rabbits, and other species) consume enormous amounts of harvested and grazed forages. Most of this animal feed is neither palatable nor of significant nutritional value to humans. Vast areas of the total global land base are of little economic value for cultivated crop production due to hilly topography, low soil fertility, climatic constraints, inadequate or poorly distributed rainfall, or combinations of these factors. Livestock utilize these nontillable areas for grazing to produce a valuable human food resource on otherwise nonproductive land. In addition, huge areas of cropland are used for postharvest grazing and scavenging by ruminants and swine to transform otherwise wasted crop residues to edible products. The world numbers of the major species of domesticated ruminant and nonruminant animals used in agriculture, their primary uses, and the countries with the largest number of each are listed in Table 3-1 (*FAO Production Yearbook,* 1997; Taylor, 1995).

In addition to the animals listed in Table 3-1, many other animal species are important in specific countries and regions of the world and contribute significantly to improving the living standards and pleasure of the local human populations. Such animals as rabbits, guinea fowl, pigeons, and an array of rodents, including agouti, capybara, giant rat, guinea pig, hutia, mara, paca, and vizcacha as well as larger species including deer, duikers, and antelope, and lizards such as the green iguana and black iguana are important in some areas or are being studied as potentially useful animals. These little-known

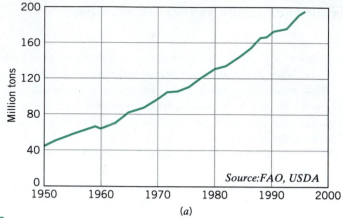

FIGURE 3-2a

World meat production, 1950–1996: Total meat produced (millions of tons).
Source: Reprinted by permission of W. W. Norton and Co., New York, NY.

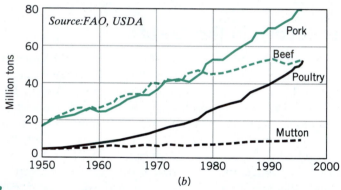

FIGURE 3-2b

World meat production, 1950–1996: Total beef, pork, poultry, and mutton (lamb) produced (millions of tons).
Source: Reprinted by permission of W. W. Norton and Co., New York, NY.

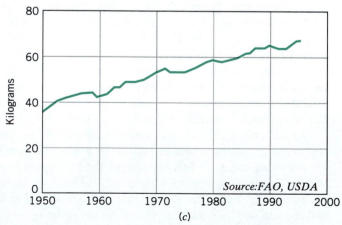

FIGURE 3-2c

World meat production, 1950–1996: Meat produced per person (kg).
Source: Reprinted by permission of W. W. Norton and Co., New York, NY.

TABLE 3-1

WORLD DOMESTICATED ANIMALS USED IN AGRICULTURE: NUMBERS, USES, AND DISTRIBUTION BY COUNTRY IN 1997

Ruminant Animals	Total Number (millions)	Leading Countries	Main Uses
Cattle	1,333	India, Brazil, USSR,[1] U.S., China,	Meat, milk, hides, draft
Sheep	1,064	Australia, USSR, China, NZ	Wool, meat, milk, hides
Goats	703	India, China, Pakistan, Nigeria	Milk, meat, hair hides
Buffalo	167	India, China, Pakistan, Thailand	Draft, milk, meat
Camels	19	Somalia, Sudan, India, Ethiopia	Packing, riding, draft, meat, milk, hides
Yaks	13[3]	USSR, Tibet	Packing, draft, riding meat, milk, hides
Llamas	13[3]	Peru, Ecuador, Other South	Packing, riding, meat, milk, hides

Nonruminant Animals			
Chickens	13,413[2]	China, U.S., USSR, Indonesia	Meat, eggs, feathers
Swine	937[2]	China, U.S., USSR, Germany	Meat
Ducks	736[2]	China, Indonesia, Vietnam	Meat, eggs, feathers
Turkeys	239[2]	U.S., USSR, France,	Meat, eggs, feathers
Horses	62	China, Mexico, USSR, Brazil, U.S.	Draft, packing, riding, meat
Asses	44[3]	China, Ethiopia, Mexico	Draft, packing, riding
Mules	15[3]	China, Mexico, Brazil	Draft, packing, riding

[1]Former USSR.
[2]Because the life cycle of these animals is less than one year, the total number produced per year exceeds the census figures listed.
[3]1992

Sources: FAO Production Yearbook (1997); adapted from Taylor (1995), by permission of Prentice-Hall, Inc., Upper Saddle River, NJ.

animals with a promising economic future are described in the book, *Microlivestock* (National Research Council, 1991). Some of these animals may offer advantages on small farms in developing countries where large capital investments are not feasible and where scale of production can be matched with limited family resources to provide a significant part of the daily food requirements plus surplus products for cash income.

The number of cattle, sheep, goats, camels, horses, and pigs in the world has increased since 1950 from 2.3 to more than 4.0 billion; poultry production grew from 3 to more than 11 billion over the same period. Total world meat consumption has more than quadrupled since 1950 to more than 170 million tons per year (more than 32 kg per capita). Pork accounts for about 40% of total consumption (75 million tons in 1995), while meat from cattle plus water buffalo (not to be confused with bison of North America, often called buffalo) accounts for about 50 million tons, poultry about 40 million tons, and sheep and goats most of the remainder. Annual meat consumption per capita tends to be highest in developed countries [U.S. is highest at 112 pounds (USDA, 1998)] and lowest in developing countries, in agreement with the acknowledged relationship between per-capita income and consumption of animal products (see Figure 1-3). World meat production continues to rise to accommodate the sustained demand for animal products. Total meat production from 52 specified countries increased from 117 million metric tons in 1989 to more than 125 metric tons in 1996 and the trend continues.

Consumption of fresh milk and processed milk products is more than 550 million tons annually (88% from cattle, 6% from buffalo, and the remainder from 14 additional species, including sheep, goat, camel, reindeer, and yak). More than 40 million tons of eggs are consumed annually from chickens as well as significant amounts of eggs from other fowl.

Fish and other marine species provide a significant source of animal protein for segments of populations in developing countries; aquaculture is the most rapidly growing animal industry in some developed countries, including the United States.

There is legitimate concern about the quality of the environment as animal production expands in a finite global space with an ever-growing human population. Water and air pollution, global warming, degradation of rangelands by overgrazing, and other potential threats to the maintenance of a stable environment must be addressed as the world becomes more crowded and resources become more limited. These challenges are considered in more detail in Chapter 11.

ANIMAL AND CROP PRODUCTION PROFILES IN THE UNITED STATES

Farms and Land in the United States

There are about 2 million farms in the United States (Table 3-2). Farm number has declined steadily since 1984, while acreage of farm land has also decreased slightly. On the other hand, average farm size climbed steadily until the late 1990s and now appears to have plateaued. (A farm is defined by the U.S. Department of Agriculture as any establishment from which $1000 or more of agricultural products were sold during the year). The United States can be divided (USDA, 1994) into farm production regions, shown in Figure 3-3.

Crop Production in the United States

Crop production in the United States includes a vast variety of plants ranging from an array of vegetables and fruits grown for direct human consumption to an array of forages grown exclusively for animal feeding. Some of the major crops are discussed here to emphasize the important role they play in animal production. Crops contribute to their di-

TABLE 3-2

NUMBER OF FARMS, LAND IN FARMS, AND AVERAGE FARM SIZE IN THE UNITED STATES, 1983–1993

Year	Number of Farms	Land in Farms	Average Farm Size (acres)
1983	2,379,000	1,023,425,000	430
1984	2,334,000	1,017,803,000	436
1985	2,293,000	1,012,073,000	441
1986	2,250,000	1,005,333,000	447
1987	2,213,000	998,923,000	451
1988	2,197,000	994,543,000	453
1989	2,171,000	991,153,000	457
1990	2,140,000	987,420,000	461
1991	2,105,000	982,766,000	467
1992	2,094,000	979,963,000	468
1993	2,068,000	978,153,000	473
1997	2,057,900	968,338,000	471

Source: USDA *Agriculture Fact Book* (1994), USDA Agricultural Statistics (1998), Table 9-9.

rect and indirect consumption by animals. An array of food processing byproducts and inedible food wastes are fed to animals. Such feed resources include milling, distillery, and brewery byproducts, oilseed meals, and low-grade cereal grains and seed legumes declared substandard for human consumption. These products, if not utilized for animal feed, would contribute to disposal problems and environmental pollution.

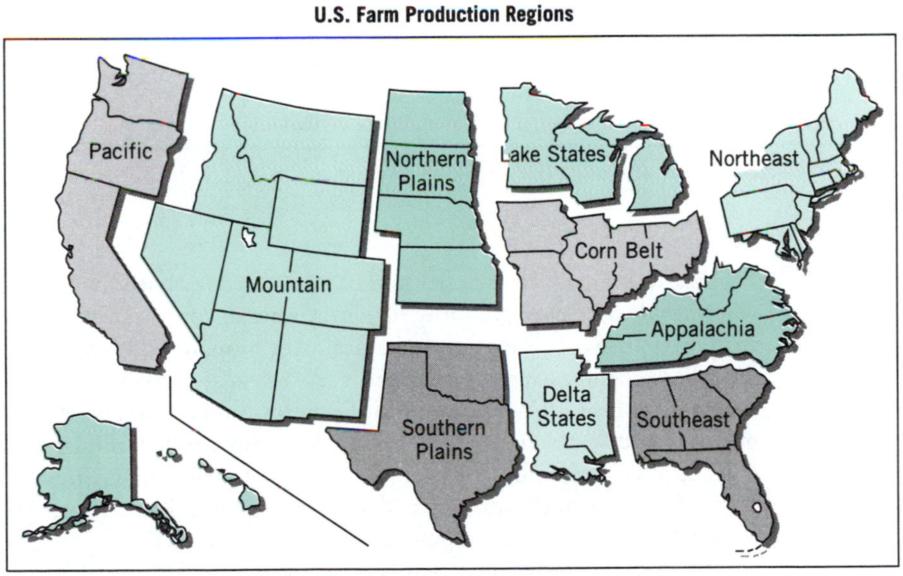

U.S. Farm Production Regions

FIGURE 3-3

U.S. farm production regions.
Source: Agriculture Fact Book, Office of Communications, USDA (1994).

TABLE 3-3

PRODUCTION OF SOME MAJOR CROPS IN THE UNITED STATES, 1993

Crop	Area Harvested (1000 acres)	Yield/Acre	Unit	Total Production (1000s)	Value of Production (1000 dollars)
Corn for grain	62,921	100.7	bushel	6,336,470	16,031,861
Corn for silage	6,831	11.9	ton	81,289	—
Wheat	62,712	38.2	bushel	2,396,440	7,644,737
Oats	3,803	54.4	bushel	206,770	291,014
Barley	6,743	58.9	bushel	398,041	812,889
Rye	381	27.1	bushel	10,340	27,149
Flaxseed	191	18.2	bushel	3,480	14,848
Cotton lint	12,783	606	bale	16,134	4,520,908
Cottonseed	—	—	ton	6,343	743,389
Rice	2,833	5510	ton	156,110	1,246,875
Sorghum for grain	8,916	59.9	bushel	534,172	1,234,500
Sorghum for silage	351	11.2	ton	3,914	—
Hay, all	59,679	2.46	ton	146,799	10,956,746
Soybeans	57,347	32.6	bushel	1,870,958	11,949,633
Peanuts	1,690	2008	pound	3,392,415	1,030,904
Potatoes	1,317	326	Cwt	428,693	2,640,628
Sunflower	2,486	1035	pound	2,572,063	328,435
Sugarcane	948.3	32.8	ton	31,101	886,285
Sugarbeets	1,409	18.6	ton	26,249	1,023,687
Apples	461	23,300	pound	10,722,800	1,360,706
Oranges	712	336	box	239,250	1,581,652
Beans, snap	87	47	Cwt	4,102	153,505
Carrots	103	306	Cwt	31,884	295,803
Tomatoes (fresh)	135	264	Cwt	35,499	1,126,387
Tomatoes (processed)	308	31	ton	9,677	581,893
Corn, sweet (fresh)	210	90	Cwt	18,834	335,213
Corn, sweet (processed)	472	5.76	ton	2,721	197,112
Lettuce, head	208	326	Cwt	67,814	1,086,756
Lettuce, leaf	41	206	Cwt	8,363	247,459

Source: USDA *Agricultural Statistics* (1994), Table 543.

Many grains, such as barley and oats, are used for both human food and animal feed, whereas wheat is used primarily for direct human consumption and grain sorghums and corn (except sweet corn grown specifically for human food) are used primarily for animal feed. Seed legumes such as peas and snap beans are grown for human food, but others such as soybeans are grown to produce oil for human use and the high-protein meal remaining after extraction of the oil is used primarily for animal feeding. Other oilseed crops grown primarily for human and industrial use include sunflower, safflower, flaxseed, canola, and cottonseed. The high protein residues remaining after extraction of the oil are used as protein supplements in animal feeds.

Some of the most important crops grown in the United States are listed in Table 3-3 to allow a comparison of the acreage, yield per acre, total yearly production, and value of

TABLE 3-4

TOP-RANKING STATES IN THE PRODUCTION OF MAJOR FIELD CROPS IN THE UNITED STATES, 1994

Corn (mil. bu)		Soybeans (mil. bu)		Hay, baled (1000 tons)		Wheat (mil. bu)		Cotton (1000 bales)		Barley (mil. bu)		Sorghum (mil. bu)		Oats (mil. bu)		Rice (mil. Cwt)	
IL	1300	IL	387	SD	8450	KS	389	TX	5144	ND	118	TX	182	ND	37	AR	62
IA	880	IA	257	CA	7590	ND	337	CA	3144	MT	64	KS	176	SD	27	CA	37
NE	785	IN	223	NE	7573	MT	204	MS	1550	IN	60	NE	74	WI	24	LA	24
IN	713	OH	154	TX	7506	WA	178	LA	1105	MN	38	MO	47	MN	24	TX	16
OH	361	MO	119	MO	7333	OK	162	AR	1094	WA	23	IL	17	PA	10	MS	13
MN	322	MN	115	KS	6430	TX	118	AZ	877	SD	15	OK	15	IA	9	MO	5
US 6,344		1,869		148,854		2,403		16,145		400		568		206		157	

Source: USDA *Agricultural Statistics* (1994), Table 700.

that production. The year 1993 was selected as a recent example (USDA, 1994). There is a year-to-year variation in acreage, yield, total production, and total value of a given crop due to fluctuations in weather, overall economy in the United States and the world, marketing and trade barriers, and other factors. Advances in technology resulting from research and development efforts in government and private industry also have an impact on overall trends in crop production.

Note in Table 3-3 that corn, wheat, hay, and soybeans are by far the most important crops in the United States in terms of acreage devoted to their production, total amount produced, and total dollar value. Of these four crops, only wheat is used primarily for direct human consumption. Crops such as potatoes, sugarbeets, apples, oranges, tomatoes, and lettuce are grown for direct human consumption; they are grown on fewer acres but have high dollar value per acre and a high total dollar value.

The areas of the country where crops are grown are determined, in addition to forces affecting local demand, by climate, topography, water supply, soil fertility, and other factors that are appropriate for optimum economy of production and marketing. For example, the Northern Plains and Cornbelt states are noted for corn and soybean production, the Southeast, Delta, and Southern Plains states for cotton and peanut production, the more arid regions of the Northern Plains, Mountain, and Southern Plains for wheat production, and the mild climate of the Pacific, lower Mountain, and Southeast states for a large portion of our fruit and vegetable supply. On the other hand, many crops, including hay and several cereal grains, are grown throughout the United States, using plant cultivars and species well adapted to particular environmental conditions in the area. Leading states for the production of some of the major field crops are listed in Table 3-4.

Note the preponderance of states in the midsection of the United States among the six highest-ranking states for most crops listed except cotton and rice, the production of which is confined mostly to the south and southwest, and hay, the production of which extends to most regions of the United States. Detailed information about a wide range of individual crops, including those listed in Tables 3-3 and 3-4 is provided throughout the

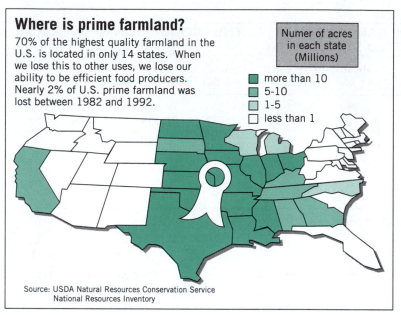

FIGURE 3-4

Where is prime farmland in the United States?

book in relation to the feeding and production of individual species and classes of animals. The brief discussion above has been intended merely to provide for the student a broad appreciation of the scope of crop production in the United States in relation to its close linkage with animal agriculture.

Seventy percent of the highest-quality farmland is located in 14 states in the midsection of the United States (Figure 3-4). These states also produce a major fraction of the meat and milk produced in the United States, underscoring again the linkage between crop and animal production. Loss of this productive land to other uses has a negative impact on our ability to produce food economically. During the past 20 years, about 2% of this prime farmland was removed from agricultural production (urbanization, roads, other nonfarm uses). In addition to losses of prime cropland, a significant acreage (17 million acres) of nonfederal rangeland (as distinguished from federally owned public grazing land) has been converted to other uses, while 7 million acres have been converted from other uses to rangeland, resulting in a net loss of 10 million acres of rangeland (408.9 million acres of rangeland in 1982 was reduced to 398.9 million acres in 1992) (USDA, 1994b).

It is noteworthy that in the Mountain states and other rangeland areas the National Forest System rangeland is managed to conserve the land and its vegetation while providing food for both livestock and wildlife. Under a multiple-use system, grazing areas also serve as watersheds, wildlife habitat, and recreation sites. Grazing permits are granted on

TABLE 3-5

FARM PRODUCTION AND OUTPUT OF ANIMAL PRODUCTS IN THE UNITED STATES 1983–1991 (100 = 1982)

Year	Farm Output	All Livestock and Products	Meat Animals	Dairy Products	Poultry and Eggs
1983	82	102	102	103	100
1984	98	100	100	99	103
1985	104	103	99	105	108
1986	100	103	99	106	112
1987	102	105	100	105	122
1988	95	108	102	107	125
1989	105	110	102	106	130
1990	112	112	102	109	138
1991	110	114	105	109	144

Source: USDA *Agricultural Statistics* (1994), Table 544.

national forests and grasslands within the National Forest System. Cattle and sheep graze under permit arrangements, for which a fee is paid to the federal government by farmers and ranchers. Annually, about 9 to 10 million animal unit months of livestock grazing are recorded on National Forest System lands. The publicly and privately owned grasslands and rangelands scattered throughout the United States clearly represent a vital crop resource of importance to animal agriculture and to maintenance of soil fertility, erosion control, and ecological stability.

Animal Production in the United States

Animal products have steadily increased in the United States as the population has grown. This growth is illustrated in Table 3-5, in which total farm output and livestock products, dairy products, poultry and eggs, and meat animal production are expressed as indices for each year from 1983 through 1991 (100 = 1982). Note the upward trend in all components of animal production.

Cash receipts from animal commodities in the United States from 1973 through 1997 more than tripled for poultry and dairy, doubled for swine, nearly doubled for beef, and remained relatively constant for sheep. Total animal receipts have represented one-half or more of total farm income in the United States throughout the past 25 years (Table 3-6).

Meat animal production listed in Table 3-5 consists of cattle and calves, sheep and lambs, and swine. Other animals, including goats and rabbits, also contribute to the meat supply in the United States. Although horses and mules are not used for human consumption in the United States, some meat from these animals is exported to France, Belgium, and other countries for human consumption.

The inventory (census) of annual calf, pig, and lamb crops, and total yearly pounds of production of live beef cattle, swine, sheep and lambs, and milk in the United States

TABLE 3-6

CASH RECEIPTS FROM ANIMAL COMMODITIES AND TOTAL FARM INCOME

Year	Poultry	Beef	Dairy	Swine	Sheep	Total Animal Receipts	Total Farm Income
				(billion dollars)			
1973	6.9	22.3	8.3	7.5	0.52	45.9	87.1
1974	6.4	17.8	9.7	6.9	0.45	41.5	92.4
1975	6.8	17.5	10.2	7.9	0.45	43.3	88.9
1976	7.2	19.3	11.8	7.5	0.49	46.4	95.4
1977	7.2	20.2	11.8	7.3	0.48	47.5	96.2
1978	8.0	28.2	12.7	8.8	0.56	59.0	112.9
1979	8.7	34.4	14.7	9.0	0.61	68.1	133.8
1980	8.9	31.5	16.6	8.9	0.59	67.8	142.0
1981	9.9	29.6	18.1	9.8	0.55	63.3	144.1
1982	9.5	29.9	18.2	10.6	0.54	70.3	147.1
1983	10.0	28.7	18.8	9.8	0.52	69.4	141.1
1984	12.2	30.6	17.9	9.7	0.47	72.9	150.7
1985	11.2	29.0	18.1	9.0	0.50	69.8	151.9
1986	12.7	28.9	17.8	9.7	0.50	71.0	147.0
1987	11.5	33.6	17.7	10.3	0.60	76.0	141.8
1988	12.9	36.8	17.6	9.2	0.50	79.4	161.1
1989	15.4	36.9	19.4	9.5	0.50	84.1	160.9
1990	15.2	39.9	20.2	11.6	0.40	89.9	169.9
1991	15.1	39.6	18.0	11.1	0.40	86.7	168.7
1992	15.5	37.3	19.7	10.0	0.50	85.6	171.3
1993	17.3	39.4	19.2	10.9	0.60	90.2	177.6
1994	18.4	36.4	19.9	9.9	0.50	88.2	181.2
1995	19.1	34.0	19.9	10.3	0.60	87.0	187.7
1996	22.3	31.1	22.8	12.7	0.60	92.0	202.3
1997[1]	21.8	36.1	21.0	13.2	0.60	96.0	204.0

[1]Preliminary.

Source: USDA.

from 1940 through 1997 are shown in Figure 3-5. This information clearly depicts the trends in production of each of these major animal products spanning the past 60 years.

Aquaculture is the most rapidly growing animal industry in the United States, due to the expansion of catfish farming in Mississippi and other Southeastern states and to a growing freshwater fish industry in other parts of the United States. In addition to the estimated 300 to 350 million fish caught annually by recreational fishermen in the United States, farm-raised freshwater fish have become an increasingly important enterprise in the United States. Farm-raised catfish production in the United States has increased dramatically from 5.7 million pounds in 1970 to nearly 500 million pounds in the late 1990s.

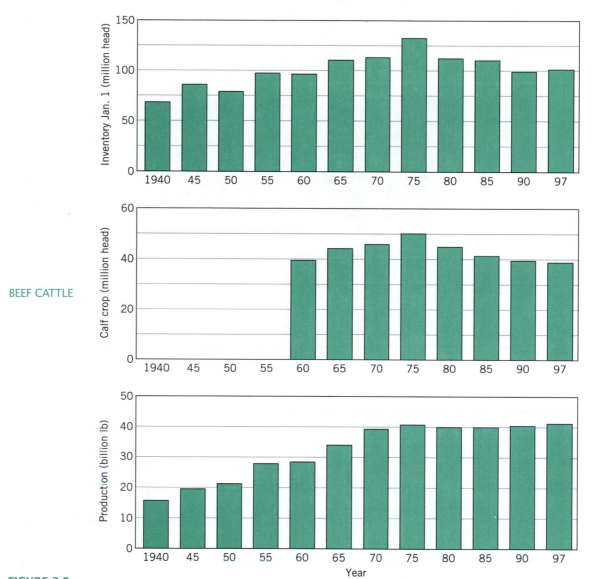

BEEF CATTLE

FIGURE 3-5

Inventory and production trends from 1940 to 1997 for beef cattle, swine, sheep, and dairy cattle.

* In general, hog numbers in the 1990s were similar to those of the 1940s, even though the U.S. population increased by nearly 115 million during those 50 years. Per-capita consumption of pork has nevertheless remained fairly constant. The increase in total pork consumed in the absence of an increase in total pigs produced is the result of increased meat produced per animal through improved technology.

**Sheep and lamb numbers peaked in the early 1940s, then gradually trended downward until 1989.

***Over the past 30 years, dairy cow numbers have declined by more than 40% while milk production per cow has more than doubled. The recent approval of the use of bovine somatotropin (bST) to increase milk production per cow may result in expanded total milk production, which may in turn stimulate a further reduction in cow numbers in the next few years.

Source: Farm and Food Facts (1992), The Kiplinger Washington Editors, Inc., Washington, D.C. and National Agricultural Statistics Service, Agricultural Statistics Board (USDA, 1998) (www.usda.gov/nass/aggraphs/graphics.htm).

SWINE

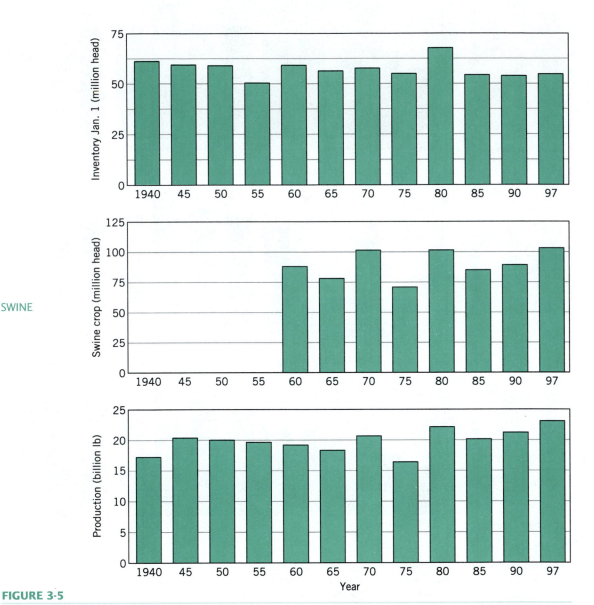

FIGURE 3-5

(Bar Inventory and production trends from 1940 to 1997 for beef cattle, swine, sheep, and dairy cattle. *(continued)*

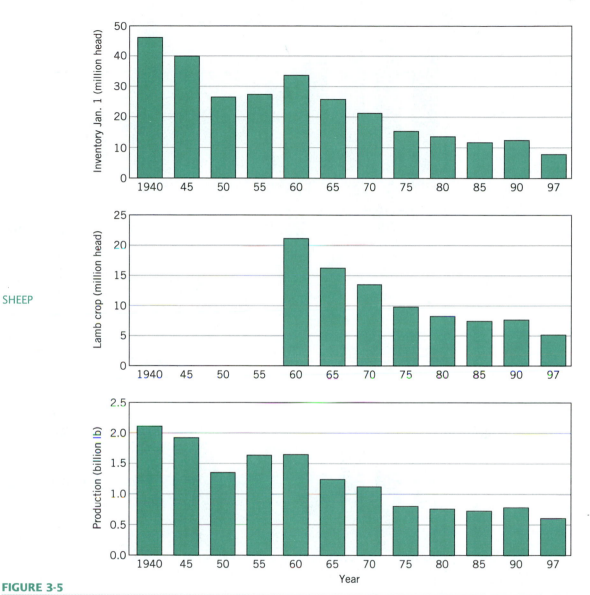

SHEEP

FIGURE 3-5

(Bar Inventory and production trends from 1940 to 1997 for beef cattle, swine, sheep, and dairy cattle. *(continued)*

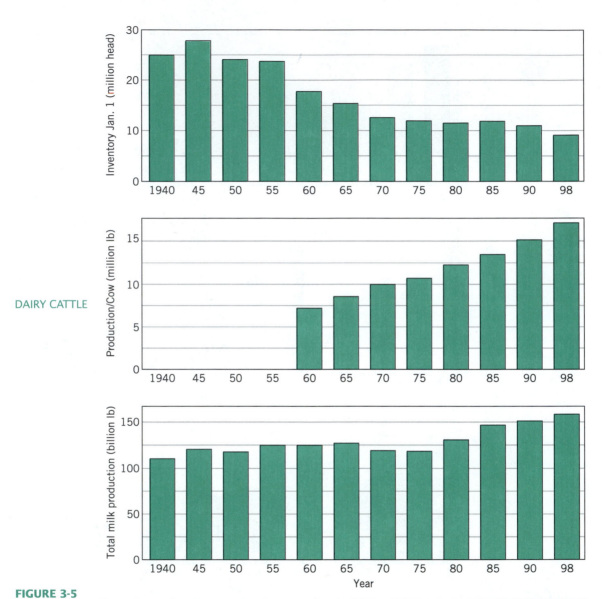

DAIRY CATTLE

FIGURE 3-5

(Bar Inventory and production trends from 1940 to 1997 for beef cattle, swine, sheep, and dairy cattle. *(continued)*

THE PLACE OF THE UNITED STATES IN WORLD ANIMAL AGRICULTURE

Animal agriculture in the United States provides a major portion of the food needs of this country plus an increasingly larger share of the animal products used in other countries. In 1994, the value of animals, animal products, animal feeds, and fish exported to all parts of the world approached 8 billion dollars out of a total value of more than 35 billion dollars for all agricultural products and 53.3 billion dollars for all U.S. exports. The global demand for food will significantly rise over the next several decades. It has been predicted that there will be stepped-up expansion of the economy in the newly industrialized nations (e.g., Hong Kong, South Korea, Taiwan), with a good chance for their economic growth to be twice as fast as that of the rest of the world. With these and other countries improving their economies, incomes will rise and demand for animal products will accordingly increase. The severe economic recession in Asia and other regions of the world in 1998 is expected to reduce the buying power of affected regions, thereby reducing the demand for exports of agricultural products, including animal products, from the United States.

It is important for American animal agriculture to continue to advance in productivity and efficiency in order to effectively compete for a reasonable share of the expanded market. Gross farm income in the United States (computed by summing the gross cash income from farming, noncash income, and the value of inventory adjustment) has been about 200 billion dollars in recent years. Generally, cash receipts from animal agriculture represent slightly more than cash receipts from crops in the United States (Table 3-6). The total contribution of agriculture to personal income in the United States is much greater than that of farm income as described above, because the personal income generated by the entire food industry must be considered. This includes personal income from jobs in all of agriculture (food processing, transportation, wholesale and retail marketing, advertising) and other industries that serve the farmer directly (feed, pharmaceutical, animal health, fertilizer, farm machinery and equipment, banking). When one adds together the value of all of these components of agriculture (the agribusiness sector) it is clear that the personal income derived from moving food, fiber, and other products of agriculture from the farm to the consumer is enormous. Personal income directly or indirectly derived from agriculture in the United States constitutes a significant share of total annual personal income from all sources. Therefore, maintenance of a prosperous U.S. agriculture is essential for general prosperity in the United States.

The progress achieved in the United States in improving the efficiency of animal production is illustrated in Table 3-7. The extent to which continued improvements in efficiency can be achieved will be governed by biological, economic, ecological, and resource constraints and by public attitudes toward animal agriculture and by government policies and a free market economy. International trade agreements such as the North American Free Trade Agreement (NAFTA) and the General Agreement on Trade and Tariff (GATT) can benefit animal agriculture by increasing the movement of food and other commodities to world markets.

TABLE 3-7

IMPROVEMENTS IN EFFICIENCY OF ANIMAL PRODUCTION IN THE UNITED STATES 1925–1990 (1925 = 100)[1]

Animal	Measure of Annual Productivity	1925		1950		1975		1990	
Beef cattle	Liveweight marketed/ breeding female (lb)	100	(220)	141	(310)	219	(482)	238	(524)
Sheep	Liveweight marketed/ breeding female (lb)	100	(60)	150	(90)	217	(130)	242	(145)
Dairy cows	Milk marketed/breeding female (thousand lb)	100	(4.2)	127	(5.3)	250	(10.5)	334	(14.0)
Swine	Lightweight marketed/ breeding female (thousand lb)	100	(1.6)	152	(2.4)	178	(2.9)	219	(3.5)
Broilers	Age to market weight (wk)	100	(15)	80	(12)	50	(7.5)	43	(6.5)
	Feed/unit of weight gain (lb)	100	(4.0)	82.5	(3.3)	52.5	(2.1)	47.5	(1.9)
	Liveweight at market (lb)	100	(2.8)	111	(3.1)	136	(3.8)	161	(4.5)
Turkeys	Age to market weight (wk)	100	(34)	71	(24)	56	(19)	47.5	(16)
	Feed/unit of weight gain (lb)	100	(5.5)	82	(4.5)	56	(3.1)	47	(2.6)
	Liveweight at market (lb)	100	(13.0)	143	(18.6)	142	(18.4)	162	(21.1)
Laying hens	Eggs/hen/yr (number)	100	(112)	155	(174)	207	(232)	223	(250)
	Feed/dozen eggs (lb)	100	(8.0)	72	(5.8)	52.5	(4.2)	50	(4.0)

[1]Number in parentheses after each entry is the absolute value for that measure of annual productivity.

Sources: Adapted from Taylor (1995) by permission of Prentice-Hall, Inc., Upper Saddle River, NJ.

SUMMARY

The goal of this chapter is to provide the background to help the student appreciate the concepts of stewardship and sustainability of animal agriculture and the principles of animal biology and the animal industries. These subjects will be explored in depth in succeeding chapters of the book. Animal and crop production are so tightly linked that both components must be considered in describing the current profile of animal agriculture. Many crops are directly consumed by humans, whereas many are processed before consumption by humans, and the processing byproducts are then available for animal consumption. Others are consumed by both humans and animals or only by animals. Vast areas unsuitable for producing food for direct human consumption are grazed by ruminant and some nonruminant animals. Grains and other crops primarily used for human consumption provide many inedible byproducts which, if not used by animals, would be environmental pollutants or would be wasted. The concept of animal agriculture as a crucial part of society is thus developed. The profiles of crop and animal production in the United States and the world are described, and the important place of U.S. animal agriculture in the world is discussed and evaluated.

REFERENCES

Brown, L. R., Renner, M., and Flavin, C. 1997. *Vital Signs.* Washington, D.C.: Worldwatch Institute.

Brown, L. S. 1990. *State of the World 1990.* New York: Norton.

Brown, L. S. 1994. *State of the World 1994.* New York: Norton.

CAST, 1990. *Food from Animals.* Council for Agricultural Science and Technology, Ames, IA.

CAST, 1999. *Animal Agriculture and Global Food Supply.* Council for Agricultural Science and Technology, Ames, IA.

Crosson, P. and Anderson, J. R. 1992. *Resources and Global Food Prospects: Supply and Demand for Cereals to 2030.* Washington, D.C.: The World Bank.

Durning, A. B. and Brough, H. B. 1992. Reforming the Livestock Economy. In L. S. Brown et al. (eds.), *State of the World 1992.* New York: Norton, pp. 66–82.

Food and Agriculture Organization (FAO). 1997. *FAO Production Yearbook.*

Kiplinger, A. 1992. Farm and food facts. *The Kiplinger Agriculture Letter.* Washington, D.C.: Kiplinger Washington Editors, Inc., pp. 1–48.

McDowell, R. E. 1991. *A Partnership for Humans and Animals.* Raleigh, NC: Kinnic Publishers, pp. 1–95.

National Research Council. 1991. *Microlivestock: Little-Known Small Animals with a Promising Economic Future.* Washington, D.C.: National Academy Press, pp. 1–448.

Taylor, R. E. 1995. *Scientific Farm Animal Production: An Introduction to Animal Science.* Upper Saddle River, NJ: Prentice Hall, pp. 1–672.

USDA, 1991. *World Livestock Situation.* Washington, D.C.: USDA-Foreign Agricultural Service, April.

USDA, 1992. *Agricultural Statistics.* Washington, D.C.: U.S. Government Printing Office, Table 442, p. 288.

USDA, 1993. World grain database, unpublished printout as quoted by L. S. Brown, Chapter 10, *State of the World 1994.* New York: Norton.

USDA, 1994a. *Agricultural Statistics.* Washington, D.C.: U.S. Government Printing Office.

USDA, 1994b. *Agriculture Fact Book.* Washington, D.C.: U.S. Department of Agriculture, Office of Communications.

USDA, 1998. *Agricultural Statistics.* Washington, D.C.: U.S. Government Printing Office.

CHAPTER FOUR
REPRODUCTION

Reproduction is the mechanism by which life perpetuates itself. Reproduction begins with the mating of the male and female. Genetic materials contained in sperm (spermatozoa) from the male and eggs (ova) from the female are united by fertilization to form an embryo. In mammals, the embryo develops in the female reproductive tract until attachment to the uterine lining of the dam occurs and then develops as a fetus until parturition. In birds, the embryo resides first within the maternal reproductive tract and later within the egg shell where it remains until hatching occurs. An understanding of the anatomy of the male and female reproductive tracts and their functions is needed to provide herd or flock management so as to maintain high reproductive efficiency and to develop and use new technologies. High reproductive efficiency is required for profitability of livestock and poultry enterprises. In this chapter, the anatomy and functions of the male and female reproductive organs are described and compared among species. Specific topics include the role of the gonadotropic hormones from the anterior pituitary gland in reproduction, the estrous cycle, gametogenesis, fertilization, pregnancy, embryo and fetal development, and parturition in mammals and egg production in birds. Current and developing technologies, including estrus synchronization, artificial insemination, embryo transfer, and other recent developments in reproductive management are described.

GONADOTROPIC HORMONES AND THEIR FUNCTIONS

Reproduction in mammals, birds, and other vertebrates is closely related to the action of several hormones, called gonadotropins, produced in the pituitary gland. These hormones are follicle stimulating hormone (FSH), luteinizing hormone (LH) and, in the case of primates and horses and other equids, chorionic gonadotropin (CG). The release of gonadotropins from the pituitary is controlled by gonadotropic releasing hormones (GnRH) in mammals and birds. All are protein hormones containing a carbohydrate moiety and are termed glycoproteins. Protein hormones act by their specific effect on target cells called receptors. The receptors for the gonadotropins are themselves proteins and are located on the surface of the target cells. Without these receptors, the hormones cannot exert their effects.

FSH acts by stimulating follicle development and the production of the steroid hormone, estrogen, in the ovary. In conjunction with LH, it also prepares the follicle for ovulation. LH causes ovulation, resulting in transformation of preovulatory follicles to corpora lutea. The corpus luteum (CL) is a specialized structure at the site of the ruptured follicle following ovulation. The CL produces another steroid hormone, progesterone, the secretion of which is required for the maintenance of pregnancy. Specialized receptor cells in the ovary allow the cells to become responsive to LH. FSH induces the production of LH receptors by the ovary. Thus, it is apparent that FSH and LH work together in orchestrating the production of steroid hormones in the ovary. In the male, FSH acts on cells (Sertoli cell) in the seminiferous tubules in which spermatozoa are produced. LH in the male stimulates the interstitial cells (Leydig cells) of the testis to produce the male hormones (androgens), mainly testosterone. In both females and males, production of gonadotropic hormones is under the influence of regulatory feedback from the target cells in the gonads and their release is controlled by GnRH.

In poultry, a condition termed molting occurs for about one month each year. Molting is characterized by a cessation of egg production and regression of the reproductive tract. Hormone changes include a decrease in LH and progesterone.

In humans, chorionic gonadotropin (hCG) stimulates the CL to continue to produce progesterone for maintenance of pregnancy. In the mare, chorionic gonadotropin is present in the blood serum during pregnancy and has been designated pregnant mare serum gonadotropin (PMSG).

Prolactin (PRL) is a simple protein pituitary hormone that stimulates milk production and may play a role in the development of the CL and of LH receptors in the ovary of some mammals. PRL inhibits gonadotropin-stimulated ovulation in poultry and depresses estrogen production by the ovary.

MALE ORGANS OF REPRODUCTION AND THEIR FUNCTIONS

The reproductive organs of the bull, ram, boar, and stallion, diagrammed in Figures 4-1a, b, c, and d, respectively, consist of the testes, epididymides, accessory organs, and penis. The testes (testicles), which descend from the body cavity in late fetal life and are housed

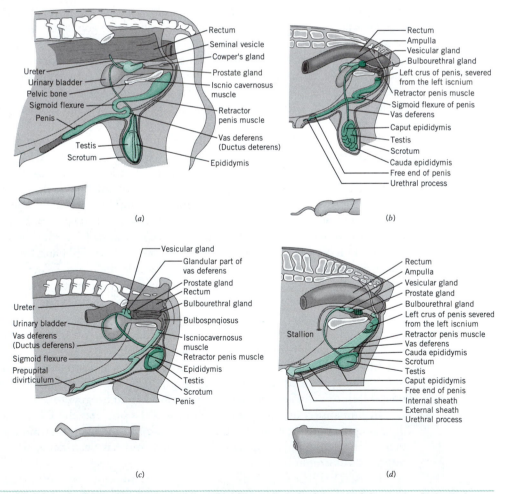

FIGURE 4-1

Reproductive organs of the bull (a), ram (b), boar (c), and stallion (d) with closeup of the penis. [Adapted from Taylor (1995), by permission of Prentice-Hall, Inc., Upper Saddle River, NJ.]

and protected by the scrotum, produce male sex cells (spermatozoa or sperm) and sex hormones. The sperm cells from each testis pass into the epididymis (one for each testis) where they are stored and acquire maturity and the capacity to become mobile. On ejaculation, fluid and spermatozoa from the epididymis move through small tubes (vas deferens) to the urethra. The urethra is the common passage for semen (the composite of sperm and fluids from the epididymis and the accessory sex organs) to the penis for ejaculation. The urethra also is the duct for excretion of urine produced in the kidney and transported via the ureter to the bladder. The accessory sex organs secrete fluids for the nutrition, buffering, and protection of the sperm. The characteristics of semen (volume and sperm concentration of ejaculate) and site of deposition during natural mating are presented in Table 4-1.

Testes (Testicles). Testes have two major functions: to produce the male gamete called sperm and sex hormones, primarily testosterone. Within the testis is a series of long coiled tubes, the seminiferous tubules, where the sperm are produced and undergo maturation. Other cells between the seminiferous tubules called interstitial cells are responsible for the production of the male hormone, testosterone. A microscopic view of a cross-section of testis depicting its internal structure is shown in Figure 4-2. Testosterone is responsible for the characteristics that govern the behavior and appearance of the male (secondary sex characteristics). Without testosterone the animal would not have male appearance, male temperament, or libido. For example, a bull is heavier muscled, has a more powerful neck and a deeper voice, and has more aggressive behavior than a steer (castrated male).

Spermatogenesis, the process by which sperm are produced, involves mitosis to increase its yield, meiosis to reduce chromosome number, and the production of billions of

TABLE 4-1

THE SEMEN VOLUME AND SPERM CONCENTRATION AND SITE OF NATURAL MATING DEPOSITION FOR VARIOUS SPECIES

Male	Volume per Ejaculate (ml)	Sperm Concentration Billion/ml	Total Sperm per Ejaculate (Billions)	Site of Deposition
Cattle (bull)	3–10	.8–1.2	4–18	Anterior Vagina
Sheep (ram)	.5–2.0	2–3	1–4	Anterior Vagina
Goat (buck)	.5–2.5	2–3.5	1–8	Anterior Vagina
Swine (boar)	150–250	.2–.3	30–60	In Cervix
Rabbit (buck)	.5–6.5	.31	1.5–6.5	Anterior Vagina
Dog (dog)	1–5	2–7	4–14	In Cervix
Human (man)	2–6	.05–.15	.1–.9	Anterior Vagina
Horse (stallion)	40–100	.15–.4	8–50	At Cervix
Chicken (cock)	.1–1.5	.4–1.5	.05–2.0	Vagina
Turkey (tom)	.1–.7	8–30	1–20	Vagina

Source: Cupps (1991), by permission of Academic Press, San Diego, CA.

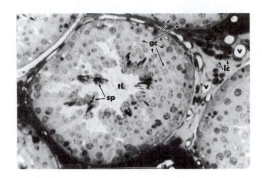

FIGURE 4-2

Microscopic section of the testis showing interstitial tissue with Leydig cells, blood and lymph vessels, and seminiferous tubules with spermatozoa in various stages of development. Key: sp = elongated spermatids; tl = tubules lumen; gc = germ cells in different stages of development; lc = Leydig cells; v = blood and lymph vessels; and bar = 100 microns. (Photo courtesy of D. D. Lunstra, USMARC, Clay Center, NE.)

specialized self-propelled gametes that carry the genome of the male to the next generation. The sperm (produced in the seminiferous tubules) when mature contain the genetic material in the head and have a tail that aids in movement (Figure 4-3). Part of the process of maturation occurs in the epididymis. The epididymis is a long convoluted duct attached to the testicle and can be palpated on the live animal. The close connection between the epididymis and testis is illustrated in the boar reproductive tract in Figure 4-4. During the time in the epididymis the sperm pass through more than 30 meters of the coiled tube during which maturation of the sperm occurs. Sperm removed from the beginning of the epididymis are less able to fertilize an ovum compared to sperm at the end of the epididymis. Sperm in large numbers are stored in the epididymis and are either moved out for ejaculation or die and are reabsorbed by the tissues. It takes 9 to 11 days (bull), 13 to 15 days (ram), and 9 to 14 days (boar) for the sperm to travel through the epididymis.

Scrotum. The scrotum is the sac-like structure that performs two very important functions: sperm protection and temperature regulation. The temperature is regulated so that viable sperm can be produced. The temperature of the testicle needs to be lower (3–7 °F lower in bulls and boars and 9–13 °F lower in the ram) than the body temperature. This is partially controlled by the scrotum. When environmental temperatures are low, the tunica dartos muscle contracts and the testicles are pulled toward the body. When temperatures are high, the muscle relaxes so that the testicles are further away from the warmth of the body. If the testes get too hot the sperm produced may not be viable, resulting in temporary sterility of the male. Management of the male during times of heat stress is critical to maintain fertile sperm.

Vas deferens. The vas deferens is simply a duct (tube) that transports the sperm from the epididymis to the urethra. In animals that ejaculate rapidly (bull, stallion, ram)

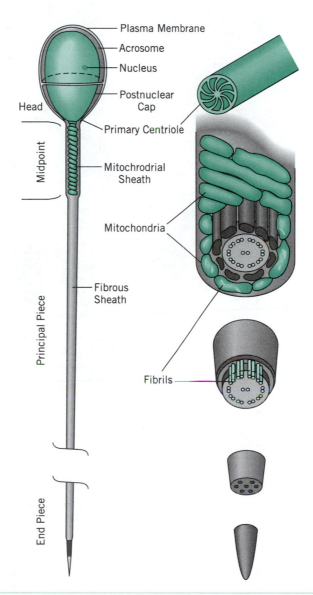

FIGURE 4-3

Anatomy of the sperm cell. [Adapted from Taylor (1995), by permission of Prentice-Hall, Inc., Upper Saddle River, NJ.]

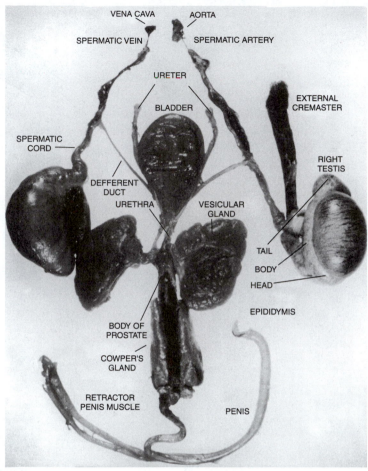

VENA CAVA   AORTA

SPERMATIC VEIN   SPERMATIC ARTERY

URETER

BLADDER   EXTERNAL
                                           CREMASTER

SPERMATIC
CORD   RIGHT
                                                        TESTIS

DEFFERENT
DUCT

URETHRA   VESICULAR
                 GLAND

                                    TAIL

                                    BODY

                                    HEAD

                              EPIDIDYMIS

BODY OF
PROSTATE

COWPER'S
GLAND

RETRACTOR
PENIS MUSCLE   PENIS

FIGURE 4-4

Reproductive tract of the boar. (Photo courtesy of R. K. Christenson, USMARC, Clay Center, NE.)

there is a widened, enlarged area called the ampulla where sperm are temporarily stored immediately before ejaculation. At the time of ejaculation the sperm are rapidly transported through the urethra and exit the penis into the female reproductive tract. There is no ampulla in animals that take several minutes for ejaculation (boar and dog). The vas deferens can be easily palpated and in fact, during mating in the boar, a quivering of the scrotum can be seen when the sperm are traveling from the epididymis through the vas deferens.

Vasectomy is simply the removal or disruption of the integrity of the vas deferens. A vasectomized animal still produces sperm and testosterone but the sperm are physically blocked from exiting the body. In a vasectomized animal the sperm die in the epididymis and are reabsorbed by the tissues. Often vasectomized rams or bulls are used to determine if the female is exhibiting "heat" or "estrus" and is receptive to the male.

Urethra. The urethra is a large-diameter tube that carries urine from the bladder and sperm and fluids from the accessory sex organs to the exterior via the penis. Along the urethra the accessory glands [seminal vesicles, prostate (absent in some species, e.g., sheep), and bulbourethral glands] secrete fluids to be added to the sperm.

Accessory glands. The seminal vesicles, prostate, and bulbourethral gland (often called cowpers gland) comprise the accessory sex glands of the male reproductive tract. The seminal vesicles secrete fluids that provide energy and buffers to the sperm. The prostate gland secretes a small volume of fluids that are high in inorganic ions. The bulbourethral glands secrete fluids before ejaculation to clean the urethra and in the boar form the gel-like portion of boar semen.

Penis. The penis provides the passageway for semen and urine and serves as the organ of copulation in the male. The erectile tissue of the penis fills with blood during sexual arousal causing the penis to become erect. The penis of bulls, boars, rams, goats, and dogs is S-shaped (sigmoid flexure) when relaxed but straightens during arousal. The penis returns to the relaxed state after copulation. The penis of the stallion and human has no sigmoid flexure and becomes enlarged and erect during arousal because of the erectile tissue engorgement with blood.

The free end of the penis is called the glans penis and is well supplied with sensory nerves. Although having the same function, the glans penis of the bull, boar, ram, and stallion are quite different. That of the bull (Figure 4-1a) is somewhat twisted with an exposed external urethral orifice; that of the ram (Figure 4-1b) has a filiform appendage extending beyond the end of the penis that acts to spray semen in the anterior vagina of the ewe. The boar (Figure 4-1c) has a corkscrew-shaped penis that meshes with the cervix of the female during copulation. The clamping of the penis by the cervix of the sow aids in causing ejaculation. The stallion (Figure 4-1d) has a relatively flat glans penis that presses up to the cervix of a mare during copulation.

FEMALE ORGANS OF REPRODUCTION AND THEIR FUNCTIONS

The female reproductive organs of mammals are quite similar with only slight variations between species. Single-bearing animals such as cows have relatively short uterine horns (Figure 4-5a and b) whereas litter-bearing animals such as pigs (Figure 4-6) have long uterine horns. The reproductive tract has two ovaries, each surrounded by a funnel-shaped membrane (infundibulum) and attached to a tube (oviduct) which connects the infundibulum to the horn of the uterus. The two horns join together forming the body of the uterus that attaches to the cervix and then the birth canal, the vagina. The portion that can be viewed externally includes the vulva and clitoris. The urethra connects the bladder to the vagina and urine is eliminated through the vagina.

Ovaries. The ovaries produce female gametes called ova (eggs) and produce estrogen and progesterone. The ovum or ova develop on the ovary in fluid-filled structures called

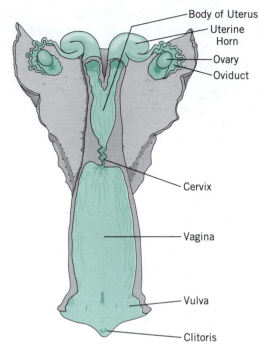

FIGURE 4-5a

Reproductive organs of the cow.

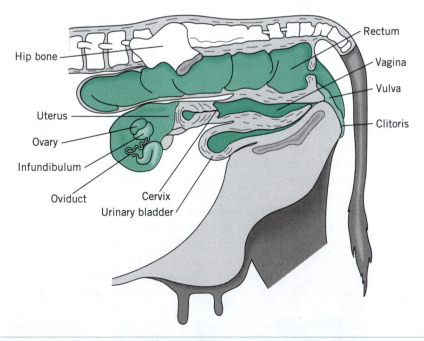

FIGURE 4-5b

Reproductive organs of the cow depicting their position in relation to other structures. [Adapted from Taylor (1995), by permission of Prentice-Hall, Inc., Upper Saddle River, NJ.]

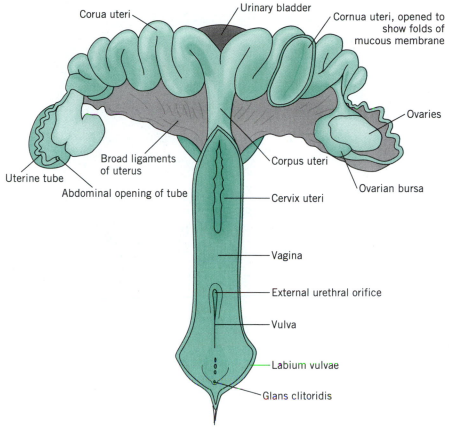

FIGURE 4-6

Reproductive organs of the sow. [Adapted from Taylor (1995), by permission of Prentice-Hall, Inc., Upper Saddle River, NJ.]

follicles. Follicles produce the hormone estrogen. After the ovum is released from the follicle, a corpus luteum (CL) forms in place of the follicle. The CL produces the hormone progesterone. The ovaries of a cow (typically releases one ovum per estrus) (Figure 4-7a) and a sow (typically releases 10 to 20 ova per estrus) (Figure 4-7b) are different. Cows usually release only one ovum[1] and form one CL whereas sows and other litter-producing animals release many ova and have several follicles and/or CLs depending on the stage of the cycle. Some breeds of sheep and some selected populations of cattle often produce twins or triplets by releasing more than one ovum and forming more than one CL.

---

[1]It is important to recognize that some breeds and lines of cattle produce twins, and in the case of sheep, triplets, and quadruplets. For example, purebred Finnsheep bear 3–5 lambs per "litter" and recent research in beef cattle by scientists at the U.S. Meat Animal Research Center, Clay Center, NE, has shown that cattle can be selected for a high rate of twinning.

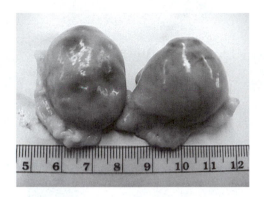

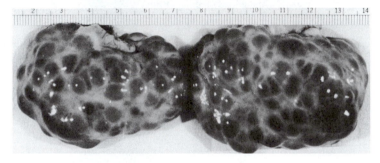

FIGURE 4-7

(a) Ovaries of the cow, one with developing follicles and one with a corpus luteum; (b) ovaries of the sow with multiple corpora lutea. [Photos courtesy of W. R. Butler, Cornell University, Ithaca, NY (a) and R. K. Christenson, USMARC, Clay Center, NE (b).]

Infundibulum. Surrounding each ovary is a funnel-shaped tissue that effectively "catches" the ova as they are released by the ovary. The infundibulum guides the ova to the oviduct.

Oviduct. The oviduct, often called the fallopian tube, is the site of fertilization. The ova pass through the infundibulum and join with the sperm cell that has made its way through the reproductive tract from the vagina or the cervix. The fertilized ova (embryo) then makes its way to the uterus in one to three days.

The role of the infundibulum and oviduct in egg-laying in poultry is described in Chapter 15.

Uterus. The site of embryonic growth and later placental and fetal development is the uterus. The uterus has two horns (one for each ovary) that join together to form the body of the uterus. Litter-bearing animals such as the pig, rabbit, and dog have long uterine horns whereas single-producing animals such as the cow or horse have relatively short horns. The placenta and each fetus develop along the horns of the uterus in the sow whereas the fetus develops in the body of the uterus in the mare.

Cervix. The major barrier and protection of the uterus and developing fetus is the cervix. The cervix is a tightly closed barrier during pregnancy, but is more open or dilated during parturition and breeding. In the sow the cervix functions during breeding by providing pressure to the end of the boar's penis, as a clamp that aids during natural breeding in swine.

Vagina. The canal between the cervix and outside of the body is the vagina. It serves as the birth canal at parturition and also as the organ of sperm deposition at mating for most species. The surface of the reproductive tract is lined with mucosal cells that vary from very moist and lubricated to almost dry depending on the stage of the reproductive cycle. The urinary tract (urethra) joins the posterior ventral vagina so that the vagina also serves as the passageway for urine elimination from the body.

Vulva. The only structure of the reproductive tract that is visible from the outside is the vulva. The vulva can be observed as an indication of fertility. Animals with small infantile vulvas often have reproductive problems. The vulva can also be observed to determine stage of the reproductive cycle or proximity to parturition.

Clitoris. The female organ that is analogous to the penis is the clitoris. The clitoris is located near the exterior of the reproductive tract at the base of the vulva. Stimulation of the clitoris during natural mating or when utilizing artificial insemination has been shown to increase fertility.

THE ESTROUS CYCLE

The female mammal has a recurring cycle that repeats as long as the female is not pregnant. The cycle is controlled by hormones that prepare the reproductive tract for ovulation and pregnancy. (A hormone is a chemical substance produced by tissues in one part of the body and carried through the bloodstream to other tissues or organs where it has specific effects on their metabolism.) A normal cycle is similar among species. The blood levels of luteinizing hormone (LH), progesterone, and estrogens for the sow are shown in Figure 4-8 to illustrate the general shape of the concentration curves of these three hormones during the estrous cycle of most domestic animals. Estrogens peak sharply at ovulation (day 0 of the estrous cycle), whereas progesterone rises gradually from day 0 to a peak midway through the estrous cycle, followed by a gradual decline to the end of the cycle. LH concentration in the blood is relatively constant from day 0 (ovulation) throughout most of the cycle, then rises gradually late in the cycle and reaches a peak just before the sharp ovulatory peak of estrogens and coinciding with the return of progesterone concentration to the baseline level. These tightly controlled changes in circulating hormones orchestrate the timing of estrus and ovulation. Exogenous administration of hormones at appropriate times and in appropriate combinations can be used to control the estrous cycle in most species, providing an effective tool for livestock producers to use to synchronize the reproductive management schedule.

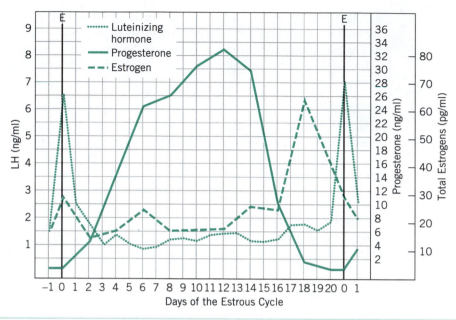

FIGURE 4-8

Blood plasma hormone levels during one normal estrous cycle of the sow. The shapes of the curves for each hormone are relatively similar to those of other mammals.
Source: From Hansel et al. (1973).

The hypothalamus of the brain produces gonadotropic releasing hormone (GnRH), which travels to and stimulates the anterior pituitary. The anterior pituitary secretes follicle stimulating hormone (FSH), which is carried via the blood to the ovaries and stimulates the growth of follicles. As the follicle grows it begins to secrete estrogen. Estrogen is carried by the blood as a negative feedback mechanism and causes the anterior pituitary to reduce the FSH released. The high level of estrogen also signals that the female is ready to accept the male, and it prepares the uterus for pregnancy and increases motility of the uterus and oviducts. The term "estrus" or "heat" denotes the time during which the female will accept the male. This should not be confused with "estrous," which pertains to the entire cycle. Estrogen in the female is analogous to testosterone in the male in the development of secondary sex characteristics.

Luteinizing hormone (LH) produced by the anterior pituitary causes the mature follicle to rupture, thereby releasing the ova, and causes the corpus luteum (CL) to form. The CL produces the hormone progesterone that prevents ovulation and continues the uterine growth initiated by estrogen. If the animal becomes pregnant, progesterone maintains pregnancy and increases development of milk-producing tissues in the udder. If the animal is not pregnant the CL degenerates and the cycle repeats itself. Table 4-2 presents the duration of estrus, length between cycles, gestation length, and ovulation time for various species.

TABLE 4-2

DURATION OF HEAT (ESTRUS), ESTROUS CYCLE LENGTH, GESTATION LENGTH, AND OVULATION TIME OF VARIOUS ANIMALS

Female	Duration Average	Duration Range	Cycle Length Average	Cycle Length Range	Gestation Length	Ovulation Time
Cattle (cow)	16h	10–27	21d	19–23	283d	30h after beginning of heat
Sheep (ewe)	30h	20–42	17d	14–19	147d	26h after beginning of heat
Goat (doe)	39h	20–80h	17d	12–27	150d	2nd day of heat
Swine (sow)	44h	1.5–4d	21d	19–23	114d	30–38h after beginning of heat
Rabbit (doe)		Constant	Estrus		31d	8–10h after mating
Dog (bitch)	9d	4–13d	2 time/year		60d	24–48h after heat begins
Cat (queen)	5d	4–7d	10d	8–14	52d	24h after mating
Horse (mare)	6d	1–37d	21d	10–37	336d	1 day from end of heat
Human (woman)	—	—	28d	21–34	270–290d	Midway between menstrual periods

Source: Adapted from Cupps (1991), by permission of Academic Press, Inc., San Diego, CA.

PREGNANCY

If pregnancy occurs, the single cell (zygote, containing the combined nuclear material from the ova and sperm) quickly divides and proliferates. It divides into 2, then 4, then 8, then 16, then 32 cells, and so on. A pig embryo at the two-cell stage is shown in Figure 4-9. There is continued embryonic growth, movement of the embryo from the oviduct to the uterus, and eventual attachment to the uterus. Attachment (sometimes also called

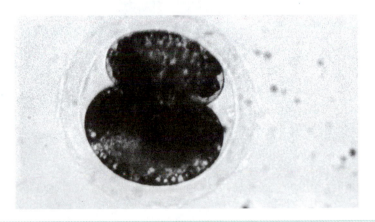

FIGURE 4-9

Fertilized pig ovum in 2-cell stage of development. (Photo courtesy of R. K. Christenson, USMARC, Clay Center, NE.)

implantation) is near completion at day 18 (sow), 22 (ewe), 28 (cow), and 36 (mare) after conception. The transition from embryonic life, during which the conceptus receives its nutrition from the surrounding uterine environment, to fetal life, during which the fetus is nourished from the maternal blood via the placenta, occurs over several hours or days, depending on the species. For example, in the pig, the inner surface of the uterus begins to change in structure at each attachment site and by day 16, each conceptus (blastocyst) is aligned to become intimately connected to the uterine lining at the point of attachment. By day 18 the attachment is complete and the nutrient supply is now derived from the maternal blood via the placenta, consisting of three cell layers of maternal uterine tissue and three cell layers of conceptus tissue (total of six layers, termed an epitheliochorial placenta) through which nutrients and metabolites pass in both directions. Thus, in the case of the pig, attachment occurs over about a 5-day period; length of the attachment process differs by species. Figure 4-10 is a diagrammatic view of pig fetal membranes and placenta.

Before and during attachment, it is important to minimize the level of stress on the pregnant dam. Fighting among animals, animal transport, or other stresses should be avoided during this stage of pregnancy or reproductive efficiency could be dramatically lower because of embryonic death.

The amnion and chorionic membranes develop and become part of the placenta surrounding the fetus. The two major fluid-filled cavities in the placental membranes con-

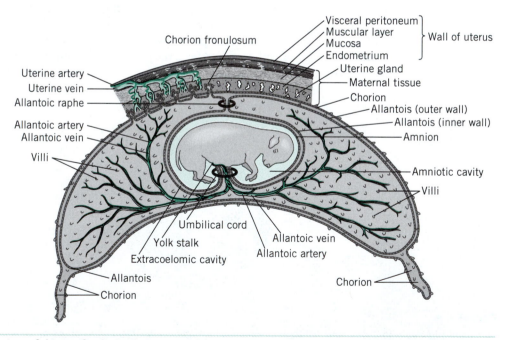

FIGURE 4-10

Diagrammatic view of the pig fetal membranes and placenta.
Source: Adapted from Harrison (1971).

tain amniotic fluid and allantoic fluid. The volume of amniotic fluid rises slowly at first, then rises rapidly to midgestation, and plateaus to term. The volume of allantoic fluid rises rapidly in early gestation, then plateaus in some species and declines in others. The amniotic and allantoic fluids provide mechanical cushioning to the fetus and collect excretory products from the fetal kidney and contain a variety of metabolic products, electrolytes, and proteins. Amniotic fluid is swallowed and moves in and out of the trachea (wind pipe).

The fetus is provided protection and exchanges nutrients and wastes through the placenta. Fetal and maternal blood are separate, but nutrients pass from the dam's blood system to the fetal blood system and fetal waste metabolites pass from the fetal blood to the maternal blood.

Depending on species there are different placenta types and ways of attachment. The mare and sow have a diffuse type of placenta and the fetal attachment can occur at several locations along the uterus. The ewe, doe, and cow have a cotylendonary type of placenta and there are specific sites along the uterus where the fetal attachment can occur. The caruncles are associated with the uterus and the cotyledons are associated with the fetus. The placenta remains functional until birth.

The fetus develops slowly at first. Most of the fetal growth occurs in the last third of gestation. The pregnancy is maintained by the hormone progesterone (produced by the CL on the ovary). In the mare, progesterone is produced and secreted by the fetus to maintain pregnancy.

PARTURITION

Close to the end of gestation the fetus initiates the parturition process by releasing the hormone cortisol from the fetal adrenal cortex. This signals the beginning of the parturition process. The level of progesterone decreases and the hormones estrogen, prostaglandin $F_{2 \text{ alpha}}$ ($PGF_{2\alpha}$), and oxytocin increase. The prostaglandin causes luteolysis (destruction of the CL), thereby reducing the secretion of progesterone, and causes initiation of uterine contractions. The hormone oxytocin is involved with the contraction of smooth muscles (uterus) and with milk letdown.

Several behavior modifications can be observed just before parturition. Females are generally restless, may exhibit nesting behavior, or become separated from the rest of the herd or flock. Frequent urination, and swelling and reddening of the vulva are often evident. Just before parturition the release of the hormone relaxin aids in the relaxation of the pelvis.

Normal parturition involves a sequential coordinated set of events. The cervix relaxes (dilates), the pelvic region relaxes (action of relaxin hormone), and the uterus begins contractions (action of oxytocin). The fetus passes through the cervix, the pelvic region, and finally through the vagina.

Litter-bearing animals have offspring that may be born oriented either head first or feet first. One uterine horn could empty first followed by the other or there may be

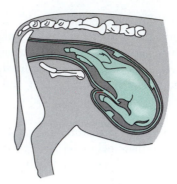

Normal presentation

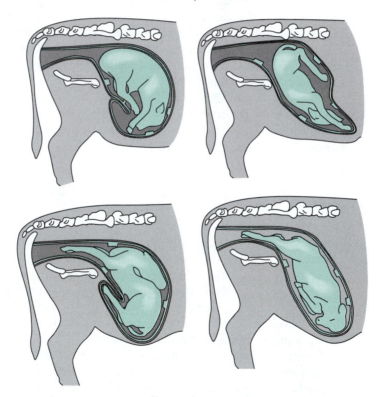

Abnormal presentation

FIGURE 4-11

Normal and abnormal presentation of the calf during parturition. [Adapted from Taylor (1995), by permission of Prentice-Hall, Inc., Upper Saddle River, NJ.]

fetuses from either side in mixed order. In the case of single births, prior to parturition the fetus normally orients itself for easy delivery (Figure 4-11). A normal presentation has the front feet extended with the head between with the curvature of the spine parallel with the backbone of the dam. Orientation with the head turned back (breech births) can reduce survival of the offspring and even cause death to the dam if assistance is not quickly attended to. The smallest opening and area of most resistance during parturition is the pelvic region. Care must be taken in selection of sires that will not cause problems during parturition due to large frame size of the offspring. Assistance during parturition may be required especially for animals in their first parturition. The placental tissues are often expelled during parturition or may be expelled several hours later. In many cases the animal is born with a partial covering of placental tissues that may interfere with breathing. Being present at parturition can save lives in such cases.

ARTIFICIAL INSEMINATION

Artificial insemination (AI) is the process of introducing semen into the female reproductive tract without contact of the female with the male. It may be used in place of natural mating to increase the number of offspring produced by superior sires, control the spread of infectious diseases, or for economic reasons. Semen collected from the male is placed into the reproductive tract of a female at the correct stage of the estrous cycle to allow normal fertilization and gestation. AI is used in several species (poultry, dairy and beef cattle, swine, horses, sheep, goats, and humans). Domesticated turkeys, because of their physical inability to mate, normally require AI for reproduction. The dairy industry has been a leader in the use and development of AI technology. Today nearly all dairy cows in the United States are bred by AI. The use of AI over the past three decades has been a major factor in the dramatic increase in milk production in dairy herds worldwide through the widespread use of superior sires. More than one-half of the pigs produced in the United States currently are produced by AI to maximize the use of genetically superior sires and to control disease. The horse industry utilizes AI but some breed associations do not allow registration of offspring originating from AI.

Most producers purchase semen from commercial sources, eliminating the need to keep sires on the premises, as well as helping control disease and allowing the use of semen from genetically superior sires that are injured or otherwise physically incapable of natural service. Use of AI, however, requires more management skill, organization, and ability to determine the correct timing of insemination.

Procedures

The rectovaginal method is used in cattle. The inseminator places one hand in the rectum and palpates for the cervix. The insemination rod is passed through the vagina and guided through the cervix and into the uterus where the semen is placed (closer to the site of fertilization than with natural breeding). Vaginal palpation is used in the mare. The inseminator places one hand in the vagina of the horse and guides and insemination rod into the cervix. In the sow the insemination rod is shaped similarly to the head of the boar's penis and the rod is turned into the cervix of the sow. With sheep and goats a speculum is used to see into the vagina and place the rod into the cervix. The method and site of insemination, insemination time, estrus detection, and sperm number and insemination volume appropriate for several species of animals are summarized in Table 4-3.

Semen Collection

Semen from the desired sires must be collected and immediately used or processed and stored for future use. There are three methods of collecting semen: use of an artificial vagina, use of a gloved hand, and use of an electroejaculator. An artificial vagina is often used with bulls, stallions, rams, and bucks. The animal must be trained to mount another animal or a phantom (mounting dummy). A female in heat can be used to train the male. The male mounts the female and the penis is diverted away from the animal mounted and positioned in an artificial vagina. The artificial vagina (AV) is an open-ended tube that simulates the vagina of the female. The AV is maintained at the appropriate body temperature, and is lubricated with nonspermicidal lubricant. The electroejaculator can be used on animals with no previous training. Electroejaculation is typically used in cattle, sheep, and goats. An electrode is inserted into the rectum of the male and a pulsating current stimulates involuntary ejaculation.

TABLE 4-3

INSEMINATION PROCEDURES IN SEVERAL MAMMALS AND BIRDS

Animal	Method and Site	Insemination Time	Estrus Detection	Sperm No. (millions)	Insemination Volume (ml)
Cow	Rectovaginal	Estrus onset plus 9 hr	Cyclic history, observation, marker bull	10–15	0.25–1.0
Ewe	Cervix, speculum & pipette	Estrus onset plus 10–20 hr	Cyclic history, marker ram	>50	0.05–0.20
Doe (Nanny)	Cervix, speculum & pipette	Estrus onset plus 12–36 hr	Cyclic history, marker buck	>50	0.1–0.2
Mare	Vaginal; cervix & uterus	Each 2nd d, start estrus d 2	Cyclic history, observation	1000	20–40
Sow	Cervix & uterus	Estrus onset plus 10–30 hr	Cyclic history, boar	5000	50
Bitch	Anterior vagina, speculum & pipettes	Estrus onset plus 1 and 2 d	Cyclic history, vasectomized dog	>50	0.5–1.0
Turkey	Midvagina, pipette	Every 3 wk	N/A	3.5	0.1–0.5
Chicken	Same as turkey	Weekly (pm)	N/A	100	0.1–0.5

Source: Adapted from Cupps (1991), by permission of Academic Press, Inc., San Diego, CA.

Semen Dilution and Storage

The male ejaculates into the AV and the semen is quickly transported for insemination or further processing. Spermatozoa do not survive well without careful control of their environment following collection. They must be protected against rapid cooling, diluted in an appropriate medium to maintain osmotic pressure and acceptable pH, inhibit microbial growth, and to provide nutrients. The dilution medium provides a suitable environment for sperm survival in extended storage and also dilutes the sperm concentration to maximize the number of inseminations possible from a single ejaculate. Many types of extenders are available for use in storage of sperm from different species. Common ingredients include natural products such as egg-yolk and milk, or both, along with a variety of buffering agents and antimicrobial agents.

Pregnancy Rates and Fertility Characteristics in Various Species

The frequency of collection can affect fertility and reproductive soundness. Collection of bulls should not exceed twice daily, two times per week. In species that are characteristically seasonal breeders, as in sheep (except in some breeds), the number of ejaculations may be several times per day for several weeks. Boar and stallion collection should not exceed every other day.

The quality of the semen is usually evaluated in terms of volume and concentration (total number of sperm), motility (70 to 80% motile sperm in an ejaculate is acceptable), and incidence of abnormalities. One collection can be extended to increase the number of females that can be inseminated. The semen extender increases the volume available and protects the sperm (providing nutrients and buffers). A typical ejaculation from a bull might be extended to provide semen for 100 cows and from a boar extended to breed 5 to 25 sows.

The pregnancy rate of females bred by AI or by natural service is seldom 100% in a given group of animals. Table 4-4 compares the fertility proficiency (pregnancy rate)

TABLE 4-4

FERTILITY AND PREGNANCY RATES OF FARM ANIMALS

| Animal | Pregnancy Rate (%) | | | | |
	Natural	Insemination: Fluid Semen (1X)	Insemination: Frozen Semen (1X)	Fertility Estimate: % Nonreturn	Sterility Estimate: % Barren
Dairy cow	60–75	50–65	50–65	70–85	8–9
Beef cow	70	60	—	—	15–20
Ewe	80–90	60–80	3–71	65	6–8
Doe (Nanny)	70–80	42–69	27–67	—	8–9
Sow	85–95	65–90	62–64	90–95	6–7
Mare	40–75	50–65	38–46	—	25–60

Source: Adapted from Cupps (1991), by permission of Academic Press, Inc., San Diego, CA.

of various species of farm animals bred by natural service or AI using fresh or frozen semen.

ESTRUS DETECTION

Although sperm viability may be normal at the time of insemination, pregnancy will not occur if the sperm and ova are not present in the oviduct at the same time. For natural mating there is no need for concern about detecting estrus because the male capably does that job. However, when the inseminator is responsible, detection of estrus is the largest limitation to successful AI.

A visual method that indicates the female is ready for the male is termed "standing heat." The female will stand and allow a male or other animal to mount her as if to breed. Cows and sows are typically checked for standing heat twice per day. In the sow, estrus can be detected by applying pressure with one's hand on the animal's back. A sow in standing heat will stand rigidly and hold her ears erect.

In cattle, sterilized males (vasectomized) or males with their penis surgically diverted are often used to check for standing heat. Placing a chin and ball marker on the bull causes the animal that the bull mounts to be painted by the marker. In sheep, the ram might be equipped with a marking harness or with grease/paint placed between the front legs. A marked ewe is one that allowed the ram to mount her. There are also pressure-sensitive patches that when attached on the tail head of cows, rupture when exposed to the pressure of an animal mounting. The mare in estrus usually is more restless, frequently urinates, and carries the tail higher than usual. Contractions of the vulva can be observed in most mares (termed "winking"). To reduce the problems associated with detecting estrus, methods have been developed to synchronize the estrous cycle, thereby having female cycle predictability.

ESTRUS SYNCHRONIZATION

The ability to predict and plan the time when an animal will be in estrus (standing heat) greatly facilitates success in AI and is required for embryo transfer. Estrus synchronization can be accomplished in some species by weaning. Sows whose pigs are weaned at about 3 weeks of age will be in standing heat about 5 days after weaning. Many large swine producers, therefore, typically wean sows on Thursday to avoid breeding on the weekend.

Hormone therapy also may be used to synchronize estrus. Melengestrol acetate (MGA) is a synthetic steroid feed additive used in feedlot heifers to suppress estrus. Cessation of MGA feeding after at least 2 weeks of feeding will cause most of the females to exhibit estrus 2 to 6 days later. An injection of prostaglandin F_2-alpha 7 days after cessation of feeding MGA causes an even higher percentage of the animals to be in estrus 2 to 5 days after injection.

SyncroMate B is a product that utilizes an implant and injection to synchronize estrus. Cows are injected with estradiol and norgestomet and implanted subcutaneously in the ear with norgestomet for nine days. Estrus should be detected 24 to 48 hours after the removal of the implant.

The use of $PGF_{2\alpha}$ to cause the CL to regress and begin another cycle has been used effectively to synchronize estrus. One injection will synchronize cows with a functional CL but a 2-injection system will synchronize all cows. Cows are injected on day one and then again on day 11, 12, or 13, causing them to exhibit standing heat 5 days after the second injection.

FERTILIZATION

Sperm deposited in the female reproductive tract naturally or by AI must reach the oviduct in order for fertilization to occur. Of the millions of sperm deposited in the female tract, only a small fraction reach the oviduct. Their transport toward the oviduct in farm animals is probably related both to the motility of the sperm and to factors associated with the female tract. The time interval from insemination to the appearance of sperm in the oviduct varies from 2 to 13 minutes in the cow to 15 to 30 minutes in the pig. The number of sperm reaching the site of fertilization (the upper end or ampulla of the oviduct) has been estimated at less than 100 in the mouse, 5 to 100 in the dog, 600 to 700 in the sheep, 1000 in the pig, and only a few in the cow. Freshly released ova are transported into the ampulla of the oviduct by the action of ciliated cells lining the infundibulum and are swept into the oviduct for fertilization. Spermatozoa are incapable of penetrating the ovum for several hours after entry into the female reproductive tract. The acquisition of the ability to fertilize the ovum, termed capacitation, involves the removal or alteration of substances on the surface of the sperm. Exposure of the sperm to the environment of the uterus and ovary appears to trigger capacitation. Capacitated sperm have changes in the structure of the acrosomal membrane covering the front of the sperm, resulting in the release of enzymes from the acrosome, which alter the structure of the ovum surface and allow penetration of the outer covering of the ovum termed the zona pellucida. Sperm that have undergone capacitation are capable of fertilizing the ovum, but only one sperm is successful, because penetration of the ovum renders closure to the entrance of other sperm. Hyaluronidase and acrosin are acrosomal enzymes thought to be responsible for penetration of the zona pellucida. (It is believed that the zona pellucida of the ova of a specific species recognizes sperm from a foreign species and rejects its penetration.)

Penetration of the ovum by a single sperm results in the erection of a barrier by the ovum to the entry of other sperm. Therefore, polyspermy (entry of more than one sperm) rarely occurs, and when it does, fertilization fails. Figure 4-12 shows a pig ovum with spermatozoa penetrating the zona pellucida. Penetration of the ovum also stimulates meiosis with extrusion of the second polar body, and the formation of male and female pronuclei. The male and female chromosomes combine to form the diploid zygote. The

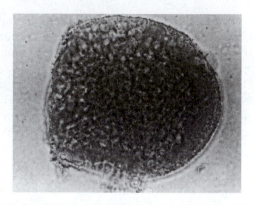

FIGURE 4-12

Pig ovum with spermatozoa penetrating the zona pellucida (lower left) and nucleus on lower periphery of ovum. (Photo courtesy of R. K. Christenson, USMARC, Clay Center, NE.)

ovum is activated to initiate cleavage and biochemical activity associated with the development of an embryo.

Survival Time and Fertility of Gametes in the Female Tract

The survival of ova and sperm in the female tract varies among species. Obviously, the inappropriate timing of the union of sperm and eggs will result in low conception rates. Table 4-5 shows the approximate survival times of gametes for males and females in the female reproductive tract. Note that in general sperm have a longer survival time than ova in most species.

EMBRYO TRANSFER

The transfer of embryos at an early stage of development from a donor female to the uterus of a recipient surrogate mother to produce a newborn was first accomplished in rabbits a century ago. The technique has now been applied commercially to improve farm livestock by propagating genetically superior animals. Well over 100,000 beef and dairy cattle pregnancies annually in the United States are produced from embryo transfers. In recent years millions of frozen cattle embryos have been shipped from the United States to other countries. The export of embryos provides a means of genetic improvement of animals in other parts of the world without as great a risk of infectious disease transmission and at a lower cost than would be the case in the traditional export of animals. The embryo transfer technique is also used commercially in goats, horses, sheep, and swine.

In order to maximize the number of ova harvested from donor females for use in em-

TABLE 4-5

SURVIVAL TIME AND FERTILITY OF GAMETES IN THE FEMALE REPRODUCTIVE TRACT

Animal	Retention of Sperm Motility (hours)	Retention of Fertility (hours)	
		Ovum	Sperm
Cow	15–56	8–12	28–50
Ewe	48	16–24	30–48
Mare	144	6–8	72–120
Sow	50	8–10	24–48
Doe (Rabbit)	43–50	6–8	28–48

Source: Adapted from Cupps (1991), by permission of Academic Press, Inc., San Diego, CA.

bryo transfer, the donor female is often given hormone injections to increase ovulation rate. Five to 12 ova are usually obtained from cows superovulated in this way. Typically 2 to 4 calves will be produced from embyros transferred from superovulated donor mothers under good embryo transfer management. The use of genetically superior donor cows and sires enhances the production of large numbers of genetically improved progeny.

Modern embryo transfer technology uses nonsurgical procedures. Steps include: (1) superovulation of donor dams; (2) artificial insemination with two doses of semen 12 to 24 hours after the onset of estrus; (3) recovery of the fertilized ova one week later by flushing the uterus with a buffered sterile solution; (4) location and collection of the embryos under microscopic low-power magnification; (5) loading the fertilized embryos into an inseminating rod similar or identical to that used in artificial insemination, and (6) transferring the embryos via the inseminating rod inserted into the reproductive tract of the recipient surrogate mother or by surgical implantation. Recipient females must be in the same stage of the estrous cycle as the donor female for highest conception (pregnancy) rate.

Embryos can be frozen in liquid nitrogen (−80°C) and stored in a viable state for months or years for later use in impregnating recipient surrogate mothers.

Embryo Splitting

Embryo transfer techniques have now advanced so that the embryo can be mechanically divided to produce identical twins from one embryo. The technique of mechanically splitting embryos is a form of cloning (creation of a genetic duplicate of an individual organism through asexual reproduction). Successes by scientists in Scotland and Japan using sophisticated techniques to produce cloned sheep and cattle (see Chapter 6) underscores the stunning advances in reproductive physiology, but raises serious ethical and moral questions that society must address (see Chapter 11).

SUMMARY

Reproduction is the mechanism by which life perpetuates itself. Without efficient reproduction (high reproductive rates) food animal production would not be profitable and food supplies for a growing human population could be threatened. The structure and function of male and female reproductive organs of representative species of farm animals are described. Details of reproduction of individual species of mammals, poultry, companion animals, and other vertebrates are not discussed in this chapter, but are covered in other chapters throughout the book. The information covered in this chapter is intended to serve only as a broad introduction to the reproductive processes of vertebrate animals. Hormonal control of sperm production in the male and of the estrous cycle in the female are briefly discussed and physiological events during pregnancy and parturition in species bearing single or multiple offspring are discussed and compared. Techniques of estrus synchronization, semen preservation, artificial insemination, and embryo transfer are described.

GLOSSARY

Abortion   Delivery of fetuses prior to the end of the normal gestation period for the species.

Accessory sex organs   Glands in the male (seminal vesicles, prostate, and bulbourethral or Cowper's) that secrete fluids which are added to the sperm to produce semen.

Afterbirth   The placenta and allied membranes with which the fetus is connected. It is expelled from the uterus after delivery.

Androgen   A general term referring to male steroid hormones, notably testosterone, produced by the testis.

Anestrous period   That time when the female does not cycle or exhibit estrus (heat); the non-breeding season.

Artificial insemination (AI)   The introduction of semen into the female reproductive tract by a technique other than natural service.

Artificial vagina   A device used to collect semen from a male when he mounts in a normal manner to copulate; the male ejaculates into this device for collection of semen.

Attachment   The process (also called implantation) occurring in the pregnant uterus in which the embryo and uterus attach to provide a vascular connection for nourishment of the fetus; this union constitutes the transformation of an embryo into a fetus.

Barren   Not capable of producing offspring.

Barrow   A male pig castrated before the developing of secondary sex characteristics.

Boar   Uncastrated male swine, any age.

Brood Animal   Females (brood sow, brood cow, brood ewe, brood mare) used for breeding and raising young.

Breed   A population of animals of common origin with distinguishing characteristics which set them apart from other groups within the species.

Bulbourethral gland   An accessory gland of the male (also called Cowper's gland).

Buck   Male sheep or goat (also synonymous with ram).

Bull   Uncastrated male of cattle, any age.

Bullock   A young bull, typically less than 20 months old.

Calf   Offspring of cattle, from birth to 1 year of age.

Calf crop   Calves produced by a herd of cattle in 1 year (90% calf crop = 90 calves per 100 cows bred).

Caruncle   The structures on the ruminant uterus where the cotyledons of the fetal placenta attach.

Castrate   To remove the testicles or ovaries.

Cervix   The portion of the female reproductive tract between the uterus and vagina.

Clitoris   The ventral part of the vulva of the female reproductive tract that is homologous to the penis of the male.

Colt   Uncastrated male horse, under 4 years of age.

Conception   The fertilization of an egg (ovum); the act of conceiving or becoming pregnant.

Conformation   Structure or shape of an animal or its carcass.

Corpus luteum   A yellowish structure formed on the ovary at the site of the ruptured ovarian follicle; it produces progesterone for maintenance of pregnancy.

Cow   Female of cattle, usually over 3 years of age.

Crossbreeding   Mating of animals of different breeds.

Cryptorchid   An animal in which the testis fails to descend from the body cavity and enter the scrotum during development; also, a testis that remains in the body cavity and is incapable of producing viable spermatozoa.

Culling   The process of eliminating undesirable animals.

Dam   The female parent.

Doe   Female goat, rabbit, deer.

Dystocia   Abnormal or difficult labor, causing difficulty in delivering the fetus during parturition.

Egg   See Ovum.

Ejaculation   Discharge of semen from the male.

Embryo   A fertilized ovum in the early stages of prenatal development (prior to the attachment to the uterus).

Epididymis   The coiled tube that leads from the testis to the vas deferens.

Equine   Pertaining to the horse.

Estrogens   A group of female steroid hormones (includes estradiol, estriol, and estrone) produced by the follicle of the ovary and by the placenta; they cause the female to enter estrus and be receptive to the male.

Estrous cycle   The cycle of events from one heat (estrus) period to the next in females.

Estrus   That period during which the female is receptive to the male (will allow mating).

Ewe   Female sheep, any age.

Farrow   To give birth to a litter of pigs.

Fertility   The capacity to initiate and support reproduction.

Fertilization   The process in which two gametes unite to form a zygote.

Fetus   Prenatal mammal attached to the uterus and nourished by the mother via the placenta.

Filly   A young female horse.

Flock   A group of sheep, goats, chickens.

Flushing   The practice of feeding females a high intake of energy before breeding to increase ovulation.

Foal   Offspring of horse, under 1 year, either sex.

Follicle-stimulating hormone (FSH)   A hormone produced by the anterior pituitary gland that stimulates the development of the ovarian follicle for ovulation.

Freemartin   Sterile heifer born twin to a bull. (About 10% of the heifers born twin to a bull are normal. These are not freemartins.)

Gamete   A germ cell possessing the haploid number of chromosomes (sperm or ovum); capable of participating in fertilization.

Gametogenesis   The process by which sperm and eggs are produced.

Gelding   Castrated male horse.

Gestation period   The period from conception to birth.

Gilt   Female of swine, under 1 year of age.

Gonad   The organ that produces the reproductive cells (testis in males, ovary in females).

Gonadotropin   A hormone that stimulates the gonads.

Hand mating Males and females separated except at mating.

Heat period That period when the female will accept the male (same as estrus period).

Heifer Female of cattle, usually under 3 years of age.

Herd A group of animals (cattle, hogs, horses).

Hormone A substance secreted by specialized tissues (endocrine glands) in the body and carried via the blood to other parts of the body for its action.

Implantation See Attachment.

Interstitial cells The cells between the seminiferous tubules of the testis that produce testosterone.

Jack A male donkey.

Jennet A female donkey (also called jenny).

Kid A young goat.

Lactation period The period of milk secretion.

Lamb A young sheep.

Lambing Giving birth to a lamb (parturition).

Libido Male sex drive.

Litter The pigs farrowed by a sow at one delivery period.

Luteinizing hormone (LH) A protein hormone produced and released by the anterior pituitary gland; it stimulates formation and retention of the corpus luteum and initiates ovulation.

Mammal A member of the class mammalia, distinguished by self-regulating body temperature, hair, and, in the female, milk production.

Mare Female horse, over 4 years of age.

Melengestrol acetate (MGA) A synthetic steroid hormone used as a feed additive to suppress estrus in cattle.

Metabolism The aggregate of chemical changes in the body, including anabolic (buildup) and catabolic (breakdown) processes.

Metabolite Any compound produced during metabolism.

Metritis Inflammation of the uterus.

Mule The hybrid animal (usually sterile) that is produced by mating a jack (male donkey) with a mare (female horse).

Multiparous Giving birth to more than one offspring at one pregnancy or having borne more than one offspring (had more than one pregnancy).

Mummified fetus Degenerated newborn (discolored and shriveled) that died before the end of the normal gestation period (common in litter-bearing mammals).

Oogenesis The process by which ova (eggs) are produced.

Open Designates a nonpregnant female.

Ovary The female reproductive organ in which eggs are formed and the hormones, estrogen and progesterone, are produced.

Oviduct The tube that carries ova from the ovary to the uterus and in which fertilization occurs.

Ovum (singular of ova) A female reproductive cell in animals.

Parity The number of times a female has borne offspring.

Parturition The process of giving birth.

Penis The male organ of copulation; serves both as vehicle for transport of urine from the bladder as an extension of the urethra, and as a copulatory organ through which sperm are deposited in the female reproductive tract.

Pheremones Chemical attractants to the opposite sex.

Photoperiod Length of day (or length of period artificial light is provided.)

Pituitary The small endocrine gland located at the base of the brain responsible for production of several hormones essential for life and reproduction.

Placenta Vascularized specialized tissue associated with the uterus and fetus during pregnancy through which the fetus is nourished.

Postpartum The period following birth.

Prepartum The period before birth.

Progesterone Ovarian steroid produced by the corpus luteum; required for maintenance of pregnancy.

Prostaglandins Chemical mediators that control many physiological and biochemical functions in the body.

Prostate A male accessory gland that secretes fluid that contributes to semen volume.

Puberty Age at which the reproductive organs become functional and secondary sex characteristics develop.

Prolific Tendency to produce many offspring.

Ram Uncastrated male sheep, any age.

Registered An animal registered (listed) in the herd book of a breed association.

Retained placenta Failure of the placental membranes to be expelled from the uterus after parturition.

Ridgling Same as cryptorchid.

Scrotum A pouch that contains the testes and serves as a thermoregulatory organ by contracting and relaxing in response to changes in environmental temperature as a means of keeping the sperm at lower than core body temperature.

Semen A mixture of sperm and accessory sex gland fluids; product of ejaculation.

Seminal vesicles Accessory sex glands of the male that contribute fluid to semen at ejaculation.

Settle To become pregnant or conceive.

Service The act of breeding or mating.

Sire Male parent.

Sow Female swine, usually over 1 year of age.

Sperm See Spermatozoa.

Spermatozoa The male reproductive cells of animals.

Stag Male animal castrated after secondary sex characteristics develop.

Stallion Uncastrated male horse, over 4 years of age.

Steer Male of cattle, castrated before secondary sex characteristics develop.

Superovulation Hormonally induced ovulation of a greater-than-normal number of eggs.

Testosterone Male steroid hormone; it stimulates the accessory sex glands, causes male sex drive, and causes development of masculine characteristics.

Testis The male sex organ that produces spermatozoa and testosterone.

Type A combination of the characteristics which make an animal useful for a specific purpose (beef type, dairy type).

Umbilical cord A cord through which arteries and veins connect the maternal and fetal blood circulation via the placenta and thereby transfer nutrients and metabolites in both directions; it is severed at parturition.

Unsoundness Structural defect in an animal.

Uterus The female reproductive organ in which the embryo and fetus live during prenatal life; fetus is sustained by the transfer of nutrients from mother to offspring.

Wean To separate nursing offspring from their dam so that they no longer receive milk.

Weanling An animal of weaning age.

Wether Male of sheep, castrated before secondary sex characteristics develop.

Yearling An animal approximately 1 year old.

Zygote The cell formed by the union of two gametes.

REFERENCES

Battaglia, R.A., and Mayrose, V. B. 1981. *Handbook of Livestock Management Techniques.* New York: Macmillan.

Bearden, H. J., and Fuquay, J. W. 1997. *Applied Animal Reproduction,* (4th ed.). Englewood Cliffs, NJ: Prentice-Hall.

Cupps, PT. 1991. *Reproduction in Domestic Animals* (4th ed.). New York: Academic Press.

Hafez, E. S. E. (Ed.). 1993. *Reproduction in Farm Animals* (6th ed.). Philadelphia: Lea and Febiger.

Hansel, W., Concannon, P. W., and Lukszewski, J. H. 1973. *Biol. Reprod.* 8: 222.

Harrison, B. M. 1971. *Embryology of the Pig and Chick.* Dubuque, IA: W. C. Brown.

King, G. J. (Ed.). 1993. *Reproduction in Domesticated Animals.* Amsterdam, The Netherlands: Elsevier Science Publishers.

Murdoch, W. J. 1994. Animal reproduction. *Encyclopedia of Agricultural Science.* San Diego: Academic Press.

Taylor, R. E. 1995. *Scientific Farm Animal Production* (5th ed.). Upper Saddle River, NJ: Prentice-Hall, Inc., pp. 1–672.

Supplementary Visuals
Videos available from:
Creative Educational Video
P. O. Box 65265
Lubbock, TX 79464

Beef Reproduction (three tapes). 1995. 87 minutes

Equine Reproduction. 1995. 27 minutes

Foaling. 1997. 28 minutes

Swine Reproduction (two tapes). 1994. 61 minutes

Artificial Insemination: Striving for Perfection. 1993. 17 minutes

Basic Animal Microgenetics. 1996. 43 minutes

Embryo Transfer. 1995. 40 minutes

Fundamental Livestock Parturition. 1997. 30 minutes

Calving Problems and Procedures. 1984. 45 minutes

CHAPTER FIVE
LACTATION

The newborn of all mammals depend on milk for normal growth and development during the first weeks or months of postnatal life. In this chapter we consider the special structure and function of the mammary gland and explore the composition and nutritional contributions of the milk of cows and other mammals during the normal lactation period. The general knowledge of the mammary gland and its product, milk, acquired in this chapter will provide the basis for understanding the many facets of lactation covered in later chapters dealing with specific mammals important in animal agriculture and biology.

THE MAMMARY GLAND

Structure

The size and shape of mammary glands and their anatomical position vary greatly among species, but the microscopic structure is similar for all mammals. In some species, including the cow, sheep, goat, and horse, the mammary glands are between the hind legs, whereas in litter-bearing animals such as the dog, cat, pig, and rabbit, the glands are distributed in two rows along each side of the ventral midline. In swine, the number of nipples and their corresponding mammary glands varies from 6 to 20 (3 to 10 pairs) or more, arranged in two parallel rows, and extending along the entire underline. A sow with her piglets is shown in Figure 5-1. In swine (both female and male) there may be an even or odd number on each side and in total; frequency distribution of even or odd is about 60:40. Each gland of the sow is separate from adjacent glands in secretory tissue. Supernumerary (nonfunctional) nipples may be present; most are underdeveloped even though they may be in association with a functional gland.

The udder of the cow has four mammary glands (four quarters), each with one teat (nipple), whereas the sheep and goat have two glands and two teats and the horse has four glands and two teats. In most species, each gland is associated with one teat. The blood supply to the mammary gland is abundant in all mammals. In the cow, most of the arterial blood is supplied by the pubic arteries via the external iliac arteries from the abdominal aorta. In swine, the blood supply is from the common carotid artery, which supplies the anterior glands, and a branch of the abdominal aorta, which supplies the posterior (inguinal) glands. However, a considerable amount of anastomosis results in some of the blood supplying the anterior (pectoral) glands, passing posteriorly to the inguinal glands

FIGURE 5-1
A sow nursing piglets. (Photo by: © Bonnie Sue Ranch/Photo Researchers.)

and, conversely, some blood supplying the inguinal glands passes forward to the pectoral glands.

Milk produced in the gland is secreted via many alveoli, the functional secretory units of the gland. Each alveolus is a vase-like structure containing on its lumen surface a single layer of secretory epithelium cells whose function is to transfer newly formed milk from the mammary cells into the lumen of the alveolus for transport into a duct system into which flows the milk contributed by many other individual alveoli. The general structure of the bovine mammary gland and the architecture of a cluster of alveoli in the duct system within the gland are depicted in Figure 5-2a and b. The collecting ducts carry the milk into large ducts, in a manner somewhat analogous to the flow of contributaries in a river. These larger ducts, called a cistern in cows and some other large species, serve as reservoirs for milk before suckling or ejection.

Development

The mammary gland begins its development (mammogenesis) during fetal life. Both males and females develop specialized cells known as mammary streaks in early fetal life. Later in prenatal life these primitive cells give rise to mammary buds which will later become teats, present in both males and females at birth.

In later prenatal life, the teat and duct structures begin to form and there is the beginning of connective tissue and fat cell development at the base of the gland. The blood and lymph supply to the gland appear and the necessary structures for eventual development of the mature mammary system are already in place. From birth until just before puberty, there is general growth of the mammary gland, but at about the same rate as that of the overall body.

Puberty (defined as the occasion of the first estrus) is characterized by a surge of hormone secretions from the ovary and pituitary gland. Accompanying these endocrine events is an increase in the rate of growth of the mammary gland in relation to that of other body organs and the whole body. This differential growth of mammary tissue is a reflection of increased branching and proliferation of the duct system and the mammary fat cell (adipocyte) tissues and the development of primitive alveoli.

During early pregnancy, there is very little change in the size or structure of the mammary gland, but from mid-pregnancy to parturition the duct system and secretory tissue proliferate in preparation for lactation. In late gestation, milk constituents begin to accumulate in the alveolar lumen and, just before parturition, the secretion of colostrum, containing high concentrations of protein and debris from the breakdown of sloughed alveolar cells, begins. After parturition, mammary tissue continues to proliferate, although to a sharply reduced degree, and milk secretion accelerates. The secretory cells of the mammary gland reach their peak at a few weeks after parturition in the cow in concert with the peak of milk production. The pattern of mammary gland development and secretion varies among species, but follows a parallel schedule related to such factors as differences in gestation length, age at puberty, and number of glands.

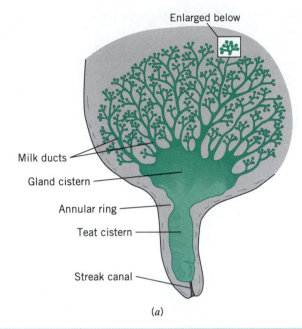

Enlarged below

Milk ducts

Gland cistern

Annular ring

Teat cistern

Streak canal

(a)

FIGURE 5-2

(a) A section through one of the quarters (mammary gland) of a cow udder, showing secretory tissue, ducts, and milk-collecting cisterns. (Adapted from Taylor (1995) by permission of Prentice-Hall, Inc., Upper Saddle River, NJ.)

MILK SYNTHESIS AND SECRETION

Milk Synthesis

The mammary glands synthesize and secrete an array of specific substances that constitute the unique product, milk. The major organic components of milk are protein, fat, and milk sugar (lactose). The minerals, calcium, and phosphorus and many constituents present in much smaller amounts, including trace elements, vitamins, and many other metabolites also are provided in milk. Some of these substances are transferred directly into the milk from blood, whereas many are synthesized in the mammary gland. In both cases (transferred or synthesized), their entry into milk is a result of secretion via the secretory epithelium cells of the alveoli of the mammary gland.

Milk fat is synthesized in the mammary gland from fatty acids and other lipids transferred from the blood and from fatty acids actually synthesized in the mammary gland cells. The fat synthesized accumulates within the epithelial cell and forms a droplet which enlarges and is eventually released into the lumen of the alveolus, enclosed in a membrane derived from the epithelial cell as it leaves. The milk fat droplet, surrounded by the milk fat membrane, is a unique biologic product. Most of the long chain fatty acids of milk are transferred directly from the blood, whereas most of the short chain fatty acids of milk are

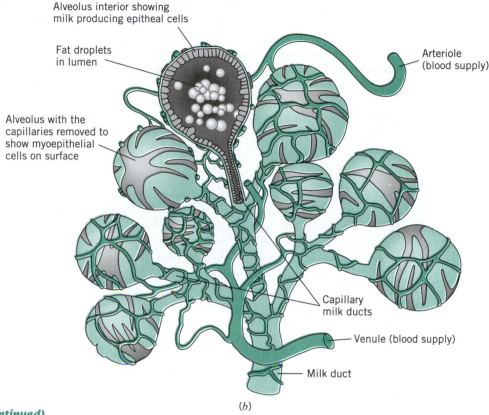

Alveolus interior showing milk producing epitheal cells

Fat droplets in lumen

Arteriole (blood supply)

Alveolus with the capillaries removed to show myoepithelial cells on surface

Capillary milk ducts

Venule (blood supply)

Milk duct

(b)

FIGURE 5-2 *(continued)*

(b) a lobe (enlarged) of the duct system, with several alveoli and their accompanying blood supply, showing an arteriole carrying oxygenated arterial blood from larger arteries, and a venule carrying venous blood from the capillaries back through larger veins for oxygenation in the lung.

Source: Drawing by Dennis Giddings; reproduced from Taylor (1995), by permission of Prentice-Hall, Inc., Upper Saddle River, NJ.

synthesized within the mammary epithelial cells from precursors. The fatty acids are combined with glycerol in the mammary epithelial cell to form triglycerides, which are the major constituent of the milk fat droplet.

Milk proteins are derived from their direct transfer into the mammary epithelial cells from the blood or are synthesized within the secretory epithelial cells from amino acids transferred from the blood plasma to the mammary epithelial cell. An example of a milk protein synthesized within the mammary epithelial cell is casein; an example of milk proteins transferred from blood plasma is the group of immune globulins present in large amounts in colostrum.

Milk sugar (lactose, a disaccharide composed of glucose and galactose) is synthesized within the mammary epithelial cell from glucose and galactose. Glucose is transported readily from the blood to the mammary epithelial cell. The union of glucose and galactose to form lactose is preceded by the conversion of some of the glucose within to another six-carbon sugar, galactose. Thus, the unique carbohydrate of milk, lactose, depends on two conversions within the mammary epithelial cell: the production of galactose from glucose and the condensation of glucose and galactose to form lactose.

Vitamins and mineral elements are transferred from the blood plasma to the mammary epithelial cell by active transport or, in some rare cases, by simple diffusion. There is no synthesis of most vitamins (except vitamin C in some species) by the mammary gland.

Milk Secretion

Milk secretion is under the control of several hormones. Hormones from the anterior pituitary gland, including thyroid stimulating hormone (TSH), adrenocorticotropic hormone (ACTH), follicle stimulating hormone (FSH), and luteinizing hormone (LH), play a role in milk synthesis and secretion through their stimulating effects on hormones of the thyroid gland, adrenal cortex, and ovaries, all of which affect mammary gland function. The sudden upsurge in milk secretion following parturition is associated with shifts in the relative amounts of estrogen and progesterone in the maternal blood plasma and with the actions of growth hormone, prolactin, and adrenal cortex hormones. Also, the appearance of the enzyme, lactose synthetase, present only in the lactating mammary gland, is associated with the onset of lactation. A subunit of this enzyme, alpha-lactalbumin, is critical in the initiation of lactose synthesis. The complex interactions among these metabolites in initiating and maintaining milk production are beyond the scope of this chapter.

The hormone, oxytocin, produced in the posterior pituitary gland, is released by suckling, or in dairy cows by massaging the udder, and has an immediate and profound effect on ejection of milk from the mammary gland (milk letdown). This milk letdown is due to the sudden contraction of the myoepithelial cells on the surface of the alveoli, which forces the milk to be ejected from the alveoli and out of the duct system. In species other than those commonly used for milk production, it is necessary to inject exogenous oxytocin into the animal to induce milk letdown.

COLOSTRUM

The first food ingested by the newborn mammal must be nutritionally adequate. It also must provide protection from infectious disease organisms to which the neonate is exposed following its entrance into the nonsterile environment of the external world from the sterile environment of the uterus. Colostrum, the first secretion of the mammary gland after parturition, meets both of these criteria. It is higher in protein than normal milk, largely because of the presence of immunoglobulins (Ig), which provide passive immunity to the neonate, whose own immune system is immature at birth. Immunoglobulins include IgA, IgG, and IgM, all of which impart immune protection. In some mammals, immunoglobulins pass into the fetus from the blood of the dam, but in most of the large domestic animals the protective immunoglobulins are obtained from the colostrum.

The newborn animal has an immature intestinal tract. When the newborn animal begins to suckle the dam, large molecules such as the immunoglobulin (Ig) proteins are able to pass intact through the epithelial lining of the small intestine of the neonate into the blood to supply the needed antibody protection. Within the first day or two after birth the intestine no longer allows these molecules to traverse the intestinal lining to reach the blood (this maturation process is called "gut closure"). If colostrum is ingested after gut closure, the Ig cannot be absorbed into the body. Therefore, colostrum must be ingested immediately after birth to provide antibody protection. This passive immunity protects the animal from infections until the immune system of the neonate produces its own active immunity to disease.

Although the Ig profile of colostrum differs among species, colostrum from one species does offer some antibody protection to the young of another species. For example, the survival of orphan newborn pigs is improved by feeding them cow colostrum for the first day after birth. Immunoglobulins also appear to stimulate protein synthesis in muscle, liver, intestine, and other tissues of neonatal pigs fed colostrum. Colostrum also contains high concentrations of one or more other factors such as insulin-like growth factor-I (IGF-I) and epidermal growth factor that stimulates protein synthesis in these same tissues (Burrin et al., 1992). These observations emphasize further the important contribution of colostrum to the development of the newborn mammal.

MILK COMPOSITION

Most mammals produce milk containing between 10 and 20% solids (the sum of fat, protein, lactose, mineral elements). Because of its nearly ideal balance of nutrients to meet the needs of the neonate, milk has come to be known as nature's most nearly perfect food. Each mammalian species has its own characteristic degree of physiological maturity at birth. The composition of milk for each species is compatible with the specific nutrient needs of the young of that species. Milk has unique composition in several ways. For example, lactose (milk sugar) is found only in milk; casein, lactalbumin, and other proteins are unique to milk; immunoglobulins, important for protection from infections in the neonate, are secreted into the milk of all species.

Differences in Milk Composition

The concentrations of lactose, proteins, fat, and mineral elements in milk vary within and among species, but each species has a characteristic range of normal values for each

TABLE 5-1

MILK COMPOSITION OF EIGHT DIFFERENT ANIMALS COMPARED WITH THAT OF HUMANS

Species	Total Solids (%)	Fat (%)	Protein (%)	Lactose (%)	Minerals (Ash) (%)
Human	13.3	4.5	1.6	7.0	0.2
Cattle (B. taurus)	12.7	3.9	3.3	4.8	0.7
Cattle (B. indicus)	13.5	4.7	3.4	4.7	0.7
Goat	12.4	3.7	3.3	4.7	0.8
Water buffalo	19.0	7.4	6.0	4.8	0.8
Sheep	18.4	6.5	6.3	4.8	0.9
Swine	19.0	6.8	6.3	5.0	0.9
Horse	10.5	1.2	2.3	5.9	0.4
Reindeer	33.7	18.7	11.1	2.7	1.2

Source: Taylor (1995), by permission of Prentice-Hall, Inc., Upper Saddle River, NJ.

nutrient. The average percent composition of these milk constituents for nine species is summarized in Table 5-1 (Taylor, 1995). Within each species, the composition of the milk changes throughout lactation. This phenomenon is illustrated for swine in Table 5-2.

The total protein concentration in milk varies considerably among species (Table 5-1), and likewise, there are significant differences among species in the total amino acid concentration in milk (Table 5-3). The concentration of total amino acids in the milk of most species decreases during lactation. For example, in the cow and horse, the concen-

TABLE 5-2

CHANGES IN COMPOSITION OF SWINE COLOSTRUM AND MILK DURING AN EIGHT-WEEK LACTATION PERIOD

	Time After Parturition								
	Hours								*Weeks*
Constituent	0	3	6	9	12	15-24	27-48	72-120	2-8
Total solids, %	30.2	28.3	26.6	23.6	20.8	19.6	21.2	21.8	21.2
Fat, %	7.2	7.3	7.8	7.8	7.2	7.7	9.5	10.4	9.3
Protein, %*	18.9	17.5	15.2	11.7	10.2	7.2	6.9	6.8	6.2
Lactose, %	2.5	2.7	2.9	3.0	3.4	3.7	4.0	4.6	4.8
Ash, %	0.63	0.62	0.62	0.63	0.63	0.66	0.72	0.77	0.95
Calcium, %	0.05	0.04	0.05	0.05	0.06	0.07	0.11	0.16	0.25
Phosphorus, %	0.11	0.11	0.11	0.11	0.11	0.12	0.13	0.14	0.15

*Note the dramatic reduction in protein during the first 24 hours. Most of the decrease is due to the decline in the immunoglobulins present in colostrum (Bourne, 1969).
Source: Perrin (1955).

TABLE 5-3
TOTAL AMINO ACIDS (GRAMS/LITER) AND TOTAL ESSENTIAL AMINO ACIDS (MILLIGRAMS/GRAM OF TOTAL AMINO ACIDS) IN PRIMATE AND NONPRIMATE MILKS

Species	Total Amino Acids (g/L of whole milk)*	Total Essential Amino Acids (mg/g of total amino acids)
Primate		
Human	8.5	400
Chimpanzee	9.2	392
Gorilla	11.5	408
Baboon	11.5	408
Rhesis monkey	11.6	421
Nonprimate		
Cattle	33.6	427
Goat	25.7	433
Sheep	54.1	422
Llama	29.6	443
Swine	35.0	379
Horse	15.8	377
Elephant	37.0	411
Cat	75.7	400
Rat	86.9	371

*Primate differed from nonprimates (P<0.001).
Source: Davis et al. (1994), by permission.

tration of total amino acids in mature milk is about half that in colostrum, whereas in the pig the concentration in mature milk is about one-third that in colostrum and in the human about one-fourth. The essential amino acid[1] concentrations (free amino acids plus those contained in intact protein) of the milk of a broad array of species is remarkably constant. This similarity among five primate and nine nonprimate species is summarized in Table 5-3. The total essential amino acid concentration in the milk of primates versus nonprimates, of ruminants versus nonruminants, or of litter-bearing versus nonlitter-bearing animals is comparable, and that of no species appears unique among all the others. Even the milk of aquatic mammals such as the Northern elephant seal, the Antarctic fur seal, the California sea lion, and the Australian sea lion (Davis et al., 1995) contains concentrations of total essential amino acids in the same range as that of mammals listed in Table 5-3.

---

[1]Essential amino acid may be defined as one that is required in the diet of one or more animal species because the animal is unable to synthesize the amino acid in its own tissues to meet its needs for growth and/or maintenance. This subject is addressed in Chapter 8.

MILK PRODUCTION

Differences Among and Within Species

It is not surprising that the amount of milk produced daily by an animal of a large species such as the cow is expected to be greater than the amount produced by a sheep or goat, because of the much greater size of the newborn calf compared with the lamb or kid. The amounts of milk produced during the typical lactation periods of several species (Figure 5-3) indicate not only differences in daily production, but also differences in the shape of the lactation curve among species. When one considers that the composition of the milk of each species is also variable, and that the number of young being raised may vary from one to 15 or 20, it becomes clear that many variables are operating to determine the total milk produced in a single lactation period, even within a single mammalian species.

Influence of Genetic and Environmental Factors

The profound effect of genetic selection for milk production is illustrated by comparing the lactation curve of Holstein dairy cows with that of beef breeds (Figure 5-3a and b). Dairy cattle have been selected over many generations for maximum milk production, whereas the selection of beef cattle has been based on a combination of several traits, including growth rate, carcass quality, and efficiency of feed utilization, along with milk production. Modern dairy cows are expected to produce upward of 25,000 pounds of milk in a single 305-day lactation. The best care and feeding of a modern high-quality beef cow could never be expected to result in a comparable level of milk production. Genetic differences in milk production also exist among dairy breeds (Holsteins are superior to most other dairy breeds) and among beef, goat, and swine breeds (see Figure 5-3b, c, and f, respectively).

The amount of milk produced daily is determined to a large degree by the extent and frequency of removal of milk from the gland. A sow nursing 10 piglets produces more milk than one nursing 5 piglets, partly because of greater total milk ingested at each suckling period by the larger litter, but also, because piglets tend to claim one nipple as their own at a few days of age, and unused glands soon cease to function. Similarly, ewes nursing twins (or triplets) produce more milk than those nursing a single lamb (see Figure 5-3d), because of the greater stimulus to milk secretion induced by two lambs. Dairy cows milked three times daily produce more milk per day than those milked twice daily, for the same reasons.

Just as genetic capacity limits total milk production of an individual animal, inadequate nutrient intake prevents the realization of genetic potential. An inadequate level of a particular dietary constituent, such as protein, has an adverse effect on milk yield. Also, an inadequate intake of total feed, even though the diet may be nutritionally well balanced, depresses milk yield. In dairy cows of exceptionally high genetic potential for milk production, their physical capacity to consume feed may be insufficient to allow them to sustain maximum production at the peak of lactation. Therefore, any management or

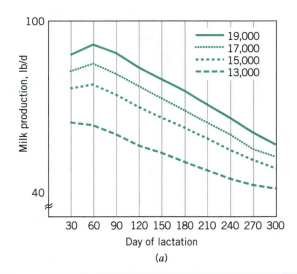

(a)

FIGURE 5-3.

Lactation curves for: (a) Holstein dairy cows. The curves were developed from the records of 356,343 Holstein cows in Dairy Herd Improvement herds in the Northeastern United States. Note the shape of the curves is similar for cows with high and low production. The curves do not show differences in production of 1st, 2nd, and 3rd lactation cows. Cows in 3rd and later lactations have a higher lactation peak (about 2 mo) and higher total production than those in 2nd lactation and cows in 2nd lactation have a higher peak and higher production than those in 1st lactation. By day 300 of lactation, cows in 1st, 2nd, and 3rd and later lactations are producing milk at a similar level.

Source: Courtesy L. E. Chase, adapted from L. R. Jones (1989), Animal Science Mimeograph Series, Cornell Cooperative Extension Service, Ithaca, NY.

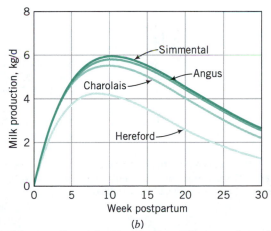

(b)

(b) Lactation curves of Angus, Charolais, Hereford, and Simmental purebred beef cows.

Source: Courtesy of C. L. Ferrell, USDA Meat Animal Research Center, Clay Center, NE.

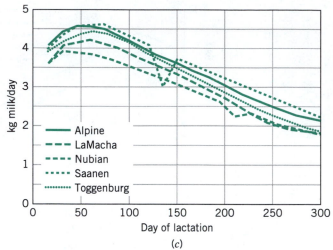

(c) Lactation curves of Alpine, LaMacha, Nubian, Saanen, and Toggenburg goats.
Source: Courtesy of George Wiggins, USDA/ARS, Beltsville, MD.

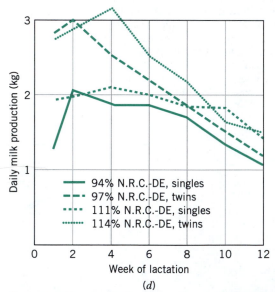

(d) Lactation curves of crossbred ewes of mixed breeding and fed at 94 to 97% or 111–114% of National Research Council–recommended levels of energy intake for singles and twins.
Source: R. W. Gardner and D. E. Hogue (1964).

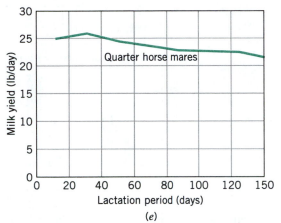

(e) Lactation curve of quarter horse mares.
Source: Gibbs et al. (1982).

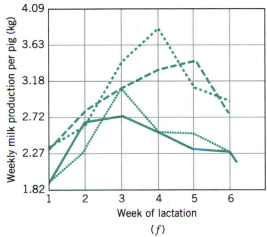

(f) Lactation curves of Duroc, Landrace, Poland China, and Landrace x Poland China sows.
Source: Allen and Lasley (1960).

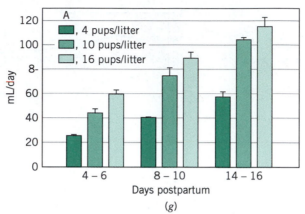

(g) Lactation curves at three stages of lactation in laboratory rats nursing 4, 10, or 16 pups. *Source:* Fiorotto et al. (1991).

husbandry change that will result in increased feed intake will benefit total milk yield. Genetically superior cows often draw on their own body stores of nutrients to offset deficits in nutrient intake during the first few weeks, corresponding to the peak of lactation. Sows with high milk-producing ability and nursing large litters also mobilize fat and protein from their own body to maintain a high level of milk production and, as a result, may become so thin as to delay their normal rebreeding schedule following weaning.

Milk production can be reduced seriously by mastitis, an infectious process that may involve one or all mammary glands for part or all of the lactation period. Any infectious disease that causes fever may interrupt lactation and decrease milk production. Extremely high ambient temperature reduces milk yield as does any stressful experience to the lactating animal.

Recently, the administration of bovine somatotropin (bST) was approved for use in the United States to increase milk yield of lactating dairy cows. The daily injection of this hormone (produced in all animals by the pituitary gland, and now available commercially in large quantities using recombinant DNA technology) results in increased milk yields of 10 to 40% in dairy cows (Peel and Bauman, 1987). The administration of bST results in the partitioning of nutrients to the mammary gland for milk synthesis. Cows receiving bST consume more feed to accommodate the extra nutrient requirement of increased lactation. The overall process is associated with improved efficiency of milk production. Less environmental resources are used when animals are made more efficient. Lactating sows also respond to somatotropin administration by increasing milk production (Figure 5-4). Pigs suckling sows given porcine somatotropin (pST) during lactation are heavier at weaning compared with pigs nursing control sows, although pST-treated sows consumed less feed and lost more weight than untreated sows (Harkins et al., 1989).[2] The use of

---

[2]The approval of pST for use in swine in the United States is under consideration.

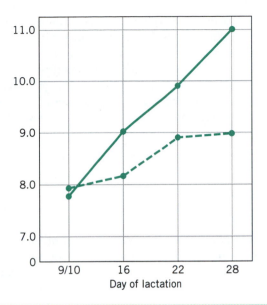

FIGURE 5-4

Milk production in sows receiving a daily subcutaneous injection of recombinant DNA-derived porcine somatotropin (pST) (solid line) or saline (untreated control) (dashed line) from day 9 to day 29 of lactation.

Source: Harkins et al. (1989), by permission of *Journal of Animal Science.*

exogenous hormones and other substances to improve lactation performance in animals has the potential to improve overall efficiency of growth and of food production in other mammals as well.

METABOLIC COST OF LACTATION

The amounts of energy, protein, minerals, and vitamins contained in milk produced over the entire lactation period (10 months in dairy cows, 2 to 5 weeks in swine, 6 to 8 weeks in sheep and goats, 25 weeks in beef cattle, 5 to 6 months in horses, 3 weeks in rats, 6 weeks in dogs and cats) is enormous in relation to the body reserves of these nutrients. Compared with the needs of the developing fetus and associated products of conception, the needs of the mammary gland, especially at the peak of lactation, far exceed the capacity of the animal to consume the needed nutrients, even when feed is unrestricted. Therefore, the body reserves of the lactating dam must make up the deficit between the output of nutrients in the milk and the intake of nutrients from the feed. For this reason, body weight is lost during lactation, the magnitude of which is related to the appetite of the dam and the nutrient density of the diet. Dairy cows with a high genetic potential for milk production lose body fat reserves and may mobilize labile protein reserves to sustain a high level of milk output (sometimes as high as 25 times her own body weight in fluid milk) throughout a 305-day lactation. Dairy goats, sows, and ewes with a high potential for milk production experience the same type of metabolic stress. The remarkable adaptability of the body to the metabolic challenge of lactation is related to a complex interaction among endocrine glands, digestive organs, physiological controls of feed intake, and genetic determinants of these responses, all of which are modulated by the environment.

SUMMARY

Lactation is a unique characteristic of all mammals. The newborn mammal depends on milk secreted from the mammary gland for sustenance during the first weeks or months of extrauterine life. We survey and describe the structure and development of the mammary gland and the process of milk synthesis and secretion. We emphasize the nature and critical importance of colostrum in the survival and immunological protection of the neonatal animal. Milk composition and production differ greatly among and within species. Milk has unique composition in several ways: lactose (milk sugar) is found only in milk; casein, lactalbumin, and other proteins are unique to milk; immunoglobulins, important for disease protection, are secreted by the mammary glands into the milk of all species. Although the chemical composition of milk varies widely among species, the essential amino acid concentrations in the milk of a broad array of species (primates vs. nonprimates; ruminants vs. nonruminants; litter-bearing vs. nonlitter-bearing) are remarkably constant. Many variables operate to determine the amount of milk produced in a single lactation period, even within an individual species. Modern dairy cows, selected for high milk production for many generations, are expected to produce upward of 25,000 pounds of milk in a 305-day lactation. Just as genetic capacity limits total milk yield of an individual animal, inadequate nutrition or a hostile environment prevent the realization of genetic potential. The administration to lactating dairy cows of bovine somatotropin (bST) results in substantial increases in the total yield of milk and improves overall efficiency of production. The use of exogenous hormones and other substances to improve lactation performance in animals has the potential to improve the efficiency of growth and of food production in other mammals as well. Lactation is a high-cost physiological process. Compared with the needs for fetal development and associated products of conception, the needs of the mammary gland far exceed the capacity of the lactating animal to consume the needed nutrients. The animal responds by depleting her own body tissues to accommodate sustained lactation. The remarkable adaptability of the body to the metabolic challenge of lactation is related to complex interrelationships among endocrine glands, digestive organs, physiological control of feed intake, and genetic determinants of these responses, all of which are modulated by the environment.

GLOSSARY

Alveolus   One of many small cavities connected to ducts within the mammary gland from which milk is secreted.

Casein   A major protein of milk.

Cistern   Milk storage tissue in the mammary gland and teat, from which milk is ejected.

Colostrum   The first secretion of the mammary gland at or immediately after parturition; it provides antibody protection to the newborn and is a concentrated source of nutrients.

Galactose   A six-carbon constituent with glucose of the disaccharide, lactose in milk.

Immunoglobulins (Ig)   Milk and colostral proteins that provide protection of the newborn from infectious disease; include IgA, IgG, and IgM.

Gut closure   The process that occurs during the first day or two following birth in which large molecules such as immunoglobulins can no longer be absorbed into the body from the intestinal lumen.

Lactalbumin   A milk protein.

Lactation   The production of milk during the period immediately following parturition; its duration varies among species from a few days to many months.

Lactose   Milk sugar, a disaccharide composed of glucose and galactose; produced only by the mammary gland, and secreted as the major carbohydrate constituent of milk.

Lactic acid   A compound formed in the body during anaerobic glycolysis; it is also produced in milk by the bacterial fermentation of lactose.

Lactoferrin   An iron-binding protein found in milk, saliva, tears, and intestinal and respiratory secretions; it interferes with iron metabolism of bacteria and may play a role in infectious disease resistance and in the growth of cells of the intestinal lining.

Mammalia   A class of vertebrate animals of more than 15,000 species, distinguished by self-regulating body temperature, hair, and in females, the secretion of milk.

Mammary gland   A milk-producing organ in female mammals, consisting of alveoli with ducts terminating in a nipple or teat.

Mammogenesis   The beginning of development of the mammary gland.

Milk   The fluid secretion of the mammary gland of all mature female mammals after they have given birth; it is the first food of the newborn and supplies all required nutrients.

Milk ejection   The release of milk from the mammary gland under the influence of oxytocin, resulting in the removal of milk from the mammary gland by suckling or mechanical manipulation.

Milk letdown   See Milk ejection; pertains to the initiation of milk release from the mammary gland in response to a stimulus.

Milk secretion   The release from the mammary gland of synthesized milk.

Milk synthesis   The metabolic process within the mammary gland that assembles the constituents that are secreted from the gland as milk.

Milk yield   The amount of milk produced by a lactating female in a prescribed period of time; in dairy cattle it is often measured in days or in a 305-day lactation.

Nipple   The small conical protuberance from the mammary gland containing the outlets of the milk ducts.

Oxytocin   A hormone produced by the posterior pituitary gland that is released by suckling or, in dairy cows, by massaging the udder to produce milk ejection.

Teat   See Nipple.

Udder   The mammary glands, which number four in the cow, two in sheep and goats, and ten or more in swine.

REFERENCES

Allen, A. D., and Lasley, J. F. 1960. *J. Animal Science,* 19: 150.

Bourne, F. J. 1969. *Animal Production,* 11: 337.

Burrin, D. G., Shulman, R. J., Reeds, P. J., Davis, T. A., and Gravett, K. R. 1992. *J. Nutrition,* 122: 1205.

Davis, T. A., Nguyen, H. V., Costa, D. P., and Reeds, P. J. 1995. *Comp. Biochem. Physiol.,* 110B: 663.

Davis, T. A., Nguyen, H. V., Garcia-Bravo, R., Fiorotto, M. L., Jackson, E. M., Lewis, D. S., Lee, D. R., and Reeds, P. J. 1994. *J. Nutrition,* 124: 1126.

Fiorotto, M. A., Burrin, D. G., Perez, M., and Reeds, P. J. 1991. *Am. J. Physiol.,* 260: R1104.

Gardner, R. W., and Hogue, D. E. 1964. *J. Animal Science,* 23: 935.

Gibbs, P. G., Poter, G. D., Blake, R. W., and McMullan, W. C. 1982. *J. Animal Science,* 54: 496.

Harkins, M., Boyd, R. D., and Bauman, D. E. 1989. *J. Animal Science,* 67: 1997.

Peel, C. J., and Bauman, D. E. 1987. *J. Dairy Science,* 70: 474.

Perrin, D. R. 1955. *J. Dairy Science,* 22: 103.

Taylor, R. E. 1995. *Scientific Farm Animal Production* (5th ed.). Upper Saddle River, NJ: Prentice Hall, pp. 1–672.

CHAPTER SIX
GENETICS[1]

Animal genetics is the study and understanding of the process by which characteristics are passed from one generation to another, the study of inheritance or heredity. The father of genetic observation was Gregor Mendel, an Austrian monk, who explained the pattern of

---

[1]The constructive comments and improvements provided by Dr. David S. Buchanan to this chapter are deeply appreciated.

inheritance using the garden pea. His observations of hereditary determinants in the plant (we now call genes) formed the basis for understanding the genetics of animals. Knowledge and understanding of genetics is a key to producing the types of animals needed for current and future production systems. Methods of selection, mating systems, and newer methods in biotechnology are critical for developing the right animal for today and tomorrow. This chapter describes the chromosome and gene, reviews the structure of the cell and its reproduction (mitosis and meiosis), describes the relationship between heredity and the environment, and describes methods of genetic selection and improvement.

GENES AND CHROMOSOMES OF THE CELL

Tissues of animals are composed of cells that contain the machinery for the maintenance and reproduction of life. A typical cell (Figure 6-1) is surrounded by a cellular membrane which contains the cytoplasm and internal structures such as the mitochondria, endoplasmic reticulum, and nucleus. From a genetics standpoint, the material contained in the nucleus is of key importance.

Chromosomes

The nucleus of the cell contains rod-like structures called chromosomes, which contain genes consisting of discrete collections of DNA, the genetic material described by Mendel as hereditary determinants. Body cells of each animal contain two pairs of each chromosome. Chromosome number is different for different species (Table 6-1). The entire set of chromosomes (karyotype) from a cell of a pig is shown in Figure 6-2. The set of chromosomes for a particular species contains all of the genes (called the genome). Each cell contains matched pairs of chromosomes and one pair of chromosomes called sex chromosomes, which can be different. From visual appearance one sex chromosome is in the shape of an X and the other of a Y. Male mammals have one of each (XY) and females have two X chromosomes (XX). In poultry, the sex chromosomes are labeled Z and W, with males ZZ and females ZW.

Genes

A unit of inheritance is called a gene, located on the chromosome. A chromosome is an elongated chain composed of a protein core surrounded by a chemical called deoxyribonucleic acid (DNA). Genes are segments of DNA on a chromosome; they contain specific information needed by the cell to make the proteins controlling the functioning of the organism (e.g., growth, development). Genes are functional units along the DNA molecule. DNA contains a sugar (deoxyribose), phosphate, and one of four nitrogenous bases (adenine, A; cytosine, C; guanine, G; and thymine, T). The compound resulting

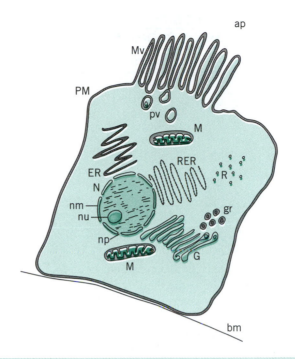

FIGURE 6-1

A generalized cell surrounded by a cellular membrane and containing internal structures. The cell is bounded by a plasma membrane (PM), which may be specialized at the apical (ap) surface and possess microvilli (Mv). At the base of the microvilli may be pinocytotic vesicles (pv). On the lateral margins, the membrane may form junctions (j) with adjacent cells. The cell may be associated at its basal surface with a basement membrane (bm), an extracellular supporting material. The nucleus (N), containing nucleolus (nu) and chromatin (ch), is bounded by a nuclear membrane (nm) with characteristic nuclear pores (np). Membranous organelles extending into the cytoplasm include smooth endoplasmic reticulum (ER) and rough endoplasmic reticulum (RER). The latter is decorated with ribosomes (R) that may also be free in the cytoplasm. The Golgi (G), a layered vesicular membrane system, forms membrane-enclosed granules (gr). These are usually secretory granules that can accumulate in the cytoplasm awaiting a secretory episode. Mitochondria (M) vary in number depending upon the metabolic activity level of the cell; they are involved in energy transformation.

from the combination of deoxyribose, phosphate, and one of the nitrogenous bases is called a nucleotide. The chemical bonding of many nucleotides forms a strand that comprises one-half of the DNA molecule. The two strands always contain complementary pairs of nitrogenous bases: A always pairs with T and C always pairs with G.

The two complementary strands wrap around each other to form the double helix arrangement of the DNA. Each member of a pair of chromosomes is of similar size and shape (called homologous chromosomes). Homologous chromosomes have genes that

TABLE 6-1
CHROMOSOME NUMBER FOR VARIOUS SPECIES

Species	Number of Pairs
Swine	19
Humans	23
Sheep	27
Goats	30
Cattle	30
Horses	32
Chickens	39
Dogs	39
Turkeys	41

code for similar information (Figure 6-3). Genes that encode for specific characteristics (traits) are at a specific and consistent location (locus) on the chromosome. If there are alternative forms of a gene they are called alleles. Genes of the same locus on homologous chromosomes that control a trait in the same way are called homozygous and those that contrast in their control of that trait are called heterozygous (-*zygous* refers to the individual; *homo-* means same and *hetero-* means different). Genes that occupy corresponding loci (plural of locus) on homologous chromosomes can affect a trait in different ways. For example, a gene may have the same or different alleles to determine whether an animal (in the case of cattle) will develop horns (horned) or will not develop horns (polled). Genes that are spacially located close together on the same chromosome tend to be inherited together; this phenomenon is termed genetic linkage.

Almost all genes code for proteins, which consist of more than 25 individual amino acids arranged in various sequences and proportions. For each amino acid making up a protein, there is at least one triplet sequence of three base pairs. By analogy, if amino acids are letters of a word and proteins are words, then one can consider that each triplet sequence of DNA can be said to code for a letter of the word and the entire encoded message, the series of base triplets, is the word (gene). The genes contained within the chromosomes are a selected grouping of base pairs on the DNA (Figure 6-4).

Transcription, Translation, and Protein Synthesis

The base pairs, in combination, code for genes along the chromosome, which in turn code for protein synthesis. The code is read and the protein is synthesized by a two-step process: transcription, then translation, both involving ribonucleic acids (RNA). The three types of RNA are: transfer RNA (tRNA), messenger RNA (mRNA), and ribosomal RNA (rRNA). Each of the three types of RNA is coded by the DNA. Transcription is the process used to make tRNA from genes, using a single strand of DNA that is temporarily partially unwound from its native state. A series of specific protein transcription factors specify which genes get transcribed. Translation is the synthesis of the primary amino acid sequence of a protein using mRNA as the template. The process is controlled by the ac-

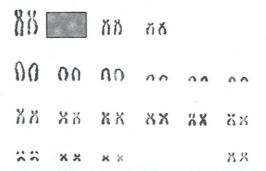

The domesticated pig has 38 chromosomes arrayed in four rows. It lacks one pair that is found in the European wild pig (below), and this absence is indicated by the square in the first row.

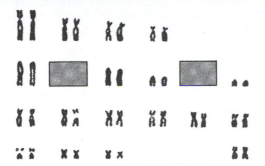

The European wild pig has only 36 chromosomes. The two pairs that are missing (but that are present in the domestic animal above) are in the second row.

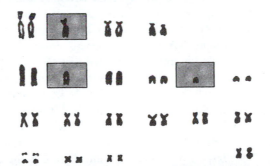

The hybrid pig has 37 chromosomes. Note that single chromosomes occupy each of the three positions in which either the domestic or the wild animal lacks a pair.

FIGURE 6-2

The karyotype of the pig.

Source: U.S. Atomic Energy Commission, Agricultural Research Laboratory, University of Tennessee, Knoxville, TN.

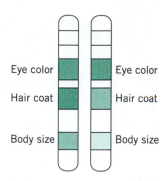

Eye color   Eye color

Hair coat   Hair coat

Body size   Body size

FIGURE 6-3

A hypothetical pair of homologous chromosomes that have sets of genes that code for various characteristics. In this example, genes at the same locus coding for expression of three different traits (eye color, hair coat color, and body size) would be described as homozygous for eye color (identical alleles) and heterozygous for hair coat color (contrasting alleles) and body size (contrasting alleles).

tion of individual triplets of nucleotide bases (codons) that specify which particular amino acid gets added to the growing peptide (ultimately ending in a complete peptide or a complete protein). Translation occurs in ribosomes which attach to and then migrate along the strand of mRNA. Amino acids are obtained by detachment from tRNA-amino acid complexes.

The first step in protein synthesis is transcription. DNA not only serves as a template for self-replication by the pairing of specific bases, it also serves as a template for mRNA. mRNA is similar to DNA but is single stranded and codes for only a few proteins. The codon (triplet sequence that codes for one amino acid in mRNA) is held in the encoded message of the DNA molecule and becomes transcribed onto the mRNA molecule. After transcription, the mRNA leaves the nucleus, enters the cytoplasm, and migrates to an organelle termed the ribosome (composed of rRNA and protein), where protein synthesis occurs. Protein synthesis proceeds by the joining of amino acids with their respective tRNA molecules which are coded by DNA. They contain an anticodon which is complementary to a mRNA codon. Each amino acid links with a specific tRNA, ensuring the integrity of the protein being synthesized. Each tRNA matches with its specific mRNA triplets, beginning at one end of the mRNA and proceeding down its length until all codons of the respective amino acids are aligned in the appropriate order. As the mRNA traverses the ribosome, the amino acids of the evolving protein join each other in peptide bond linkage. The completed protein dissociates from the mRNA-tRNA complex. In this way the entire array of proteins in the body is synthesized, each to perform one of the myriad functions required to sustain life, including the roles in enzyme systems, in hormonal control of metabolism, and as structural constituents and secretory products in the body. The term gene expression, at the molecular level, refers to the production of the protein whose synthesis is controlled by a specific gene. The presence of mRNA in a tissue suggests, but does not ensure, that significant gene product will be formed.

The story of heredity is the story of a chemical symphony buried deep within the nucleus of the cell. When an animal is conceived it receives a haploid ("half") set of chromosomes, from its dam (the female genetic parent) and a similar half from its sire (the male genetic parent). Together, these contributions form the diploid ("double") array of paired chromosomes that contains all of the information needed to transform a fertilized ovum into an animal with its own set of individual characteristics.

The alphabetic code used to spell out this remarkable compilation of information has only four letters, known as nucleotides and represented in biochemical shorthand as A, C, G, and T. When linked together in pairs in ladder-step fashion, nucleotides take on the well-known helical shape of DNA, the primary substance that comprises chromosomes.

It is from special, functional stretches of DNA, known as genes, that the cellular machinery makes proteins, the basic building blocks of life. A gene may consist of fewer than a thousand nucleotides, or of hundreds of thousands. It may code for an entire protein or for just part of one.

In the same way that digital variations determine the notes and pitches and hues that emanate from a compact disc, the order in which A, C, G, and T appear in a particular gene dictates the exact nature of the proteins under construction—and ultimately, the form and function of the symphony we know as a living organism.

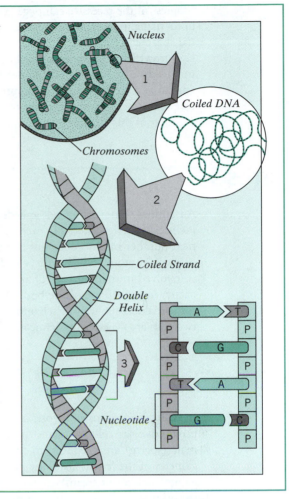

FIGURE 6-4

A detailed look at the genetic system including the nucleus, chromosomes, DNA, and nucleotides. (Adapted from Schook, 1995); by permission of L. B. Schook.

The genes that are on the chromosome of an individual are the same in every cell of the individual and were originally transmitted from the parents. Cell division resulting in somatic cells (mitosis) and sex cells (meiosis) is described below.

Occasionally in nature, errors are made in the process of cell division whereby slight changes occur in the delicate steps of passing genetic information to the next generation. Such an error is termed a mutation. The individual differing from the parental strain as a result of a mutation is a mutant. Mutations can be induced by environmental insults (e.g., x-irradiation, toxic chemicals), but many mutations occur by chance. Recent examples of chance mutations in farm animals are the "callipyge" gene in sheep and the "spider" gene in sheep. Both are recessive genes (defined later). Individual sheep carrying two "copies" of the recessive callipyge gene (homozygous) have a high proportion of their lean body tissue in the rear quarters and a higher-than-expected total lean body mass. Individual sheep carrying two copies of the recessive spider gene have abnormal bone and cartilage growth and become crippled and debilitated at an early age. Therefore, it is clear that mutations may be beneficial or detrimental to the functional development of the affected animal and to its usefulness in animal production. A better understanding of the structure and functions of genes and of their actions and interactions will be gained in the remainder of this chapter.

MITOSIS

An animal starts as one cell and develops into a multicellular functional organism with identical genetic material in each cell. The division of cells to produce like cells with identical number of chromosomes is called mitosis. During mitosis two cells form from an original "mother" cell (Figure 6-5). Mitosis causes the growth of an embryo to a fetus and is involved in maintenance of an organism by replacing old cells with new ones. Mitosis occurs in most parts of the body throughout life. The DNA contained in each chromosome makes a replica of itself and one copy goes to each of two new "daughter" cells. The two cells are genetically identical.

MEIOSIS

In contrast to mitosis, meiosis is the division of cells that results in the production of reproductive sex cells (gametes) by the process called gametogenesis. The gametes of the male (sperm) are produced in the testicles in a process called spermatogenesis, and the gametes of the female (ova) are produced in the ovary in a process called oogenesis. Each gamete (sperm or ovum) contains only half the genetic material (haploid) contained in the original cell (only 1 chromosome per pair). The general process of meiosis is similar in both the testis and ovaries (Figure 6-6). The chromosomes in each cell replicate, and homologous chromosomes form into bundles of four. One pair of joined replicas (originally from the sire, termed paternal chromosome) goes to one end of the cell and the other pair (originally from the dam, termed maternal chromosome) goes to the other end of the cell and the cell divides. The replicas in the new cells then separate with one chromosome going to each end of the cell and a second division occurs resulting in cells with only one chromosome of the pair in the new cell. The division in the production of sperm results in four cells of approximately equal size. In the female, the first and second division result in the majority of the size associated with one cell so that only one large viable ovum is formed. The smaller cells called polar bodies usually die and are not functional. The joining of the sperm and ova during fertilization results in a return to the full complement of chromosome pairs (diploid), one-half of the chromosomes from the male and one-half of the chromosomes from the female.

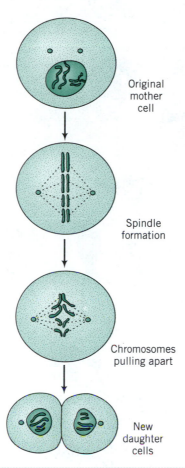

Original
mother
cell

Spindle
formation

Chromosomes
pulling apart

New
daughter
cells

FIGURE 6-5

The process of cell division called mitosis whereby an original cell is replicated to obtain two identical cells. [Adapted from Taylor (1995), by permission of Prentice-Hall, Inc., Upper Saddle River, NJ.]

FERTILIZATION AND GROWTH

The ovum uniting with a sperm (fertilization) initiates life and reestablishes the diploid number of chromosomes. The united male and female gametes (sperm and ovum) form the zygote. Fertilization has then occurred. Following fertilization, the zygote divides to form 2-, 4-, 8-, 16-, 32- (etc.) cell stages with each cell containing the identical genetic material. The subject of fertilization and subsequent differentiation and growth was covered in Chapter 4 and will be considered in Chapter 7. The growth in size and structure is genetically controlled and modified by the environment. The resulting animal is a product of both genetics and environment.

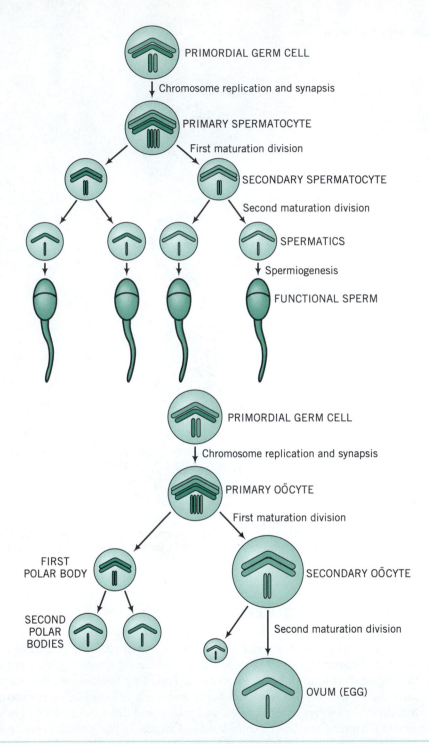

FIGURE 6-6

The process of meiosis in the testes and ovaries. The divisions result in four sperm cells compared to only one viable ovum (oocyte). [Adapted from Taylor (1995), by permission of Prentice-Hall, Inc., Upper Saddle River, NJ.]

DOMINANT AND RECESSIVE ALLELES FOR A SINGLE TRAIT: SIX POSSIBLE OUTCOMES

Chromosomes contain genetic information in each pair that codes for characteristics of animals. Some characteristics are controlled by one set of alleles (genes in similar locations on homologous chromosomes). A good example of this is the presence or absence of horns in breeds of cattle of European origin. Cattle exhibit horns or are polled (do not develop horns) based on the genetic information (genotype) contained on one pair of alleles on homologous chromosomes. The animal can have both genes for polled that indicates the animal will be polled, have both genes for horned that indicates the animal will be horned, or have a combination of both genes indicating the animal will be polled. The gene for polled covers the gene for horns and is termed the dominant gene. The gene for horns is recessive; thus, it is covered by the presence of the dominant gene for polled.

An individual receives one chromosome in each pair from each of the parents. There are three possible combinations for an individual. The individual could have genes that are both dominant for polled, that are both recessive for horns, or have one gene for polled and one gene for horns. Generally a letter is assigned to a gene that codes for a trait, with uppercase letters representing dominant genes and lowercase letters representing recessive genes. An individual with two dominant genes for polled might be abbreviated PP and individuals with one of each designated Pp. The letter designation would indicate the genetic makeup (genotype) of the animal and the characteristics exhibited would be called the phenotype (what you can see). Here are the examples for presence or absence of horns:

Genotype	Phenotype	Description
PP	Polled	Homozygous dominant
Pp	Polled	Heterozygous
pp	Horned	Homozygous recessive

A sire or dam will produce sperm or ova that contain the genes represented by his or her genotype. A homozygous dominant will only produce gametes (sperm or ova) with chromosomes containing the P allele (gene). Similarly a homozygous recessive will only produce gametes with chromosomes containing the p allele. The heterozygous individual will produce sperm or ova with 50% P and 50% p alleles of the gene on the chromosome. Therefore using one trait with 2 alleles (1 recessive and 1 dominant), the following mating combinations are possible: PP $\times$ PP, Pp $\times$ PP, PP $\times$ pp, Pp $\times$ pp, Pp $\times$ Pp, and pp $\times$ pp. There are six possible outcomes of the mating of sires and dams for the horned/polled trait. Knowledge of the parents' genotype can be used to determine the traits of the offspring or from the characteristics of the offspring the genotype of the parents can be determined. For example, horned cattle mated together will have 100% horned calves with a pp genotype. However, two polled cattle could produce a horned calf. How? The sire and dam would both have to be heterozygous (i.e., one horned allele and one polled allele of the gene). The P allele dominates over the recessive p allele of the gene so the parents were polled, but they both carried the p allele for horns. Uniting a sperm containing an allele of the p gene and an ovum containing an allele of the p gene will result in horned (pp) offspring.

Looking at more than one trait at a time is more complicated, but similar procedures can be followed. First consider the genetic makeup of the parents and determine possible combinations of genes that could be present in the gametes (sperm and ovum). Let us use the example for polled dominant over horned and add the trait color, in which black is dominant over red. The following genotypes are possible:

Genotype	Phenotype	Polled Genotype	Color Genotype
PPBB	polled, black	homozygous dominant	homozygous dominant
PpBB	polled, black	heterozygous	homozygous dominant
PpBb	polled, black	heterozygous	heterozygous
Ppbb	polled, red	heterozygous	homozygous recessive
ppBB	horned, black	homozygous recessive	homozygous dominant
ppBb	horned, black	homozygous recessive	heterozygous
ppbb	horned, red	homozygous recessive	homozygous recessive
PPBb	polled, black	homozygous dominant	heterozygous
PPbb	polled, red	homozygous dominant	homozygous recessive

Determining the genotype of gametes is simple if we know the genotype of the parents. Then the possible combinations can be charted. Genetic markers for some genes are available commercially to determine which alleles are carried by an animal.

These examples have been used to illustrate genetic principles of inheritance. Most traits are not determined by only one gene. Usually several genes at different loci are active in determining the characteristics of the individual. Characteristics affected by multiple loci provide the opportunity to exploit genetic variation. Such opportunities would be impossible if all traits were controlled by one gene.

TYPES OF GENE ACTION

Additive, Dominance, and Epistasis

There are three basic categories of gene action: additive, dominance, and epistasis. There are several qualitative (observed phenotype) traits which are largely determined by one or two gene pairs in which the type of gene action can be clearly discerned. Quantitative (measured phenotype) traits are likely to be influenced by many pairs of genes with varying degrees of all categories of gene action.

For a locus where the gene action is entirely additive (no dominance), the phenotype of the heterozygote is exactly midway between that of the two homozygotes. This is accomplished because each allele has a specific value which, when present, adds a specific amount to the phenotype. There may also be a dominance effect expressed at a given locus. Dominance is an interaction between genes within the locus. If there is complete dominance, the heterozygote is exactly equal in value to the homozygous dominant. Overdominance is present when the heterozygote is outside the range of the homozygotes. Examples of additive gene action and various degrees of dominance are illustrated (both qualitative and quantitative traits) as follows:

Qualitative Traits

RR	red	PP	polled
Rr	roan	Pp	polled
Rr	white	pp	horned
No Dominance		*Complete Dominance*	

Quantitative Traits

AA	+4	BB	+4	CC	+4	DD	+4
Aa	+2	Bb	+4	Cc	+3	Dd	+6
aa	+0	bb	+0	cc	+0	dd	+0
Additive		*Complete Dominance*		*Partial Dominance*		*Overdominance*	

Epistasis refers to the concept of having an interaction of genes at different loci. For example, in horses there is a primary locus for hair color that determines whether the horse will have black points (bay) or nonblack points (sorrel or chestnut). Horses that are BB or Bb are bay, whereas horses that are bb are sorrel or chestnut. However, there is another locus that can limit the expression of pigment in the hair coat. Horses with the ww genotype have normal expression of pigment and will be bay or chestnut, but horses that have the Ww or WW genotype will have white hair, no matter what is their genotype at the B locus.

Sex-Linked, Sex-Influenced, or Sex-Limited Traits

Sex-linked traits are those that are genetically controlled by genes located on the sex chromosomes. Although there are some genes on the Y chromosome, generally sex-linked genes are on the X chromosome because of its larger size. Traits such as hemophilia and color blindness in humans are controlled by a gene on the X chromosome. Sex-limited traits are those which are expressed in only one sex. Milk production and egg production are examples of traits limited to females, whereas cryptorchidism (failure of testes to descend into the scrotum during development) is limited to males. Sex-influenced traits are those in which the relation between genotype and phenotype differs between the sexes. Color inheritance in Ayrshire cattle is influenced by sex as shown below.

Genotype	Male Phenotype	Female Phenotype
DD	Dark red and white	Dark red and white
Dd	Dark red and white	Red and white
dd	Red and white	Red and white

QUANTITATIVELY INHERITED TRAITS

Most traits of economic importance to livestock production are quantitatively inherited. A quantitative trait is one that can be measured. This is in contrast to a qualitative trait, in which phenotypes fall into discrete classes. Phenotypes for quantitatively inherited traits usually follow a normal distribution (a bell-shaped curve) (Figure 6-7).[2] Such traits include weight, size, growth rate and efficiency, carcass characteristics at a given weight, and milk production. Some traits are measured by scoring systems composed of a small number of classes, although they may have a large number of underlying genotypes. These traits include body condition score (1 to 5 or 1 to 9), sheath score in cattle (1 to 5), and temperament score (1 to 5). Litter size is also measured in such a manner. Such traits may not follow a strict normal distribution, but the underlying variation is normally distributed. The phenotypes for traits with a normal distribution are affected by both genetic and environmental influences.

---

[2]Normal distribution is determined entirely by two constants (or parameters): (1) the mean or average, which locates the center of the distribution and (2) the standard deviation, which measures the variation of the individual measurements. The unit of measurement for both the mean and the standard deviation (SD) is the same as the unit of measurement for the trait itself.

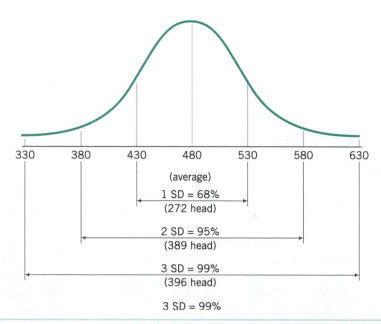

FIGURE 6-7

A normally distributed bell-shaped curve descriptive of a normally distributed population. The example is the distribution for weaning weights of 400 calves. (One standard deviation will include 68% of the calves, two standard deviations will include 95% of the calves and three standard deviations will include 99% of the calves.)

The center of this distribution (Figure 6-7) is the average performance level of that group of animals. How wide or narrow this bell shape appears is determined by the amount of variation among animals for that trait, measured in standard deviation units. Consider a large group of calves in which the average weaning weight is 480 lb and the phenotypic standard deviation is 50 lb. This tells us several things about this group of calves. For any population with normal distribution, 68% of the group is expected to be within one standard deviation of the mean, 95% is expected to be within two standard deviations of the mean, and 99.5% is expected to be within three standard deviations of the mean. So, for this group of calves we should have 68% that weigh between 430 and 530 lb, 95% that weigh between 380 and 580 lb, and 99.5% that weigh between 330 and 630 lb. This illustrates that animals that are very much smaller or larger than the mean are relatively rare. Such extreme phenotypes are frequently associated with an unusual environmental effect instead of an unusual genetic effect. Identification of both extremes is important in a selection program because both culling of animals below the average and making parents of those above the average help to genetically improve animal populations.

SELECTION

The process of selection deals with the concept of deciding which animals will become parents, and how many offspring these animals will produce. There are two major types of selection in regard to animals involved in agriculture: natural selection and artificial selection. The effectiveness of artificial selection for a given trait is influenced by the heritability of that trait. The expected progeny difference compares predictions of genetic merit of potential breeding animals.

Natural Selection

Natural selection refers to the reproduction of the fittest concept that was proposed by Charles Darwin and Alfred Wallace. This means that some animals are more likely to survive in their environments and be able to reproduce due to their characteristics. If these characteristics have a genetic component, the animals that survive and reproduce pass on their genes to the next generation. Animals that have certain disadvantages which prevent them from living long enough to reproduce do not pass on their genes. Animals that survive to puberty, but are inefficient at reproduction have fewer chances to pass on their genes than animals that are more fertile. This concept applies to farm animals just as it does to wild animals.

Artificial Selection

Artificial selection refers to the process of humans dictating which animals will reproduce and how many offspring they will have. Castration of a boar pig or ram lamb ensures that they will never produce offspring. This is one way to propagate only the genes carried by the animals with the most desirable phenotypes. Unfortunately, not all animals with superior phenotypes have superior genotypes because environmental influences can have significant effects upon the performance of an animal for a quantitatively inherited trait.

Heritability

Heritability refers to the proportion of the total variation among animals in a particular trait that is due to heredity. Environment and heredity both influence animal performance traits (phenotypes). In regard to a particular trait, how well an animal's phenotype (performance) indicates its breeding value (genetic merit) for that trait is referred to as the heritability (h^2). The ratio of the breeding value variation to the phenotypic variation defines the heritability; the possible range in heritability is 0 to 1. This means that if none of the differences in animals' phenotypes are due to differences in breeding values, then the heritability is 0. If all of the differences in phenotypes are due to differences in breeding values, the heritability is 1.0. It is easier to make genetic change in a group of animals when h^2 is high because ranking animals from most superior to most inferior for phenotypes will correspond closely with these animals being ranked from most superior to most inferior for breeding values. Heritability estimates for several traits are included in Table 6-2. This is a little like driving down a road that may have fog. As less fog exists, it is easier to see where one is going. When selecting for traits high in heritability, there is less fog on the road. When dealing with traits low in heritability, the performance of a group of animals does not indicate their breeding values very well, and it is more difficult for one to see where one is truly headed. It is also important to remember that heritability deals with the concept of variation and is the property of a distinct group of animals. A single animal does not have a heritability value, but a group of animals does. In addition, heritability for a given trait will vary from one herd to another because genetic and environmental variability differs among herds.

Expected Progeny Difference

It is important to be able to compare predictions of genetic merit (breeding value) of animals both within and between herds. The Expected Progeny Difference (EPD) is the method of expressing predicted genetic merit for beef cattle, sheep, and swine. The meaning of the EPD is contained in the name. The difference between the EPDs of two potential parents is a prediction of the difference between the offspring of those two parents. It is essentially the same as the Predicted Transmitting Ability (PTA), used in dairy cattle. The EPD combines information from the animal's own performance and that of its relatives (e.g., sire, dam, siblings, progeny) into a single prediction of genetic merit. The beef industry routinely uses EPDs for birth-, weaning-, and yearling-body weight as well as for some traits associated with carcass merit, reproduction, or maternal performance. The swine industry has instituted EPDs for growth, backfat thickness, and litter size and weight. The dairy industry has PTAs for milk production, type, and numerous milk constituents. EPDs are routinely used by both purebred and commercial producers to evalu-

TABLE 6-2

ESTIMATES OF HERITABILITY (H²) AND PHENOTYPIC STANDARD DEVIATION (σ) FOR CERTAIN QUANTITATIVELY INHERITED TRAITS IN FARM ANIMALS

Species	Trait	h^2	σ
Cattle (beef)	calving interval	.05	20 days
	birth weight	.40	10 lb
	weaning weight	.30	50 lb
	yearling weight	.40	60 lb
	mature weight	.65	85 lb
	feed conversion (lb feed/lb gain)	.40	0.5 lb feed/lb gain
	scrotal circumference	.50	2 cm
Cattle (dairy)	calving interval	.10	75 days
	milk yield	.25	560 lb
	percent fat	.55	0.5%
	percent protein	.50	0.4%
Horses	Wither height	.40	1.8 in
	cannon bone circumference	.45	0.23 in
	time to trot one mile		3.5 sec
	time to run one mile	.35	1.3 sec
	cutting ability	.12	10.3 points (cutting score)
Swine	litter number born alive	.15	2.8 pigs
	litter number weaned	.10	2.8 pigs
	21-day litter weight	.15	15 lb
	days to 230 lb	.25	12 days
	feed conversion	.35	0.2 lb feed/lb gain
	loin eye area	.50	0.25 sq in
	backfat thickness	.50	0.15 in
Sheep	number born	.15	0.3 lambs
	birth weight	.30	3 lb
	60-day weaning weight	.20	8 lb
	yearling weight	.40	30 lb
	loin eye area	.45	0.1 sq in
	grease fleece weight	.40	1.1 lb
	staple length	.50	0.5 in
Poultry	500-day egg production	.25	
	first-year egg production		3 eggs
	egg size	.45	4.6 g (egg weight)
	hatchability (layers)	.10	2.2%
	body weight	.45	0.9 kg (broilers)
	shank length (turkeys)	.50	0.5 mm

Source: Adapted from Bourdon (1997).

ate potential breeding stock from their herds and from other herds. The amount of information used in determining the EPD is important in determining the degree of confidence in the EPD. The accuracy is used to evaluate confidence. Young animals usually have only a small amount of information from their sire and dam or from siblings; therefore, the accuracy is low for such animals. However, as the animal becomes a parent and has numerous progeny the accuracy greatly increases.

MATING SYSTEMS

The decision as to which sires mate with which dams is the mating system. There can be random mating (all males have equal chance to breed any female), positive assortative mating (mating of animals with similar phenotypes), negative assortative mating (mating of animals with dissimilar phenotypes), inbreeding (mating of related animals), outbreeding (mating of unrelated animals within a breed), or crossbreeding (mating of unrelated animals from different breeds). Proper utilization of these different possibilities can greatly increase production efficiency.

Inbreeding

The genetic effect of inbreeding is production of animals that are more homozygous than the typical non-inbred animal of that breed or strain. When animals are related, they tend to possess genes that are identical by descent. This is why offspring resemble their parents and siblings resemble each other. If the parents are related, there is a higher chance of their offspring getting identical alleles from them. The more related the parents, the higher the level of homozygosity expected in their progeny. As a result, animals can be made more uniform in genetic makeup, and thus performance, through inbreeding. However, severe levels of inbreeding tend to reduce performance in traits related to reproduction, vigor, and growth. This effect is termed inbreeding depression.

Heterosis (Hybrid Vigor) and Crossbreeding

Just as inbreeding tends to increase homozygosity, mating unrelated animals tends to increase heterozygosity. If two inbred but unrelated animals are mated, their offspring are not inbred and such a mating produces offspring that can show an advantage because of increased heterozygosity. Such an advantage should be even greater when the mating occurs between distinct breeds. This advantage is called heterosis. Heterosis is defined as the advantage of the crossbred individual when compared to the average of the component purebreds. Levels of heterosis (individual, maternal, and paternal) are shown in Table 6-3. In general, traits that are low in heritability benefit the most from heterosis and traits high in heritability do not benefit much from heterosis. The concept of heterosis has been important in the development of crossbreeding programs in the beef cattle, swine, and sheep industries. In addition to heterosis, there is an advantage from crossing breeds that excel in growth and carcass merit and dam breeds that excel in fertility and maternal

TABLE 6-3

LEVEL OF HETEROSIS (INDIVIDUAL, MATERNAL, AND PATERNAL) FOR VARIOUS TRAITS IN BEEF CATTLE, SWINE, SHEEP, AND DAIRY CATTLE

Trait	Heterosis (%)		
Beef Cattle	*Individual*	*Maternal*	
Calving %	3.4	6.6	
Birth weight	2.7	1.6	
Weaning weight	4.7	4.2	
Postweaning average daily gain	3.9	−1.4	
Loin eye area	2.8		
Fat thickness	2.3		
Quality grade	0.7		
Swine	*Individual*	*Maternal*	*Paternal*
Conception rate		3.8	3.4
Litter size born	1.0	4.7	
Birth weight	3.1	1.5	
Litter size at 21 days	8.0	8.7	
21-day weight	3.1	3.7	
Average daily gain	9.4	0.0	
Age at 230 pounds	−6.5	−1.2	
Backfat thickness	−2.5	−4.4	
Loin eye area	1.8	0.4	
Sheep	*Individual*	*Maternal*	
Birth weight	3.2	5.1	
Weaning weight	5.0	6.3	
Conception rate	2.6	8.7	
Survival to weaning	9.8	2.7	
Lambs born per ewe exposed	5.3	11.5	
Weight of lamb per ewe exposed	17.8	18.0	
Dairy cattle	*Individual*		
Milk yield	5.1		
Fat yield	5.5		
Protein yield	5.7		
Age at first calving	0.2		
Calving interval	2.7		

Source: Beef: Long, C. R. (1980. *J. An. Sci.* 51: 1197; Swine: Buchanan, D. S. 1987. *J. An. Sci.* 65: 117; Sheep: Nitter, G. 1978. *An. Breed. Abs.* 46: 131; Dairy: McDowell, R. E. 1982. *South Coop. Ser.* 259.

ability. In this way, the strengths of various breeds can be utilized while weaknesses are hidden.

Many crossbreeding systems have been developed to take advantage of heterosis and breed complementarity. The expected levels of heterosis used in the dams and the off-spring are shown in Table 6-4 for several crossbreeding systems.

Crossbreeding systems can be broadly grouped into two main types of systems,

TABLE 6-4

EXPECTED LEVELS OF HETEROSIS IN VARIOUS CROSSBREEDING SYSTEMS WHEN NO INBREEDING OCCURS

System	Direct Heterosis[1]	Maternal Heterosis[2]
Terminal F_1 production	100%	0%
Terminal F_2 production	50%	100%
Three-breed terminal	100%	100%
Two-breed rotation	67%	67%
Three-breed rotation	86%	86%
Two-breed composite (50% each breed)	50%	50%
Four-breed composite (25% each breed)	75%	75%

[1]Direct heterosis refers to the amount of heterosis of offspring produced.

[2]Maternal heterosis refers to the amount of heterosis of dams that produce offspring.

terminal (or specific) and rotational. The main distinction between these two types deals with the production of replacement females. Terminal systems in themselves do not automatically produce a type of animal that is worked back into the breeding herd, whereas rotational systems by design produce replacement types of females. This is best illustrated with an example. Consider a three-breed terminal cross. This typically refers to breeding a large, growthy breed of sire (such as Charolais, Limousin, Simmental, Gelbvieh), to a smaller breed of cow (such as an Angus-Brahman F_1 or a Hereford-Angus F_1). This produces a calf that is one-half the makeup of the sire breed and one-fourth each of the two breeds in the dam (or one-half the makeup of the dam type). The calf itself has a high degree of heterosis for various traits of importance such as growth and survivability. The cow, being an F_1, has 100% heterosis for traits of importance such as fertility and milk production. The calf is a blend of the sire and dam types and is expected to be intermediate between them for traits of economic importance. Finally, producing calves in this specific manner, heterosis is present in the cow, and a smaller mature size can be utilized on the cow side to have lower maintenance costs. This type of calf could also be produced by breeding F_1 bulls to purebred cows but it probably would not be as efficient. As can be seen, the type of calf is different from the type of cow in this system; the progeny should not be utilized as a replacement of the F_1 cow because a yet different type of calf would then be produced. Several rotational crossbreeding systems have been developed to produce a type of calf that will be a replacement for the breeding herd. These systems provide high levels of heterosis in the calves produced as well as the cows. One example of this is a two-breed rotational system, sometimes referred to as a criss-cross system, in which the breeds of sires are rotated. Cows that are sired by one breed are bred to the other breed. In this manner sire breeds are rotated, and there are two distinct types of cows and calves in this system. After several generations, the types of calves produced are basically two-thirds the composition of their sire type and one-third the composition of the other breed.

Heifers kept for replacements are bred to the type of sire least represented in them. For a two-breed rotation involving Gelbvieh and Hereford, calves sired by Gelbvieh bulls would be 2/3 Gelbvieh and 1/2 Hereford; this type of female would be bred to Hereford bulls and produce calves that are 2/3 Hereford and 1/3 Gelbvieh, which would be bred to Gelbvieh bulls, and so on. Two-breed rotational systems maintain 67% heterosis in calves and cows. One aspect to consider for rotational crossbreeding systems is that the number of required breeding groups increases as the number of involved breeds increases. In addition, variation in the offspring is more pronounced than in a terminal crossing system.

Many breeds have been developed from crossbred bases of animals. Brangus, Santa Gertrudis, and Beefmaster cattle, and Columbia, Polypay, and Corriedale sheep are examples. Most breeding lines of swine from seedstock companies are some type of "composite." Composite breeds are those developed from a crossbred base for the purpose of forming a new population of breeding animals by combining traits from traditional breeds.

MOLECULAR GENETICS

The field of biotechnology, broadly defined, includes any techniques that use living organisms to make or modify products, to improve plants or animals, or to develop microorganisms for specific purposes. It focuses on two powerful molecular genetics techniques, recombinant deoxyribonucleic acid (rDNA) (also termed gene splicing) and cell fusion technologies. Using these techniques, scientists are able to visualize the gene, and to isolate, clone, and study its structure. The application of molecular genetics to improvements in animal production has resulted in many new advances in animal biology. Animal genetic engineering, including gene splicing, cloning, and embryo transfer, is being used like never before to improve economically important production traits, including growth, reproduction, and lactation.

Recombinant DNA Technologies

Recombinant DNA (rDNA) technology, because of its power to alter life forms, is considered a major achievement of biological science. With this technology, DNA fragments from two different species can be fused together to form a recombinant type. Such rDNA molecules might contain, for example, a gene from bovine somatotropin (growth hormone) fused to DNA that regulates the reproduction of bacteria. When such molecules are inserted into bacteria, they instruct those bacteria to produce human somatotropin. It is currently possible to insert molecules of rDNA into an array of bacteria, yeasts, and animal cells, where they replicate and produce a variety of useful proteins. Examples are: somatotropin, insulinlike growth factors (IGF-1 and IGF-2), enzymes, blood proteins, amino acids, and microbial protein feed supplements. The basic steps in the recombinant DNA technology for these applications are diagrammed in Figure 6-8. Bovine somatotropin

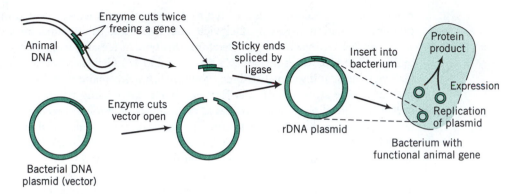

Animal DNA — Enzyme cuts twice freeing a gene — Sticky ends spliced by ligase — Insert into bacterium — Protein product — Expression — Replication of plasmid — Bacterium with functional animal gene — rDNA plasmid — Enzyme cuts vector open — Bacterial DNA plasmid (vector)

FIGURE 6-8

Recombinant DNA procedure used in gene splicing in molecular biology. An animal gene is spliced into a carrier DNA (called a vector) for insertion into a micro-organism (a bacterium is shown) or alternate animal host cell, and is made to replicate and express its protein product.

Source: Office of Technology Assessment (OTA), Congress of the United States, Washington, D.C.

(bST) produced in this way is currently used commercially in many dairy herds throughout the United States to enhance milk production and increase efficiency of dairy herd operations. Porcine somatotropin (pST) produced with the same recombinant DNA technology has also been shown to increase lean tissue growth in swine, but its commercial use awaits approval by the U.S. Food and Drug Administration.

TRANSGENIC ANIMALS. Combining the techniques developed in embryo manipulation with rDNA technology has permitted genes for specific traits to be inserted into the reproductive cells of animals and poultry. The main method of producing transgenic animals is to microinject DNA into the pronucleus of fertilized oocytes under a microscope. The injected ova are cultured for several hours in a culture medium, then transferred directly into the oviduct of a time-matched surrogate mother. In 1983, the insertion of the rat growth hormone gene into the embryo of a mouse resulted in a transgenic mouse twice normal size. Later, USDA scientists produced transgenic pigs by injecting pig embryos with the human growth hormone gene and transferring the embryos into surrogate mothers for the remainder of prenatal life. The transfer of the somatotropin (growth hormone) gene is accomplished using a fusion gene[3] produced by fusing the regulatory region of the matallothionine (MT) gene, which causes MT synthesis in liver, kidney, and other tissues, with the structural region of the somatotropin (growth hor-

---

[3]The structural component of the gene contains the DNA coding sequences that determine the structure of the messenger RNA (mRNA) which, after leaving the nucleus, binds to ribosomes in the cytoplasm and directs the synthesis of a specific protein metabolite such as an enzyme or hormone. The regulatory component of the gene contains the DNA coding sequences that control the timing, location, and amount of mRNA produced by the structural component.

mone, GH) gene. Thus, when the MT-GH fusion gene is introduced into the fertilized pig ovum, the resulting transgenic pigs express the GH gene not only in the pituitary gland (the normal source of GH), but also in several other tissues in the body as a result of the presence of the regulatory region of the MT gene. Since the original research with MT-GH fusion gene, many other fusion genes have been studied to improve GH expression in transgenic pigs.

Transgenic pigs with the MT-GH gene have increased somatotropin in the blood, but health problems, including stomach ulcers, and reduced reproduction have been noted. Transgenic mice and other laboratory animals are now widely used in biomedical research. Transgenic techniques are used to produce animals completely lacking a specific gene (termed "knockout") as a tool for learning more about physiological effects on the animal. Research in the application of gene transfer to produce transgenic animals for agriculture continues to be an active field of endeavor for molecular geneticists and physiologists. In the future, it may be possible to improve animals in economically important traits such as growth rate, body composition, disease resistance, and milk production through the application of these gene transfer techniques. As more information is obtained about transgene regulation in animals, the application of this technology in animal agriculture is expected to increase.

GENE MARKERS. A gene marker is a sequence of DNA that is linked to a gene affecting some trait. Several institutions are involved in mapping genes related to economically important traits in farm animals. Researchers have identified genes related to ovulation rate in sheep and swine, and to growth rate in cattle and swine. There is a commercially available gene marker for the horned/polled gene and the red/black gene in cattle. This type of technology allows the identification of heterozygotes and eliminates the need for progeny testing for these traits. Other markers have been identified for litter size and meat quality in swine.

CLONING ANIMALS. Cloning is defined here as the creation of a genetic duplicate of an animal organism through asexual reproduction, as by stimulating a single cell. The first cloning of a farm animal from the cells of an adult was reported by Scottish animal scientists in 1997 with the announcement of the birth of Dolly, the now-famed Dorset sheep. This breakthrough (Campbell et al., 1996; Wilmut et al., 1997) research established that somatic cell nuclear transfer can clone a viable sheep from the DNA of a mammary cell of an adult mammal. Japanese animal scientists were the first to report the birth of calves cloned from the DNA of reproductive cells from a mature cow (Kato et al., 1998). These were breakthrough events because they demonstrated that differentiated cells could be programmed to start over as the first cell of a new embryo.

At about the same time as the cloning of sheep from the DNA of mammary tissue from adult sheep, other lambs were produced in the same laboratory by cloning from fetal, rather than adult, cells (Schnieke et al., 1997). These lambs carry extra genes introduced into the cells before they were cloned. To produce cloned lambs from fetal cells, fetal skin cells (fibroblasts) were exposed to DNA that included both the human gene being transplanted and a marker gene. Cells that expressed the marker gene were then tested to determine which of these cells took up the human gene. The selected nuclei from the fetal cell were then inserted into enucleated mature egg cells. The egg cells containing the inserted transgenic nuclei were then transferred to a surrogate mother to carry to term. The genetic instructions now came from the fetal cell DNA. Transgenic fetal cells are more efficient than adult cells in getting the egg to develop (about one live birth per 60 nuclear transfers, a rate several times greater than achieved with adult cells). Of five new lambs resulting from this landmark experiment, all carried the marker gene and one carried the human gene. Using these techniques, the Scottish team (Schnieke et al., 1997) produced transgenic sheep with the human factor IX gene (FIX) by transferring nuclei from transfected fetal fibroblasts, as used in the earlier work. Human FIX is responsible for the production of human blood clotting factor, which plays an essential role in blood coagulation; its deficiency results in hemophilia in humans. The FIX protein is secreted into the milk of transgenic sheep carrying this gene, providing a new and valuable source of that protein for hemophiliac patients.

The rapid pace of research in animal molecular genetics, involving manipulation of the genetics of animals, raises important moral and ethical issues for society. These issues pertain mainly to the possibility that many of these techniques of gene transfer and cloning, and other techniques emerging from biotechnology, might eventually be applied in bizarre ways to humans. Concern for the implications of cloning humans, for example, must be addressed. The successful cloning of farm animals offers many potential benefits to society, but if cloning of humans became a reality, who would regulate its use and how would it be regulated? These are profound questions for a society not used to dealing with such issues. Many new and emerging issues related to all aspects of animal science are addressed in more detail in Chapter 11.

SUMMARY

A working knowledge of the basic principles of animal genetics is critical to the understanding of animal selection and improvement. The gene is a component of the nucleus of all cells of the body and is responsible for transmitting characteristics (traits) of animals from one generation to the next. Genes (segments of DNA) are located on chromosomes within the nucleus of all cells. Chromosomes occur in pairs, the number of which is constant for each animal species (e.g., chickens have 39 pairs, cattle 30, pigs 19, humans 23). Because chromosomes are in pairs, genes are also in pairs. Animals contain thousands of genes, each pair located at a specific special position (locus) on the chromosome. Each gene pair contributes to the unique nature of each individual. The transmission of genes from parents to offspring depends on the transmission of chromosomes. In males the spermatozoa and in females the ova produce gametes containing one-half (haploid) of the genetic material to be transmitted to the progeny. Thus, half of the genes of the offspring are transmitted randomly by each parent. The genes located at corresponding loci on homologous chromosomes may correspond to each other in the way they control a trait (homozygous, identical alleles) or they may contrast (heterozygous, contrasting alleles). If an animal is heterozygous for a trait, the allele that dominates the other in its effect on the trait is said to be dominant; its counterpart allele is recessive. Other traits such as growth rate are under the control of many genes. Such traits are termed quantitatively inherited. The degree to which a trait is influenced by heredity (as contrasted with environment) is termed heritability. Traits high in heritability, such as body fatness or milk production, lend themselves to more rapid improvement through selection than do traits of low heritability, such as litter size in pigs. In meat animals, crossbreeding is used to improve level of performance in economically important heritable traits. The reason for the practice is that the performance of crossbred offspring exceeds that of the average of the parents because of greater heterozygosity; the effect is termed heterosis (hybrid vigor). Modern tools of animal molecular genetics, including gene transfer, cloning, and advances in identification of most or all of the genes (the genome) of animals can be expected to result in improvements in efficiency of productive processes such as growth rate, nutrient utilization, animal protein production, and milk and egg production.

GLOSSARY

Additive   A type of gene action which indicates independent effects of one gene of an allelic pair on the phenotypic expression of the other member of the pair, with no interaction among them, in contrast to dominant or epistatic effects.

Allele   One of the inherited forms of a particular gene or stretch of DNA. An animal carries two alleles of each gene, one from each parent.

Anaphase   The stage during mitosis when sister chromatids, attached to filaments of the spindle apparatus, separate from each other toward two poles as the filament shortens.

Apoptosis   Programmed cell death.

Autosomal   Refers to chromosomes other than the sex chromosomes.

Breed   Group of animals with a common ancestry and characteristics which distinguish them from other groups within the same species.

Breeding value   A genetic measure of one trait of an animal; can be estimated by combining into one number several performance values accumulated on the animal and its relative.

Cell cycle   A general term to describe the events occurring between identical stages of consecutive generations of dividing cells, such as from one mitosis to the next.

Chromosomes   Discrete collections of DNA that contain the genetic information that is passed from one generation to the next. Each animal species has a characteristic number of chromosomes.

Clone (noun)   Descriptive of a population in which every individual is genetically identical, and traced back to a single cell.

Clone (verb)   To create an identical duplicate of an individual organism through asexual reproduction, as by stimulating a single cell.

Culture   The growth and maintenance of cells

under laboratory conditions in a controlled set of conditions and with provisions of nutrients and growth factors.

Coinheritance   The passing to the next generation of two traits together. Loci that are tightly linked (close together on the chromosome) have a high probability of being coinherited.

Crossbred   Animal whose parents are of two different breeds.

Crossbreeding   Mating of animals of differing breeds.

Crossover   A process that occurs during the creation of ova and spermatozoa in which chromosomes exchange segments of DNA, enhancing the possibility of increased variability in the offspring.

Culling   The process of eliminating undesirable animals.

Dam   Female parent.

Daughter cells   The pair of progeny cells arising from a preceding cell division.

DNA (deoxyribonucleic acid)   The fundamental unit of the gene, contained within the nucleus of every cell in the body of all living things, and serving as the basis of inheritance.

Differentiation   Term descriptive of when daughter cells acquire new characteristics relative to the parent cell (usually because of expression of a new set of genes); differentiated cells may have reduced capacity for or complete loss of capacity for further division (mitosis).

Diploid   The condition of a zygote containing a full set of chromosomes, half of which came from the dam and half from the sire.

Dominance   A condition in which the gene of one allelic pair prevents the phenotypic expression of the other member of the allelic pair.

Economic trait loci (ETL)   Loci that code for traits of economic importance to producers (e.g., litter size, carcass leanness, growth rate, disease resistance).

Environment   All of the conditions to which an animal is subjected.

Epistasis   The process in which one gene influences the expression of another pair of genes.

Gamete   A germ cell possessing the haploid number of chromosomes and capable of participating in fertilization.

Gene   A segment of DNA within a chromosome that contains specific information needed by the cell to make a protein that controls the functional and anatomical characteristics of the organism.

Genome   The set of DNA molecules that specify the inherited characteristics of an animal. Essentially every cell in the body contains the entire genome within its nucleus.

Genotype   The genetic makeup of an organism.

Genotyping   The process of identifying which alleles an organism carries for a specific trait(s).

Grade animal   One that possesses the major characteristics of a breed, but is not purebred or eligible for registration as a purebred.

Halothane gene test   A method in which halothane gas anesthesia is used to test for the presence of the gene that causes porcine stress syndrome (PSS).

Haploid   A cell containing half the normal number of chromosomes, as in the ovum and sperm.

Heritability   That portion of the total variation in a specific trait in a group of animals that is due to heredity.

Heredity   The genetic transmission of characteristics from parents to offspring.

Heterosis ("hybrid vigor")   The genetic phenomenon in which crossbred individuals are superior to the average of their parents in a particular quantitatively inherited trait.

Heterozygosity   The degree to which a specific gene occurs in different forms in different animals.

Hyperplasia   Increase in cell number.

Hypertrophy   Increase in size of a cell or organ; a nonproliferative growth process.

Inbreeding   Mating of animals more closely related than the mean of the population.

Karyokenesis   The division of the nucleus and formation of two discrete nuclei within mitosis; occurs during telophase, when the cell divides and forms two daughter cells.

Linkage map   A map that describes the location

of genes relative to other genes rather than as points on specific parts of specific chromosomes.

Locus The location of a particular DNA segment on a chromosome.

Mammal The phylogenic class of animals distinguished by self-regulating body temperature, the presence of hair, and the secretion of milk from mammary glands for suckling young.

Major histocompatibility complex (MHC) A length of DNA that contains numerous genes involved in regulating the process by which the body distinguishes itself from invaders (e.g., microbes, foreign proteins).

Marker A portion of DNA that appears in more than one form in a population, the variations of which can be detected by laboratory testing, and so used to identify patterns of heredity.

Marker-assisted selection (MAS) Selection of animals for propagation or culling based on the presence or absence of genetic markers that are linked to desired or undesired characteristics.

Meiosis The process that creates haploid ovum and sperm cell.

Meiotic Reductive cell division in which the resultant cells contain a haploid (N) number of chromosomes rather than the typical 2N; the process gives rise to gametes.

Metaphase The stage of mitosis in which condensed chromosomes are aligned on the spindle apparatus.

Mitosis The process of cell division to produce like cells with an identical number of chromosomes; starts with prophase, leads to metaphase, then anaphase, and finally telephase.

Mitotic figure Term to describe readily visible condensed chromosomes in cells undergoing mitosis; they are apparent during metaphase and anaphase.

Mutagen A substance that causes alterations to the sequence of bases in DNA, thereby deranging the native state of DNA, resulting in mutation.

Nucleotide The compound resulting from the combination of deoxyribose, phosphate, and one of the four nitrogenous bases which, when linked together into DNA, creates the code that determines the inherited characteristics of an organism.

Pedigree A record of ancestry.

Phenotype The expressed characteristics of an organism; characteristics are determined by environment and genetics to varying degrees, depending on the trait.

Polled Naturally hornless.

Polymorphism One of the various forms of a gene.

Progeny Offspring.

Proliferation Cell multiplication.

Prophase The first part of mitosis when the nuclear envelope breaks down and the organization of DNA and protein changes to allow chromosomal condensation.

Purebred An animal of a recognized breed that is eligible for registration in the official herd book (registry) of that breed.

Quantitative trait loci (QTL) Genes that contribute to the expression of a trait that is expressed on a continuum (e.g., growth rate).

Recessive gene A gene that has its phenotype masked by its dominant allele when the two alleles are present together.

Registered animal One listed in the official registry (herd book) of a recognized breed association.

RNA (ribonucleic acid) Present in cells in three forms: transfer RNA (tRNA), messenger RNA (mRNA), and ribosomal RNA (rRNA).

Sire Male parent.

Somatic cells All cells other than gametogenic cells or the very earliest embryonic cells.

Telephase The final stage of mitosis when newly separated chromosomes become enveloped with nuclear membranes and the remainder of the cell divides into two daughter cells.

Telomere A tract of nucleotides at the end of strands of DNA in chromosomes.

Transcription The processes used to make RNA transcripts from genes, using a single strand of DNA that is temporarily partially unwound from its native state; an array of proteins are involved in the transcriptional process and specific transcription factors specify which genes will be transcribed.

Transgenic animal An animal that possesses genes transferred from another animal, usually from a different species.

Translation The synthesis of the primary amino acid sequence of a peptide or protein using mRNA as the template; individual triplets of nucleotide bases (codons) specify which amino acid gets added to the growing peptide. Translation occurs in ribosomes.

Zygote The cell formed by the union of two gametes.

REFERENCES

Bourdon, R. M. 1997. *Understanding Animal Breeding.* Upper Saddle River, NJ: Prentice-Hall, pp. 1–523.

Bowling, A. 1990. Putting it all together: Color genotypes and phenotypes. *Horse Genetics,* Ch. 8.

Campbell, K. H. S. et al. 1996. *Nature* 380: 64.

Cockett, N. E., and Jackson, S. P., et al., 1994. Chromosomal localization of the callipyge gene in sheep (ovis aries) using bovine DNA markers. *Proc. Natl. Acad. Sci.,* USA, 91: 3019.

Crawford, R. D. 1990. *Poultry Breeding and Genetics.* New York: Elsevier Science Publishing.

Cundiff, L. V., Van Vleck, L. D., Young, L. D., and Dickerson, G. D. 1994. Animal breeding and genetics. *Encyclopedia of Agricultural Science.* San Diego: Academic Press.

Jackson, S. P. 1993. Investigation of the productivity and carcass composition of sheep with a muscle hypertrophy gene. PhD Thesis, Texas Tech University, Lubbock, TX.

Jones, W. E. 1982. *Genetics and Horse Breeding.* Philadelphia: Lea & Febiger.

Kato, Y., et al. 1998. Eight calves cloned from somatic cells of a single adult. *Science,* 282: 2095–2098.

Lasley, J. F. 1987. *Genetics of Livestock Improvement.* Englewood Cliffs, NJ: Prentice-Hall.

Lawrence, T. L. J., and Fowler, V. R. 1997. *Growth of Farm Animals.* Wallingford, UK and New York: CAB International, Chapter 2, Cells, pp. 9–25.

Office of Technology Assessment. 1986. Technology, public policy, and the changing structure of American agriculture. Washington, D.C.: OTA, U.S. Congress.

Pennisi, E. 1997. Transgenic lambs from cloning lab. *Science,* 277: 631.

Rice, V. A. *Breeding and Improvement of Farm Animals.* New York: McGraw-Hill.

Schnieke, A. E., et al. 1997. Human Factor IX transgenic sheep produced by transfer of nuclei from transfected fetal fibroblasts. *Science,* 278: 2130–2133.

Schook, L. B. 1995. Mapping the pig genome: A practical primer. Minnesota Report 234–1995, Minnesota Agricultural Experiment Station, St. Paul, MN.

Taylor, R. E. 1995. *Scientific Farm Animal Production* (5th ed.). Upper Saddle River, NJ: Prentice-Hall, Inc., pp. 1–672.

Van Vleck, L. D., Oltenacu, P. A., and Pollack, J. 1986. *Genetics for the Animal Sciences.* New York: W. H. Freeman.

Watson, J. F., and Crick, F. H. C. 1953. The double helix structure of DNA. *Nature,* London, 171: 737.

Wilmut, I., et al. 1997. *Nature,* 385: 810.

Young, L. D. (Ed.). 1991. Genetics of swine. North Central Regional Swine Breeding Committee, USDA/ARS, Clay Center, NE.

Other Resources

Basic Animal Microgenetics. 1996. 43 minutes

Swine Breeds. 1994. 21 minutes (CD available)

Cattle Breed Identification:

British. 1992. 21 minutes (CD available)

Composites I. 1992. 21 minutes

Composites II. 1992. 20 minutes

Continental. 1992. 30 minutes

Dairy. 1992. 21 minutes (CD available)

Zebu. 1992. 20 minutes

CHAPTER SEVEN
GROWTH

Growth is a fundamental trait of all biological systems. The characteristic S-shaped growth curve of all biological systems, whether it describes the increase in body weight of an animal from conception to maturity or the increase in number of yeast cells in a population (Brody, 1945), is shown in Figure 7-1. The term growth, as applied to animals, may be viewed in its simplest form to be an increase in body weight or height of a young animal over some time interval on the way to becoming an adult. In this chapter we develop a broader concept of growth. Growth includes all the processes of cell multiplication and differentiation beginning with the newly formed embryo, and extending through fetal development, postnatal growth and development, and into adulthood. Growth also includes processes in specialized tissues and organs, for example, uterine and fetal membranes during pregnancy, and mammary gland during lactation. Animal agriculture requires a high level of efficiency of resource utilization. Efficiency is determined, to a large extent, by the degree to which the genetic potential of an animal for maximum growth rate is matched by inputs of environmental factors such as adequate nutrition, control of infectious diseases, comfortable housing, and other husbandry practices that enhance growth performance.

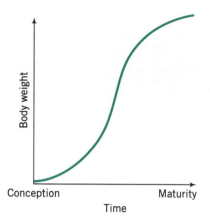

FIGURE 7-1

S-Shaped growth curve typical of all biological systems.
Source: Brody (1945).

In this chapter, we describe briefly the nature of growth in animal cells, tissues, and organs, and in the whole animal. This information is intended to provide a foundation for understanding the variation that exists among animal species in rate of body weight gain, in body composition, and in mature body size. Understanding the basis for these differences should be helpful in applications to animal production related to specific animal species.

METHODS OF EXPRESSING GROWTH

The characteristic S-shaped growth curve of all biological systems is shown in Figure 7-1 (Brody, 1945). This curve applies to such diverse systems as the number of yeast cells in a population and the increase in body weight of a plant or animal. Growth, as indicated by increase in body weight, may be expressed as absolute gain in a given period of time (for example, grams/day) or as relative gain (or percentage gain).

Absolute growth rate

larger weight minus smaller weight/final time minus initial time

can be misleading in the sense that the average value may not represent the actual value at any one point in time. For example, a pig that weighed 1 kg at birth and 91 kg at slaughter at 180 days of age would have an average daily gain of 500 g from birth to slaughter:

91 kg minus 1 kg ÷ 180 d = 500 grams/day

This pig might never have gained exactly 500 g on more than one or a few days (see S-shaped growth curve, Figure 7-1). The absolute weight gain the day after conception may have been a few micrograms, followed by a gain of 50 g the day after birth, and 1000 g the last day before slaughter. Nonetheless, the absolute average daily weight gain to slaughter is an important practical measure of growth as applied in the broad sense.

Relative growth rate

$$\text{larger weight minus smaller weight/smaller weight}$$

declines steadily as the animal advances in weight. For example, a newborn pig might weigh 1000 g at birth and 1100 g at two d of age:

$$1100 \text{ g minus } 1000 \text{ g} \div 1000 \text{ g} = 10\% \text{ relative growth rate}$$

In contrast, a market-weight pig might weigh 100 kg two days before slaughter and 102 kg at slaughter:

$$102 \text{ kg minus } 100 \text{ kg} \div 100 \text{ kg} = 2\% \text{ relative growth rate}$$

As an animal approaches mature size, the relative growth rate diminishes toward zero, and at maturity, growth ceases and body weight remains constant, unless energy intake exceeds the maintenance requirement, in which case body fat increases and the animal continues to gain body weight. This increased weight is not considered to be true growth in the context of animal production, yet the increased fat deposition, by definition, represents "growth" of adipose tissue.

BODY WEIGHT AS A MEASURE OF GROWTH

In practical animal production, the most meaningful and useful measure of growth is the increase in body weight per unit of time. Each animal species has its own characteristic growth, related to mature body weight and average rate of growth. The phenomenal growth of animals from conception to maturity is illustrated in Table 7-1 in which the absolute and relative weight of the pig at various stages of prenatal and postnatal growth are reported (Lowrey, 1911). Data derived from pigs were used to illustrate differences in

TABLE 7-1

ABSOLUTE AND RELATIVE WEIGHT OF THE PIG AT VARIOUS STAGES OF PRENATAL AND POSTNATAL GROWTH

Stage of Development	Weight (grams)	Multiple of 21-day Weight
Ovum	0.000003	—
21 days	0.25	—
112 days (birth)	1,000.0	4,000
135 days (3 weeks postnatal)	5,000.0	20,000
274 days (23 weeks postnatal)	90,000.0	360,000

Source: Adapted from Lowrey (1911).

weights of organs and in body protein, water, ash, and lipid composition during prenatal and postnatal life. Similar patterns of differences exist in other animal species studied, although less information is available than in pigs. The stomach, liver, and kidneys increase in weight proportionately faster than the whole body immediately after birth. The changes in weight of several organs from 98 d after conception (about 2 wk before birth) to 6 d after birth are shown in Table 7-2. It has been known for many years that the growth rates of individual parts of the animal are not identical. The head and shoulders reach mature size before the posterior parts of the body. That is, early in life, the head and shoulders represent a higher proportion of the total body weight than they do later. Similarly, individual organs and tissues grow at different rates as illustrated in Table 7-2, and indeed, individual cell types within a single organ grow at different rates. Changes in proportion of fat with increased age and weight of three genotypes of pigs (contemporary, lean, and obese) are illustrated in Figure 7-2. Protein and ash, as proportions of total body weight, remain relatively constant throughout growth, whereas the proportion of water changes reciprocally with fat (i.e., as fat increases, water decreases proportionately). Boars (males) are leaner than gilts (females) at a given weight during growth, and both sexes are leaner than castrated males at the same weight. This difference in leanness among males, females, and male castrates is also illustrated in Figure 7-3, which depicts changes in body protein mass and in daily protein accretion from birth to about 2.5 years of age. Note that in the pig, protein accretion plateaus at about 2 years of age, signifying the approach of mature size. Fat deposition would be expected to continue beyond the age of 2 years if feed intake is not restricted, resulting in steady increases in body weight.

It is important to recognize the close relationship in food animals between ultimate body size (within species) and body composition during growth. Animals within a species that reach maturity at a relatively low body weight attain a desirable body fat content at a

TABLE 7-2
ORGAN WEIGHT CHANGES IN LATE PRENATAL AND EARLY POSTNATAL LIFE IN SWINE

Organ	Days from Birth						
	−16	−12	−8	−4	+2	+4	+6
Whole body, kg	0.89	1.11	1.18	1.35	1.45	1.71	1.96
Carcass (minus internal organs), kg	0.40	0.52	0.54	0.64	0.72	0.81	0.93
Liver, g	22.8	27.0	28.5	37.5	37.8	51.8	64.3
Stomach (empty), g	6.0	6.8	7.0	6.8	8.5	10.5	12.5
Heart, g	7.3	9.0	10.0	9.8	10.5	12.8	14.0
Kidneys, g	10.0	10.0	9.5	10.3	12.5	12.8	15.0
Spleen, g	2.8	2.0	2.8	1.1	2.0	3.0	4.0
Brain, g	22.8	24.5	25.5	29.3	32.8	35.3	36.8
Lungs, g	28.9	31.5	32.5	22.3	20.3	25.8	29.0

Source: Brooks and Davis (1969).

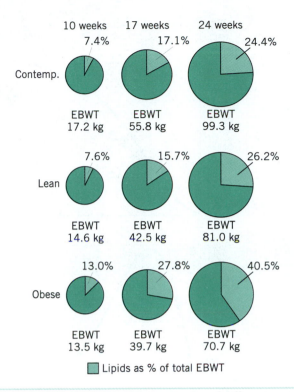

FIGURE 7-2

Changes in body composition with increasing age in pigs of different genetic background. Percentages shown are for carcass lipids as a fraction of empty body weight (EBWT). *Source:* Tess (1981), by permission.

lower body weight than larger animals. For example, breeds of cattle of medium size (e.g., Angus or Hereford) may be marketed at a lower weight than breeds of larger size (e.g., Simmental or Chianina). This is because their body fat content is sufficient to produce top carcass value at a lower body weight than larger breeds (animals of large frame size must reach a heavier body weight to achieve a body fat concentration equal to that of medium-frame animals).

HYPERPLASIA, HYPERTROPHY, AND DIFFERENTIATION

Growth of tissues, organs, and of the whole organism occurs in two phases: increase in number of cells (hyperplasia) and increase in size of cells (hypertrophy). Immediately after conception, most growth is by hyperplasia. Implicitly related to the increase in cell number and size is cellular differentiation. Differentiation of cells into those with specialized structure and function begins early in embryonic development. For example, long

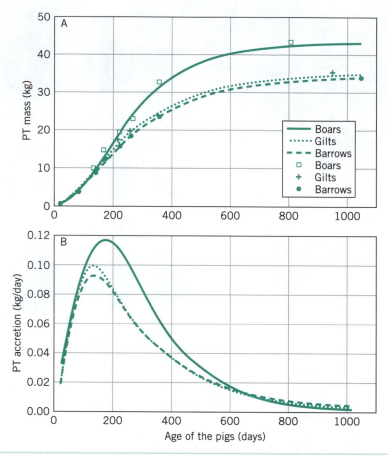

FIGURE 7-3

Protein mass (upper panel) and daily protein accretion (lower panel) generated from computer simulation.
Source: Pomar et al. (1991), by permission of *Journal of Animal Science.*

before it is possible to tell whether an embryo is to become a female or a male, certain large cells become differentiated from their neighbors. These large cells, termed primordial sex cells, soon become established in the gonads, and sexual differentiation begins. As in sexual differentiation, many other cell types appear during early development, ultimately producing the unique characteristics of tissues and organs in the female and male adult of each species. The layers of cells that form the early embryo (endoderm, mesoderm, and ectoderm) each give rise to specific organ systems. The inner layer, endoderm, differentiates into the digestive tract, lungs, and bladder; the outer layer, ectoderm, differentiates into the skin, hair, brain, and spinal cord; the intermediate layer, mesoderm, differentiates into the skeleton, skeletal muscle, and connective tissue. The study of embryology is beyond the scope of this chapter, but its fundamental relationship to growth at the whole animal level must be appreciated.

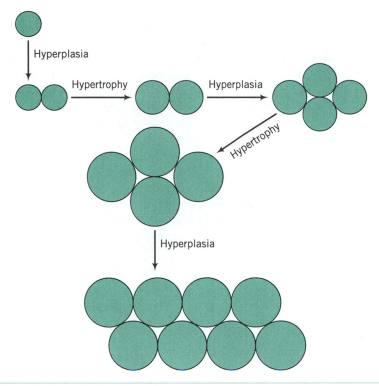

FIGURE 7-4

Diagram of growth by hyperplasia and hypertrophy.

From early prenatal life throughout most of the postnatal growing period, the two processes of hyperplasia and hypertrophy occur concurrently. Finally, at some point in postnatal life, cell division ceases (except in some tissues), and growth occurs only by hypertrophy. This gradual transition from hyperplasia, through a combination of hyperplasia and hypertrophy, and finally hypertrophy alone, is illustrated diagrammatically in Figure 7-4. The time during animal development when maximum rate of growth of various tissues occurs is somewhat variable among species. The growth "spurt" of the brain occurs first (in some species such as the guinea pig, before birth; in others such as the pig and human, just before until just after birth), followed in order by skeleton, muscle, and adipose tissue. Of course, all tissues grow simultaneously, but the time of the growth spurt of each tissue varies and the pattern differs among species.

Although nervous and muscle tissues cease hyperplasia at some finite point for the species, other tissues, such as the epithelium of the skin and digestive tract and cellular elements in blood, have continuous turnover throughout the life of the animal. Life of the red blood cells is about 70 days in most species, and that of the mucosal (epithelial) cells in the small intestine is only a few days. It is generally considered that fat cell hyperplasia ceases prenatally or around birth in most animal species. If this is the case, fattening during postnatal life involves hypertrophy alone.

It is well known that hormones and a series of growth factors affect the growth of individual cell types and tissues in young animals. These effects on growth are mediated through effects on enzyme systems that control anabolic (synthesis of tissues) and catabolic (breakdown of tissues) reactions of nutrients and metabolites. The physiological effects of hormones and growth factors are modulated by the presence of receptors on the surface or extending into the cytoplasm of cells and by binding proteins. Receptors interact with the hormone or growth factor to allow its entrance into or association with the cell to accomplish its effect. Serum-binding proteins may prevent the biological effects of the growth factors with which they bind or otherwise affect their activity.

Thus, we see that animal growth, in keeping with the broad definition of growth cited earlier (Brody, 1945), proceeds from a fertilized zygote to a mature adult through a process of cell hyperplasia and hypertrophy, and through differentiation of cells, tissues, and organs. Whole-animal growth, as well as that of individual cells and organs, is under the influence of genetically and environmentally controlled metabolic systems within the body, many aspects of which still elude our complete understanding.

GROWTH OF BRAIN, SKELETON, MUSCLE, AND ADIPOSE TISSUE

As discussed earlier, the growth spurt of individual organ systems is predictable in the sense that the general pattern is similar in all animal species for which information is available.

Brain

The brain, like other organ systems, has its own developmental pattern, characterized by a period of very rapid growth, the stage of the life cycle and duration of which is peculiar to each animal species. In general, the period of most rapid growth of the central nervous system, which includes the brain, precedes that of other tissues. The brain growth "spurt" of several animal species and that of humans has been plotted by Dobbing (Figure 7-5). Note that the growth is expressed by plotting the weight of the brain as a percentage of adult body weight (*y*-axis) at each age (*x*-axis) in relation to conception (left of birth date) and to maturity (right of birth date). Most of the available information on brain growth in animals is from laboratory animals; less is known in farm animals. The growth pattern of the pig brain appears to resemble that of humans more closely than does that of other species studied, in that the growth spurt spans the period just before birth to just after birth. This similarity has led to the use of the pig as an animal model in research into brain development in human infants.

Skeleton

Bones of the skeleton undergo continuous remodeling throughout life. The process consists of a balance between bone accretion (apposition) and breakdown (resorption). Dur-

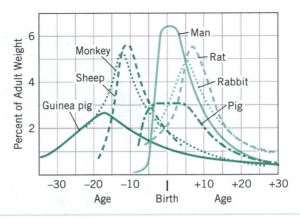

FIGURE 7-5

Comparative growth spurt of the brain in relation to prenatal or postnatal age in several species of animals and in humans.

Source: Dobbing (1968), by permission of M.I.T. Press, Cambridge, MA.

ing skeletal growth, bone apposition exceeds resorption, resulting in increased bone mass, whereas, in adulthood, rate of apposition tends to equal resorption, resulting in a constant size and density of bones. The main constituents of the skeleton are the mineral elements, Ca, P, and Mg, and an organic protein matrix, upon which the organized bone structure is built. (Bone metabolism in relation to Ca and P homeostasis is described briefly in Chapter 8.) As growth of the skeleton proceeds from fetal to mature skeletal tissue, the cartilage tissue that is included in the organic matrix which forms the framework for mineralization (ossification) of bone makes up a progressively smaller portion of the skeleton. The timing of ossification of bone in prenatal and early postnatal growth is followed readily by X-rays taken at intervals throughout the period. It is remarkably constant and predictable within animal species.

Growth of long bones is accomplished by progressive proliferation of chondrocytes (cartilage-forming cells) in the growth plate to add cartilage. The epiphyseal growth plate is located near the end of the shaft of each long bone. Figure 7-6 shows a section through the proximal end of the humerus (upper front leg bone) of a pig, illustrating the epiphyseal growth plate demarcating the head (epiphysis) of the humerus from the shaft (diaphysis). Cessation of growth in length of long bones occurs when ossification of the cartilaginous tissue in the epiphyseal growth plate is complete. This "closure" of the growth plate signifies the end of growth in length of the long bone. In some species, such as the rat, epiphyseal closure does not occur; therefore the skeleton of the rat can continue to grow throughout life.

All bones, including not only the long bones, but also the skull, ribs, and vertebrae, are remodeled by the same processes of apposition and resorption. Vertebrae and ribs are composed of trabecular bone, which undergoes the same metabolic processes as long bones. The cells involved include chondrocytes (those involved in cartilage); osteoblasts (cells that secrete the organic matrix which is ultimately mineralized); and osteocytes

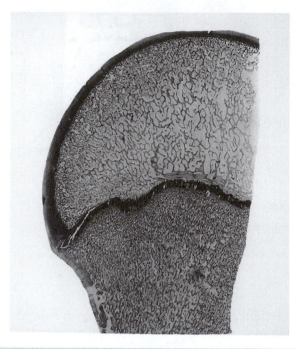

FIGURE 7-6

Head of the humerus of a pig showing the epiphysis, epiphyseal growth plate and end of di-aphysis. Note the dark line representing the cartilage tissue at the site of the growth plate, indicating that long bone growth is still underway. Photo, courtesy of L. P. Krook, Cornell University.

Source: From Hsu, F. S., Ph.D. Thesis, Cornell University (1974), page 85.

(osteoblasts that are embedded in mineralized bone matrix). Mineralization occurs by de-position of apatite, the form of calcium phosphate unique to bone; and osteoclasts (cells involved in resorption from bone surfaces). This process is called osteoclasia; resorption deep within bone, called osteolysis, is part of the normal process of maintaining normal bone composition.

Muscle

Muscles of the animal body include specialized types: skeletal (or voluntary) muscle, which represents the major portion of total muscle mass; smooth (or involuntary) muscle, which consists of muscles in the digestive, respiratory, urogenital, circulatory, and other systems not related directly to locomotion; and cardiac muscle, which has special proper-ties related to normal heart contractions and rhythm. We are concerned mainly with skeletal muscle in dealing with growth of organ systems in animal production, for it is skeletal muscle that constitutes the product we call meat.

Mature muscle cells are large, complex, and have many nuclei. Skeletal muscle structure and composition are covered in Chapter 22. We emphasize here the general nature of muscle growth. Individual muscles consist of a variable number of elongated fibers (or cells), each multinucleated. They are arranged parallel to one another, and range in diameter from 10 to 100 micrometers and may be several centimeters long. The number of fibers as well as the diameter and length of each fiber both contribute to the size of a particular muscle in a given species of animal. There are different types of muscle fibers, each with its own unique metabolism and properties. Fiber types differ in diameter, so the total size of a particular muscle is influenced by the relative amounts of each fiber type in that muscle.

Muscle development begins in the embryo as myogenesis. Myogenesis originates in muscle precursor cells (from the mesoderm). Myogenic cells (myoblasts) proliferate and differentiate, and then fuse to form multinucleated myotubes. The myotubes begin to synthesize contractile proteins that are specific to muscle and to assemble them into myofibrils. Myotubes are unable to divide, so the number of muscle fibers in an animal is fixed after the termination of the formation of myotubes. Because this process is completed before birth, the number of muscle cells is fixed at birth in most animal species. The major events in the formation of muscle fibers are summarized in Figure 7-7.

In addition to multinucleated muscle fibers, there exists in postnatal life a significant amount of mononucleated myogenic cells known as satellite cells. These cells are closely associated with but distinct from each muscle fiber. Some evidence suggests that satellite cells proliferate and fuse with existing muscle fibers to provide nuclei needed during muscle growth postnatally. Thus, muscle hypertrophy, which accounts for muscle growth from birth to maturity, is influenced by satellite cells. Factors such as exercise and the force of gravity (astronauts returning from space flights experience muscle atrophy), along with an array of hormones and growth factors all affect muscle hypertrophy.

Muscle consists mostly of protein. Therefore, factors that affect protein synthesis and

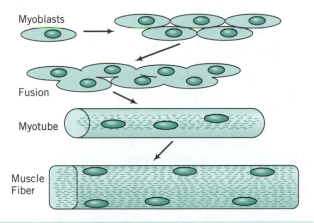

FIGURE 7-7

Main events in striated muscle fiber formation.
Source: Novakofski and McCusker (1993), by permission of CAB International, Wallingford, UK.

degradation may be expected to influence rate of muscle growth. The accretion of muscle in the growing animal is determined by the difference between the amount of protein synthesized and the amount degraded. Many factors affect each process. Growing animals fed a protein-free diet obviously cannot increase their muscle size. They excrete more nitrogen (N) than they store, so they are in negative N balance. This does not necessarily mean that protein synthesis ceases, although protein synthesis is reduced to a rate less than the rate of protein degradation, so the animal loses muscle mass. On the other hand, growing animals fed a diet containing adequate amounts of protein and other nutrients can be expected to maximize their muscle protein accretion by increasing synthetic rate to match their genetic potential (assuming no other limiting management or environmental factors). Because hormones and other growth factors, through their effects on enzyme systems and other metabolic traits, modify muscle growth, continuous research is underway to develop strategies to modify the process. Some of these strategies are briefly discussed later in this chapter.

Adipose Tissue

Adipose tissue is the main site of stored energy in animals. Dietary fat and carbohydrates and, to a lesser extent, the carbon skeleton of amino acids, are stored in "fat depots" throughout the body. The anatomical location and size of each depot varies among species and between males and females. Females deposit more fat in the mammary gland than males and in some species, such as humans, females have larger fat depots in the thighs and buttocks. In swine, most of the depot fat is subcutaneous, whereas in cattle and sheep, a higher proportion is located in internal body fat depots and intramuscular (within muscles), described as "marbling." In the fat-tail sheep of the Middle Eastern areas of the world, a major deposit is the tail, and in the camel, the hump is a major depot. In all species, there is a significant fat depot around the kidneys and viscera and at other sites within the body cavity. These internal fat depots provide an available source of energy to the animal during periods of scarce feed supplies.

The adipose cell (adipocyte) is a specialized form of connective tissue. The number of adipocytes in an animal appears to be determined prenatally. This is true despite the fact that the growth in body fat stores occurs last among the main tissue types (nervous, skeletal, and muscle tissues mature earlier than adipose tissue). The increase in body fat content characteristic of the period from birth to maturity in all animals is due to an increase in adipocyte size (hypertrophy) and not to an increase in total number of adipocytes (hyperplasia) in the body. Genetic propensity to deposit body fat varies considerably. For example, pigs selected for many generations for body leanness or fatness (Hetzer and Harvey, 1967) are distinctly different in their body composition and appearance (Figure 7-8). The difference between the lean and obese pigs in body fatness is due not to adipocyte number, but to average adipocyte diameter and volume. Obese piglets have larger adipocytes than lean piglets as early as at birth, even though the difference is not visually detectable until a few weeks of age. The average adipocyte diameter and volume of genetically obese pigs at 6 mo of age (about 80 kg body weight) were found (Mersmann, 1985) to be 88.8 micrometers and 4.94×10^{-5} cubic micrometers, compared with 72.0

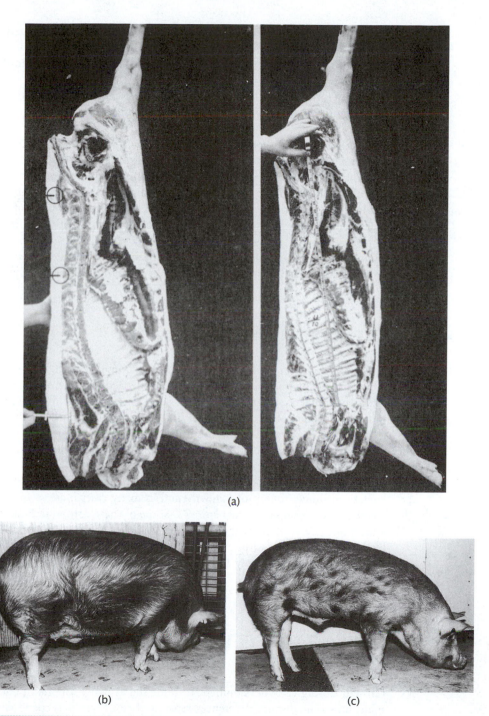

(a)

(b)   (c)

FIGURE 7-8

Genetically lean and obese pigs and carcasses.
Source: USDA/ARS.

micrometers and 2.64×10^{-5} cubic micrometers, respectively, in lean pigs. Similar, though less striking, differences in genetic tendency to fatten exist in most or all animal species. Differences among breeds of beef cattle and other animals in this regard are well recognized.

Body fat accretion, as in the case of body protein accretion, involves a balance between synthesis (lipogenesis) and breakdown (lipolysis). Differences among animals in rate of fattening (lipid accretion) appear to be related to variation in lipogenesis rather than to differences in lipolysis.

The adipocyte is filled with triglycerides whose fatty acid composition tends to reflect that of the diet consumed, in the case of nonruminant animals. In ruminants, the microflora in the rumen alter fatty acid carbon chain length and degree of unsaturation, resulting in a relatively constant triglyceride composition typical of the animal species (tallow from cattle has a different fatty acid composition than fat from sheep).

Most animal species have two types of adipocytes, brown and white. White adipocytes are quantitatively the most prominent in most farm animals. The role of brown adipocytes (brown fat) is notable in hibernating species such as the bear.

STRATEGIES FOR REGULATING GROWTH

Many hormones and growth factors influence animal growth. These substances not only affect rate of total body growth, but also influence body chemical composition and may affect the efficiency of growth. Genetic selection of animals for rapid weight gain or improved efficiency of feed utilization has been practiced successfully for many decades. Changes in animal productivity resulting from selection over many years have been associated with and brought about by changes in physiological traits, including modified endocrine function and other metabolic factors.

In recent years, several exogenously administered hormones and other metabolites have been shown to improve growth, and in many cases increase muscle growth and decrease fat accretion in growing animals. Some of these compounds are listed in Table 7-3 with a brief description of their mode of action. All such compounds must be approved by the U.S. Food and Drug Administration (FDA) for use in the United States based on firm evidence of their safety and efficacy. Some have been approved; others have not, but may be in the future.

GROWTH OF PLACENTA, FETUS, AND MAMMARY TISSUES IN MAMMALS AND EMBRYO IN BIRDS

Growth during early development in birds shares many aspects in common with mammals, but some distinct differences separate them. Mammals spend embryonic and fetal life in the uterus and depend during fetal life on maternal transfer of nutrients from the

TABLE 7-3
EXOGENOUSLY ADMINISTERED AGENTS EFFECTIVE IN REGULATING GROWTH

Compound	Description of Action	Use Status
Growth hormone (Somatotropin, bST*, pST**)	Increase muscle growth, decrease fat	bST approved, pST not approved
Synthetic androgens (Trenbolone acetate)	Increase muscle growth, decrease fat	Approved for ruminants
Synthetic estrogens (Estradiol-progesterone)	Increase muscle growth, decrease fat	Approved for ruminants
Combinations of synthetic androgens and estrogens	Increase muscle growth, decrease fat	Approved for ruminants
Growth hormone releasing factor (GRF)	Increase muscle growth, decrease fat	Effective in pigs, sheep, calf; used only experimentally
Beta-adrenergic agonists***	Increase muscle growth, decrease fat	Effective in pigs, birds, ruminants, but not approved

*Bovine somatotropin is used to improve milk production in dairy cows.

**Porcine somatotropin may be used to improve carcass leanness in pigs; its use awaits FDA approval.

***Beta-adrenergic agonists are synthetic analogs of the natural hormone, epinephrine. The three most extensively studied are raptopamine, clenbuterol, and cimaterol. The commercial use of one or more awaits FDA approval.

blood of the mother for their survival and growth until birth, after which they depend on milk during the early postnatal period. During the first days or weeks after conception, the developing mammalian embryo grows and develops within the uterine lumen and receives its nutrients first from the fluids in which it is bathed. Later, fetal and maternal placental membranes develop, and the growing embryo becomes attached to the uterine wall (the process of implantation) and the nutrients are then supplied directly from the blood of the mother via the umbilical vein. The growth and differentiation of the placenta and the implantation of the embryo in the uterine wall represents the transformation of the embryo to a fetus. This transformation marks a point of departure between the subsequent development of mammals and birds.

The early development of the bird is in sharp contrast to that just described for the mammal. The chicken is used here to illustrate the contrast. All of the nutrients required for the fertilized chick embryo to grow into a fully developed newly hatched chick are present in the egg when it is laid. The hen deposits protein, carbohydrates, lipids, vitamins, and minerals and other metabolites in the egg as it traverses the oviduct. These nutrients are distributed in the yolk and white of the egg and packaged in the egg shell, familiar to everyone. The fertilized egg, if incubated at the appropriate temperature, is transformed into a newly hatched chick 21 days later. There is little resemblance between the chick and the egg from which it came. Yet, there has been no input of nutrients into the egg and no appreciable loss of nutrients from it in the interval from laying until hatching. The cell hyperplasia, hypertrophy, and differentiation characteristic of mammals during intrauterine life occurs in the bird before hatching. The proteins and lipids of the egg have been transformed during embryonic development to an entirely different set of proteins and lipids in the newly hatched chick, using the C, N, and other elements as the building blocks. This transformation, amazing as it may seem, is only one of myriad examples of the complex, highly programmed biological transformations in the early growth process.

Growth of the fetus in mammals requires nutrient transfer from the pregnant dam across the placenta via the umbilical vein. The beginning of pregnancy is associated with changes in the maternal endocrine system that trigger the development of the blood supply to the uterus and the eventual implantation of the developing embryo in the uterine wall and the beginning of fetal life. After implantation, the fetus is nourished entirely by the transfer of nutrients from the dam across the placenta. The fetus has a direct effect on placental growth through its own production of hormones such as insulin and insulin-like growth factors (IGF-I and IGF-II) and through its own influence on uterine blood flow. The placenta also produces hormones, notably, placental lactogen in some species, and it has effects on maternal metabolism, including the induction of increased cardiac output and increased release of maternal lipids. The ultimate result of the actions of the fetus and the placenta is an increase in uterine blood flow which enhances fetal growth and development. A detailed discussion here of the hormonal and physiological interactions that drive fetal and placental metabolism for the benefit of fetal survival and growth is beyond our intent. Suffice it to say that the critical early development of the embryo to become a viable fetus and ultimately a neonate depends on adequate placental growth and development. The growth of the placenta is complete in most species by the beginning of the third trimester of pregnancy. The relationships between fetal and placental growth are depicted in Figure 7-9 using the pig as an example. Note that the placenta growth spurt precedes the steep part of the fetal growth curve.

Interference with placental development caused by insults such as malnutrition of the dam during pregnancy have permanent detrimental effects on subsequent growth and development of the progeny. Mature body size, therefore, is determined not only by the genetic background of the animal (breed differences in mature size can be cited in virtually every species of animals and birds), but by environmental factors related to nutrition and to uterine environment (illustrated by the classic experiment in which the size of the offspring of the mating of horses with ponies was influenced greatly by whether the dam was a horse or a pony).

Mammary gland tissue is first formed early in embryonic life near the time coinciding with the appearance of limb buds. Mammary buds, which later give rise to teats, soon begin to proliferate and the teats and cistern form, followed by the development of connective tissue and fat cells. All structures of the mammary gland are in place before birth. The gland remains undeveloped during postnatal life until puberty, when accelerated growth of the gland begins, under the influence of estrogen and progesterone from the newly functioning ovaries, along with the influence of pituitary hormones. The growth

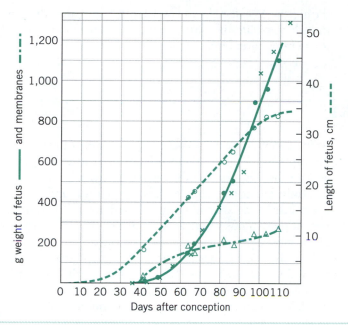

FIGURE 7-9

Length (from end of snout to base of tail) and weight of pig fetuses and weight of membranes during pregnancy. X indicates American results; solid circles, open circles, and triangles indicate Danish results.
Source: Moustgaard (1962).

rate of the mammary gland exceeds that of the body as a whole during this time; the extension and branching of milk ducts and the increase in parenchymal cells accompany this accelerated growth. During pregnancy, the secretory tissue proliferates and the mammary fat pad expands. In late pregnancy, there is limited secretion of milk proteins and other milk constituents which are transported into the lumen of the alveoli from the blood. Thus, at the time of parturition, milk solids high in immune globulins (colostrum) are already available for secretion as the first food of the newborn offspring. As in the growth of other tissues and organs, the mammary gland develops on a timetable appropriate for the function it is designed to serve, under the influence of a highly orchestrated series of hormonal changes and adaptations. The excessive deposition of fat in the mammary gland due to overconsumption of energy before pregnancy may be associated with reduced milk yield in high-producing dairy cows, due to suppressed secretory tissue growth when mammary gland fat deposition is overabundant. Thus, not only undernutrition, but also overnutrition, is important in mammary tissue development.

In birds, all cell differentiation and development of tissue and organ systems occur within the fertilized egg and are present at hatching. Therefore, the newly hatched chick is in a position similar to that of the newborn mammal, in that its future development depends on an exogenous supply of nutrients. In the case of the hatched bird, the food must come from its surroundings, whereas the neonatal mammal relies on mother's milk during the first few days or weeks. In both cases, the physiology of growth is similar, though the source of nutrients to permit growth during early development (after hatching in birds, after birth in mammals) is different.

SUMMARY

Animal growth occurs by increased cell number (hyperplasia) and increased cell size (hypertrophy) and by cell differentiation into structurally and functionally unique tissues and organs. The growth of the nervous, skeletal, muscle, and adipose tissues occurs concurrently, but at rates characteristic of the tissue and the animal species. Growth is under the control of an array of hormones and other factors whose actions orchestrate the pattern of growth of each organ system. The number of muscle and fat cells is fixed before birth; therefore postnatal accretion of muscle and fat is accomplished by hypertrophy of these cells. Some tissues such as skin, digestive tract, and bone, continue to undergo cell renewal (turnover) throughout life, whereas others normally do not regenerate (nervous tissue) or do so only by hypertrophy (muscle and adipose tissue).

Several exogenously administered hormones and other metabolites have been shown to regulate muscle and fat accretion in animals. Their ultimate use in animal production is determined by their safety and efficacy and by public acceptance of them as growth promoters.

Growth of the fetus is influenced by placental growth and the fetus, in turn, affects placental growth and the blood supply to the placenta. Growth of the developing unhatched bird is programmed genetically and proceeds by utilization of nutrients and their precursors present in the egg at laying.

Growth of the mammary gland begins in early embryonic life. Differentiation into mammary gland ducts, secretory cells, fat pad, and other tissues accelerates at puberty and further mammary growth occurs in pregnancy to accommodate the needs of the newborn offspring at parturition.

The ultimate body size and composition of the adult mammal or bird is under genetic control of the total growth process, but can be modulated by nutritional and other environmental factors, some of which may be imposed prenatally or prehatching. The metabolic controls of growth are similar in mammals and birds, and the same modulators of the growth process operate in both.

GLOSSARY

Agonist   A substance that enhances a particular physiological action, in opposition to a contradictory force.

Anabolism   Metabolic process by which simple substances (nutrients) are assembled into living tissue, resulting in an increase in tissue mass.

Anabolic agent   A substance that stimulates tissue growth when administered to an animal.

Beta-adrenergic agonist   A group of natural or synthetic compounds effective in increasing muscle growth and decreasing fat deposition when administered to animals.

Catabolism   Metabolic process that results in tissue or metabolite breakdown in an animal.

Differentiation   The changes in cells during the growth process that result in specialized structure and function in cells and tissues.

Endocrine   Pertains to internal secretions; endocrine glands are those that produce one or more internal secretions (hormones) that enter directly into the blood and are carried to cells in other parts of the body where they affect specific metabolic processes.

Growth   An increase, as in size or number; in animals and plants, development from a simpler to a more complex form; includes the processes of cell multiplication and differentiation and of increases in cell, tissue, and organ size in living organisms; may be expressed as an absolute change per unit time (e.g., grams per day) or as a relative change (e.g., percentage gain).

Growth hormone   See Somatotropin.

Hormone   An endocrine secretion carried in the bloodstream to other parts of the body; each hormone has specific effects on metabolism in specific cells.

Hyperplasia   Increase in cell number.

Hypertrophy   Increase in cell, tissue, or organ size.

Insulin-like growth factors (IGF-I and IGF-II)   A class of polypeptides, produced by most or all cells in the body, that are involved in cellular differentiation and multiplication; they have a role in insulin and growth hormone action and perhaps other hormones.

Nutrient   Any substance required in the diet for growth, reproduction, or lactation, and for life itself.

Ontogeny   The developmental pattern of an organism or its organs.

Somatotropin   Anterior pituitary hormone active in promoting protein and mineral accretion in growing animals and milk production in lactating animals.

REFERENCES

Brody, S. 1945. *Bioenergenics and Growth.* New York: Hafner.

Brooks, C. C., and Davis, J. W. 1969. *J. Anim. Sci.,* 29: 325.

Dobbing, J. 1968. Effects of experimental undernutrition on development of the nervous system. In: N. S. Scrimshaw and Gordon, J. E. (eds.), *Malnutrition, Learning, and Behavior.* Cambridge, MA: The M.I.T. Press.

Hetzer, H. O., and Harvey, W. R. 1967. *J. Anim. Sci.,* 26: 1244.

Hollis, G. R. 1993. *Growth of the Pig.* Wallingford, UK: CAB International.

Lawrence, T. L. J., and Fowler, V. R. 1997. *Growth of Farm Animals.* Wallingford, UK and New York: CAB International.

Lowrey, L. G. 1911. *J. Anatomy,* 12: 107.

Mersmann, H. J. 1985. *J. Anim. Sci.,* 60: 131.

Moustgaard, J. 1962. In J. T. Morgan and D. Lewis (eds.), *Nutrition of Pigs and Poultry.* London: Butterworths.

Novakofski, J., and McCusker, R. H. 1993. Physiology and principles of muscle growth. In G. R. Hollis (ed.), *Growth of the Pig.* Wallingford, UK: CAB International.

Pomar, C., Harris, D. L., and Minvielle, F. 1991. *J. Anim. Sci.,* 69: 1468.

Pond, W. G., Maner, J. H., and Harris, D. L. *Pork Production Systems.* New York: Van Nostrand Reinhold.

Smith, S. B., and Smith, D. R. 1995. *The Biology of Fat in Meat Animals.* Champaigne, IL: American Society of Animal Science.

Tess, M. W. 1981. Simulated effects of genetic change upon life-cycle production efficiency of swine. PhD thesis, University of Nebraska, Lincoln, NE.

CHAPTER EIGHT
NUTRITION AND FEEDING

Animal life depends on an adequate supply of food from a variety of sources to ensure the maintenance of normal bodily functions throughout the life cycle. No single food source contains the optimum amount of all constituents required. These constituents are termed nutrients; adequate nutrition is determined by an adequate intake of all nutrients. A nutrient may be defined as any chemical element or compound required in the diet to support normal reproduction, growth, lactation (in the case of mammals), or maintenance of life processes. Animals (including humans) require a long list of specific nutrients. In contrast, the requirements for plants are relatively simple. Plants, in general, require only water (H_2O), inorganic nitrogen (N, in the form of nitrate or ammonia), several inorganic elements present in soil, and carbon (C), taken up by photosynthesis from atmospheric carbon dioxide (CO_2) to synthesize all of the compounds that are constituents of plant structure. These constituents include inorganic nutrients (mineral elements) as well as organic nutrients (amino acids, proteins, carbohydrates, lipids, and vitamins) required by animals, whose metabolism does not provide for their synthesis. Thus, plants are essential to sustain animal life. Some animals, including cattle, sheep, and deer, are ruminants. That is, they have a compound stomach which includes a rumen (fermentation vat) inhabited by microbes capable of synthesizing organic nutrients. These microorganisms synthesize protein from inorganic N and break down indigestible carbohydrates. Microbial breakdown of complex carbohydrates provides a means by which vast quantities of fibrous plants, otherwise useless for humans, can be converted to valuable edible products (meat, milk).

In this chapter, the following aspects of animal nutrition and feeding are briefly described and explored: nature, function, and metabolism of each class of nutrients; digestive anatomy and physiology of ruminant and nonruminant animals; composition, processing, and feeding value of a variety of feedstuffs; and diet formulation for life-cycle feeding of animals. Photographs of animals and animal tissues showing typical deficiency signs of specific nutrients are provided in textbooks (Pond et al., 1995; Miller et al., 1991) and on the home page of several universities on the Internet World Wide Web.

NUTRIENTS

The broad categories of nutrients are: water, energy (supplied by carbohydrates, fats, and proteins); proteins and amino acids; vitamins; mineral elements. All animal species require these nutrients or their precursors (for example, ruminants can obtain part of their protein requirement from the microbes residing in the rumen capable of synthesizing amino acids from inorganic N). The amounts of specific nutrients required for normal life vary among species and according to the stage of the life cycle (e.g., growing versus adult animal), productive function (e.g., lactating vs. nonlactating), and other factors.

Water

Water makes up about 70% of the body mass of adult animals and up to 90% of that of newborn animals, and accounts for more than 99% of the molecules in the body (because water molecules have a lower mass than most others).

FUNCTIONS. Water serves two broad functions in all terrestrial animals: (1) it plays a key role in many phases of body metabolism and (2) it is a critical factor in control of body temperature. All of the biochemical reactions that occur in an animal require water. It acts as a solvent for a wide variety of compounds, and serves as a medium for transport of dissolved substances in blood, tissue fluids, cells, and secretions, and in excretions such as urine and sweat. Water is part of many chemical reactions: in hydrolysis, it is a substrate in the reaction, and in oxidation it is a product of the reaction. Metabolic water, or water of oxidation, results from the oxidation of organic substances within the body cells. Ingestion of food results in increased respiration and heat dissipation and increased urinary excretion, which increase water requirement. In hybernating animals, metabolic water is apparently adequate to sustain normal body functions.

Water, as a major constituent of the body, allows animals to maintain body temperature within desired limits. Factors that allow the animal to maintain a relatively constant body temperature are: the fluidity of the blood and its rapid circulation, the large evaporative surface of the lungs, the body surface area for sweating or panting during exposure to high temperatures, and the ability of the animal to restrict blood flow to the body surfaces during exposure to cold temperatures.

SOURCES. Water available to body tissues can be supplied from: (1) drinking water; (2) water contained in feed; (3) water liberated from metabolic reactions; and (4) preformed water associated with body fat and protein breakdown during a period of negative energy balance (such as starvation or illness).

LOSSES. Losses of water from the body occur via urine, feces, insensible water (that lost by vaporization from the lungs and through the skin), and sweat. The route of water loss is affected by environmental temperature, physical activity, and water intake in relation to immediate needs.

REQUIREMENTS. Most domestic animals drink water soon after or during a meal if it is nearby. Frequency of drinking and the amount consumed is increased in hot weather. Many factors govern the amount of water needed to meet physiological needs. Such factors include level of physical activity, physiological state (i.e., growth, pregnancy, lactation), relative humidity, water content of the diet, and ambient temperature. Water requirement is related to the animal's heat production and to energy consumption and body surface area. At environmental temperatures that do not result in heat stress, there is a close relationship between dry matter consumption and water consumption, but when temperature reaches a stressful level water intake increases greatly and feed consumption declines. Animals can be expected to consume 2 to 5 kg of water for every kg of dry feed consumed. Some animals that are able to conserve water require less; for example, sheep are more efficient than cattle in conserving water, so their intake tends to be in a ratio of 2.5 to 3 kg water to 1 kg feed, whereas the ratio for cattle tends to be about 4 to 1. Growing animals need more water per unit of dry feed consumed than adults and pregnant and lactating animals need more than nonpregnant and nonlactating animals. Low water intake may reduce feed consumption and level of production of milk or meat.

Energy

Quantitatively, energy is the most important component of the animal diet, other than water. Energy can be measured only in its transformation from one form to another. In nutrition, energy is defined in terms of chemical energy, measured in terms of heat produced upon the oxidation of organic metabolites and expressed as calories. The calorie is defined as the heat required to raise the temperature of 1 gram water from 16.5 to 17.5 degrees Centigrade. The joule has been adopted by many countries as the standard unit of expression. The calorie[1] is defined relative to the joule such that 1 calorie = 4.184 joules.

The energy content of feeds is usually expressed as kilocalories per gram (kcal/g). Gross (total) energy is measured in a bomb calorimeter as the increase in temperature of a known amount of water upon complete oxidation of a sample of material of known

---

[1]One Calorie (uppercase C, kilocalorie) is equivalent to 1000 calories (lowercase c). For practical usage, the kilocalorie (Calorie), equivalent to 1000 calories, and megacalorie, equivalent to 1000 kilocalories, are more commonly used.

quantity. Gross energy values of feedstuffs (kcal/g) are determined by the relative amounts of the three major classes of organic nutrients present: carbohydrates, 4.1; proteins, 5.7; fats (lipids), 9.4. Thus, feedstuffs high in fat are higher in energy concentration than are feedstuffs high in carbohydrates. The gross (total) energy of a feed is not an accurate index of the amount of energy available to the animal because of differences among feeds in the degree of utilization by the animal. The energy flow through an animal is diagrammed in Figure 8-1. The gross energy is partitioned into that lost in feces and in gases produced by fermentation in the gastrointestinal tract (gross energy minus fecal and gaseous energy = digestible energy); and that lost in urine, gill (in fish), from the body surface, and as heat production related to basal metabolism, voluntary activity, and other metabolic transformations. The energy remaining after one accounts for all processing losses in the energy flow through the animal is considered to be recovered energy. This

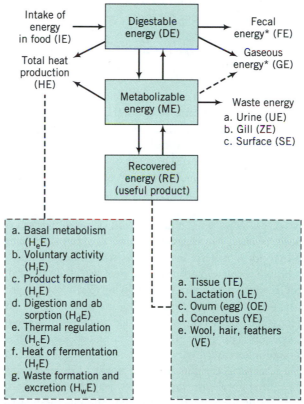

*Under some circumstances the energy contained could be considered to be a useful product of fuel.

FIGURE 8-1

Schematic representation of the energy flow through an animal.
Source: NRC (1981).

recovered energy can be present as animal tissue, milk, eggs, conceptus, wool, hair, or feathers. It is this amount of productive energy that determines the net energy value of a given feedstuff for various productive functions. Therefore, it is clear that gross energy of a particular substance is of little use in estimating its value as a source of dietary energy for an animal. For example, the gross energy of oat straw, a very poor source of energy for animals, is 4.5 kcal/g, whereas that of corn grain, an excellent source of energy for animals, is about the same (4.4 kcal/g). Knowledge derived over many years concerning energy utilization has provided a broad array of feedstuffs for animals. The subject of energy and its metabolism, known as bioenergetics, is fundamental to advancing the efficient utilization of natural resources in animal production and human endeavor.

Carbohydrates

Carbohydrates are the major components in plants. They comprise up to 70% of the dry matter of forages and up to 85% of that of some seeds, especially the cereal grains. In contrast, carbohydrates comprise less than 1% of the weight of animals, mainly in the form of glucose and glycogen. The conversion of plant carbohydrates to animal tissues therefore involves major metabolic transformations of plant energy constituents within the animal body.

STRUCTURE. Carbohydrates are composed of carbon (C), hydrogen (H), and oxygen (O), usually in the ratio of about 1C:2H:1O. Carbon (C) is combined with H and O, which are in about the same ratio as in water. When 2 or more molecules of simple sugars (monosaccharides) are joined together, the formula represents the loss of 1 or more molecules of water. Structures of some of the common monosaccharides and disaccharides are shown in Figure 8-2. Classification and occurrence of simple and complex carbohydrates are shown in Table 8-1.

FUNCTIONS. The main function of carbohydrates in animal nutrition is to serve as a source of energy to support life processes. In plants, simple sugars formed from C, H, and O by photosynthesis are stored as starch, hemicellulose, cellulose, and lignin. Relatively insoluble forms of carbohydrate such as cellulose, hemicellulose, and lignocellulose provide structural support for the living plant. Although the simple sugar, glucose, is the basic unit of both starch and cellulose, the linkage of glucose polymers of these two polysaccharides is different (starch is a glucose-4-alpha-glucoside, cellulose is a glucose-4-beta-glucoside). This slight difference in linkage has a major effect on the utilization of these two complex carbohydrates by the animal. The digestive enzymes of the animal are capable of splitting the glucose-4-alpha glucoside, rendering the released glucose available to the animal for absorption into the body from the digestive tract. In contrast, the digestive enzymes of the animal cannot split the glucose-4-beta-glucoside. Therefore, leaves and other vegetative portions of plants high in cellulose cannot be processed by the animal digestive system without the intervention of cellulolytic microbes residing in the digestive tract (e.g., rumen and large intestine), whose function for the host animal is to break

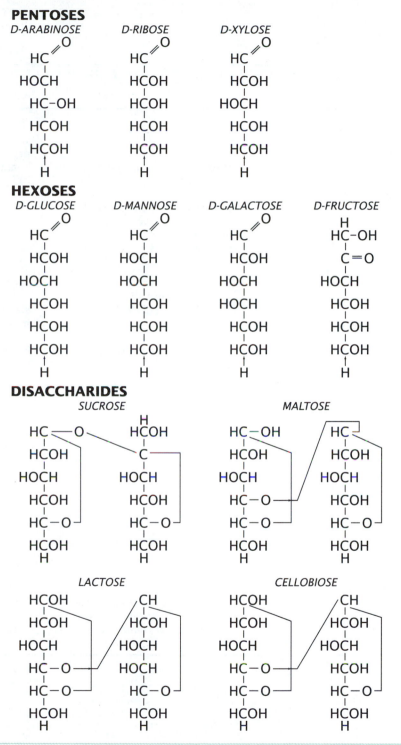

FIGURE 8-2

Structure of monosaccharides and disaccharides.

Source: Pond et al. (1995).

TABLE 8-1

CLASSIFICATION OF CARBOHYDRATES AND THEIR OCCURRENCES

Compound	Monosaccharide Content	Occurrence
Monosaccharides (simple sugars)		
Pentoses (5-C sugars) ($C_5H_{10}O_5$)		
Arabinose		pectin; polysaccharide,
Xylose	corn cobs, wood; polysaccharides	araban
Ribose	nucleic acids	
Hexoses (6-C sugars) ($C_6H_{12}O_6$)		
Glucose	disaccharides; polysaccharides	
Fructose	disaccharides (sucrose)	
Galactose	milk (lactose)	
Mannose	polysaccharides	
Disaccharides ($C_{12}H_{22}O_{11}$)		
Sucrose	glucose–fructose	sugar cane, sugar beets
Maltose	glucose–glucose	
	(glucose-4-α-glucoside)	starchy plants and roots
Lactose	glucose–galactose	milk
Cellobiose	glucose–glucose	
	(glucose-4-β-glucoside)	fibrous portion of plants
Trisaccharides ($C_{18}H_{32}O_{16}$)		
Raffinose	glucose–fructose–galactose	certain varieties of eucalyptus,
		cottonseed, sugar beets
Polysaccharides		
Pentosans ($C_5H_8O_4$)$_n$		
Araban	ababinose	pectins
Xylan	xylose	corn cobs, wood
Hexosans ($C_6H_{10}O_5$)$_n$		
Starch (a polyglucose glucoside)	glucose	grains, seeds, tubers
Dextrin	glucose	partial hydrolytic product of
		starch
Cellulose	glucose	cell wall of plants
	(glucose-4-β-glucoside)	
Glycogen	glucose	liver and muscle of animals
Inulin (a polyfructose fructoside)	fructose	potatoes, tubers, artichokes
Mixed polysaccharides		
Hemicellulose	mixtures of pentoses and hexoses	fibrous plants
Pectins	pentoses and hexoses mixed	
	with salts of complex acids	citrus fruits, apples
Gums (partly oxidized to acids)	pentoses and hexoses	acacia trees and certain plants

down the cellulose and produce volatile fatty acids (VFA) as an energy source for absorption by the animal.

The ultimate source of energy for most animal cells is glucose. This basic unit is made available to animal cells either by ingestion of glucose or its precursors by the animal or by conversion from other metabolites. Energy storage in the animal body is largely as fat, in contrast to the plant, which stores its energy largely as carbohydrates. Humans, cats, dogs, mink, and several other animal species consume a large proportion of their energy from animal sources. Therefore, the proportion of dietary energy coming from carbohydrates is less in these species than in most farm animals. For example, the average human diet in the United States contains more than 30% of the energy as fat.

METABOLISM. Metabolism of carbohydrates (as with all other nutrients) includes the many aspects of processing them from the point of absorption from the digestive tract into the body, transport through the body, biochemical transformations within the body, and their ultimate fate (e.g., storage in the body, conversion to other metabolites, excretion from the body).

Preparation for Absorption. Only simple sugars (monosaccharides) can be absorbed from the gastrointestinal tract (GI-tract), except in newborn animals capable of absorbing larger molecules. Thus, for absorption to occur, complex carbohydrates must be hydrolyzed by digestive enzymes produced by the animal or by the microbes inhabiting the GI-tract. The carbohydrate-splitting enzymes (carbohydrases) are effective in hydrolyzing most complex carbohydrates to monosaccharides (those with a glucose-4-alpha-glucoside linkage such as starch but not those with a glucose-4-beta-glucoside linkage such as cellulose). Starch occurs in two important forms, amylose and amylopectin, both of which are digested and used efficiently by animals.

Microflora of the rumen of ruminants and of the large intestine of some nonruminants such as the horse, rabbit, and to a lesser extent, the pig, are able to hydrolyze cellulose. Large amounts of short chain fatty acids (volatile fatty acids or VFA) are produced in the rumen and large intestine by anaerobic fermentation of the hydrolyzed cellulose. Ruminants rely on absorption and utilization of VFAs as their main source of energy. Some nonruminants, including the pig and human, utilize cellulose through anaerobic fermentation by microbes residing in the cecum and colon. Cellulase (the enzyme that hydrolyzes cellulose) is produced by microorganisms but not by animal tissues. The symbiotic relationship between the microbes residing in the rumen and lower GI-tract and the host animal is an important factor in the utilization of vast quantities of high-cellulose plants for animal production and ultimately for human nutrition. Cellulose and hemicellulose are often present in plants in combination with lignin, a highly insoluble and biologically unavailable mixture of phenolic acid polymers. Lignification increases with plant maturity and, in mature trees, is the chief structural component. Vegetables and cereals are low in lignin, whereas grasses are intermediate and legumes are high in lignin. Lignin depresses the bioavailability of cellulose for microbial use and, therefore, the nutritional value of plants.

ABSORPTION AND TRANSPORT. Carbohydrate is absorbed in the form of simple sugars (monosaccharides) and in the case of ruminants and some nonruminants, as VFAs produced from anaerobic fermentation of cellulose by microbes in the rumen or large intestine. The upper (proximal) end of the small intestine (duodenum and jejunum) is the major site of absorption of monosaccharides. The lower (distal) end of the small intestine (ileum) absorbs less, and the stomach and large intestine absorb little if any sugars. Glucose and galactose (the two constituents of the disaccharide, lactose or milk sugar) are absorbed very efficiently, but other 6-C sugars (mannose and fructose) and 5-C sugars (arabinose, ribose, and xylose) are less efficiently absorbed. Glucose and galactose are absorbed by active (energy-dependent) transport, whereas other monosaccharides are transported mostly, if not entirely, by simple diffusion. Conversion of some monosaccharides to glucose occurs within the intestinal mucosal cell during transit from the intestinal lumen to the blood.

Metabolic Conversions. The animal body stores very little energy as carbohydrate, but some glucose is converted to glycogen, which is stored in liver and muscle. Glycogen is a polysaccharide that can be hydrolyzed to glucose to supply a ready source of energy. In this way, the blood glucose level is maintained within a relatively narrow range in normal animals by conversion of blood glucose to glycogen (glycogenesis) after a meal and by reconversion to glucose by the reverse process (glycogenolysis) during fasting. The glucose available to body cells for normal metabolism is kept relatively constant through this homeostatic control mechanism. In normal animals, the hormones insulin and glucagon are secreted in response to changes in blood glucose level to decrease and increase, respectively, the circulating level of glucose. Glycogen storage is limited; therefore, when carbohydrate ingestion exceeds the current needs for glycogenesis, glucose is converted to fat. This is accomplished by the breakdown of glucose to pyruvate, which is the two-carbon fatty acid available for fat synthesis (described later in this chapter). In addition to glycogen as a source of glucose for cellular metabolism, glucose can be formed by body tissues from noncarbohydrate metabolites, including amino acids and lipids (a process called gluconeogenesis). The breakdown of glucose to produce energy for body functions (glycolysis) is termed the glycolytic or Embden-Meyerhof pathway. The process by which carbohydrates, amino acids, and fatty acids are utilized to release energy is described in the citric acid or Krebs cycle. These two important metabolic cycles, the Krebs citric acid cycle and the Embden-Meyerhof glycolytic pathway, form the basis for understanding energy metabolism in animals. The total energy released in the conversion of glucose to carbon dioxide and water is 673 kcal/mole. This is illustrated as follows:

$$C_6H_{12}O_6 \rightarrow 6\ CO_2 + 6\ H_2O + 673\ kcal$$

PLANT FIBERS AS ENERGY SOURCES. Plant tissues contain easily digestible carbohydrates, but also large amounts of complex carbohydrates indigestible by the digestive enzymes secreted by animals. These indigestible fractions, contained in plant cell walls, include cellulose and hemicellulose, in combination with lignin. Other plant fibers include gums and beta-glucans. The microflora residing in the rumen of ruminant animals and in the large intestine and cecum of some herbivores (e.g., horse, rabbit) and omnivores (e.g., swine, some birds) produce enzymes capable of hydrolyzing the cellulose for utilization by the host animal. The digestibility and utilization of the energy of these high-fiber plant constituents can be estimated accurately by chemical analyses of the feedstuffs. The Van Soest neutral detergent and acid detergent fiber methods have become standard procedures for determining the digestible energy content of feedstuffs high in plant cell wall constituents.

Lipids

Lipids are organic compounds relatively insoluble in water and composed primarily of C, H, and O, and often P or N. Simple lipids are esters of fatty acids with various alcohols. Fats and oils are esters of fatty acids with glycerol. Plant and animal lipids are abundant in triglycerides (the ester of three fatty acids with glycerol). Triglycerides make up the largest fraction of lipids in most foods. They are characterized by their high energy value. A typical fat yields about 9 kcal per g when completely combusted, compared with about 4 kcal per g for a typical carbohydrate. Sterols are lipids with complex ring structures; examples are testosterone, estrogens, progesterone, cholesterol.

STRUCTURE. The generic structures of fatty acids, glycerol, triglycerides, and sterols are shown in Figure 8-3. Fatty acids (FA) consist of chains of carbon (C) atoms ranging from 2 to more than 24 in length. There is a carboxyl group on the end of each chain; the structure is RCOOH, where R is a carbon chain of variable length. The formula of the shortest fatty acid, acetic acid, is CH_3COOH. Fatty acids in which all C atoms are associated with two hydrogen (H) atoms are termed saturated FA; those in which two hydrogen (H) atoms are removed from one or more C atoms to form a double bond between two C atoms are termed unsaturated FA. Fats that are solid at room temperature tend to contain mostly saturated short-chain FA, whereas those that are liquid at room temperature contain a high percentage of unsaturated long-chain FA. Examples of saturated fats are butter and coconut fat; examples of unsaturated fats are corn and soybean oil.

Glycerol is the alcohol component of all triglycerides (also called triacylglycerol) in animal and plant tissues and is a constituent of the phospholipids lecithin, cephalin, and sphingmyelin. Triglycerides contain three FA, diglycerides contain two FA, and monoglycerides contain one FA esterified with glycerol.

FUNCTIONS. Lipids have the following general functions in animals: (1) supply energy for normal maintenance and productive functions; (2) source of essential FA (linoleic and linolenic); (3) carrier of the fat-soluble vitamins; (4) serve as an integral constituent of cell membranes; (5) sterols serve as important hormones and as precursors of vitamin D.

METABOLISM. Lipids are synthesized in all body cells. Fatty acids are elongated stepwise in two-C units to form short-chain and long-chain FA from which triglycerides are formed by esterification and stored in body tissues, primarily adipose cells. Triglycerides

$$CH_3(CH_2)_4CH = CHCH_2CH = CH(CH_2)_7COOH$$

a   *Linoleic Acid*

Linoleic acid, a constituent of corn oil and other plant oils high in polyunsaturated fatty acids, has 18 carbons and two double bonds. Its formula is shown above.

Most fatty acids commonly found in animal tissues are straight chained and contain an even number of carbons. Branched-chain fatty acids and those with an odd number of carbons are more common in microorganisms; however, tissues of ruminant animals, particularly, contain relatively large amounts of these fatty acids as a result of rumen fermentation and the subsequent absorption of these microbially derived acids. Conjugated linoleic acids (CLA) have two double bonds, but in different positions on the carbon chain than shown here.

b   *Glycerol*

The formula for glycerol is:

$$HOCH_2$$
$$|$$
$$HOCH$$
$$|$$
$$HOCH_2$$

GLYCEROL

Glycerol is the alcohol component of all triglycerides common in animal and plant tissues and is a component of the phosphatides—lecithin, cephalin, and sphingomyelin.

d   *Sterols*

The most abundant sterol in animal tissue is cholesterol, shown below:

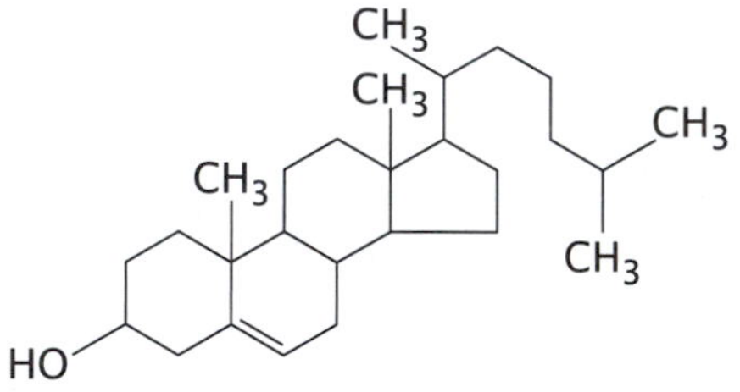

$$CH_3$$
$$CH_3$$
$$CH_3$$
$$CH_3$$
$$CH_3$$

HO

Other important sterols in animals are ergosterol (yields vitamin D_2 when irradiated), 7-dehydrocholesterol (yields vitamin D_3 when irradiated), bile acids, androgens (male sex hormone), and estrogens and progesterones (female sex hormones).

c   *Mono-, Di-, and Triglycerides*

Monoglycerides, diglycerides, and triglycerides are esters of glycerol and fatty acids. An ester is formed by reaction of an alcohol with an organic acid; the structure of an ester and the linkage between glycerol and fatty acids in glycerides is illustrated:

$$\begin{array}{cc} O & O \\ \| & \| \\ R-C-OH + HOR' \rightleftharpoons R-C-OR' + H_2O \end{array}$$

A monoglyceride, diglyceride, and triglyceride would have the following general structures, where R, R', and R" represent three different fatty acids:

$$
\begin{array}{cccc}
\alpha & H_2COH & H_2COH & H_2COOCR \\
 & | & | & | \\
\beta & H-COH & H-COOCR' & H-COOCR' \\
 & | & | & | \\
\alpha' & H_2COOCR'' & H_2COOCR'' & H_2COOCR''
\end{array}
$$

The fatty acid composition of triglycerides (triacylglycerols) is variable. The same or different fatty acids may be in all three positions; for example, if stearic acid occupied all three positions, the compound would be termed tristearin (a simple triglyceride), whereas if butyric, lauric, and palmitic acid each occupied one position, the compound would be called butyrolauropalmitin (glyceryl butyrolauropalmitate), a mixed triglyceride.

FIGURE 8-3

The structure of lipids. (a) Fatty acids are made up of a carbon chain and a carboxyl-group at one end of the chain. Linoleic acid, a fatty acid required in the diet of animals, is shown as an example; it has 18 C atoms and 2 double bonds. (b) Glycerol is the alcohol component of all triglycerides common in animal and plant tissues. (c) Mono-, di-, and triglycerides are esters of fatty acids and glycerol. One of the hydroxyl (-OH) groups on glycerol forms an ester with the carboxyl (-COOH) group of a fatty acid, with the release of one molecule of water (H_2O). A monoglyceride is glycerol with one fatty acid ester, a diglyceride is glycerol with two fatty acid esters, and a triglyceride is glycerol with three fatty acid esters as shown. (d) Sterols include vitamin D, sex hormones, and cholesterol, the most abundant sterol in animal tissues, shown here.

are broken down in the body to glycerol and FA for use as a source of energy for normal body functions. In addition to lipid synthesis by body cells, lipids that are ingested in the diet can be absorbed into the body from the intestinal tract after breakdown by digestive enzymes and emulsification into absorbable units. Unabsorbed lipids and those secreted into the intestinal lumen from the body are excreted in the feces. Lipids are stored as body fat when energy intake exceeds energy requirement for maintenance and are oxidized to carbon dioxide and water during fasting or undernutrition.

ABSORPTION.   The upper small intestine is the site of the main processes of preparation for absorption. Dietary lipids (mostly triglycerides) pass slowly through the stomach after ingestion and are mixed with bile from the liver and with pancreatic and intestinal secretions. Emulsification occurs by the detergent action of bile acids and by the churning action of the intestine. The smaller particle size resulting from emulsification allows greater surface exposure to fat-digesting enzymes (lipases) secreted by the pancreas and small intestine. The lipases hydrolyze the triglycerides to their constituent FAs and glycerol. Bile acids are secreted from the liver via the bile duct in copious amounts and are readily reabsorbed from the intestinal tract (lower jejunum and ileum) and recycled to the liver for reuse. Common bile acids are cholic, deoxycholic, taurocholic, and glycocholic acid.

The main site of lipid absorption is the proximal jejunum, although some absorption occurs all along the small intestine. Glycerol and short-chain FA are absorbed by passive transport into the portal blood system. Monoglycerides and long-chain FA enter the intestinal mucosal cells by diffusion. Long-chain FA are reesterified to triglycerides within the mucosal cell before transfer to the lymphatic system.

Lipid droplets that enter the intestinal mucosal cell are then coated with a thin layer of protein to form chylomicrons, consisting of triglycerides, phospholipids, cholesterol esters, and protein. The chylomicrons leave the mucosal cell and enter the lymphatic system, which carries the chylomicrons to the blood via the thoracic duct.

The absorption of lipids therefore differs from that of carbohydrates in that both the portal blood system and the lymphatic system participate, depending on the nature of the lipid. The routes of absorption also differ among species. Mammals absorb most of the long-chain FA into the lymphatic system, whereas the chicken absorbs them directly into the portal blood.

TRANSPORT AND DEPOSITION.   Absorption of lipids after a meal is associated with a large increase in lipid level in the blood (lipemia). Blood lipids consist of chylomicrons (formed in the intestinal mucosal cell during absorption) and lipids arising from mobilized depot stores and from synthesis in the liver and adipose tissues. Lipids in the blood include triglycerides, FA, and cholesterol. Blood lipids are combined with proteins and transported as lipoproteins varying in size and composition. The type and amount of dietary lipid and the time after a meal affect the composition and concentration of lipids in the blood at a given time.

All body tissues, notably adipose tissues (fat depots), store triglycerides. Adipose tissue, in addition to storing ingested fat, is capable of synthesizing fat from carbohydrate and of oxidizing FA. Triglycerides in depot fat tend to have a FA composition characteristic of the species. In ruminants, the depot fat composition is relatively independent of the diet fat composition because of the action of the rumen microflora. In nonruminants, the FA composition of the depot fat resembles that of the diet, because ingested FAs are absorbed and deposited unchanged. Body lipids are in a dynamic state of metabolism. Changes in dietary intake, diet composition, physiologic state (pregnancy, lactation), and endocrine status have immediate effects on lipid metabolism and turnover.

Differences in lipid metabolism among animal species are associated with the susceptibility to atherosclerosis. For example, the dog is resistant, whereas the pig and rabbit are highly susceptible to dietary induction of atherosclerosis. For this reason the pig and rabbit are used extensively as animal models in biomedical research in lipid metabolism and atherosclerosis for application to cardiovascular disease in humans.

Protein and Amino Acids

Proteins are essential constituents of animal cells and are the class of nutrients in highest concentration in muscle tissues. All cells synthesize protein as an obligatory part of life processes. Except in animals whose intestinal microflora can synthesize protein from nonprotein N sources, protein or its constituent amino acids must be provided in the diet to allow normal growth and other productive functions. Cell turnover is very rapid in some tissues such as intestinal epithelial (mucosal) cells. The percentage of protein required in the diet is highest in young growing animals and declines gradually to maturity, when only enough protein to maintain body tissues is needed. Protein requirement is increased during pregnancy and lactation in mammals and for egg production in birds because of increased accretion of protein in the products of conception, increased output in milk, and increased output in eggs, respectively, and because of increased metabolic rate in conjunction with all of these productive functions.

Proteins are composed of simple units, amino acids, the building blocks of protein. Although there are more than 200 naturally occurring amino acids, only about 20 are present in significant amounts in most proteins and up to about 10 are believed to be required in the diet of animals because of inadequate tissue synthesis to meet metabolic needs.

STRUCTURE OF AMINO ACIDS. The basic structure of amino acids is illustrated by glycine, the simplest amino acid. The essential constituents are a carboxyl group, as in FA (-COOH), and an amino group (-NH2) attached to the C atom adjacent to the carboxyl group. This NH2 group is identified as the alpha-amino group. The structure of glycine is depicted in Figure 8-4.

The generic structure representing all amino acids can be depicted as:

$$R\text{-}C\text{-}COOH$$
$$NH_2$$

where R is the remainder of the molecule attached to the C atom associated with the alpha-amino group of the amino acid. Amino acids with a straight-chain arrangement of

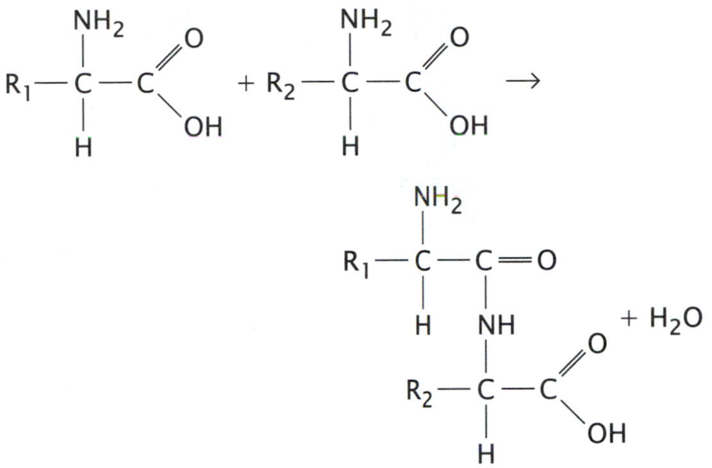

FIGURE 8-4

Synthesis of protein from amino acids. The process occurs by joining of individual amino acids to form long chains. The length of the chain and the order of arrangement of amino acids within the chain are two of the main factors determining the characteristics of the protein.

C atoms are termed "aliphatic"; examples are glycine and isoleucine. Amino acids with some of the C atoms arranged in a ring structure are termed "aromatic"; examples are phenylalanine and tyrosine. Amino acids containing sulfur include cysteine, cystine, and methionine. Some amino acids are "heterocyclic" because they have an N atom attached to two C atoms; examples are tryptophan and proline. Those amino acids that contain more than one amino group are termed "basic" and those with two carboxyl groups are termed "acidic." Examples of basic amino acids are lysine and arginine; examples of acidic amino acids are aspartic acid and glutamic acid.

STRUCTURE OF PROTEINS. Protein is synthesized by joining amino acids to form long chains. This linkage of one amino acid to another in the formation of proteins is depicted in Figure 8-5. The carboxyl group of one amino acid reacts with the alpha-amino group of another amino acid resulting in the loss of one molecule of water. The resulting linkage is called a peptide bond. The peptide bond of alanine and glycine forms the dipeptide, alanylglycine. Elongation of the chain of amino acids proceeds from tripeptides to polypeptides, and ultimately to an entire protein molecule. Each protein has its own specific amino acid content and sequence. The exact amino acid composition and sequence of hundreds of proteins has been determined. The molecular weight (sum of the atomic weights of all atoms in the molecule) of most proteins is about 35,000 to 500,000 daltons with 350 to 5000 amino acid residues. Plant and animal tissues have their own unique proteins, each with its own unique amino acid composition. A single feedstuff may contain several different proteins; therefore, its nutritional adequacy for animals will depend on the composite amino acid mixture provided by the individual protein fractions.

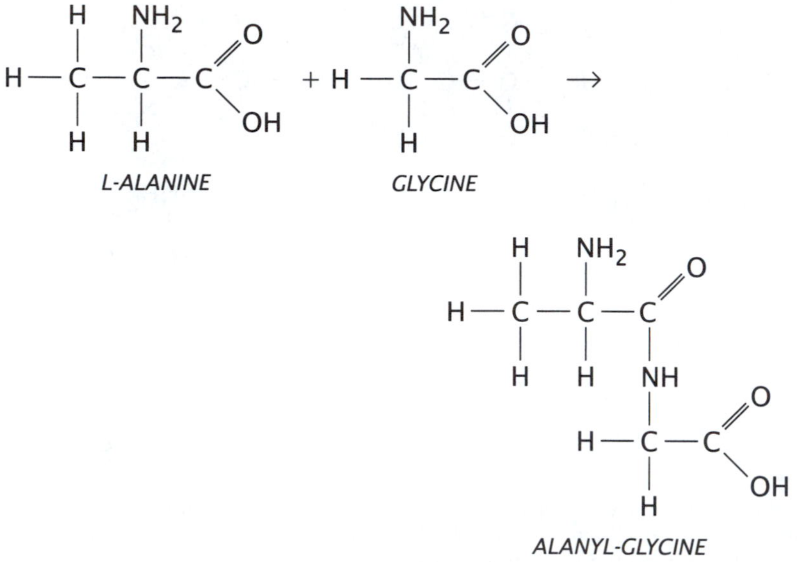

FIGURE 8-5

Linkage between one amino acid and another to form a peptide bond. In the example, alanine and glycine are linked to form the dipeptide, alanylglycine.

FUNCTIONS OF PROTEINS. Most proteins in the animal body are present in virtually all organs as constituents of a variety of tissue and cell types: muscle; skin, hair,
hooves; bone and other connective tissue; blood; nerves; and fat depots. Muscle tissue includes collagen, elastin, and myofibrillar and contractile proteins. Hair, wool, feathers,
hooves, horns, claws, and beaks contain a high proportion of keratins, which are highly
resistant to acid, alkali, and heat treatment and to digestive enzymes, and therefore of
limited nutritional value. The main proteins of blood are albumin, globulins, clotting
proteins (thromboplastin and fibrinogen), hemoglobin, an array of apoproteins (protein
moiety of lipoproteins), and small quantities of many enzymes, hormones, and peptides.
All of these proteins have specific functions in body metabolism. Enzymes, often referred
to as organic catalysts, are all protein in nature and have specific actions, some in degradation of metabolites (as the digestive enzymes in the intestinal tract), and some in synthetic processes (as in fat synthesis from carbohydrates). The action of enzymes is restricted generally within the same cell or in close proximity to the site of origin.
Hormones, like enzymes, are produced in minute amounts and have profound effects on
metabolism, but all have their action at sites removed from their origin (for example,
growth hormone or somatotropin is produced in the anterior pituitary, but acts on cells
throughout the body). Not all hormones are protein in nature (some are steroids). Many
peptides and polypeptides (for example, insulin-like growth factors, nerve growth factor)
have been identified as important in modulating metabolic activities. Some exert their action locally within the cell in which they are produced (autocrine effect), or in close prox-

imity to their origin (paracrine effect), whereas others have classical hormone action (endocrine effect). Immune antibodies are specific proteins that perform a vital role in protecting the animal from infectious agents.

PROTEIN METABOLISM. Protein metabolism consists of two general processes, anabolism (synthesis) and catabolism (breakdown). Individual amino acids, the basic units required in metabolism of the animal, are present in the diet largely as constituents of intact proteins which must be catabolized to amino acids to be absorbed into the body. The absorbed amino acids are used by cells throughout the body as the building blocks from which proteins characteristic of each tissue are synthesized. Protein synthesis and breakdown in the body is a dynamic continuous process. The final breakdown product of protein and amino acid catabolism is urea in mammals and uric acid in birds. The structures of urea and uric acid are depicted as:

The degree to which ingested protein is utilized by the animal is determined by the efficiency of hydrolysis of the protein in the digestive tract and, in turn, the absorption and utilization of the amino acids. Proteins can be characterized nutritionally on the basis of absorption of amino acids released from them during hydrolysis and the degree of utilization of amino acids after absorption. Dietary proteins not containing the correct proportion of amino acids to meet the animal's needs cannot be used efficiently for tissue protein synthesis. Nitrogen from dietary amino acids not absorbed from the digestive tract (exogenous N) is excreted in the feces along with N from protein and amino acids broken down in normal metabolism such as from sloughed intestinal mucosal cells and digestive secretions (endogenous N). The difference between the N excreted in the feces and that ingested represents the amount absorbed by the animal. Nitrogen lost in urine (as urea, and other nonprotein N) represents the end-product of protein catabolism after absorption. Animals that are consuming the same amount of N as they are excreting in feces plus urine are said to be in N balance. Growing animals are in positive N balance and starving animals are in negative N balance.

Amino Acid Absorption. Except in the newborn animal, whose intestine allows the passage of large molecules such as immune globulins from colostrum, the intestinal lining is an effective barrier to absorption of intact proteins and other large molecules. Amino acids, in contrast, are absorbed efficiently. In ruminant animals, certain di- and tripeptides are absorbed, but the biological importance is unclear. Absorption of amino acids occurs by active transport.

Fate of Amino Acids after Absorption. Absorbed amino acids may be used for tissue protein synthesis or for synthesis of enzymes, hormones, and other metabolites; or may be deaminated or transaminated and the C skeleton used for energy. (Deamination is the removal of the alpha amino group; transamination is the transfer of an amino group from one amino acid to the C skeleton of an amino acid that has undergone deamination.)

Essential (Indispensable) and Nonessential (Dispensable) Amino Acids. Some amino acids cannot be synthesized by animals at a rate sufficient to meet the metabolic requirements. Others can be synthesized from other amino acids or from other compounds. The quantitative requirement for individual essential amino acids varies among animal species and differs for each physiological function (growth, gestation, lactation), but most animals (except ruminants) have a nutritional requirement for most or all listed by Rose (1948) as required by the laboratory rat:

Essential	Nonessential
Arginine	Alanine
Histidine	Aspartic acid
Isoleucine	Citrulline
Leucine	Cystine
Lysine	Glutamic acid
Methionine (can be replaced partly by cystine)	Glycine
	Hydroxyproline
Phenylalanine (can be replaced partly by tyrosine)	Proline
	Serine
Threonine	Tyrosine
Tryptophan	
Valine	

Arginine is required in the diet of some species for maximum growth. In most species, adults do not require dietary arginine for maintenance, but mature dogs and cats do require it. Citrulline can completely replace arginine in the diet of cats and some other species. Glutamine may be important in normal digestive tract immune function and in normal pancreas and liver metabolism. The cat has a high sulfur amino acid requirement and is the only species known to require dietary taurine. Taurine is not a constituent of protein, but it may be present as a free amino acid in the diet. Histidine may be needed in the diet of adult humans and some other species. Proline appears to be required for egg production in hens and for growth in chicks and some mammals. Thus, it is clear that the dietary essentiality of some amino acids is related to animal species and stage of the life cycle.

In ruminant animals and in those whose lower intestinal tract microflora synthesize protein from nonprotein N, the amino acid composition of the diet is of minor nutritional importance, except for high-producing animals under some circumstances.

Protein Synthesis and Degradation. Protein synthesis in animals requires the presence of nucleic acids. Deoxyribonucleic acid (DNA), a chromosomal component of cells, carries the genetic information in the cell and transmits inherited traits from one generation to the next. DNA is composed of phosphate-linked deoxyribose and four nitrogenous bases: adenine, cytosine, guanine, and thymine. The DNA molecule is in the form of a long double-helix chain of nucleotides composed of phosphate-linked deoxyribose sugar groups, to each of which is attached one of the four bases. The bases are always paired, adenine with thymine and guanine with cytosine. The sequence of pairs can vary infinitely. A particular gene sequence determines the exact protein to be synthesized by the cell.

DNA controls development of the individual by regulating the formation of ribonucleic acid (RNA). Three types of RNA are present in cells: ribosomal RNA, transfer RNA, and messenger RNA. All three are involved in protein synthesis. Ribosomal RNA is part of the structure of the ribosome, the enzyme sequence that forms protein in the cell. Transfer RNA carries specific amino acids to the ribosome, where they interact with messenger RNA. The sequence of amino acids in the protein being synthesized is determined by messenger RNA. Synthesis of each protein is controlled by a different messenger RNA.

Dietary protein deficiency, particularly in young growing animals, depresses cellular growth and development by interfering with these vital genetically controlled protein synthetic processes.

Protein degradation in muscle tissue is controlled by enzymes such as cathepsins and calcium-dependent proteases (calpains). The processes of protein synthesis and protein degradation are dynamic. Net protein accretion (growth) in the animal is determined by the rate of protein synthesis and the rate of protein degradation. The relative importance of the two metabolic processes in regulation of the growth of muscle and other tissues is not completely understood. As animal scientists continue to discover the many factors that control the processes of protein synthesis and degradation in animals, the efficiency of animal production and the quality of animal products continues to improve.

Urea Cycle. The production of urea from the catabolism of protein and amino acids involves a complex series of metabolic conversions. The urea or ornithine cycle is a key metabolic process in protein metabolism. Urea is excreted in the urine and is the main route of excretion of N in mammals. In birds, ornithine synthesis does not occur; the main route of N excretion is as uric acid.

MEASURES OF THE NUTRITIVE VALUE OF PROTEINS. Protein sources are evaluated in several ways, including digestibility, biological value (BV), protein efficiency ratio (PER), net protein utilization (NPU), and net protein value (NPV). Protein utilization is conventionally estimated by determining N content of feed and animal excreta and multiplying by $N \times 6.25$ to convert to protein equivalent (proteins contain, on average, about 16 percent N; $6.25 \times 16 = 100$). Perhaps the two most commonly used measures are digestibility and BV. Protein digestibility refers to that portion of the protein ingested (measured as N) that does not appear in the feces. It is usually expressed as a percentage; thus if 100 g of protein is ingested and 20 g appears in the feces, 80 g has been digested and absorbed, giving an apparent digestibility of 80%. Proteins can be highly absorbable, but poorly utilized for growth, because of large losses of N in the urine due to an imbalanced essential amino acid pattern or a deficiency of a single amino acid in the protein. Therefore, protein sources often are evaluated on the basis of their biological value (BV). BV is defined as that percentage of N absorbed from the digestive tract that is available for productive body functions. BV is determined by measuring the total N intake and N losses in feces and urine. It provides an estimate of the efficiency of use of the absorbed protein for combined maintenance and growth. BV values of feedstuffs range from 91 for whole egg protein to less than 40 for wheat gluten. High-quality proteins such as milk casein and beef muscle have BV values of 60 to 70.

Vitamins

Vitamins are required in minute quantities for normal metabolism. Each has its own specific function. The omission of a single vitamin from the diet of a species that requires it results in specific deficiency signs and may result in death of the animal. The known vitamins and their signs of deficiency are listed in Table 8-2. Vitamins can be divided on the basis of their solubility properties into fat soluble and water soluble. The fat-soluble vitamins are A, D, E, and K. The water-soluble vitamins are thiamin (B1), riboflavin (B2), niacin (nicotinic acid), pantothenic acid, pyridoxine (B6), vitamin B12, biotin, choline, ascorbic acid (vitamin C), myoinositol, and para-aminobenzoic acid (PABA). The fat-soluble vitamins are required by ruminant and nonruminant animals. The water-soluble vitamins are synthesized by microbes residing in the rumen and in the large intestine of some nonruminants, such as the horse and rabbit, and are consequently of less concern in the diets of ruminants, horses, and some other nonruminants.

VITAMIN A. Vitamin A is required for normal night vision, for normal epithelial cells (cells lining the respiratory, urogenital, and digestive tracts, and skin), and for normal bone growth. Vitamin A can occur as the alcohol (retinol), as the aldehyde (retinal), or as the acid (retinoic acid). It also can be provided as its precursor, carotene. Retinol is considered to have 100% biopotency; other forms of vitamin A are less potent. More than 500 carotenoid pigments have been identified in addition to beta-carotene, the most abundant form. The relative biopotency of beta-carotene is 50% (one molecule of beta-carotene produces 2 molecules of retinol). Other forms are less potent.

Deficiency of vitamin A causes night blindness, thickened skin, changes in intestinal mucosal cells, lungs, and conjunctiva, reduced liver vitamin A concentration, embryonic death, abnormal skeletal development in newborn, xerophthalmia (scarring of the cornea and poor vision), abnormal bone formation, and reproductive failure in males, abortions, and poor growth of surviving young. All of these symptoms are related to defects in metabolism and structure of epithelial cells in various body tissues and organs. Vitamin A deficiency reduces thyroxin secretion from the thyroid gland. The most sensitive measure of vitamin A nutritional status is liver vitamin A concentration, which can be estimated by liver biopsy.

Toxicity of vitamin A (and other fat-soluble vitamins) may occur as a result of excessive intakes over an extended period of time or the acute ingestion of a large excess. Fat-soluble vitamins are not excreted readily, and surplus intakes above the metabolic require-

TABLE 8-2

VITAMINS REQUIRED BY ANIMALS

Vitamin	Deficiency Signs
Vitamin A	Night blindness, thickened skin, embryonic death, abnormal bone formation, abortion, xerophthalmia
Vitamin D	Impaired calcium utilization; rickets in growing animals, osteoporosis in adults
Vitamin E	Muscular dystrophy in mammals and birds; encephalomalacia and exudative diathesis in birds; mulberry heart disease (cardiac muscle degeneration) in pigs; liver necrosis
Vitamin K	Prolonged blood-clotting time, generalized hemorrhages
Thiamin (B1)	Enlarged heart, muscle weakness, edema, elevated blood pyruvic and lactic acids
Riboflavin (B2)	Cataracts; conjunctivitis; curled toe paralysis in chicks; vesicular stomatitis (lesions around lips and mouth) in humans
Niacin (Nicotinic acid)	Ulcerated intestine in swine; diarrhea, dermatitis; poor feathering and "spectacle eye" in chicks; darkening of the tongue (black tongue) in dogs; pellagra in humans
Pantothenic acid	Dermatitis in chicks; graying of the hair (achromotrichia) in foxes and rats; degeneration of the adrenal cortex; fetal death and resorption; fatty infiltration of the liver; nerve degeneration and "goose-stepping" (a peculiar gait in pigs)
Vitamin B6	Reduced immune function; altered lipid metabolism and increased fat deposition; demyelination of peripheral nerves; convulsions
Vitamin B12	Anemia, rough hair and feather coat; kidney damage; impaired thyroid function; demyelination of nerves; numerous abnormalities in blood chemistry
Folacin	Macrocytic hyperchromic anemia (indistinguishable from vitamin B12 deficiency)
Biotin	Scaly dermatitis; alopicia (loss of hair); birth defects; reproductive failure
Vitamin C (Ascorbic acid)	Structural defects of bone, teeth, and connective tissue; bleeding gums; scurvy in humans (only required by humans and other primates, rainbow trout, coho salmon, and a few other animals)
Choline	Fatty liver, hemorrhagic kidneys; perosis (slipped tendon) in chicks

ments are stored in liver and adipose tissue depots. Chronic toxicity of vitamin A results in loss of appetite (anorexia), weight loss, skin thickening, scaly dermatitis, crusting of the eyelids, hemorrhaging, decreased bone strength (leading to fractures), malformed young in pregnant animals, embryonic death, skeletal defects, eyelessness in the newborn, and death. Daily intakes for several weeks of 50 to 500 times the metabolic requirements produce toxic signs.

VITAMIN D.   Several steroid compounds have vitamin D activity, but the most important are vitamin D2 (irradiated ergosterol or calciferol, present mostly in plants) and vitamin D3 (irradiated 7-dehydrocholesterol, present in animal tissues). Mammals tend to use either form with equal efficiency, but birds use D2 only one-seventh as efficiently as D3. Ultraviolet light converts each precursor to its respective active form (exposure of harvested green forage to sunlight converts plant sterols to D2, whereas exposure of animals to sunlight converts skin sterols to D3. Sun exposure thereby decreases the need for dietary vitamin D in animals and humans.

Vitamin D functions to increase blood Ca and P levels for normal bone mineralization and prevention of tetany caused by hypocalcemia (low blood Ca). The active metabolite of vitamin D (1,25-dihydroxycholecalciferol) is produced in the kidney in response to hypocalcemia. This metabolite stimulates intestinal absorption, removal from bone, and possibly kidney tubular reabsorption of Ca and P to maintain blood Ca within normal limits. Vitamin D acts in conjunction with several hormones in regulating Ca homeostasis: parathyroid hormone is released to mobilize bone Ca when blood Ca is low and calcitonin is released to inhibit mobilization of bone Ca when blood Ca is high.

Deficiency of vitamin D results in inadequate bone calcification (rickets in growing animals, osteomalacia in adults). Toxicity causes abnormal deposition of Ca in soft tissues, including kidneys, aorta, and lungs.

VITAMIN E.   Vitamin E consists of a mixture of tocopherol compounds. The most active form of vitamin E is alpha-tocopherol. Other less active forms include beta- and gamma-tocopherol. Vitamin E is very unstable and can be oxidized easily by the presence of unsaturated FA or mineral salts. Vitamin E functions as an antioxidant and as a free radical scavenger in animal tissues. It is closely linked with the mineral element Se in protecting animals from several vitamin E-Se-deficiency diseases, including muscular dystrophy in calves, lambs, pigs, chicks, turkeys, and rabbits; encephalomalacia and exudative diathesis in chicks; mulberry heart disease (cardiac muscle degeneration) in pigs. Newborn pigs and lambs are especially vulnerable to vitamin E-Se deficiency, probably because placental transfer of the vitamin is inefficient. Vitamin E deficiency results in reproductive failure, derangement of cell permeability, and muscular lesions. Storage occurs in liver, skeletal muscle, heart, lung, kidney and other organs and in adipose depots. Reports of vitamin E toxicity are rare. Apparently the range of safe level of intake is broader than for other fat-soluble vitamins.

VITAMIN K.   Vitamin K exists in two common forms: phylloquinone (K1), common in green vegetables, and menaquinone (K2), a product of microbial flora in the digestive tract of animals and humans. A synthetic compound, menadione (K3), is widely used commercially as a source of vitamin K. Vitamin K is required for synthesis of prothrombin, a factor in normal blood clotting. A deficiency of vitamin K results in prolonged blood-clotting time, generalized hemorrhages, and death in severe cases. Microflora in the digestive tract normally synthesize sufficient vitamin K to meet metabolic needs of the animal. The vitamin is available either from its absorption from the lower intestinal tract or by coprophagy (feces-eating), which serves as an important source of nutrients for many animal species. Vitamins K1 and K2 are nontoxic, even at high dosages, but the synthetic, menadione, is toxic to the skin and respiratory tract of several animal species. However, its bisulfate derivatives are not. A well-known natural antagonist of vitamin K is dicoumerol, often present in weather-damaged sweet clover hay. This antagonist causes massive hemorrhages and death in calves consuming the hay. Warfarin, a commercial product with dicoumerol activity, is a commonly used rat poison.

THIAMIN (B1).   Thiamin, as in the case of all water-soluble vitamins (except vitamin B12), is stored in the body in limited amounts, so it must be supplied in the diet on a daily basis. It is required in normal carbohydrate and fat metabolism; it is converted in the liver to form the coenzymes cocarboxylase (thiamin pyrophosphate, TPP) and lipothiaminide (LTPP). In thiamin deficiency, blood pyruvic and lactic acids are elevated, and appetite is reduced. Deficiency signs include enlarged heart, muscle weakness, unsteady gait, and edema. The deficiency syndrome is called beriberi in humans and polyneuritis in chicks. Some raw seafoods and fish contain specific enzymes (thiaminases) which destroy thiamin and produce deficiency signs. Toxicity has not been reported.

RIBOFLAVIN (B2).   Riboflavin is a yellow fluorescent pigment consisting of ribose (a 5-C sugar) and the organic ring compound, isoalloxazine. Riboflavin functions in the coenzymes FAD (flavin adenine dinucleotide) and FMN (flavin mononucleotide). FAD and FMN are present in virtually all animal cells and occur as coenzymes in a large number of enzyme systems in energy metabolism. Specific deficiency signs include corneal opacities (cataracts), conjunctivitis; in chicks, curled-toe paralysis; in humans, lesions of the lips and mouth (vesicular stomatitis). Riboflavin is absorbed rapidly from the small intestine and excreted readily in the urine. Toxicity is highly unlikely, due to its rapid urinary excretion when intake exceeds the requirement.

NIACIN (NICOTINIC ACID).   Niacin was first recognized as a nutrient when it was found to cure the human disease, pellagra. Its essentiality in the diets of animals was later clarified. It is readily absorbed from the small intestine by simple diffusion. It functions as a constituent of two important coenzymes in energy metabolism. These coenzymes are NAD (nicotinamide adenine dinucleotide) and NADP (nicotine adenine dinucleotide phosphate). Niacin deficiency signs include diarrhea, vomiting, dermatitis, and an ulcerated intestine in swine; poor feathering and "spectacled eye" in chicks; darkening of the tongue (black tongue) in dogs; bright red tongue, mouth lesions, anorexia, and nausea in humans (pellagra).

If animals are deprived of dietary niacin, the metabolic requirement can be met partially by supplying a slight excess of the essential amino acid tryptophan in the diet. Tryptophan can be converted by the body to niacin. However, the cost of supplemental niacin is far less than that of tryptophan.

PANTOTHENIC ACID.   Pantothenic acid is present in feeds in various forms, including coenzyme A (CoA) and as the free vitamin. It is readily absorbed from the intestine in either form. Pantothenic acid functions in the body as a component of the coenzyme

CoA, which is required in the formation of two-C fragments from fats, carbohydrates, and amino acids for entry into the Krebs citric acid cycle and for synthesis of steroids. Deficiency signs include growth failure, as in deficiencies of other water-soluble vitamins. Specific symptoms include: dermatitis in chicks; graying of the hair (achromotrichia) in rats and foxes; hemorrhaging and degeneration of the adrenal cortex in rodents; fetal death and resorption in rats; nervous derangement, skin lesions, and degeneration of intestinal and pancreatic cells in chicks; fatty infiltration of the liver in several species; and "goose-stepping," a peculiar abnormal gait in pigs, resulting from nerve degeneration. Toxicity is unlikely.

VITAMIN B6. Vitamin B6 occurs as pyridoxine, pyridoxal, and pyridoxamine. Pyridoxine is absorbed from the intestine at a higher efficiency than other forms of the vitamin. Transfer to the liver is in all three forms. Vitamin B6 functions as a coenzyme for a vast array of enzyme systems associated with protein and amino acid metabolism. Its dietary requirement increases with high protein intakes. This is because pyridoxal phosphate, the coenzyme of transaminases, must be increased in activity to metabolize extra protein. The most common deficiency sign of vitamin B6 involves the nervous system. Convulsions have been observed in all species studied. Demyelination of the peripheral nerves, swelling of the myelin sheath, and other degenerative changes occur in nerve cells. Vitamin B6 deficiency results in reduced antibody response to various antigens, reduced immunocompetence in the progeny of depleted female rats, and produces a variety of changes related to lipid metabolism, including reduced carcass fat, fatty liver, and high blood lipids and cholesterol. Vitamin B6 is required for normal reproduction in rats and normal egg production and hatchability in hens. Toxicity is unlikely, although high doses can produce convulsions, impaired coordination, paralysis, and death.

VITAMIN B12. Vitamin B12 is the most recently discovered vitamin (isolated in 1948). It was first known as the animal protein factor (APF) because animals not consuming a diet containing animal protein were susceptible to the abnormal blood cell picture and nervous signs later shown to be prevented or cured by vitamin B12. It is stored in small amounts in animal tissues and excreta, although it is not synthesized by plant or animal tissues. Microorganisms are the only known primary source of vitamin B12.

The fundamental form of vitamin B12 is cyanocobalamin; derivatives of similar structure also are found in nature, but only a few have some vitamin B12 activity. Vitamin B12 functions as a coenzyme in several important enzyme systems involved in energy metabolism. It is closely linked to the action of pantothenic acid in the oxidation of certain FA and another water-soluble vitamin, folacin, in the metabolism of sulfur-containing amino acids in bacterial and animal cells. Vitamin B12 deficiency leads to secondary folacin deficiency.

Absorption of B12 from the intestine requires the presence of an enzyme, termed the intrinsic factor (IF), secreted by the mucosal cells lining the stomach and upper small intestine. If the IF is absent, B12 deficiency develops even in the presence of adequate B12 in the diet. Vitamin B12 deficiency symptoms include manifestations of many metabolic derangements, including poor feathering in birds and rough hair coat in mammals, kidney damage, impaired thyroid function, anemia, and numerous abnormalities in blood chemistry. In ruminant animals, whose rumen bacteria produce enough B12 to meet the requirement of the animal under normal conditions, a dietary deficiency of the trace mineral element, cobalt (Co), produces B12 deficiency because Co is an integral constituent of the vitamin B12 molecule. In the absence of Co, the rumen bacteria cannot synthesize B12.

Vitamin B12 deficiency in humans results in neurological disease, including demyelination of the spinal cord, brain, and peripheral nerves. Breast-fed human infants nursing vegetarian mothers may show signs of vitamin B12 deficiency, including anemia, apathy, and involuntary movements. Mothers of these infants have mild anemia and low concentrations of B12 in blood plasma and milk. Vitamin B12 toxicity has not been reported in animals or humans.

FOLACIN. Folacin is the generic term for several derivatives of folic acid, each of which has some biological activity. Folacin functions with vitamin B12 in a number of important metabolic reactions as described briefly in the section on B12. The most prominent feature of folacin deficiency in humans and animals is anemia indistinguishable from that of vitamin B12 deficiency. The anemia (reduced red blood cells) is described as macrocytic (large cells), hyperchromic (high concentration of red pigment). Folacin is distributed widely in nature; therefore, a deficiency is unlikely in birds and animals fed common diets. However, folacin deficiency remains at a relatively high frequency in human nutrition.

BIOTIN. Biotin is required in extremely small amounts relative to the amount present in common feedstuffs and it is synthesized by intestinal microflora. Therefore, biotin deficiency is unlikely under normal conditions. However, deficiency has been reported in animals kept in cages and not allowed to practice coprophagy (feces are a source of microbially synthesized biotin). Also, animals fed large quantities of raw egg white develop signs of deficiency due to the presence in raw egg whites of a protein, avidin, which binds biotin in the digestive tract and prevents its absorption. Avidin is destroyed by heat, so the problem is absent when the eggs are cooked. Biotin is a component of several enzyme systems involved with amino acid, carbohydrate, and lipid metabolism. Deficiency results in scaly dermatitis, alopecia (loss of hair), birth defects, and reproductive failure. There is no evidence of biotin toxicity, even at large doses.

VITAMIN C (ASCORBIC ACID). Vitamin C was first recognized as a factor in citrus fruits capable of preventing scurvy in humans. It is formed in animal tissues by conversion from glucose. Most animal species can synthesize vitamin C, but those unable to do so lack the enzyme, L-gulonolactone oxidase, which is involved in a key step in ascorbic acid synthesis from glucose. Vitamin C is involved in several enzyme systems that catalyze oxidation and reduction reactions. Ascorbic acid itself is easily oxidized and reversibly reduced, serving as a reducing agent. It has become widely recognized as an important antioxidant in body tissues of humans and animals. It is also required for the formation of the amino acid, hydroxyproline, from proline in normal connective tissue metabolism.

Signs of deficiency include edema, weight loss, bleeding gums, and diarrhea, as in scurvy, and structural defects in bone, teeth, cartilage, and connective tissue.

Species requiring dietary vitamin C include: humans and other primates, guinea pigs, rainbow trout, coho salmon, and several other mammals and nonmammals. The common domestic animals and birds do not require dietary vitamin C under normal conditions.

CHOLINE. Choline is widely distributed in animal tissues as free choline, acetyl choline, and as a component of phospholipids. It has the following broad functions: structural component of tissues (phospholipids in cell membranes); involved as acetyl choline in nerve impulse transmission; supplies biologically labile methyl groups in metabolic pathways; prevents accumulation of liver fat (fatty liver). Unlike other water-soluble vitamins, it appears not to be required as a cofactor in enzyme reactions. Signs of choline deficiency include hemorrhagic kidneys, fatty liver, and changes in cell membrane structure of lipoproteins needed for lipid transport in several species; perosis in chicks, and abnormal gait in swine. Choline toxicity has not been reported in humans or animals.

MYOINOSITOL. Myoinositol is required for the growth of cells in tissue culture and has been reported to be required for growth of gerbils, rats, and other animals under certain conditions. Tissue synthesis has been reported in several mammalian species. It appears to have important functions in lipid metabolism not previously recognized in animal nutrition. However, it is not considered to be needed as a supplemental vitamin in diet formulation, because of its abundance in plant materials and its microbial synthesis in the digestive tract. Phytic acid, a major source of phosphorus (P) in cereal grains and other seeds, is the hexaphosphoric acid ester of inositol. The release of free inositol by the removal of P through the action of the enzyme, phytase, occurs only to a limited degree in the intestinal tract of nonruminant animals, because phytase is not produced by animal tissues.

Inorganic Mineral Elements

More than 25 inorganic mineral elements are known to be required by one or more animal species for one or more productive functions (maintenance, work, growth, reproduction, lactation). Those of greatest nutritional concern in animal feeding and important signs of their deficiency are listed in Table 8-3. Those required in relatively large amounts, termed macrominerals, are calcium (Ca), phosphorus (P), sodium (Na), chlorine (Cl), potassium (K), magnesium (Mg), and sulfur (S). Ca, P, and Mg are required as structural components of the skeleton, whereas Na, Cl, and K, are electrolytes that function in acid-base balance and S is a constituent of an array of organic compounds involved as structural components of soft tissue and skeleton and in metabolism. Those required in much smaller amounts are termed trace or microminerals. Trace mineral elements required in the diet of one or more animal species are: boron (B), cobalt (Co), chromium (Cr), copper (Cu), florine (F), iodine (I), iron (Fe), manganese (Mn), molybdenum (Mo), selenium (Se), silicon (Si), and zinc (Zn). Still others whose dietary essentiality is suggested

TABLE 8-3

INORGANIC MINERAL ELEMENTS REQUIRED BY ANIMALS*

Mineral Element	Deficiency Signs
Calcium (Ca)	Poorly mineralized bone (rickets in growing animals, osteomalacia and osteoporosis in adults); low blood calcium, resulting in calcium tetany (parturient paresis or "milk fever" in cows and ewes); impaired blood clotting and generalized hemorrhage
Phosphorus (P)	Poorly mineralized bone (rickets, osteomalacia and osteoporosis as in calcium deficiency); nutritional hyperparathyroidism; depraved appetite manifested by wood-chewing (termed pica); impaired fertility in cattle
Magnesium (Mg)	Reduced blood magnesium, resulting in magnesium tetany (also called grass tetany)
Potassium (K)	General overall weakness, abnormal electrocardiogram, emaciation
Sodium (Na)	Weight loss; reduced milk production; extreme craving for salt
Chloride (Cl)	See Sodium
Sulfur (S)	Reduced wool and feather growth in sheep and birds; reduced rumen microbial activity and lower S-amino acid synthesis in ruminants
Iron (Fe)	Microcytic hypochromic anemia
Copper (Cu)	Anemia (reduces Fe absorption and utilization); incoordination and ataxia (known as "swayback" in sheep); bone abnormalities; abnormal hair and wool development; lack of hair pigmentation; cardiovascular lesions (aortic rupture in turkeys)
Manganese (Mn)	Skeletal abnormalities; low reproductive rates
Cobalt (Co)	Anemia (functions as a constituent of the vitamin B12 molecule; therefore, deficiency results in a failure in vitamin B12 synthesis by intestinal microorganisms
Iodine (I)	Low basal metabolic rate and goiter
Selenium (Se)	Same signs as for vitamin E deficiency (muscular dystrophy, encephalomalacia, exudative diathesis, liver necrosis, mulberry heart disease)
Zinc (Zn)	Skin lesions and growth failure; parakeratosis in pigs

*More than 25 inorganic mineral elements are known to be required by one or more animal species. Those included in this table are the most likely to be deficient in commonly used feedstuffs and need special attention in animal nutrition. Many are routinely added to the diet in mineral supplements.

by limited evidence include aluminum (al), arsenic (As), cadmium (Cd), nickel (Ni), vanadium (V), tin (Sn), bromine (Br), lead (Pb), and lithium (Li). Some of this latter group of trace minerals (Cd, Pb, As) are known to have toxic properties. Only those clearly established as required mineral elements for normal body functioning by animals are discussed further. Only the salient features of function and deficiency signs of each required macro- and micromineral element are addressed.

Virtually all mineral elements are toxic when ingested in excessive amounts. The

National Research Council has published a list of the maximum tolerable levels of dietary minerals for some of the domestic animals. Continuous long-term feeding of nutritionally essential minerals above the maximum tolerable levels may cause adverse effects.

CALCIUM (CA). Approximately 99% of the Ca stored in the body is in the skeleton (bones and teeth). Its functions are: structural component of the skeleton (bone is in a dynamic state of continuous remodeling and turnover of Ca and other bone constituents; Ca concentration of blood plasma is kept relatively constant under the influence of homeostatic control by hormones that regulate accretion and resorption of Ca in bone); required for controlling excitability of nerve and muscle; required for normal blood clotting. Calcium deficiency results in weakened and poorly mineralized bone (rickets in growing animals and osteoporosis in adults). Severe Ca deficiency produces hypocalcemia (low blood Ca), which results in tetany and convulsions. The classic example of Ca tetany in animals is parturient paresis or "milk fever" in dairy cows. The tetany occurs usually in early lactation during the period of serious depletion of body Ca for milk production. The condition is reversed quickly by the intravenous administration of Ca lactate or other Ca salts, which restore the blood plasma Ca level to normal. Ca deficiency in rats and dogs has resulted in generalized hemorrhage due to impaired blood clotting in severe Ca depletion.

PHOSPHORUS (P). Approximately 80% of the P stored in the body is in the skeleton (bones and teeth), in a Ca:P ratio of about 2:1. The remaining 20% is distributed in blood plasma (in both organic and inorganic forms) and in muscle, nervous, and adipose tissue and in liver, heart, kidney, brain, skin, and other organs, mostly in organic form. Its functions are: (1) structural component of the skeleton; constituent of phospholipids (important in lipid metabolism and transport and in cell membrane structure); (2) constituent of high-energy phosphate bonds (adenosine mono-, di-, and triphosphate, AMP, ADP, and ATP, respectively), as key substances in energy metabolism; (3) constituent as phosphate of DNA and RNA; (4) constituent of several enzyme systems (flavoproteins, FMN, FAD, and nicotinamide adenine dinucleotide phosphate, NADP). Signs of P deficiency include: rickets and osteoporosis as in Ca deficiency; depraved appetite manifested by wood-chewing (termed pica); impaired fertility in cattle.

MAGNESIUM (MG). Magnesium is widely distributed in the body, about 50% in bone and 50% in soft tissues, mostly within cells. Highest concentration is in liver and muscle. Functions of Mg are: required for normal skeletal development; required for oxidative phosphorylation in mitochondria; required for activation of many enzyme systems. Deficiency signs include: reduced blood serum Mg, resulting in Mg tetany. Cattle grazing on pastures low in Mg or high in K or in an organic acid, trans-aconitic acid, are prone to Mg tetany (also called grass tetany) because of reduced blood serum Mg. The problem is overcome by providing inorganic Mg as a supplement to grazing cattle.

POTASSIUM (K), SODIUM (NA), AND CHLORINE (CL). Potassium, sodium, and chlorine are discussed together because they function together in performing several vital bodily functions. They are all electrolytes that maintain osmotic pressure in the extracellular and intercellular fluids and help to maintain acid-base balance. Normal ratios among electrolytes in body tissues are remarkably constant among animal species. K is located mainly within cells (about 90% of body K is intracellular) and is exchangeable readily with Na in the extracellular fluid. Na is located primarily in the extracellular fluid (about 90%) with less than 10% within cells. Of the extracellular Na, about half is adsorbed to the hydroxyapatite crystal of bone and half is present in blood plasma and interstitial fluids. Cl is located almost exclusively in the extracellular fluid. It acts with bicarbonate (HCO_3-) to electrically balance the Na of the extracellular fluid. When excess Na is excreted by the kidney, it is accompanied by Cl excretion. Thus, we see that the cations, $K+$ and $Na+$, and the anions, $Cl-$ and HCO_3-, act in synchrony to keep the body tissues in electrolyte and acid-base balance.

K, in addition to its role in maintaining osmotic pressure and acid-base balance, is required in enzyme reactions involving energy utilization, is important in facilitating the uptake of neutral amino acids by cells, and is required for normal protein synthesis, and for integrity of heart and kidney muscle and for a normal electrocardiogram. Na functions extracellularly through an energy-dependent "Na pump," and in nerve impulse transmission by virtue of the potential energy associated with its separation from K by the cell membrane. Cl, in addition to its role in regulating osmotic pressure and acid-base balance, is the chief anion of gastric juice where it unites with $H+$ ion to form HCl.

Deficiency of K results in abnormal electrocardiograms, reversible by K administration; general overall muscle weakness; emaciation; and death. K deficiency can be produced by Mg deficiency, which results in failure to retain K and consequent signs of K deficiency. The main signs of Na deficiency are reduced growth in young animals and reduced milk production and weight loss in adults. Animals deprived of Na (as supplied by common salt, NaCl) display a craving for it and have been observed to drink urine in an effort to satisfy their craving. Depressed growth rate is the main sign of Cl deficiency.

Toxicity of K, Na, and Cl is unlikely, because the kidney normally regulates their excretion when intakes are excessive. Severe water restriction, the presence of excessive levels of the electrolytes in drinking water (salinity), or kidney malfunction may produce toxicity signs. K toxicity results in enlarged adrenal gland cortex and disturbances in energy metabolism; Na toxicity results in hypertension associated with degenerative vascular disease; Cl toxicity results in disturbed acid-base balance.

SULFUR (S). Sulfur is required by animals mainly as a constituent of organic compounds, including amino acids (methionine, cystine, and cysteine); vitamins (biotin and thiamin); mucopolysaccharides; heparin; glutathione; and coenzyme A. Proteins are present in every cell of the body, and S-containing amino acids are present in virtually all proteins. Therefore, S is widely distributed throughout the body in every cell and makes up about 0.15% of body weight. Because most of body S is present in amino acids, it follows that urinary S excretion parallels that of N excretion. High-protein diets result in large amounts of urinary S and N. In ruminant animals fed nonprotein N for use by rumen microflora in synthesis of protein, a source of inorganic S is needed in the diet to allow microbial S-amino acid and protein synthesis for use by the animal. Wool and feathers are unusually high in S-containing amino acids, so sheep and birds have a higher S requirement than most other animals. S toxicity is not a practical problem because inorganic S is poorly absorbed from the intestine. Excesses of S-containing amino acids cause growth depression, but such an effect is seen with excesses of amino acids in general, not specifically the S-containing amino acids.

TRACE (MICRO-) MINERAL ELEMENTS. The trace minerals likely to be deficient in commonly used feedstuffs for animals are listed in Table 8-3 along with signs of their deficiency. Trace elements function as activators of enzyme systems or as constituents of organic compounds. Interactions among and between macrominerals and between individual macrominerals and microminerals are increasingly recognized as important. For example, a dietary Ca-to-P ratio of less than 1:2 or greater than 2:1 may cause bone abnormalities; a high ratio of K to Mg in pasture may be associated with increased incidence of magnesium tetany in ruminants; high dietary Ca may precipitate zinc deficiency in swine; high dietary aluminum decreases P availability by forming insoluble complexes in the intestine, resulting in reduced bone mineralization.

DIFFERENCES IN REGIONAL DISTRIBUTION OF TRACE ELEMENTS. Regional distribution of some trace elements in soil has been described and mapped. Such information is useful in identifying problem areas for trace element deficiencies and excesses. For example, selenium (Se) is known to be deficient in the soils of some areas of the United States, resulting in low Se content of the plants grown on those soils and Se deficiency in animals consuming these plants. Other areas are known to contain very high levels of soil Se, resulting in plant accumulation of Se and Se toxicity in animals consuming those plants. Some trace elements vary among geographic areas in their concentration in the soil, as in the case of Se, but soils deficient in a particular element (for example, zinc), result in reduced plant yield with no change in concentration of the trace element in the plant tissues and therefore no effect on the zinc status of the animal consuming the plant.

COMMONLY DEFICIENT TRACE MINERAL ELEMENTS. Trace minerals most likely to be deficient in animals fed commonly used feedstuffs are: Fe, Mn, Co (required as a constituent of vitamin B12), I (supplied easily as iodized salt), Zn, Cu (only in regions where soil Mo is high), and Se. Feed manufacturers usually add small amounts of one or more of these trace minerals to macromineral supplements to ensure an adequate intake of each element.

Fe is a component of many enzymes and proteins in animals. Its most notable function is as a component of hemoglobin in red blood cells (erythrocytes) and myoglobin in muscle, and as such is required for oxygen transport within the body. Fe deficiency results in anemia (described as microcytic, hypochromic), which is characterized by smaller-than-normal red blood cells containing less-than-normal hemoglobin. Fe-deficiency anemia is common in baby pigs, whose body stores of Fe at birth are low due to limited placental transfer of Fe to the fetus during pregnancy coupled with low Fe concentration in the milk. Fe-deficiency anemia is a major nutritional problem in humans worldwide.

Mn is present in common feedstuffs at marginal levels and is therefore of nutritional concern in animal production. Mn is required for formation of chondroitin sulfate, a constituent of mucopolysaccharides of bone. It is also a component of enzymes involved with carbohydrate and lipid metabolism. Deficiency causes an array of skeletal abnormalities. Low reproductive rates and reduced egg production are also associated with Mn deficiency.

Co, as a component of the vitamin B12 molecule, is important in preventing vitamin B12 deficiency. No other function has been ascribed to Co in animal or human nutrition. Deficiency in ruminant diets results in signs of vitamin B12 deficiency because of the inability of rumen microflora to synthesize the vitamin in the absence of Co.

I is a constituent of the thyroid hormones, thyroxin (T4) and triiodothyronine (T3). These thyroid hormones are required for normal basal metabolism in all higher animals. A dietary deficiency of I therefore produces goiter and low basal metabolism. I is usually supplied in the diet as iodized salt, either incorporated into the mixed diet or as a component of a NaCl (salt) block for ruminants and horses.

Zn is a constituent of many metalloenzymes. It activates some enzymes and plays a role in the configuration of DNA and RNA. The most common signs of deficiency are reduced growth rate and thickening and hyperkeratinization of the skin. The prime example is parakeratosis in swine. Correction of skin lesions in Zn-deficient animals with supplemental Zn is dramatic; within days, feed intake returns to normal and skin lesions disappear. Zn deficiency is precipitated by reduced absorption of Zn from the digestive tract due to consumption of a high Ca diet in combination with high levels of phytic acid (phytate), present in corn, cereal grains, and plant protein supplements.

Cu is required for the activity of enzymes involved with Fe metabolism, and for connective tissue formation, melanin (pigment) production, and integrity of the central nervous system. Deficiency signs include anemia (reduces Fe absorption and utilization), incoordination and ataxia (in sheep the condition is known as swayback or enzootic neonatal ataxia), bone abnormalities, abnormal hair and wool development, lack of hair pigmentation, and cardiovascular lesions (aortic rupture in turkey poults). Cu is apt to be toxic in sheep. A level of Cu in the diet that is well tolerated by cattle and swine is fatal to sheep, due to excessive liver Cu accumulation.

Se was recognized as a toxic mineral many years before it was discovered to be dietary essential. It functions as a component of the enzyme glutathione peroxidase and in this role protects the cell from lipid oxidation and damage from peroxides. Thus, it has a major role in maintenance of the integrity of cell membranes. Several deficiency diseases thought earlier to be due to vitamin E deficiency now are known to be prevented also by Se. These diseases, all related to cell membrane damage due to peroxidation, include: nutritional muscular dystrophy in lambs, pigs, poultry, and calves; liver necrosis in pigs and rats; exudative diathesis in poultry. Note that these diseases are the same as those described earlier in this chapter under vitamin E deficiency. Either vitamin E or Se will prevent all of these diseases; however, vitamin E, but not Se, prevents encephalomalacia in chicks. Se toxicity is still encountered in geographic areas with high soil Se, but diet formulation in these areas with feedstuffs grown in nonseleniferous areas alleviates the problem.

Other trace mineral elements known to be required in the diet of animals, but normally present in adequate amounts in common feedstuffs, are not discussed here. Many reviews and textbooks covering in detail the field of minerals in nutrition are available. Some are cited in the reference list at the end of this chapter.

THE GASTROINTESTINAL TRACT: STRUCTURE, DIGESTION, AND ABSORPTION

The gastrointestinal tract (GIT) represents the organ systems responsible for assimilating food for utilization by the animal to support life. The specialized structures of the GIT are concerned with procuring, chewing, and swallowing food and with its processing in preparation for entering the body. The terms digestion and absorption are frequently used in describing these processes. They represent the ways by which feedstuffs or mixed diets ingested by the animal are transformed into products that can be utilized for performing normal life functions. Digestion may be defined as the preparation of food for absorption. It may include mechanical forces (mastication, muscular contractions of the GIT); chemical action (hydrochloric acid in the stomach, bile in the small intestine); and biological action (breakdown of food into its component nutrients by enzymes produced in the GIT and by microorganisms residing within its lumen). The overall purpose of these various digestive processes is to reduce ingesta to a molecular size or solubility that allows absorption of the nutrients into the body for use. Absorption is the summation of processes that result in the passage of nutrients from the lumen of the GIT into the epithelial (mucosal) cells lining the lumen for metabolism there or for transport into the blood and lymph systems to be carried to body cells for metabolism.

Structure and Functions of the GIT

The GIT is essentially a modified tubular structure designed for ingestion, digestion, and absorption of food and the elimination of some undigested food residues and of the products of metabolism. Wide variations in GIT structure exist among animal species. Evolution has produced many variations in GIT structure and function to accommodate the utilization by a particular species of feedstuffs differing greatly in composition and quality. Thus, the GIT of carnivores (species such as cats, dogs, and mink, which depend on nonplant material, e.g., meat, fish, insects) is characterized by a simple stomach and a relatively short and uncomplicated intestine. Omnivores (species such as humans, swine, and poultry, which depend on both animal and plant sources of food) and herbivores (species such as cattle and other ruminants; and rabbits and horses, which depend entirely on plant sources of food) have a more complicated GIT modified in various ways to improve utilization of plant materials. Diagrams of the GIT of the sheep, rabbit, pig, and dog are shown in Figure 8-6 to illustrate major differences among herbivores, omnivores, and carnivores in digestive tract anatomy. Photographs of the GIT of a pig, chicken, rabbit, and sheep showing differences in relative size of the various parts in each species are in Figure 8-7.

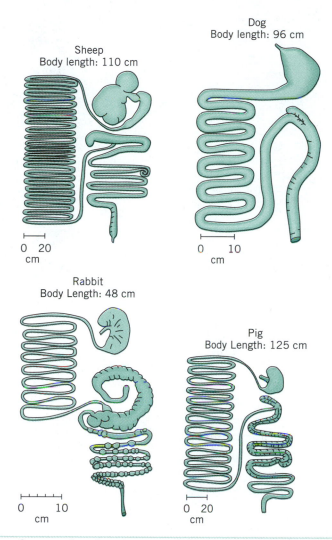

FIGURE 8-6

Some examples of mammalian digestive tracts drawn to illustrate major anatomical differences. The sheep represents pregastric digesters. There is some similarity between the cecum of the pony and the pig (both hindgut fermenters). Sacculation is a distinguishing characteristic of herbivores whether in the stomach, cecum, or large intestine. The cecum is small in the dog.

Source: Reprinted from Pond, Church, and Pond (1995), with permission from John Wiley and Sons, Inc., NY and *Dukes' Physiology of Domestic Animals,* 9th ed. (Swenson, 1977).

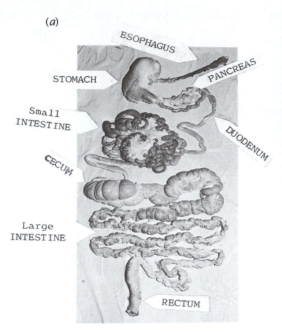

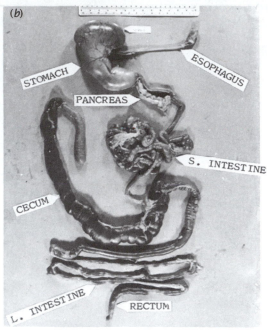

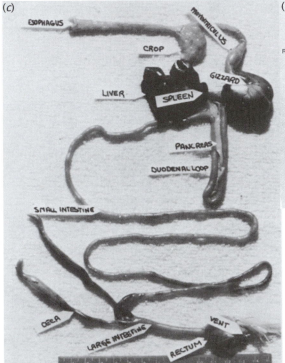

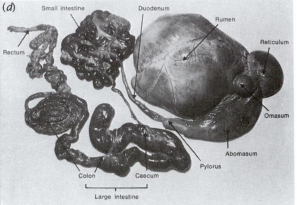

FIGURE 8-7

Digestive tracts from (a) the pig (nonruminant mammalian omnivore), (b) rabbit (nonruminant mammalian herbivore), (c) chicken (nonruminant avian omnivore), and (d) sheep (ruminant herbivore). Note the relative differences among species in size of the stomach and cecum and length and structure of the small and large intestine.
Source: Adapted from Pond et al. (1995).

The GIT of birds differs considerably from that of other nonruminant species. The beak has no teeth to reduce particle size for swallowing, but some species have a crop or proventriculus where some fermentation occurs and a gizzard that acts to physically reduce food particle size by muscular grinding action. The intestinal tract of the chicken is uncomplicated and consists of a small intestine, large intestine, and two ceca, where limited fermentation occurs. Total digestibility of fibrous diets by chickens is similar to or less than that in pigs.

Pigs, rabbits, and horses and ponies are all nonruminants with a simple stomach, but the intestinal tract of pigs differs considerably from that of rabbits and horses. The pig has a long but simple small intestine, a relatively large cecum, and sacculated large intestine (colon). The pig has microbial fermentation in both the cecum and large intestine. In herbivores, such as the rabbit and horse, most of the fermentation in the GIT occurs in the cecum (rabbit), or cecum and large intestine (horse and pony).

Ruminants (e.g., cattle, sheep, deer) have a large complex stomach (rumen) with extensive fermentation, followed by a long but simple small intestine, a relatively large cecum, and a short large intestine. Therefore fermentation in ruminants occurs both in the foregut (rumen) and the hindgut (large intestine), although the rumen is by far the more important. Ruminants represent a highly specialized class because of their ability to digest dietary fiber and other complex carbohydrates more completely than other animals. The ruminant stomach has four compartments—rumen, reticulum, omasum, and abomasum. The reticulum and rumen are not completely separated, but have different functions. The reticulum moves food into the rumen or into the omasum, and functions in regurgitation of ingesta during rumination (the process by which rhythmic contractions of stomach compartments result in regurgitation of ingesta up the esophagus for remastication, i.e., cud-chewing, followed by reswallowing of the bolus formed in the process). The reticular groove allows milk to bypass the reticulorumen and escape bacterial fermentation. It does not remain functional in nonsuckling animals. The rumen, as discussed earlier, acts as a large fermentation vat with a high microbial population. The omasum aids in reducing particle size of feed and in controlling passage of ingesta into the lower intestinal tract. The abomasum is comparable to the stomach of nonruminants. Eructation (belching of gas) is important to ruminants as a means of releasing the large volume of gases produced in the process of fermentation. Failure to eructate results in accumulation of these gases within the rumen, causing bloat, a condition that can be fatal if not relieved. Some feedstuffs contain substances that cause froth accumulation, which blocks the escape of gases during eructation.

In animals that depend heavily on cecal fermentation (e.g., rabbit, rat), there often is an association with coprophagy (feces-eating). This practice allows the animal to consume plants that are poor sources of vitamins and amino acids and obtain these nutrients by absorbing them from the hindgut following synthesis by microbial populations residing there.

Processes of Digestion and Absorption

The preparation of food for absorption requires first that the ingesta be transformed to components capable of passing through the epithelial cells lining the intestinal lumen.

Digestive secretions play important roles in this process. In nonruminants, digestive enzymes (organic catalysts, all protein in nature) break down the ingesta before it is subjected to microbial action in the lower intestine. In ruminants, the digestive enzymes act on the ingesta after it is subjected to fermentation by rumen microbes. The stomach (or proventriculus in birds, abomasum in ruminants) produces the proteolytic (protein-splitting) enzyme, pepsin, which is activated by its precursor, pepsinogen under the influence of HCl, also produced in the stomach. Other proteolytic enzymes, carbohydrases (carbohydrate-splitting), and lipases (lipid-splitting) are produced in the pancreas and small intestinal cells and released for action in the lumen of the small intestine. The pancreatic enzymes are secreted into the intestine via the pancreatic duct. Some of the principal digestive enzymes and their characteristics are shown in Table 8-4. The end-products of protein digestion are amino acids, those of carbohydrate digestion are glucose and other monosaccharides, and those of fats (triglycerides) are fatty acids and glycerol. Amino acids and glucose are absorbed by diffusion and active (energy-requiring) transport. Fatty acids are mixed with bile acids (produced in the liver and transported to the intestinal lumen via the bile duct) to form micelles, which enhance solubility and allow absorption either through the intestinal epithelial cells or the lymphatic system.

Nutrient digestion and absorption requires the influence of neurohumeral control processes of enzyme secretion, motility of specific segments of the intestine, and other functions of the GIT. These functions are affected by the nervous system, the endocrine system, and interactions between these systems and the diet of the animal. Some of the important hormones related to the activity of the GIT (organ of origin is listed in parentheses) are gastrin (stomach), secretin (upper small intestine), cholecystokinin (upper small intestine and brain), and somatostatin (upper small intestine). These and other hormones act in concert to maintain normal digestive function in animals fed diets of varying composition.

Fecal and Urinary Excretion

Fecal material excreted by animals is comprised of undigested residues of feeds; residues of secretions from the GIT, including pancreatic and intestinal enzymes and other substances; sloughed intestinal epithelial cells; microbial cell debris from the large intestine (or in the case of ruminants, from the rumen); and breakdown products of body metabolism excreted into the intestinal lumen. The term "apparent digestibility" of a nutrient refers to the amount of the nutrient consumed during a fixed time period minus the total amount excreted in the feces during the same period, divided by the total amount of the nutrient consumed. This fraction is multiplied by 100 to express the value as a percentage. For example, if 100 g protein is ingested, and 20 g appears in the feces, the apparent digestibility of the protein is 80/100 = 0.80 or 80%. The true digestibility of a protein is represented by only the amount of fecal protein that originated from the diet. Therefore, apparent digestibility, as measured, gives a lower than actual value for the amount of dietary protein absorbed. On the other hand, apparent digestibility discloses the net protein available to the animal for use in body metabolism.

Urine represents the main route of excretion of nitrogenous and sulfurous metabo-

TABLE 8-4

PRINCIPAL DIGESTIVE ENZYMES SECRETED BY THE GASTROINTESTINAL TRACT (GIT), THEIR ORIGIN, SUBSTRATE, AND SUBSTRATE END-PRODUCTS

Type, Name	Origin	Substrate	End Product
Amylolytic		*Carbohydrates*	
salivary amylase	saliva	starches	dextrins, maltose
pancreatic amylase	pancreas	starches	maltose
maltase	small intestine	maltose	glucose
lactase	small intestine	lactose	glucose, galactose
sucrase	small intestine	sucrose	glucose, fructose
Lipolytic		*Lipids**	
pancreatic lipase	pancreas	triglycerides	monoglyceride + 2 FAs
intestinal lipase	small intestine	triglycerides	glycerol + 3 FAs
Proteolytic		*Proteins*	
pepsin**	stomach	protein	polypeptides
rennin**	abomasum (ruminants)	milk protein (casein)	calcium caseinate
trypsin**	pancreas	protein, polypeptides	peptides
chymotrypsin	pancreas	protein, polypeptides products of rennin digestion	peptides
carboxypeptidase A	pancreas	peptides	small peptides
carboxypeptidase B	pancreas	peptides	basic amino acids
aminopeptidases	small intestine	peptides	amino acids
dipeptidases	small intestine	dipeptides	amino acids
nucleases	pancreas, small intestine	nucleic acids	nucleotides
nucleotidases	small intestine	nucleotides	purine and pyrimidine bases, pentose sugars

*Bile acids from the liver enter the small intestine via the bile duct and aid digestion and absorption of lipids by reducing particle size and increasing solubility.

**These enzymes are released in inactive precursor forms, probably as a means of protecting the body tissues. Pepsinogen is activated by hydrochloric acid (HCl) to the active form, pepsin; trypsinogen by an intestinal enzyme, enterokinase, and by trypsin. The pro-forms of chymotrypsin, carboxypeptidases, and amino acid peptidases are activated by trypsin.

lites of body tissues, and is the principal route for excretion of some of the inorganic minerals, notably P, and electrolytes, K, Na, and Cl. Urine contains urea and other N compounds and small amounts of vitamins and trace elements. Water-soluble vitamins consumed in amounts exceeding the requirement are rapidly lost in the urine. Protein is normally found in urine only in traces; the presence of significant amounts indicates kidney disease in adults, although it may be present in the urine in young animals under some conditions. Carbohydrate (glucose) sometimes may be found in urine after a meal high in soluble carbohydrates, but its presence usually denotes diabetes. Ketones may be present in animals suffering from starvation or ketosis.

In birds, feces and urine are voided together through a common excretory opening. Nitrogen excretion in urine is mainly as uric acid, rather than as urea, the end-product of protein metabolism in mammals (an exception is the Dalmation dog, in which uric acid is a major end-product of protein metabolism).

FACTORS AFFECTING FEED CONSUMPTION

Feed represents the major cost in animal production (for example, in swine production, feed costs are more than half of total costs and may reach 80 to 85% of total costs on many farms. Therefore, efficiency of feed utilization is an important consideration in all of animal agriculture, and level of feed consumption by individual animals is directly related to efficiency of growth and lactation.

Many factors affect feed consumption by animals. Taste, odor, physical texture, and chemical composition of the diet may alter feed intake. Several terms often used in describing eating behavior and short- and long-term feed consumption are defined here.

- Appetite is the desire of an animal to eat.
- Satiety is the lack of desire to eat.
- Hunger is the physiological state that results from the deprivation of feed; hunger is relieved by the ingestion of feed.
- Hunger and satiety centers located in the brain are responsible for short-term changes in feed intake in response to signals from the GIT, liver, and perhaps other organs.
- Long-term feed intake (over periods of days or months) is controlled by factors such as physiological state (lactating animals have greater intake than nonlactating animals; growing animals eat more per unit body weight than adults maintaining constant body weight); energy status of the animal (underfed, thin animals tend to eat more feed when given the opportunity as a compensatory measure); and environmental temperature (high temperatures decrease feed intake and low temperatures increase it).

Most adult animals are able to maintain a relatively stable body weight over long periods of time. This indicates that the animal is generally able to adjust intake to match energy expenditure by some unclearly defined means of appetite control. The main dietary factor in determining feed intake appears to be energy density. Diets high in fat are consumed in lower amounts so, in such cases, other nutrients such as protein must be increased in the diet to ensure adequate nutrition. If a diet is diluted with an indigestible ingredient, the animal will eat more total feed to compensate for the lower calorie concentration of the energy-diluted diet. The increased intake will occur up to the point at which its GIT can no longer accommodate the bulk in the diet; this is an example of physical fill as a limiting factor in intake. Chemostatic control of appetite also plays a role in feed intake; for example, in nonruminant animals, when blood glucose concentration is decreased by fasting, hunger contractions of the stomach are increased and eating is stimulated. Other chemostatic agents such as the hormone cholecystokinin also affect short-term intake.

FEEDS AND FEEDING

Feed Processing

Not only is a nutritionally adequate diet important to encourage consumption and maximize efficiency of feed utilization, but equally important is appropriate processing of feedstuffs. Feed processing is accomplished by physical, chemical, thermal, bacterial, or other alterations of a feed ingredient before it is fed. Feeds are processed to alter physical form or particle size, to preserve, to isolate specific parts, to improve palatability or digestibility, to alter nutrient composition, or to detoxify. Many processing techniques are done on the farm (e.g., hay drying, baling; grain drying; grinding; silage making) whereas many are done by commercial feedmills (e.g., grinding, pelleting, cubing, steam-flaking), or by distilleries (e.g., barley malting), meatpackers (e.g., production of blood meal, meat meal,[2] tallow), food processors (e.g., soybean and other oil seed meals, corn gluten meal), and other industries related to food and feed production.

Feed processing is of particular importance for animals consuming feed for high levels of production (e.g., lactation, growth). However, increases in relative fuel costs have resulted in more selectivity of processing methods based on differences in efficiency of fuel use among various procedures. Forages and roughages require some degree of processing when they are incorporated into complete diets, to facilitate diet mixing and the use of feed distribution systems. Feed wastage can be significantly reduced in forage feeding systems by appropriate processing and in complete high-concentrate diets for nonruminants by pelleting and by the use of well-designed and adjusted self-feeding systems.

Diet Formulation

The success of any animal production enterprise depends on adequate nutrition and feeding management based on economical, nutritionally balanced diets matched to each phase of the life cycle and physiological state. Diet formulation is a procedure that matches nutrient requirements of the animal with optimum combinations of available feed ingredients. The two sets of information needed to balance a diet are: (1) the nutrient requirements of the animal and (2) the chemical (nutrient) composition of the available feedstuffs.

---

[2]The use of meat meal from cattle and sheep has been curtailed because of reports of certain nervous system diseases in humans (Creutzfeldt-Jacobs disease) possibly related to bovine spongioform encephalopathy (BSE, "mad cow disease") in cattle in Europe.

Resources Available on Approaching Animal Nutrient Needs

Nutrient requirements are expressed in terms of energy, fat, protein (and amino acids), vitamins, and inorganic mineral elements. The National Research Council, National Academy of Science, publishes an ongoing series of recommended dietary levels of nutrients entitled "Nutrient Requirements," with separate publications for beef cattle, dairy cattle, sheep, goats, swine, poultry, laboratory animals, fishes, dogs, cats, and horses. These publications are widely used in the United States as the basis for diet formulation for each of these animal species. Titles of most of these and other related publications are listed in the References section at the end of this chapter. As new knowledge is gained, teams of experts active in research in the nutrition of each animal species gather to revise recommendations for each nutrient for a particular species. Thus, the field of animal nutrition is in a dynamic state of change, based on advances in science and technology.

CHEMICAL COMPOSITION OF FEEDSTUFFS. Tables of feed composition (as in Table 8-5) may be used as the basis for diet formulation. Most commercial feed manufacturers maintain a quality-control laboratory in which chemical composition of individual feed ingredients is frequently monitored and adjustments in combinations and levels of ingredients are made to produce diets meeting all nutrient requirements of the animal for a specific purpose or a particular level of production. Feed tags attached to bagged commercial concentrate feeds state guaranteed minimum (and sometimes maximum) concentrations of selected nutrients contained therein.

Because many nutrients must be balanced in a diet, computer software programs often are used to formulate modern diets. Such programs include upper and lower limits of acceptable concentrations of each nutrient, and ingredient costs are included in the formula to develop diets low in total cost. Least-cost diet formulation is performed by linear programming techniques, using computers to balance diets quickly and efficiently. Such techniques are part of normal instruction in undergraduate animal nutrition courses. For diets that contain only a few feedstuffs and in which nutritional parameters such as energy and protein are fixed, the techniques are simple and do not require linear programming. In these cases algebraic equations, solved mentally, with an electronic calculator, or with a simple spreadsheet are used. When diets are more complex and some predetermined level of production is included in the equation, mathematical programming with a computer is needed.

It is important to recognize that the most sophisticated and accurate method of diet formulation may not reveal such factors as ingredient or diet palatability, acceptance by the animal, possible presence of toxic substances, or other characteristics of the feedstuff(s) that might affect level of intake of the final mixed diet by the animal. Such variables can only be evaluated by observing the animal to which the diet is fed.

EXPRESSION OF ENERGY IN DIET FORMULATION. As described earlier in this chapter, calorie (or joule) is the unit of energy in animal and human nutrition. The partitioning of energy during its transit through the body is based on losses to the animal during digestion, absorption, and metabolism (see Figure 8-1). Tables of nutrient composition of feedstuffs usually express energy content as "digestible energy, DE" or

TABLE 8-5

COMPOSITION OF SOME COMMON FORAGES AND ROUGHAGES FED TO RUMINANT AND NONRUMINANT ANIMALS

Feed Class and Ingredient Name	Dry Matter	Composition, Dry Basis (percent)					
		Crude Protein	Crude Fiber	Ca	P	Digestible Protein	DE*
*Pasture, immature***							
Bermuda	39	9.1	28	0.49	0.27	—	2.53
Bluegrass, KY	30.5	17.3	25.1	0.58	0.47	12.6	3.18
Bluestem	31.6	11.0	28.9	0.63	0.17	7.2	2.82
Brome	32.5	20.3	23.9	0.59	0.37	15.1	3.00
Fescue, meadow	25.0	17.6	23.6	0.76	0.48	12.9	3.01
Orchard grass	23.8	18.4	23.6	0.58	0.55	13.5	2.87
Timothy	26.1	15.7	22.7	0.47	0.43	11.2	2.92
*Green legumes***							
Alfalfa	20.9	21.2	23.6	2.26	0.35	15.9	2.74
Clover, ladino	18.0	14.1	24.7	1.27	0.42	19.5	3.31
Clover, red	19.7	19.4	23.3	2.26	0.38	13.9	3.05
*Other pasture crops***							
Rape	16.9	17.6	14.7	1.47	0.43	12.9	3.37
Sudangrass	20.8	14.1	27.5	0.49	0.44	9.9	3.04
Wheat	25.9	16.0	22.9	0.31	0.31	11.7	3.50
*Silages***							
Grass-legume	29.3	11.8	31.4	0.78	0.28	6.0	2.47
Corn, well-eared	27.9	8.4	26.3	0.28	0.21	4.9	3.09
*Grass hays***							
Bermuda, coastal	91.5	9.5	30.5	0.46	0.18	5.1	2.36
Fescue, tall	88.5	10.5	31.2	0.55	0.36	6.0	2.73
Orchard grass	93.5	9.1	30.1	0.58	0.16	5.8	2.51
Prairie	91.0	8.1	32.0	0.34	0.31	4.1	2.20
Timothy	88.4	8.5	33.5	0.41	0.19	4.6	2.56
*Legume hays***							
Alfalfa	90.0	18.4	29.8	1.25	0.23	12.7	2.51
Clover, ladino	91.2	23.0	19.2	1.38	0.40	14.5	2.69
Clover, red	87.7	14.9	30.1	1.61	0.22	8.9	2.60
Straw							
Barley	88.2	4.1	42.4	0.34	0.09	0.5	2.16
Wheat	90.1	3.6	41.5	0.17	0.08	0.4	2.03
Miscellaneous							
Corn cobs, ground	90.4	2.8	35.8	0.12	0.04	0.0	2.07
Cottonseed hulls	90.3	4.3	47.5	0.16	0.10	0.2	1.90

*Digestible energy, megacalories per kilogram.

** Values are based on immature stage of growth (pre-bloom or early bloom) at time of harvest; as plants mature, protein and digestible energy contents decline steadily.

Source: NRC publications.

"metabolizable energy, ME" or "net energy, NE." (As a rule of thumb, $ME = 0.95 \times DE$ in nonruminants, less in ruminants).

Gross energy (GE) represents the total energy content of a substance (the calories released from an organic substance on complete combustion, measured with a bomb calorimeter). In animal nutrition, GE of a feed minus energy lost in the feces = DE. Metabolizable energy (ME) is absorbed energy (DE) not lost in urine and sweat or as methane produced by microbial metabolism in ruminants and lost as eructated gas. Net energy (NE) represents the energy available to the animal for body maintenance and for productive functions, including growth of body tissues, egg production, milk production, wool production, and work after heat production losses are deducted from metabolizable energy (ME). Net energy (NE) value of feedstuffs is often expressed according to the productive function for which it will be used. For example, NE for maintenance is designated NEm; NE for lactation is designed NEl; NE for growth is NEg.

Earlier, total digestible nutrients (TDN) was the standard way of expressing digestible energy value of a feedstuff. This term was based on experimental data in which the digestible energy was calculated from the sum of the digestible protein, crude fiber, and soluble carbohydrates (nitrogen-free extract, calculated by difference), and of ether extract (multiplied by 2.25, to account for its 2.25 times higher calorie content than that of carbohydrate and protein). A feed with a TDN value of 80 would be considered to have a high energy value, whereas one with a TDN of 50 would be considered to have a low energy value.

The TDN system is gradually being replaced by the Van Soest detergent fiber method of energy evaluation of fibrous feeds. This method is based on the differences in solubility of fiber fractions of a feedstuff in acid or neutral detergent conditions. The Van Soest system of feed analysis takes into account the differences between plant cell wall constituents and cell contents in their utilization by animals. Cell walls contain large amounts of cellulose and lignin, whereas cell contents contain simple sugars and starches and are readily hydrolyzed to glucose by the enzymes secreted by the host's digestive system. Fibrous portions of plants (stems, leaves, seed coats) are high in cellulose. Therefore, their energy is unlocked by microbial fermentation in the rumen or large intestine to yield volatile (short-chain) fatty acids (FA). These FA are absorbed and used as energy by the animal. The Van Soest system of fibrous feed evaluation and other systems like it have had a major impact on roughage and plant fiber evaluation in animal nutrition.

Feedstuffs

A feedstuff may be defined as any component of a diet that serves some useful function. Most feedstuffs provide an array of nutrients. Ingredients may be included to provide bulk, to reduce oxidation of readily oxidized nutrients, to emulsify fats, or to provide flavor, color, or other attributes related to palatability. Feedstuffs and the diets formulated from them are the raw materials for animal production. More than 2000 feed products have been characterized for animal feeding, not counting varietal differences in various forages and grains. Most products fed to animals are either not edible for humans or are produced in excess of demand for human consumption in a given location. Because of our imperfect systems of distribution and differences in agricultural productivity, a grain or other food in surplus in the United States may be in high demand for export to other regions of the world for use in animal feeds or for human use. The conventional classes of feedstuffs and their characteristics and properties as well as special features of selected common feedstuffs within each class are described here.

The classification scheme used here is roughages (includes harvested grass, and legume forages and pasture and high-fiber byproducts of harvested crops, e.g., corn cobs and cottonseed hulls), silages, energy concentrates, protein concentrates, mineral element supplements, and vitamin supplements.

FORAGES AND ROUGHAGES. Forages and roughages are the primary feedstuffs for all herbivorous animals. The two terms are often used interchangeably. Technically, forage usually refers to the vegetative portions (leaves and stem) of a plant, whereas roughage usually refers to other fibrous parts, such as citrus pulp, beet pulp, corn cobs, soybean hulls, peanut hulls, straw, and other plant byproducts. Forages and roughages share the common property of being relatively high in fiber and low in digestible energy. Harvested and stored forages (hays, silages, and other forms) and other roughages provide energy and other nutrients for animals from plant sources of limited or no value in human nutrition. Roughages are of primary value for ruminants and for nonruminant herbivores (e.g., rabbits, horses, ponies) that depend on fermentation of insoluble carbohydrates in the gastrointestinal tract (GIT) for most of their energy supply. Other species such as swine also can utilize roughages, but with less efficiency than ruminants and other herbivores.

Roughage is bulky and has a low weight per unit of volume. Most roughages have a high fiber content and are digested less efficiently than are concentrates. Exceptions are lush young grass (whose weight per unit of volume is relatively low and fiber content relatively high, yet its fiber digestibility is high) and soybean hulls, whose high fiber content belies its high energy value for ruminants.

Most forages are provided either as harvested grass or legumes or as pasture. A wide variety of vegetation is utilized directly as pasture by herbivorous animals. In some regions, such as in the untillable grazing lands of the western United States, cattle and sheep are used to harvest native grasses. In agricultural production, cultivated species of grasses and legumes are used to improve productivity, extend the period of grazing, or improve the versatility of crop production.

TYPES OF HERBAGE USED BY GRAZING ANIMALS. Herbage used for grazing or browsing by domestic and wild animals is divided as follows:

■ Grasses are members of the family Gramineae (more than 6000 species). Based on their growth patterns and climatic adaptation, grasses are divided into cool season and warm season species. Cool season grasses make their best growth in the spring and fall; warm season grasses grow slowly in the early spring and most actively in early summer, setting seed in late summer or fall.

- Legumes are members of the family Leguminoseae (more than 14,000 species), unique in that they capture atmospheric N for use in their own growth and therefore do not need N fertilization. Through this process of "N fixation," they improve soil N fertility.

- Forbs are primarily broadleaf, nonwoody plants.

- Browses are woody plants consumed to some degree by ruminants, especially selective eaters such as deer and antelope.

Grasses. Grasses are by far the most important group of plants used in agriculture, because they include not only all of the wild and cultivated species used for grazing and forage harvesting, but also the cultivated cereal grains (e.g., barley, oats, wheat) and sorghum species. Most grass species are palatable and of high nutritional value when they are immature. Many grasses grow well in environments (except arctic regions) where herbivores can survive. Cultivated cool season and warm season grasses include perennial ryegrass, Italian ryegrass, foxtail, tall fescue, and orchard, blue, brome, Bermuda, and bahia grasses. Subtropical and tropical grasses include buffelgrass, pangola, digitgrass, napiergrass, molasses grass, and kikuyu grass. In many regions of the United States, cereal grains are used for pasture during the vegetative stage of growth. Wheat, barley, rye, and oats often can be grazed in the winter and early spring with no appreciable effect on grain yield. Several species of sorghum (e.g., Sudan grass and Johnson grass) are used for pasture or harvested forage. They are prone to be highly toxic during regrowth following drought or frost, so careful grazing management is crucial.

Legumes. Alfalfa is the most common legume used for pasture, silage, or hay in North America. It finds favor because of its high yield, persistence as a perennial crop, and high palatability and nutritive value. Other common legumes used for hay or pasture are ladino, red, white, and subterranean clover; lespedeza; lupines; and vetches. Legumes are higher than grasses in protein content, and are higher in Ca, Mg, and S than grasses, but tend to be lower in Mn and Zn.

Some legumes, notably alfalfa and clovers, are prone to cause bloat in grazing ruminants. Bloat is a life-threatening condition caused by accumulation of gases (methane and others) produced during fermentation of carbohydrates in the rumen. It results from the presence of foam-producing compounds produced by the plant that interfere with the normal process of gas eructation.

HARVESTED DRY FORAGES. In temperate and tropical regions, roughages are stored in the dry form for use during the time of the year when grazing is not available or in facilities in which animals are housed in confinement.

Hay. Grass or legume hay is grown and harvested almost exclusively for animal feeding. It is usually handled by packaging in square bales or in large round bales as shown in Figure 8-8A. The usual intent is to harvest the crop at the optimum stage of maturity so as to capture the maximum yield of nutrients without damage to the next crop. Good-quality hay requires that the water content be reduced to a point low enough to ensure that stor-

FIGURE 8-8A

Hay baler capable of producing bales weighing 650 to 2000 lb. Such bales can be surface-wrapped to preserve the hay in outdoor storage.

Source: Reprinted from Pond, Church, and Pond (1995), courtesy of John Deere & Co.

FIGURE 8-8B

Gas-tight silos for fermenting and preserving forages and high-moisture grain.

Source: Reprinted from Pond, Church, and Pond (1995), courtesy of A. O. Smith Co.

age occurs without spoilage or marked nutritional losses. The water content must be reduced to about 15% or less to achieve adequate storage properties. Moisture content of freshly harvested forage may range from 65 to 85% or more, depending on plant maturity at harvest and on species. Rapid drying, provided it is not done at excessively high temperatures, results in minimum changes in nutritional quality of the hay. Machines such as crimpers or conditioners may be used to crush the stems and hasten the drying process. Nutritive properties of hays are similar to those of the fresh forages from which they came, except for any losses induced by weather damage or method of harvesting.

Straw and Chaff. Straw consists mainly of stems and variable amounts of leaves remaining after the harvest of the seeds from cereal grains. Chaff consists of the small particles removed from the seed head and of fragments of small or broken seeds. In addition to straw and chaff from cereal grain harvest, substantial amounts may be available in some areas from the grass or legume seed industry. Straw is generally very low in digestible protein and very high in fiber and is of low feeding value by itself. However, straw may be used as the basal feed for nonpregnant or pregnant beef cattle and other ruminants when properly supplemented with protein, minerals, and vitamins, particularly vitamin A.

Other Dry Forage Byproducts. Most of the corn and cereal grains grown in the United States are harvested in the field, leaving cobs or threshed seed heads, often along with significant amounts of uncaptured and broken seeds as potentially useful products. These materials provide an otherwise wasted animal feed resource. In cotton-growing areas, cottonseed hulls and cotton gin trash are used in substantial amounts for feeding ruminants. Other useful high-fiber byproducts of the food processing industry include: pineapple greenchop, pineapple press meal, pineapple juice press cake, rice mill feed, sugarcane bagasse, sugarcane strappings, and citrus pulp.

HARVESTED HIGH-MOISTURE FORAGES

Greenchop (Soilage). This is forage that has been cut and chopped in the field and is fed to livestock without further processing. Plants used as greenchop include forage grasses and legumes, sudan grass, sorghums, corn (vegetative portion), and residues of food crops harvested for human consumption (pea and bean vines, cull vegetables).

Silage. Silage is the product of controlled fermentation of high-moisture herbage. When herbage is stored under anaerobic conditions and contains an adequate supply of fermentable carbohydrates, sufficient lactic acid is produced to stabilize the mass so that fermentation stops. If undisturbed, silage will keep for an indefinite period. High-quality silage is palatable and of high nutritional value. Most silage in the United States is made from the entire corn plant harvested at the appropriate stage of maturity, or sorghum, grass, and legume plants. Tower silos and trench (or bulk) silos for silage storage are shown in Figure 8-8B. For most crops, a dry matter content of about 35% and a soluble carbohydrate content of about 6 to 8% (dry weight basis) provide optimum conditions for silage making. In some cases, preservatives or sterilants (e.g., formic acid or sulfur dioxide) may be added. If the herbage is too high in moisture or the soluble carbohydrate content is too low, the acidity produced by fermentation will not drop to the desired pH of 4.0. Additional dry matter from sources such as corn cobs or straw may be used to reduce the moisture content, and soluble carbohydrates in the form of grain or molasses may be added to increase soluble carbohydrate into the desired range.

HIGH-ENERGY FEEDSTUFFS (CONCENTRATES). High-energy feedstuffs are added to the diet primarily to increase energy intake of the animal. They include corn, cereal grains, and some of their milling byproducts, and root crops, as well as fats. Energy from high-energy feeds is supplied primarily by soluble carbohydrates (sugars and starches) or by fat. Other nutrients (amino acids, vitamins, inorganic minerals) are provided as well by these feedstuffs, but the quantity is usually less than required by the animal, so supplementation is required. Average concentrations of some nutrients in corn and cereal grains are shown in Table 8-6.

The energy value of corn is used as a standard of comparison for other high-energy feedstuffs for cattle, swine, and poultry. Its high energy value appears to be due to the low fiber content of the corn kernel and the high digestibility of its starch.

The milling of corn and cereal grains for the production of flour, starch, and other products results in a number of byproducts of value in animal-feeding. Milling byproducts account for a significant portion of the seed. For example, byproducts from wheat account for about 25% of the weight of the kernel. The bran and middlings are fibrous materials from the outer layers of the seed; they contain higher amounts of protein and water soluble vitamins than the remaining portion of the kernel and are relatively bulky and laxative. Milling byproducts of barley, oats, and sorghum are similar to those of wheat and of comparable nutritional value.

Corn-milling byproducts are slightly different from wheat byproducts because corn is often milled for purposes other than flour production. When milled for corn meal, hominy feed is produced, consisting of bran (hulls), germ, and part of the endosperm (starch-rich central portion).

Root crops used in animal feeding, particularly in northern Europe, include turnips, beets, carrots, and parsnips. The bulky nature of these crops limits their use for nonruminants, so most are fed to cattle. A tropical root crop, cassava (also called yuca, manioc, tapioca, or mandioca) is grown in large quantities in many parts of the world and is used as an energy source for both humans and animals. Tubers such as cull potatoes are used for feeding to cattle and sheep in areas of commercial potato production.

Dried bakery products are produced from reclaimed (unused) bakery products, candy, nuts, and other pastries and fill a need as a feed energy source that would otherwise be wasted. Molasses produced as a byproduct of cane sugar and beet sugar refining is another example of an otherwise wasted food industry byproduct used in animal feeding.

Surplus animal and vegetable fats frequently are used in commercial feeds, depending on relative prices. Most feeding fats are derived from rendering of beef, swine, and poultry tissues. Adding fat at moderate levels (2 to 10%) may increase total energy intake in young early-weaned animals, but other reasons for its use are to decrease dustiness and improve pellet stability in pelleted diets.

TABLE 8-6
AVERAGE COMPOSITION OF THE MAJOR CEREAL GRAINS, DRY BASIS

Item	Corn, Dent	Opaque-2 Corn	Wheat Hard Winter	Wheat Soft Winter	Rice, with Hulls	Rye	Barley	Oats	Sorghum (Milo)
Crude protein, %	10.4	12.6	14.2	11.7	8.0	13.4	13.3	12.8	12.4
Ether extract, %	4.6	5.4	1.7	1.8	1.7	1.8	2.0	4.7	3.2
Crude fiber, %	2.5	3.2	2.3	2.1	8.8	2.6	6.3	12.2	2.7
Ash, %	1.4	1.8	2.0	1.8	5.4	2.1	2.7	3.7	2.1
NFE, %	81.3	76.9	79.8	82.6	75.6	80.1	75.7	66.6	79.6
Total sugars, %	1.9		2.9	4.1		4.5	2.5	1.5	1.5
Starch, %	72.2		63.4	67.2		63.8	64.6	41.2	70.8
Essential amino acids, % of DM									
Arginine	0.45	0.86	0.76	0.64	0.63	0.6	0.6	0.8	0.4
Histidine	0.18	0.44	0.39	0.30	0.10	0.3	0.3	0.2	0.3
Isoleucine	0.45	0.40	0.67	0.44	0.35	0.6	0.6	0.6	0.6
Leucine	0.99	1.06	1.20	0.86	0.60	0.8	0.9	1.0	1.6
Lysine	0.18	0.53	0.43	0.37	0.31	0.5	0.6	0.4	0.3
Phenylalanine	0.45	0.56	0.92	0.57	0.35	0.7	0.7	0.7	0.5
Threonine	0.36	0.41	0.48	0.37	0.25	0.4	0.4	0.4	0.3
Tryptophan	0.09	0.16	0.20		0.12	0.1	0.2	0.2	0.1
Valine	0.36	0.62	0.79	0.56	0.50	0.7	0.7	0.7	0.6
Methionine	0.09	0.17	0.21	0.19	0.20	0.2	0.2	0.2	0.1
Cystine	0.09	0.22	0.29	0.34	0.11	0.2	0.2	0.2	0.2
Minerals, % of DM									
Calcium	0.02		0.06	0.09	0.06	0.07	0.06	0.07	0.04
Phosphorus	0.33		0.45	0.34	0.45	0.38	0.35	0.30	0.30
Potassium	0.33		0.57	0.44	0.25	0.52	0.63	0.42	0.39
Magnesium	0.12		0.11	0.11	0.11	0.13	0.14	0.19	0.22

Source: NRC (1982) and several NRC publications on the Nutrient Requirements of Domestic Animals.

HIGH-PROTEIN FEEDSTUFFS (CONCENTRATES). High-protein feedstuffs (protein concentrates or supplements) are more expensive than high-energy feedstuffs, so adequate but not excessive levels are important in formulating diets. Protein supplements (generally greater than 20% crude protein) are available from a wide variety of plant and animal sources. In addition, nonprotein N sources such as urea and ammonium phosphates are available from commercial synthetic chemical manufacturing processes. Table 8-7 contains information on the composition of several common plant and animal protein supplements. Protein supplements of animal origin are derived from inedible tissues from meat packing or rendering plants, from surplus milk or milk byproducts, or from marine sources. Meat-packing byproducts include meat meal, blood meal, hair and feather meals; milk products include dried skim and whole milk and dried whey; fish

TABLE 8-7

COMPOSITION OF SEVERAL IMPORTANT PROTEIN SUPPLEMENTS

Item	Alfalfa, Dehy.	Dried Skim Milk	Meat Meal[a]	Fish Meal, Herring	Feather Meal	Cottonseed Meal, Sol. Ext.[b]	Soybean Meal, Sol. Ext.[b]	Brewers Grains, Dehy.[c]
Dry matter, %	93.1	94.3	88.5	93.0	91.0	91.0	89.1	92.0
Other components, %[d]								
Crude protein	22.1	36.0	55.0	77.4	93.9	45.5	52.4	28.1
Fat	3.9	1.1	8.0	13.6	2.6	1.0	1.3	6.7
Fiber	21.7	0.3	2.5	0.6	0.0	14.2	5.9	16.3
Ash	11.1	8.5	21.0	11.5	3.5	7.0	6.6	3.9
Ca	1.63	1.3	8.0	2.2	0.4	0.2	0.3	0.29
P	0.29	1.09	4.0	1.7	0.5	1.1	0.7	0.54
Essential amino acids								
Arginine	0.97	1.23	3.0	4.5	6.9	4.6	3.8	1.4
Cystine		0.48	0.4	0.9	4.1	0.7	0.8	
Histidine	0.43	0.96	0.9	1.6	0.6	1.1	1.4	0.5
Isoleucine	0.86	2.45	1.7	3.5	4.8	1.3	2.8	1.6
Leucine	1.61	3.51	3.2	5.7	8.7	2.4	4.3	2.5
Lysine	0.97	2.73	2.6	6.2	2.0	1.7	3.4	1.0
Methionine	0.32	0.96	0.8	2.3	0.6	0.5	0.7	0.4
Phenylalanine	1.18	1.60	1.8	3.1	4.8	2.2	2.8	1.4
Threonine	0.97	1.49	1.8	3.2	5.1	1.3	2.2	1.0
Tryptophan	0.54	0.45	0.5	0.9	0.7	0.5	0.7	0.4
Valine	0.11	2.34	2.2	4.1	7.8	1.9	2.8	1.7

[a]Meat meal from ruminants cannot be fed to ruminants because of recent reports linking certain nervous system diseases in humans (Creutzfeldt-Jakob disease) to bovine spongiform encephalopathy (BSE, "mad cow disease") in cattle in Europe.

[b]Solvent extracted.

[c]Dehydrated.

[d]Composition on dry basis.

Source: NRC (1982) and several NRC publications on the nutrient requirements of domestic animals.

products include fish meal consisting of organs and tissues from an array of fish species or other marine species. Generally, animal protein supplements are higher in protein, vitamins, and inorganic mineral elements than plant protein supplements.

The most important plant protein supplement is soybean meal, the byproduct of soybean oil production. Other important commercial sources of plant protein supplements are cottonseed meal, and the residue from fat extraction of peanuts, flax (linseed), sunflower, sesame, safflower, and rapeseed (canola). As a group, the oilseed meals contain 40% or more of crude protein. Most meals are relatively deficient in the essential S-containing amino acids, methionine and cystine. Other plant protein supplements include coconut (copra) meal, and the legume seeds, field beans, field peas, and other legumes. Most of these legumes contain 20 to 30% crude protein.

As the world population continues to expand, protein supplies are becoming more critical and efforts continue to identify and develop additional sources for use in animal feeding. Potential sources include animal wastes, seaweed, and single-cell protein products such as algae, bacteria, and yeasts. In addition, new and underutilized plant resources not previously exploited for feed production are being examined and evaluated for future use.

Ruminant animals, because of microbial populations residing in the rumen, do not require large amounts of preformed dietary protein. Nonprotein sources of N, less expensive than intact protein, are widely used in cattle and sheep feeding. The most common nonprotein N (NPN) source is urea. Other NPN compounds available for use are ammonium salts such as ammonium phosphate. The rumen microflora use the ammonia released from NPN for incorporation into amino acids for their own protein synthesis; the host animal, in turn, uses these microbially synthesized amino acids to satisfy its own requirement.

Vitamin and Mineral Supplementation

Nearly all feedstuffs contain some vitamins and minerals, but their concentrations vary widely among plant species and plant parts, and, in the case of animal sources of vitamins, among specific tissues and organs. Generally, animal tissues are higher than plant sources in most vitamins. Vitamin concentrations in plants are affected by harvesting, processing, and storage conditions. Some vitamins are destroyed by heat, others by sunlight or by oxidizing conditions or storage conditions that support mold growth. With current technology, the vitamins are commercially synthesized and are available in pure form at relatively low cost. Therefore, it is customary for complete mixed diets to contain pure sources of supplemental vitamins to ensure their adequacy in the diet.

As in the case of vitamins, nearly all feedstuffs contain some minerals, but often the level present is below the requirement of the animal. Therefore, mineral supplementation is required. Minerals of most concern include common salt (NaCl), Ca, P, Mg, S, Cu, Fe, I, Mn, and Zn, and in some geographic areas, Co and Se. To ensure adequate macro- and trace mineral intakes, mineral supplements normally are added to the mixed diet or offered as a separate supplement available free-choice. Common mineral supplements used in animal diets and the amounts of Ca and P they supply are shown in Table 8-8.

TABLE 8-8
CALCIUM AND PHOSPHORUS CONTENT OF COMMON MINERAL SUPPLEMENTS (IN PERCENT)

Supplement	Calcium	Phosphorus
Bone meal, raw	21	9–10
Bone meal, steamed	24–29	12–14
Bone black, spent	27	12
Dicalcium phosphate	23–26	18–21
Defluorinated rock phosphate[a]	31–34	13–17
Raw-rock phosphate[b]	24–29	13–15
Soft phosphate[a]	18	9
Curaçao phosphate[a]	35	15
Oyster shell	38	—
Limestone	38	—
Calcite, high grade	34	—
Gypsum	22	—
Dolomite limestone	22	—
Wood ashes	21	—

[a]Usually less than 0.2% F.

[b]2.0–4.0% F.

Feed Additives

In addition to the nutrients contained in feedstuffs used in diet formulation, many non-nutritive additives are used to improve performance. Only additives approved by the U.S. Food and Drug Administration based on their safety and efficacy can be used in animal feeds. Currently used additives include antibiotics, arsenicals, and nitrofuran compounds, all of which have been shown to improve animal performance (growth, feed utilization, or some other productive function). Antibiotics are compounds produced by one microorganism that inhibit the growth of another organism. Chlortetracycline, oxytetracycline, and bacitracin have been used most widely, but new antibiotics continue to be introduced for approval after careful testing. Arsenicals and nitrofurans are used primarily for swine and poultry. When used for growth promotion, these antimicrobial agents are added to feed at low levels, much below therapeutic levels used to cure infectious diseases. The beneficial effects of antibiotics on growth and efficiency of feed utilization when added to the diet of growing pigs are illustrated in Table 8-9. These results have continued to be impressive over the entire span of nearly 50 years of use.

Other types of antibiotics, monensin and lasalocid, are produced by various strains of streptomyces bacteria and are used widely in beef cattle. They are referred to as ionophore antibiotics because they interfere with the passage of ions through cell membranes. These substances were used first in poultry to prevent coccidiosis, a highly devastating disease of poultry.

Other feed additives include zeolites, naturally occurring aluminosilicate compounds with cation exchange properties that may be useful in improving animal performance.

TABLE 8-9

EFFECTS OF DIETARY ANTIBIOTICS
ON GROWTH PROMOTION OF PIGS

Stage	Control	Antibiotic	Improvement (%)
Starter phase (7–25 kg)			
Daily gain (kg)	0.39	0.45	16.4
Feed gain	2.28	2.13	6.9
Growing phase (17–49 kg)			
Daily gain (kg)	0.59	0.66	10.6
Feed/gain	2.91	2.78	4.5
Growing-finishing phase			
(24–89 kg)			
Daily gain (kg)	0.69	0.72	4.2
Feed/gain	3.30	3.23	2.2

Data from 453, 298, and 443 experiments, involving 13,632, 5783, and 13,140 pigs for the three phases, respectively.
Source: Cromwell (1991), adapted from Hays (1977) and Zimmerman (1986).

Zeolites, formed from volcanic eruptions, are common in many parts of the world. They are only now being seriously tested for their biological properties. Other types of additives include digestive enzymes such as pepsin and trypsin, plant enzymes such as phytases to improve dietary P availability, and flavoring agents intended to improve feed palatability and intake. The cost of such additives must always be weighed against the expected benefits in decision making in diet formulation.

SUMMARY

Animal life requires an adequate supply of food from a variety of sources. Whereas plants thrive with only a source of nitrogen, carbon dioxide, water, inorganic minerals and sunlight for photosynthesis, animals depend on plants to supply many of the dietary factors that are synthesized by plants. Nutrients are the substances that animals require in their diet because they are unable to synthesize them in their own body tissues. The broad classes of nutrients are: water, proteins and their constituent amino acids, carbohydrates, lipids (fats), vitamins, and inorganic mineral elements. Carbohydrates and lipids (and proteins under some conditions) provide energy, measured in calories (or joules), to carry out all life processes. This chapter describes the nature and functions of each nutrient (there are more than a dozen vitamins and more than two dozen inorganic mineral elements known to be required in the diet of most animal species) followed by an overview of nutrient metabolism. The structure and functions of the gastrointestinal tract are described and compared among the various animal species. Animals with a complex stomach (ruminants) have fewer nutrient requirements and a different structure and function of the gastrointestinal tract than do nonruminant animals. Birds differ in digestive anatomy and physiology from mammals, and herbivores (animals that eat only plant products) differ from omnivores (those that eat both plant and animal products) and carnivores (those that eat only animal products). The processes of digestion and absorption of nutrients and some of the factors that affect the amount of feed consumed and its utilization are described. Finally, the vast array of available feed resources is sketched and the concepts of feedstuff processing, diet formulation, and feeding are addressed. Feed costs represent 50 to 80% or more of the total costs of the animal production enterprise. Therefore, efficient and wise use of feed resources and adequate nutrition are vital to prosperous animal production and adequate human nutrition. The dependence of animal production on an adequate feed supply and the interdependence of plants and animals and the human population are fundamental to environmental stability.

GLOSSARY[3]

A significant number of the terms defined in this glossary have been taken directly from the glossary on pp. 499–510 of *Principles of Nutrition* by E. D. Wilson, K. H. Fisher, and M. E. Fuqua, 3rd ed., 1975, John Wiley and Sons, Inc., New York. In addition to the terms given, the reader interested in feed terms is directed to Appendix Glossary 1, Bulletin 479, by L. E. Harris, J. M. Asplund, and E. W. Crampton, Utah Agricultural Experiment Station, Utah State University, Logan, UT (1968).

Abomasum   The fourth compartment of the ruminant stomach; it functions similarly to the true stomach of nonruminant animals and is the most important compartment in the young ruminant.

Active transport   The movement of substances (particularly electrolyte ions) across cell membranes, usually against a concentration gradient. Unlike diffusion or osmosis, active transport requires the expenditure of metabolic energy.

Adenine   One of four nitrogenous bases found in DNA.

Adenosine triphosphatase (ATPase)   An enzyme in muscle that catalyzes the hydrolysis of the terminal phosphate group of adenine triphosphate.

Adenosine triphosphate (ATP)   A compound that consists of one molecule each of adenine (a purine) and ribose (a five-carbon atom sugar) and three molecules of phosphoric acid; it is required for energy transfer and the phosphorylation of compounds.

ADF   Acid detergent fiber, the fraction of a feedstuff analyzed by the Van Soest scheme of detergent analysis used to divide carbohydrates in plant constituents into those highly available and those poorly available to animals; ADF content of a feed reflects the amounts of carbohydrates not solubilized by acid detergent.

Adrenaline   See Epinephrine.

Albumin   A group of globular proteins; a major constituent of blood serum protein.

Amine   A chemical compound formed from ammonia (NH_3) by replacement of one or more of the hydrogen atoms with hydrocarbon groups (—CH_3 or —C_2H_5 and others).

---

[3] *Source:* Adapted from Pond, Church, and Pond (1995).

Amino acids   The simplest organic structure of which proteins are formed; many different amino acids occur in nature of which about 10 (for most animals) are required in the diet; all have common property of containing a carboxyl group and an amino group on the adjacent C atom.

Amino group   A chemical structure, —NH$_2$; a constituent of all amino acids, attached to the C atom adjacent to the carboxyl group.

Anemia   A deficiency in the blood of red cells, hemoglobin, or both.

Hyperchromic anemia: A decrease in hemoglobin that is proportionately much less than the decrease in the number of erythrocytes (where the color index is high).

Hypochromic anemia: A decrease in hemoglobin that is proportionately much greater than the decrease in the number of erythrocytes (where the color index is low).

Macrocytic anemia: A condition in which the erythrocytes are much larger than normal.

Megaloblastic anemia: A condition in which there are megaloblasts in the bone marrow.

Microcytic anemia: An anemia in which the erythrocytes are smaller than normal.

Nutritional anemia: Hypochromic and microcytic anemia resulting from insufficient Fe, Cu, vitamin B12, or other causes.

Antagonist   A substance that exerts a nullifying or opposing action to another substance.

Antibody   A protein produced by the body in response to the presence of a foreign agent (antigen). Antibodies are part of the body's natural defense against invasion by foreign substances.

Antigen: Any substance not normally present in the body that produces an immune reaction upon introduction into the body.

Antioxidant   A substance that inhibits the oxidation of other compounds.

Antivitamin   A substance that interferes with the synthesis or metabolism of a vitamin.

Anus   The distal opening of the gastrointestinal tract through which undigested feed residues are excreted as feces.

Appetite   A desire for food or water; generally a long-term phenomenon, in contrast to short-term satiety.

Arachidonic acid   A 20-carbon atom fatty acid with four double bonds; in the body it is synthesized from the essential fatty acid linoleic acid.

Ascorbic acid (vitamin C)   A water-soluble vitamin required in oxidation—reduction reactions (electron transport) and for normal tyrosine oxidation and collagen metabolism and in hydroxylation reactions (i.e., hydroxyproline from proline).

Ash   The residue remaining after complete combustion at 500 to 600 °C of a feed or animal tissue or excreta during proximate analysis.

Atherosclerosis   A condition in which the inner walls of the arteries have been thickened by deposits of plaques of lipid substances including cholesterol.

Basal metabolic rate   The basal metabolism expressed as kilocalories per unit of body size (square meter of body surface; weight to the three-fourths power ([W$^{0.75}$]).

Basal metabolism   The energy expenditure of the body at rest, under comfortable environmental conditions, and in the postabsorptive state (12 h after the ingestion of food).

Beriberi   A deficiency disease caused by an insufficient intake of thiamin and characterized by polyneuritis, edema (in some cases), emaciation, and cardiac disturbances (enlargement of the heart and an unusually rapid heartbeat).

Beta-adrenergic agonist   A structural analog of epinephrine or norepinephrine that increases skeletal muscle growth and decreases fat deposition in an animal when added to its diet. Examples are cimaterol, clenbuterol, and raptopamine.

Bile   A secretion from the liver, containing metabolites such as cholesterol and important bile acid conjugates that aid in emulsification of fats for digestion and absorption.

Bile duct   The tube carrying bile from the liver to the duodenal lumen.

Biopsy   The removal and examination of tissue

or other material from the living body, usually for diagnosis.

Biotechnology   Any technique that uses living organisms or processes to make or modify products, to improve plants or animals, or to develop microorganisms for specific uses.

Biotin   A water-soluble vitamin required as a constituent of several enzymes related to energy and amino acid metabolism.

BMR   Basal metabolic rate.

Bolus   The solid mass of ingesta regurgitated for remastication during rumination. (Secondary: a medicant or capsule administered orally in a discrete mass.)

BST (bovine somatotropin)   Growth hormone from cattle; recombinant DNA–derived BST is available in large amounts and has been approved for use in lactating dairy cattle to increase milk production.

Calcitonin (thyrocalcitonin)   A polypeptide secreted by the thyroid glands that lowers the level of calcium and phosphorus in the plasma.

Calcium (Ca)   A mineral required as a structural component of the skeleton and for controlling excitability of nerve and muscle.

Calorimeter   The equipment used to measure the heat generated in a system. In nutrition it is an instrument for measuring the amount of heat produced by a food on oxidation or by an individual.

Carboxyl group   The chemical structure—C—OH

$$\parallel$$
$$O$$

a constituent of all amino acids and the characteristic group of all organic acids.

Carboxypeptidase   A proteolytic digestive enzyme secreted by the pancreas; hydrolyzes peptides to amino acids.

Cartilage   A connective tissue characterized by nonvascularity (without blood vessels) and firm texture; consists of cells (chondrocytes), interstitial substance (matrix), and a ground substance (chondromucoid).

Cassava   A tropical plant of the spurge family with edible starchy roots.

Catalyst   A substance that either increases or decreases the rate of a particular chemical reaction without itself being consumed or permanently altered; enzymes are special chemical catalysts of biological origin.

Catecholamine   Any of a group of sympathomimetic amines, including dopamine, epinephrine, and norepinephrine, that affect heart rate, blood pressure, and other physiological functions.

Cecum   A blind pouch just distal to the small intestine and containing a large population of anaerobic bacteria that ferment complex carbohydrates; appendix in humans corresponds loosely with a rudimentary cecum.

Cellulose   A polymer of glucose in linkage resistant to hydrolysis by digestive enzymes.

Ceruloplasmin   A copper-containing protein (an alpha-globulin) in blood plasma.

Chlorine (C1)   A mineral required in regulation of extracellular osmotic pressure and in maintaining acid–base balance.

Cholecystokinin   A hormone secreted by duodenal cells and perhaps by certain brain cells; release stimulated by fat in lumen of duodenum and perhaps by concentrations of metabolites in blood circulating in brain; causes gall bladder contraction and may exert short-term effect on food intake.

Cholic acid   A family of steroids comprising the bile acids; they are derived from cholesterol.

Choline   A water-soluble vitamin required as a structural component of tissues (i.e., lecithin, sphingomyelin) and of acetylcholine and as a donor of labile methyl groups; there is no evidence for a role as a cofactor in enzymatic reactions.

Chromium (Cr)   A trace mineral required as trivalent ion for normal glucose metabolism.

Chylomicron   A particle of emulsified fat present in lymph; they are especially numerous after a meal high in fat content.

Chyme   A semiliquid material produced by the

action of gastric juice on ingested food; it is discharged from the stomach into the duodenum.

Chymotrypsin A proteolytic digestive enzyme secreted by the pancreas.

Cirrhosis of the liver A progressive destruction of the liver cells and an abnormal increase of connective tissue.

Citric acid cycle The major series of pathways through which carbohydrates are oxidized to produce energy in animal cells.

Cobalt (Co) A trace mineral required as a constituent of vitamin B12.

Coenzyme An organic molecule that is required for the activation of an apoenzyme to an enzyme. The vitamin coenzymes are niacin, pyridoxine, thiamin, riboflavin, pantothenic acid, and folic acid.

Coenzyme A A complex molecule containing pantothenic acid; it is required for fatty acid oxidation and synthesis and for the synthesis of cholesterol and phospholipids; it combines with acetate to form acetyl coenzyme A (active acetate), which in turn combines with oxaloacetate to form citrate and enter the tricarboxylic acid cycle.

Collagen A group of fibrous proteins: resistant to digestive enzymes, prevalent in muscle from aged animals; become gelatin on acid or alkaline hydrolysis.

Colon The large intestine, distal to the cecum and small intestine; contains a large population of anaerobic bacteria that ferment complex carbohydrates, which may represent a significant energy contribution in some animals.

Convulsion An involuntary spasm or contraction of muscles.

Copper (Cu) A trace mineral required for normal red blood cell formation, apparently by allowing normal iron metabolism, and as a component of several oxidases involved in normal wool and hair growth.

Creatine A nonprotein nitrogenous substance in muscle; it combines with phosphate to form phosphocreatine, which serves as a storage form of high-energy phosphate required for muscle contraction.

Creatinine A nitrogenous compound that is formed as a metabolic end product of creatine; creatinine is produced in the muscle, passes into the blood, and is excreted in the urine.

Crude fiber The insoluble carbohydrates remaining in a feed after boiling in acid and alkali during proximate analysis; this fraction represents the poorly digested part of a feed by animals.

Crude protein The content of nitrogen in a feed or animal tissue or excreta, multiplied by a factor (usually 6.25, since most proteins contain about 16% N) to provide an estimate of protein content; both nonprotein N (amino acids, amines, ammonia, etc.) and true protein may be present.

Cud The solid mass of ingesta regurgitated and masticated in the process of rumination.

Cyanocobalamin (B12) A water-soluble vitamin required as a coenzyme in several enzymes, including isomerases, dehydrases, and enzymes involved in methionine biosynthesis.

Cystine A sulfur-containing, nonessential amino acid that occurs notably in keratin and insulin; in the diet, it exerts a sparing effect on methionine.

Cytosine One of four nitrogenous bases found in DNA.

Deamination The removal of the amino group from a compound.

Degradation The conversion of a chemical compound to one that is less complex.

Dehydrogenase Any of a class of enzymes found in plant and animal tissues that catalyze oxidation by the transference of hydrogen ions to hydrogen acceptors.

Diabetes mellitus A disease characterized by elevated blood sugar (hyperglycemia), sugar in the urine (glucosuria), excessive urination (polyuria), increased appetite (polyphagia), and general weakness.

Diet A regulated selection or mixture of feedstuffs or foodstuffs provided on a continuous or prescribed schedule; a balanced diet supplies all nutrients needed for normal health and productive functions.

Digestibility, apparent That percentage of a

feed nutrient that is apparently digested and absorbed from the gastrointestinal tract, as indicated by intake minus fecal output of the nutrient; differs from true digestibility in that feces contain endogenously derived as well as feed-derived nutrients, so true digestibility must be estimated indirectly by feeding a diet devoid of the nutrient of concern.

Digestibility, true   See apparent digestibility.

Disaccharide   A dimer of simple sugars: sucrose (common cane or beet sugar) yields glucose and fructose.

Diuresis   The excretion of urine; commonly denotes production of unusually large volumes of urine.

Diuretic   A substance that promotes the excretion of urine; diuretic drugs are used chiefly to rid the body of excess fluid.

Dopamine   See catecholamine.

Dry matter   That portion of a feed or tissue remaining after water is removed, usually expressed as a percentage.

Duodenum   The upper part of small intestine, into which empty the secretions of the exocrine pancreas and liver bile.

Edema   An abnormal accumulation of fluid in the intercellular spaces of the body.

Elastin   A group of fibrous proteins; similar to collagen but not converted to gelatin; a major constituent of tendons and cartilage.

Electrolyte   Any substance that, when in solution, dissociates into charged particles (ions) capable of conducting an electrical current.

Emaciation   Excessive leanness; a wasted condition of the body.

Endemic   A disease of low morbidity that persists over a long period of time in a certain region.

Endocrine   Pertains to internal secretions; endocrine glands are those that produce one or more internal secretions (hormones) that enter directly into the blood and affect metabolic processes.

Endogenous   Produced within or caused by factors within the organism.

Enterocrinin   A hormone secreted by jejunal cells; release perhaps stimulated by food digestion products; stimulates secretion of intestinal fluids and enzymes.

Enterogastrone   A hormone secreted by duodenal cells; release is stimulated by fat and fatty acids and bile in the lumen of the duodenum; inhibits gastric secretion and motility.

Epinephrine   The adrenal medulla hormone that stimulates autonomic nerve action; increases heart rate, perspiration.

Ergosterol   A sterol found chiefly in plant tissues; on exposure to ultraviolet irradiation, it becomes vitamin D.

Eructation   Belching of gas by ruminants as a normal means of expelling products of fermentation such as carbon dioxide and methane.

Erythrocyte   Red blood cell.

Erythropoiesis   The formation of erythrocytes.

Esophageal groove   A muscular structure at the lower end of the esophagus that, when closed, forms a tube from the esophagus to the omasum; functions in suckling animals to allow milk to bypass the reticulorumen and escape bacterial fermentation.

Ether extract   The fraction of a feed or animal tissue that is soluble in a fat solvent, such as ethyl ether, and removed by extraction during proximate analysis.

Exogenous   Originating outside or caused by factors outside the body.

Fatty acids   Organic acids, composed of carbon, hydrogen, and oxygen, that combine with glycerol to form fat.

Feces   The excretory product of undigested feed residues plus endogenously produced digestive secretions, sloughed cells of the intestinal lining, and metabolites reexcreted into the intestinal lumen in the bile from the liver.

Ferritin   The form in which iron is stored in the body; it is an iron–protein complex made up of iron and the protein apoferritin.

Fistula   An abnormal passage from an abscess, cavity, or hollow organ to the surface or from one abscess, cavity, or organ to another.

Fluorine (F)   A trace mineral required for protection against dental caries.

Fluorosis (dental)   A mottled discoloration of the enamel of the teeth caused by chronic ingestion of excessive amounts of fluorine.

Folacin (folic acid)   A water-soluble vitamin required as a cofactor in a variety of metabolic reactions involving incorporation of single-C units into large molecules.

Folic acid   See Folacin.

Fortification   The addition of one or more nutrients to a food in amounts so that the total amount will be larger than that contained in any natural (unprocessed) food of its class, for example, the fortification of fruit juices with vitamin C; the FDA has not established standards for fortification.

Galactosemia   The accumulation of galactose in the blood resulting from a genetic lack of the enzyme galactose-1-phosphate uridyl transferase, which is necessary for the conversion of galactose to glucose; it is characterized by vomiting and diarrhea, abdominal distension, enlargement of the liver, and mental retardation.

Gastrin   A hormone secreted by intestinal cells near the pylorus; release is stimulated by distension and movement of the stomach; stimulates acid secretion by gastric glands in the stomach.

Globulin   A group of globular proteins; alpha-, beta-, and gamma-globulins are major constituents of blood serum protein.

Glossitis   Inflammation of the tongue.

Glucagon   A compound secreted by the alpha cells of the islets of Langerhans that is hyperglycemic (produces a rise in the blood glucose concentration), is glycogenolytic (hydrolyzes glycogen to glucose), and stimulates gluconeogenesis.

Gluconeogenesis (glyconeogenesis)   The formation of glucose from noncarbohydrate sources, chiefly certain amino acids and the glycerol portion of the fat molecule.

Glucose tolerance test   A test indicating the efficiency of the body in its use of glucose; changes are noted in the concentration of glucose in the blood at determined intervals after ingestion of a standard amount of sugar.

Glutelins   A group of globular proteins.

Glyceride   A compound (ester) formed by the combination of glycerol and fatty acids and the loss of water (the ester linkage); according to the number of ester linkages, the compound is a mono-, di-, or triglyceride.

Glycerol (glycerin)   The three-carbon atom alcohol derived from the hydrolysis of fat.

Glycogenesis   The formation of glycogen from glucose.

Glycolysis   The conversion of glucose to lactic acid in various tissues, notably muscle; since molecular oxygen is not consumed in the process, it is referred to as "anaerobic glycolysis."

Goitrin   The antithyroid, or goitrogenic, compound obtained from turnips and the seeds of cruciferous plants.

Gram (g)   A metric unit of weight that is equivalent to about 1/28 of an ounce (1 oz = 28.4 g), 1/1000 of a kilogram, or 1000 milligrams.

Growth factors   A group of specific substances elaborated by cells that have trophic effects on growth and differentiation of cells, tissues, and organs. Examples are EGF (epidermal growth factor), FGF (fibroblast growth factor), IGF (insulin-like growth factor), and NGF (nerve growth factor).

Guanine   One of four nitrogenous bases found in DNA.

Hematocrit   The volume percentage of erythrocytes in whole blood; it is determined by centrifuging a blood sample to separate the cellular elements from the plasma; the results of the test indicate the ratio of cell volume to plasma volume and are expressed as cubic millimeters of packed cells per 100 mL of blood.

Hematopoiesis   The production of various types of blood cells and blood platelets.

Heme   The nonprotein, insoluble pigment portion of the hemoglobin molecule; the prosthetic group of the hemoglobin molecule.

High-energy bonds (energy-rich bonds) The pyrophosphate bonds; on hydrolysis they yield a standard free energy near -8000 kcal per molecule, whereas simple phosphate bonds on hydrolysis yield only -1000 to -4000 kcal of standard free energy.

Histones A group of globular proteins.

Homeostasis The tendency of the body to maintain uniformity or stability in its internal environment or fluid matrix.

Homeothermal (homothermal) Warm-blooded animals.

Hunger Desire for food; the antithesis of satiety.

Hydrogenation The addition of hydrogen to a compound, especially to an unsaturated fat or fatty acid; adding hydrogen at the double bond solidifies soft fats or oils.

Hydrolysis A chemical process whereby a compound is broken down into simpler units with the uptake of water.

Hypoglycemia A condition characterized by a lower than normal level of glucose in the blood.

Hypomagnesemia An abnormally low magnesium content of the blood plasma.

Hypothalamus A portion of the brain, lying beneath the thalamus at the base of the cerebrum, and forming the floor and part of the walls of the third ventricle; it contains centers for temperature regulation, appetite control, and others.

IGF See Growth Factors and Insulin-like growth factors.

Ileum The lower part of the small intestine, distal to the jejunum and proximal to the large intestine; absorption of most nutrients occurs in the jejunum and ileum.

Immunoglobulin (Ig) A serum globulin having antibody activity; most of the antibody activity appears to be in the gamma fraction of globulin.

Inorganic Compounds that do not contain carbon.

Insulin A hormone secreted by the beta cells of the islets of Langerhans of the pancreas; it facilitates glucose oxidation, as well as the synthesis of glycogen, fat, and protein.

Insulin-like growth factors (IGF-I and IGF-II) A class of polypeptides, produced by most or all cells in the body, that are involved in cellular differentiation and multiplication. Their paracrine and endocrine roles in fetal and postnatal development and in adult metabolism are related to insulin and somatotropin action and perhaps other hormones and are modulated by several binding proteins whose functions are not well understood.

Interferon A family of glycoproteins, the production of which is stimulated by viral, bacterial, and parasitic infections, or by bacterial endotoxins. Interferons exert antiviral activity and have immunoregulatory functions.

Interleukin A generic name for a group of proteins produced by leukocytes in response to antigenic or mitogenic stimulation. Some interleukins are used as anticancer drugs.

Interstitial Relates to space in any structure, such as tissue.

Intestinal peptidase A group of poly-, tri-, and dipeptide digestive enzymes secreted by epithelial cells in the small intestine.

Intolerance An allergy or sensitivity, for example, to certain foods or medicines.

Intrinsic factor A transferase enzyme (mucoprotein) secreted by the mucosal cells of the stomach which is required for the absorption of vitamin B12 through the intestinal wall; a lack of this factor will produce pernicious anemia.

Iodine (I) A trace mineral required as a constituent of thyroxine.

Ionophore Any molecule, as of a drug or xenobiotic, that increases the permeability of cell membranes to a specific ion.

Iron (Fe) A trace mineral required for hemoglobin and myoglobin formation as a constituent of several heme enzymes and of several nonheme metalloenzymes.

Isomer A compound having the same percentage composition and molecular weight as another compound but differing in chemical or physical properties; for example, L (levorotary) amino acids are biologically active but D (dextrorotary) amino acids generally are not (see also Racemic mixture).

Isotope One of two or more atoms, the nuclei of which have the same number of protons but different numbers of neutrons; for example, ^{14}N and ^{15}N are both stable isotopes of nitrogen.

Jejunum The middle segment of the small intestine, distal to the duodenum and proximal to the ileum; absorption of most nutrients occurs in the jejunum and ileum.

Joule (J) A unit of energy that is equal to 0.0002 kcal.

kcal See Kilocalorie.

Keratin A group of fibrous proteins; resistant to digestive enzyme; a major constituent of skin, hooves, and horns.

Krebs cycle See Citric acid cycle.

Ketogenic That which is conducive to the formation of ketone bodies, such as a high-fat, low-carbohydrate diet.

α-Ketoglutaric acid A compound that is common to the metabolic pathways of carbohydrates, fats, and certain amino acids.

Ketone A chemical compound that contains the carbonyl group (CO); ketone bodies include betahydroxybutyric acid, acetoacetic acid, and acetone.

Kilocalorie (kcal) The quantity of heat required to raise the temperature of 1 kg of water 1 °C (or, more precisely, from 15 °C to 16 °C).

Kilogram (kg) A metric unit of weight that is equivalent to 2.2 pounds, or 1000 grams.

Kwashiorkor A disease of infants and young children, caused primarily by protein deficiency; it is characterized by edema, "pot belly," and pigmentation changes of skin and hair.

Lactic acid A compound formed in the body during anaerobic glycolysis; it is also produced in milk by the bacterial fermentation of lactose.

Lactoferrin An iron-binding protein found in milk, saliva, tears, and intestinal and respiratory secretions; it interferes with iron metabolism of bacteria and may play a role in infectious disease resistance and in the growth of cells of the intestinal mucosa.

Lecithin The traditional term for phosphatidylcholine.

Leucine An essential amino acid.

Lignin A biologically unavailable mixture of polymers of phenolic acids; it is a major structural component of mature plants and of trees; its presence affects the bioavailability of cellulose and hemicellulose in plants.

Linoleic acid The essential fatty acid; it is unsaturated; and occurs widely in plant glycerides.

Lipids Substances that are diverse in chemical nature but soluble in fat solvents (such as ethanol, ether, chloroform, benzene); lipids include fats and oils; phospholipids, glycolipids, and lipoproteins; fatty acids, alcohols (glycerol, sterols [including vitamin D and vitamin A], and carotenoids).

Liver A large internal organ of the body, which lies in the upper right section of the abdomen directly beneath the diaphragm. Among other things, it produces bile, glycogen, and antibodies; interconverts proteins, carbohydrates, and fats; stores iron, copper, and vitamins A and D; and detoxifies harmful substances.

Lymph A fluid that circulates within the lymphatic vessels and is eventually added to the venous blood circulation; it arises from tissue fluid and from intestinal absorption of fatty acids; it is colorless, odorless, slightly alkaline, and slightly opalescent.

Lymphatic system All of the vessels and structures that carry lymph from the tissues to the blood.

Lysine An essential amino acid.

Malnutrition An overall term for poor nourishment; it may be due to an inadequate diet or to some defect in metabolism that prevents the body from using the nutrients properly.

Magnesium (Mg) A mineral required as a constituent of bone, for oxidative phosphorylation of mitochondria of cells, activation of numerous energy-related enzymes.

Manganese (Mn) A trace mineral required for formation of chondroitin sulfate and as a component of metalloenzymes and as a cofactor in several enzymes.

Marasmus Extreme emaciation resulting from insufficient food.

Megaloblast A large, nucleated, embryonic type of cell; it is found in the blood in cases of pernicious anemia, vitamin B12 deficiency, and folacin deficiency.

Metabolic pool The total amount of a specific substance in the body that is in a state of active turnover, such as the amino acid pool or vitamin D pool; subtractions from and additions to the pool are constantly being made.

Metabolic size The body weight raised to the three-fourths power ($W^{0.75}$).

Metabolite Any compound produced during metabolism.

Metalloenzyme An enzyme containing a metal (ion) as an integral part of its active structure.

Methane (CH_4) A major product of anaerobic fermentation of carbohydrates in the rumen; its loss through eructation represents a significant reduction in available dietary energy to the ruminant.

Methionine A sulfur-containing essential amino acid.

Microgram (μg) A metric unit of weight that is equivalent to one-millionth of a gram or 1/1000 milligram.

Micelle An aggregate of molecules of lipids and bile acids formed in the lumen of the gastrointestinal tract during preparation of dietary lipids for absorption.

Milligram (mG) A metric unit of weight that is equivalent to 1/1000 gram or 1000 micrograms.

Milliliter (mL) A metric unit of liquid measure that is equivalent to 1/1000 liter.

Millimeter (mm) A metric unit of length that is equivalent to 1/10 centimeter.

Miscarriage The spontaneous expulsion of the product of conception early in pregnancy.

Mitochondria The largest organelles in the cytoplasm; the cell mitochondria contain important enzymatic, oxidative, and respiratory systems.

Molecular weight The weight of a molecule of a chemical compound as compared with the weight of an atom of hydrogen; it is equal to the sum of the weights of the constituent atoms.

Molybdenum (Mo) A trace mineral required as a constituent of the metalloenzyme, xanthine oxidase.

Monogastric Simple stomach; the term is often used for simple stomached (nonruminant) animals; technically it is a misnomer, since ruminants have only one stomach with four compartments.

Monosaccharide A simple sugar of five (pentoses) or six (hexoses) C atoms; glucose is a prime example.

Mucin Secretions containing mucopolysaccharides.

Mucopolysaccharide A complex of protein and polysaccharides.

Mucoprotein A complex of protein and oligosaccharides (yield on hydrolysis: 2 to 10 monosaccharides).

NDF Neutral detergent fiber, the fraction of a feedstuff analyzed by the Van Soest scheme of detergent analysis, containing mostly cell wall constituents of low biological availability.

Necrosis The death of a cell or group of cells resulting from irreversible damage.

Neuropeptides Molecules composed of short chains of amino acids found in brain and nervous tissue; they function as regulatory metabolites and are characterized by a duration of action exceeding their short half-lives. Examples are endorphins, enkephalins, and vasopressin.

Neurotransmitter A substance released from a neuron on excitation, which diffuses across the synapse to excite or inhibit the target cell. Neurotransmitters include a large group of peptides involved in a broad array of metabolic actions.

Examples are gamma-amino butyric acid (GABA), neuropeptide Y (NPY), peptide YY (PYY), cholecystokinin (CKK), and several endogenous opioid peptides, including beta-endorphin and dynorphin, all of which affect feed intake; epinephrine and norepinephrine, which affect heart rate, blood pressure, and other physiological functions; and serotonin (5-HT), which affects growth hormone secretion and behavior.

NFE (nitrogen-free extract)   Consists primarily of readily available carbohydrates such as sugars and starches, but may contain hemicellulose and lignin; NFE is calculated by difference during proximate analysis by subtracting all measured components from 100.

Niacin (nicotinic acid)   A water-soluble vitamin required as a constituent of coenzymes, nicotinamide adenine dinucleotide (NAD), and nicotinamide adenine dinucleotide phosphate (NADP) (another form of the vitamin is nicotinamide).

Nicotinic acid   See Niacin.

Nitrogen free extract   See NFE.

Norepinephrine   A hormone secreted by sympathetic nerve endings; it is a vasoconstrictor.

Nucleic acid   Complex, high molecular weight molecules that contain phosphate, ribose, and four bases—adenine, guanine, cytosine, and thymine; DNA and RNA, which are nucleic acids, are responsible for inherited characteristics.

Nucleoprotein   A complex of protein and nucleic acid.

Nucleotide   A combination of purine and pyrimidine bases, five-carbon atom sugar, and phosphoric acid; a hydrolytic product of nucleic acid; a constituent of the coenzymes NAD and NADP.

Nucleus   Typically the largest structure within cells; it contains DNA, RNA, and usually a distinct body the nucleolus.

Nutrient   A chemical substance that nourishes, such as protein, carbohydrate, mineral, or vitamin.

Obesity   The accumulation of body fat beyond the amount needed for good health.

Oleic acid   An 18-carbon fatty acid that contains one double bond; it is found in animal and vegetable fat.

Omasum   Third compartment of ruminant stomach; aids in reducing particle size of ingesta and is site of some nutrient absorption.

Ornithine cycle   See Urea cycle.

Osmosis   The passage of a solvent through a membrane separating two solutions from the solution of lesser concentration to that of greater concentration.

Osteomalacia   Adult rickets; a softening of the bones caused by a vitamin D deficiency in adults.

Osteoporosis   A reduction in the normal quantity of bone.

Oxidation   The increase of positive charges on an atom or loss of negative charges; oxidation is one of the changes that take place when fats become rancid.

Palmitic acid   A saturated fatty acid with 16 carbon atoms; it is common in fats and oils.

Pancreas   An organ located in the abdominal cavity whose functions are both endocrine and exocrine; that is, its specialized cells produce the hormones insulin and glucagon for control of energy and protein metabolism, and other cells produce several digestive enzymes for food digestion.

Pancreatic duct   A tube carrying pancreatic secretions, including lipases, amylase, chymotrypsin, and trypsin, from the pancreas to the duodenal lumen.

Pancreozymin   A hormone secreted by duodenal cells; release is stimulated by acid and nutrients in the lumen of the duodenum; stimulates pancreatic secretion of enzymes.

Pantothenic acid   A water-soluble vitamin required as a constituent of coenzyme A, needed for acetylation of numerous compounds in energy metabolism.

Parturition   The birth of offspring.

Phenylketonuria (PKU)   An affliction characterized by mental retardation that is caused by the congenital lack of the enzyme required to convert phenylalanine to tyrosine; phenylpyruvic acid and other phenyl compounds are excreted in the urine.

Phosphorus (P)   A mineral required as a structural component of the skeleton; as a component of phospholipids, which are important in lipid metabolism and cell membrane structure; and as a component of ATP, creatine phosphate, and other essential compounds in energy metabolism.

Phosphocreatine   A creatine-phosphoric acid compound that occurs in muscle; the energy source in muscle contraction.

Phospholipids   Fatlike substances consisting of glycerol, two fatty acids, a phosphate group, and a nitrogen-containing compound, such as choline (found in the phospholipid lecithin).

Phosphorylation   The addition of phosphate to an organic compound (such as glucose) to form glucose monophosphate.

Photosynthesis   The process by which chlorophyll-containing cells in green plants convert sunlight to chemical energy and synthesize glucose from carbon dioxide and water and release oxygen.

Phytic acid (inositolhexaphosphoric acid)   A phosphorus-containing organic acid; phytin is the mixed salt of phytic acid with calcium and magnesium.

Plasma   The fluid portion of the blood in which corpuscles are suspended; serum is plasma from which the fibrinogen has been removed.

Polyamine   A compound containing two or more amino groups. Putrescine, spermidine, and spermine are important polyamines in the initiation and regulation of cellular division and tissue growth in plants and animals.

Polyneuritis   An inflammation encompassing many peripheral nerves.

Polyunsaturated fatty acids   Fatty acids containing two or more double bonds, such as linoleic, linolenic, and arachidonic acids.

Polyuria   Excessive excretion of urine.

Potable water   Water fit to drink.

Potassium (K)   A mineral required for maintenance of acid-base balance, for activation of several enzymes, for normal tissue protein synthesis, for

integrity of heart and kidney muscle, and for a normal electrocardiogram; it is located mostly within cells.

Progesterone   An ovarian steroid hormone produced by the corpus luteum; required for maintenance of pregnancy.

Prostaglandin   Any of a group of naturally occurring derivatives of arachidonic acid, which have numerous important physiological functions, including stimulation of contractility of uterine and other smooth muscle; regulation of blood pressure, stomach acid secretion, body temperature, blood platelet aggregation; control of inflammation and vascular permeability; and modulation of the action of certain hormones.

Protein-bound iodine (PBI)   The binding of almost all thyroxine in the blood to protein (PBI); the measure of the amount of PBI is useful as an indicator of the quantity of circulating iodine.

Proximate analysis   A combination of analytical procedures used to quantify the protein, lipid, dry matter, ash and carbohydrate (nitrogen-free extract) content of feed, animal tissues, or excreta.

PST (porcine somatotropin)   Growth hormone from swine; recombinant DNA-derived PST can be produced in large quantities for administration to swine as a means of increasing body lean tissue accretion and decreasing body fat.

PTH (parathyroid hormone)   A hormone secreted by the parathyroid gland; maintains blood plasma calcium homeostasis by promoting calcium resorption from bone in hypocalcemia.

Purine   The parent substance of the purine bases; adenine and guanine are the major purine bases of nucleic acids; other important purines are xanthine and uric acid.

Pylorus   The muscular sphincter separating the stomach from the duodenum, which controls the rate of movement of ingesta out of the stomach.

Pyridoxine (B6)   A water-soluble vitamin required as a coenzyme in a large array of enzymes associated with protein and nitrogen metabolism (other forms of the vitamin are pyridoxamine and pyridoxal).

Pyrimidine   The parent substance of several nitrogenous compounds found in nucleic acid—suracil, thymine, and cytosine.

Pyruvic acid   A keto acid of three-carbon atoms; it is formed of carbohydrate in aerobic metabolism; pyruvate is the salt or ester of pyruvic acid.

Radioactive   The emission of particles during the disintegration of the nuclei of radioactive elements; the emissions include alpha particles, beta particles, and gamma rays.

Radioisotope   A radioactive form of an element; the nucleus of a stable atom when charged by bombarding particles (in a nuclear reactor) becomes radioactive and is called "labeled" or "tagged."

Racemic mixture   Pertaining to a chemical compound consisting of equal amounts of dextrorotary (D) and levorotary (L) isomers so that it does not rotate the plane of polarized light.

Ration   A fixed portion of feed, usually expressed as the amount of a diet allowed daily.

Rectum   The distal portion of the gastrointestinal tract, joined proximally to the colon and opening to the exterior via the anus.

Reduction   The gain of one or more electrons by an ion or compound; for example, ferric iron (Fe^{3+}), which is the common form that is found in food, is reduced to ferrous iron (Fe^{2+}) in the acid medium of the stomach.

Rennet (rennin)   A partially purified milk-curdling enzyme that is obtained from the glandular layer of the stomach of the calf.

Reticular groove   See Esophageal groove.

Reticulum   Closely associated with the rumen of ruminant animals; functions in moving ingesta with the rumen or omasum and in regurgitation of ingesta during rumination.

Riboflavin (B2)   A water-soluble vitamin required as a constituent of the coenzymes flavin adenine dinucleotide (FAD) and flavin mononucleotide (FMN).

Ribosome   A ribonucleic acid–containing particle in the cytoplasm of a cell; the site of protein synthesis.

Rumen   The largest compartment of a ruminant stomach, containing enormous populations of anaerobic microorganisms capable of degrading complex carbohydrates and synthesizing amino acids and vitamins from inorganic constituents to provide nutrients for the host animal.

Rumination   The process in ruminants whereby semiliquid ingesta is regurgitated into the esophagus, remasticated by the animal, and reswallowed for further digestion.

Satiety   The condition of being fully satisfied with food; the antithesis of hunger.

Secretin   A hormone secreted by duodenal cells; release is stimulated by acid and nutrients in the lumen of the duodenum; stimulates pancreatic secretion of water and electrolytes.

Selenium (Se)   A trace mineral required as a constituent of the enzyme glutathione peroxidase which destroys peroxides arising from tissue lipid oxidation.

Serotonin (5-hydroxytryptophan, 5-HT)   A neurotransmitter produced in the brain and involved with many physiological functions, including growth hormone secretion, tryptophan metabolism, and behavior.

Serum   The clear portion of any fluid from an animal's body that remains after the solid elements have been separated out (blood serum is the clear, straw-colored liquid that remains after blood has clotted); the plasma from which fibrinogen has been removed.

Silicon (Si)   A trace mineral required for initiation of the mineralization process in bones.

Sodium (Na)   A mineral required for maintenance of acid-base balance, for transfer of nerve impulses, and as an extracellular component of an energy-dependent sodium "pump"; it is located mostly in extracellular fluids.

Somatomedin   See Insulin-like growth factor.

Sphingomyelin   A group of phospholipids found in the brain, spinal cord, and kidney; on hydrolysis it yields phosphoric acid, choline, sphingosine, and a fatty acid.

Spleen   A large organ situated under the ribs in the upper left side of the abdomen; it functions in the normal destruction of old red blood cells.

Sprue   A chronic disease caused by the imperfect absorption of nutrients (especially fats) from the small intestine.

Starch   A polymer of glucose readily hydrolyzed by digestive enzymes.

Stearic acid   A saturated fatty acid composed of 18 carbon atoms.

Sterol   An alcohol of high molecular weight, such as cholesterol and ergosterol.

Stillbirth   The birth of a dead fetus.

Stomach   The first portion of the gastrointestinal tract, within which chemical action occurs on ingested feeds in most animal species; in humans, pigs, and many other species it is a single compartment (simple stomach); in ruminants such as cattle, sheep, goats, and deer, it contains several compartments.

Sulfur (S)   A mineral required as a constituent of several organic metabolites, including methionine, cystine, thiamin, biotin, coenzyme A, and mucopolysaccharides.

Taste   To distinguish flavors between or among feed or water components.

Tetany   A condition characterized by sharp bending (flexion) of the wrist and ankle joints, muscle twitchings, cramps, and convulsions; inadequate calcium in the blood causes irritability of the nerves and muscles so that they respond to a stimulus with greater sensitivity and force than normally.

Tetraiodothyronine   A thyroid hormone active in regulation of the basal metabolic rate (BMR); its chemical formula is $C_{15}H_{11}I_4NO_4$.

Thiamin (B1)   A water-soluble vitamin required as a constituent of the enzymes cocarboxylase and lipothiamide.

Threonine   An essential amino acid.

Thymine   One of the four nitrogenous bases in nucleic acid.

Thymus gland   A two-lobed ductless gland lo-cated behind the upper part of the sternum and extending into the neck; it is fairly large in young animals but usually shrinks in adulthood; it is structured like a lymph node and contains lymphatic follicles; it may play a role in immune reactions.

Thyroxin   An iodine-containing hormone that is produced by the thyroid gland; it is a derivative of the amino acid tyrosine and has the chemical name tetraiodothyronine.

Transferrin (siderophilin)   An iron-binding protein in the blood that transports iron.

Tricarboxylic acid cycle (Krebs cycle and citric acid cycle)   A series of biochemical reactions by which carbon chains of sugars, fatty acids, and amino acids are metabolized to yield carbon dioxide, water, and energy.

Triglyceride (fat)   An ester composed of glycerol and three fatty acids.

Tristearin   A triglyceride of stearic add.

Tryptophan   An essential amino acid; a precursor of niacin.

Trypsin   A proteolytic digestive enzyme secreted by the pancreas; its precursor trypsinogen is activated to trypsin by enterokinase.

Tyrosine   A nonessential amino acid; it spares the essential amino acid phenylalanine.

Undernutrition   A condition resulting from insufficient food.

Urea   The chief end product of protein metabolism in mammals and one of the chief nitrogenous constituents in the urine.

Urea cycle   The major pathway of nitrogen excretion in mammals.

Uric acid   A nitrogenous end product of purine metabolism; it is present in the blood and excreted in the urine.

Valine   An essential amino acid.

Vasoconstrictor   An agent (motor nerve or chemical compound) that acts to decrease the caliber of blood vessels.

Vitamin A A fat-soluble vitamin required for normal night vision, normal epithelial cells, and normal bone growth and remodeling.

Vitamin B1 See Thiamin.

Vitamin B2 See Riboflavin.

Vitamin B6 See Pyridoxine.

Vitamin B12 See Cyanocobalamin.

Vitamin D A fat-soluble vitamin required for normal absorption of calcium from the intestinal tract as a precursor of 1,25-dihydroxycholecalciferol, which acts in the control of mobilization of calcium from bone and stimulation of calcium absorption from the gastrointestinal tract.

Vitamin E A fat-soluble vitamin required as an antioxidant in preventing a wide variety of diseases relating to maintaining integrity of cellular membranes.

Vitamin K A fat-soluble vitamin required for normal blood clotting, specifically for synthesis of prothrombin in liver.

Xanthurenic acid A metabolite of tryptophan; it is found in normal urine but appears in increased amounts in cases of vitamin B6 deficiency.

Xenobiotic Any of a group of nonnutritive substances not normally present in or synthesized by the body, that produces a beneficial physiological response, e.g., improved growth, higher efficiency of feed utilization, increased leanness of the body, when fed or otherwise administered to the animal.

Zinc (Zn) A trace mineral required as a constituent of an array of enzyme systems in several body tissues, as an activator of several metalloenzymes, and in binding reactants to the active site of enzymes.

REFERENCES

Church, D. C. (Ed.). 1987. *The Ruminant Animal.* Englewood Cliffs, NJ: Prentice-Hall.

Cromwell, G. L. 1991. Chapter 17, p. 297 in E. R. Miller et al. (eds.), *Swine Nutrition.*

Feed Additive Compendium. 1998. Minnetonka, MN: Miller Publ. Co. and Alexandria, VA: Animal Health Institute.

Hays, V. W. 1977. *Effectiveness of Feed Additive Usage of Antibacterial Agents in Swine and Poultry Production.* Office of Technology Assessment, U.S. Congress, Washington, D.C.

Mertz, W. (Ed.). 1986. *Trace Elements in Human and Animal Nutrition* (5th ed., vols. 1 and 2). Orlando, FL: Academic Press.

Miller, E. R., Ullrey, D. E., and Lewis, A. J. 1991. *Swine Nutrition.* Boston: Butterworth-Heinemann.

NRC. 1973. *Effect of Feed Processing on the Nutritive Value of Feeds.* National Research Council, National Academy Press, Washington, D.C.

NRC. 1980. *Mineral Tolerances of Domestic Animals.* National Research Council, National Academy Press, Washington, D.C.

NRC. 1981. *Nutritional Energetics of Domestic Animals and Glossary of Energy Terms.* National Research Council, National Academy Press, Washington, D.C.

NRC. 1982. *U.S.–Canadian Tables of Feed Composition.* National Research Council, National Academy Press, Washington, D.C.

NRC. 1987. *Predicting Feed Intake of Food-Producing Animals.* National Research Council, National Academy Press, Washington, D.C.

NRC. 1987. *Vitamin Tolerance of Animals.* National Research Council, National Academy Press, Washington, D. C.

NRC. 1988. *Designing Foods: Animal Product Options in the Marketplace.* National Research Council, National Academy Press, Washington, D.C.

NRC. 1994. *Metabolic Modifiers: Effects on the Nutrient Requirements of Food-Producing Animals.* National Research Council, National Academy of Science, Washington, D.C.

NRC. 1997. *Minerals and Toxic Elements in Diets and Water for Animals.* National Research Council, National Academy of Science, Washington, D.C.

NRC. 1997. *Environmental Implications of Livestock Feeding Symposium.* National Research Council, National Academy of Science, Washington, D.C.

NRC. 1998. *The Role of Chromium in Animal Nutrition.* National Research Council, National Academy of Science, Washington, D.C.

Pond, W. G., Church, D. C., and Pond, K. R. 1995. *Basic Animal Nutrition and Feeding* (4th ed.). New York: Wiley.

Pond, W. G., Maner, J. H., and Harris, D. L. 1991. *Pork Production Systems.* New York: Van Nostrand-Reinhold.

Stevens, C. E. 1977. Chapter 18 in M. J. Swenson (ed.), *Duke's Physiology of Domestic Animals.* Ithaca, NY: Cornell University Press.

Zimmerman, D. R. 1986. *J. Anim. Sci., 62* (Suppl. 3): 6.

Series of National Research Council Publications on the Nutrient Requirements of Domestic Animals
  NRC. 1977. Nutrient Requirements of Rabbits
  NRC. 1981. Nutrient Requirements of Goats

NRC. 1982. Nutrient Requirements of Mink and Foxes

NRC. 1985. Nutrient Requirements of Dogs

NRC. 1985. Nutrient Requirements of Sheep

NRC. 1986. Nutrient Requirements of Cats

NRC. 1989. Nutrient Requirements of Horses

NRC. 1993. Nutrient Requirements of Fish

NRC. 1994. Nutrient Requirements of Poultry

NRC. 1995. Nutrient Requirements of Laboratory Animals

NRC. 1996. Nutrient Requirements of Beef Cattle

NRC. 1998. Nutrient Requirements of Dairy Cattle

NRC. 1998. Nutrient Requirements of Non-Human Primates

NRC. 1998. Nutrient Requirements of Swine

CHAPTER NINE
ANIMAL HUSBANDRY: FULFILLING ANIMAL NEEDS

S. E. CURTIS
UNIVERSITY OF ILLINOIS
URBANA, IL

Animals need many resources from the external environment. Animal husbandry aims to fulfill these needs. Rudimentary knowledge of these needs and how they may be fulfilled enables one to analyze animal-environmental relationships. Nutritional requirements are discussed elsewhere (Chapter 8).

SPACE AND PLACE

Agricultural animals are social creatures that naturally perform many adaptive and maintenance behaviors. To do so, they often must move, so they need space. An animal in a group needs access to space in which to eat, drink, defecate, urinate, socialize, groom, change posture, play, and move about. Space requirements of livestock and poultry must be characterized in terms of quality as well as quantity; physical floor area is not necessarily synonymous with the living space that is perceived by the animal.

Relocation in a pen of important resources (such as feeders and waterers) so they are more accessible than before in effect increases the amount of usable space as perceived by an animal. When the feed trough on a layer cage was moved from a short side to a long side (increasing its length by half), the hens' access to feed—and their state-of-being and performance—increased.

Addition of resources may alter animal perceptions of quantity of living space. When the walls are designed so they can project their heads outside the cage, hens consider the alleyway to be part of their living space. Pigs provided small hiding places in a pen partition into which they can put their heads to terminate a fight consider their pen's living space to have been increased.

Pen shape also may affect the amount of perceived space. Cattle and swine (which are prey species) prefer to lie with their backs next to a partition, often leaving the middle of a pen largely unused, which is inefficient. Pens with the same area but different plan shapes may offer animals quite different amounts of usable living space. An isosceles-triangular pen has 28% more perimeter, and a square one 13% more, than a circular pen of equal area. Rectangles are intermediate, but triangles maximize pen perimeter:area ratio, and thus efficiency of area use.

Environmental Enrichment

Some contemporary artificial livestock and poultry environments are simpler than the naturalistic settings in which the animals evolved, causing the animals to experience understress (see below). Such environments may be intentionally enriched with features providing needed or wanted stimuli and resources.

There can be alternative ways and means of offering feed that increase the effort and time an animal must spend to find and ingest its daily ration. The drastically reduced time animals may have to spend eating in intensive production systems compared to naturalistic settings probably constitutes the greatest constraint on normal behavior. Space often can be rearranged to provide enhanced opportunities for movement, locomotion, and access to resources. Hiding areas, perches, mazes, mezzanines with ramps, and visual screens allow animals to distance themselves from one another, thereby in effect reducing animal density. Special features such as manipulatable objects, dust baths, nesting materials, levering bars, and rubbing posts increase animals' opportunities to engage in play and other maintenance behaviors (provided use of the specific feature is attractive to the animal).

Other aspects of the social environment can be enhanced, too. Group composition is crucial in terms of age, gender, number of individuals, and continuity. Changing group membership, for whatever reason, always results in aggression, stress, and sometimes trauma as animals engage in one-on-one encounters to reestablish social order.

Unfortunately, little is yet known about how different means of enrichment affect the environment as it is actually perceived by the animals. Sometimes animals provided several novel features intended to enrich the environment use one of them almost to the exclusion of all others. Is an enrichment feature used less than 1 minute per day nonetheless important? Would limiting the offering to the most preferred feature(s) suffice? The potential for flexibility in enrichment strategies and tactics nevertheless should be considered.

THERMAL ENVIRONMENT

An animal body naturally tends to assume the temperature of its surroundings. A warm-blooded (homeothermic) animal continuously regulates its body temperature (thermoregulation) as it struggles to resist that tendency and maintain steady temperature in its body core, regardless of the nature of its thermal environment.

Energy Flow

Animals are open thermodynamic systems. Energy continuously flows through them, organizing vital processes along the way. That energy originates in the sun, from which animals receive it both directly and indirectly. Indirect routes include plants, which have captured solar energy and then are eaten, digested, absorbed, and assimilated by the animal, as well as other features of the thermal surroundings—such as air, soil, rocks, and trees that have themselves been warmed by solar radiation. Eventually, after passing through and doing work in an animal, all of this energy completes the loop as it is dissipated in the form of heat from the biosphere near earth to outer space.

Thermoregulation

Livestock and poultry are homeothermic animals. Despite fluctuating external temperature, a homeotherm maintains temperature in its body core (including its cranial, thoracic, and abdominal cavities) more or less constant over time. But temperature does vary from one part of the body to another (for example, the skin ordinarily is cooler than the core), and even core temperature varies regularly from time to time each day and from season to season each year. In contrast to external temperature, though, internal temperature is remarkably steady, usually staying within ±1 °C of average for the location (Table 9–1).

Warm-blooded animals regulate body temperature by balancing heat losses, gains, and storage. Thermoregulatory processes—involving numerous, various physiological, anatomical, and behavioral effectors throughout the body—alter the time rates at which body heat is produced, gained, and lost.

TABLE 9-1
NORMAL RECTAL TEMPERATURE

Animal	°C
Horse	37.7
Beef cow	38.3
Dairy cow	38.6
Sheep	39.1
Pig	39.2
Chicken	41.7
Dog	38.9
Cat	38.6

Source: B. E. Andersson and H. Jonasson (1993), Chapter 47 in M. J. Swenson and W. O. Reece (eds.), *Dukes' Physiology of Domestic Animals*, 11th ed. Ithaca, NY: Comstock Publishing Associates.

On the positive side of the heat-balance equation are heat production and heat gain. Heat-production rate (HP) is comprised of metabolic rate while fasting plus the heat increments associated with ingesting, digesting, and assimilating nutrients, with productive and reproductive processes, with physical activities, and with adaptive and stress responses. In hot environments, animals may reduce HP by cutting back on voluntary feed intake, synthetic processes, and physical activity. They can raise HP in the cold by sequentially calling several specific metabolic responses into play.

Heat-loss rate (HL) can be varied severalfold by passive and active physiological, anatomical, and behavioral mechanisms. In warm situations, heat flow from the warm core to the cooler surface is passively increased by cardiovascular responses, including increased heart rate and dilation of (peripheral) blood vessels in and near the skin. If the environment becomes hot, the animal shifts to active heat-loss mechanisms, including panting and sweating. Species differ greatly in the panting:sweating ratio. Birds have no sweat glands. Pigs' sweat glands do not respond to heat, and those of sheep are only moderately reactive, whereas those of cattle are quite reactive. Animals, especially those with low or no sweating response, may instead wallow in water or mud to get water on the body surface for evaporation.

In cool and cold conditions, animals constrict blood vessels at the body surface and call upon other heat-conserving circulatory mechanisms. They also erect hairs or feathers to increase cover insulation; change posture to minimize surface exposure; and seek a calm place to reduce effects of wind on boundary-layer insulation.

These various thermoregulatory mechanisms are invoked in integrated fashion by effector signals originating in the hypothalamic thermoregulatory center (HTC), which receives temperature information from special sensory nerves—a variety of thermoreceptors—located in the skin, the viscera, and the brain itself. The HTC operates as a room thermostat does, comparing actual temperature against a setpoint, and, when much differential is detected, calling for negative feedback response(s) to reestablish heat balance.

Over a certain range of environmental temperature, an animal can maintain normal core temperature with minimal thermoregulatory effort. With neither heat-loss-enhancing nor -reducing processes much engaged, its minimal HP at its current feed intake rate (FI) is exactly balanced with its HL. This range is called the thermoneutral zone—"neutral" because it does not provoke the animal to respond in any special way to maintain normal body temperature.

Regulating Energy Metabolism and Heat-Production Rate (HP)

Metabolic reactions are not completely energy efficient, so they always give off some heat as a byproduct. The HP of an animal that is fasting, not physically active, and experiencing neither heat stress nor cold stress (thermoneutral) is called the standard metabolic rate (SMR), similar to basal metabolic rate in humans. For an animal weighing W (kg), SMR (kcal/day) is calculated as SMR = $W^{.75}$. So, for each 100-percent increase in W, SMR increases by only 68%. At W = 2.5, 5, 10, 20, 40, 80, 160, 320, or 640 kg, SMR approximates 139, 234, 394, 662, 1,113, 1,872, 3,149, 5,296, or 6,448 kcal/day. And a 256-fold increase in W (from a 2.5-kg piglet to a 640-kg cow) is associated with a 46-fold increase in SMR (from 139 kcal/day to 6,448).

A healthy animal's total HP ordinarily does not fall below SMR, but it may rise considerably higher. When the animal is ingesting, digesting, absorbing, and assimilating feed, additional heat is given off by physical and metabolic processes. Also, the more nutrients processed, the greater the heat increment of feeding (HIF). Proteins, high-fiber feeds, and nutritionally imbalanced diets tend to have higher HIF than do carbohydrates and fats, grains, and well-balanced diets, respectively. Also, due to the different digestive processes, the HIF of a given diet is higher for ruminant animals than for nonruminant animals. Of course, higher HIF can be of benefit when extra body heat is needed (as in cold weather), but may be a hindrance otherwise.

In order to compensate for high HL to cold surroundings, a homeothermic animal may raise HP to reestablish heat balance. The initial thermogenic response to cold by an unadapted animal is shivering (thermogenic muscle spasm), which is relatively inefficient and gradually replaced by thermogenic muscle tonus and finally by nonshivering thermogenesis (increased general metabolic rate). The fuel for these metabolic responses may be either recently ingested nutrients (mostly carbohydrates and proteins) or body reserves (mostly fat). When completely oxidized, these compounds yield heat at the rate of their respective metabolizable-energy (ME) densities: carbohydrates, approximately 4 kcal/gram; proteins, 4.5; and fats, 9 (Chapter 8). There is a limit, however, to the rate at which animals can process nutrients. For healthy, mature animals, the summit HP (sustainable for weeks, provided feed supply is adequate) usually is around 5 times the SMR. The maximal HP (ordinarily sustainable for only a day or so) is around 20% higher than the summit HP.

Regulating Heat-Loss Rate (HL) and Heat-Gain Rate (HG)

Heat naturally flows along temperature gradients via radiation, convection, and conduction (sensible avenues), and along vapor-pressure gradients via evaporation and occasionally condensation (insensible avenues). Heat usually is dissipated from warm metabolic sites to the animal's external environment by flowing through successive stages: mainly by circulatory convection from the warm core (the body cavities already mentioned) through the cooler shell (musculoskeletal system); then mainly by conduction through the still-cooler cover layer (haircoat or feathercoat plus the still air it entraps) and also via evaporation at the skin; and then mainly by radiation and conduction through the still-cooler boundary layer (a film of still air [up to .35 cm thick] surrounding the body); and finally on to the suroundings via sensible avenues and evaporation.

In some infrequent instances, effective environmental temperature (EET) is higher than body core temperature. Then the temperature gradient—and thus the direction of net heat flow—is the reverse of normal, and the animal will be experiencing a net gain of heat from the environment. Of course, this cannot go on for very long without progressing to heat death (positive feedback leading to spiraling hyperthermy). The animal also may gain heat from solar radiation while at the same time having significant heat loss to the environment via thermal radiation, convection, conduction, and evaporation.

An animal has three thermal insulators between its core and the external environment: tissue insulation (core to skin); cover insulation (skin to edge of cover); and boundary insulation (beyond cover). In a pig, the tissue insulation obtaining when peripheral blood vessels are fully constricted is around .15 °C h/kcal; by the cover in still conditions, .40 units; and by the boundary layer in still conditions, .15 units.

Animals control HL mainly by varying tissue and cover insulations and by behavior. Tissue insulation may be varied threefold by altering core-to-skin blood flow rate. By erecting hairs or fluffing feathers, animals increase cover depth and thus cover insulation. Boundary insulation (and cover insulation somewhat) may be greatly reduced by air movement, even at low speeds. Boundary insulation may be reduced by 2/3 as air speed rises from nil to 20 cm/s.

When they have the opportunity, animals thermoregulate behaviorally by huddling with one another, by changing surface-area exposure via postural adjustments, or by seeking windbreaks or sunshades. They also wallow in water or mud to maximize the amount of water on the body surface available for evaporation.

Environmental Heat Demand (EHD) and Effective Environmental Temperature (EET)

At any given moment, from any given animal, the total set of thermal factors in the surroundings will "demand" a certain net HL. This is called environmental heat demand (EHD). An animal's EET theoretically expresses the total effect of an environment on that animal's heat budget. It represents the temperature of an isothermal (that is, all features at the same temperature), still-air environment that results in the same EHD as the environment of interest. By referring to EET, an attempt is made to more fully characterize a thermal envionment in terms of its effect on the animal than by simply referring to air temperature.

Factors Determining EHD and EET

Although EET is still difficult to accurately quantify, its concept is nevertheless useful when evaluating thermal environmental effects on animals. Factors other than air temperature are always important determinants of EHD: thermoregulatory behavior, by which an animal can alter HL and HG, respectively, by a factor of three; the nature of the floor or ground, which can serve either as a conductive heat sink or an insulator against conductive, convective, and radiant HL; the thermal nature of surrounding surfaces, which may be either radiant heat sinks or sources; solar radiation, which when present may be responsible for HG exceeding SMR; aerial water vapor, which when very low can facilitate evaporative HL but when very high can stifle it; air movement, as it drives convective and evaporative HL; and inclement weather in outdoor environments—cold, rainy, windy weather which can virtually destroy cover and boundary insulations and thus greatly increase total HL.

Estimating EET: An Example

An animal's EET can be estimated by adjusting air temperature for temperature-equivalent impacts of other thermal factors (including solar radiation outdoors). Using values generated by Laurence Mount and others, it is possible to estimate the EET for young pigs in groups residing indoors. Starting with air temperature, other factors are accounted for one by one:

Air speed at pig level is a major determinant of convective HL. As it increases from nil to .2, .5, or 1.5 m/s, then 4 °C, 7 °C, or 10 °C are subtracted from air temperature.

Growing pigs lie >80% of the time, so the floor's thermal character affects EHD. Straw bedding reduces conductive, convective, and radiant HL, and raises EET by 4 °C. If pigs must lie on slatted or solid concrete (which often are wet), however, 5 °C or 10 °C, respectively, must be subtracted.

The difference between air temperature and average walls-ceiling surface temperature is directly related to radiant HL. Inside during cold weather, the better insulated the structure, the closer the average surfaces and air temperatures will be. For differences of 13 °C, 3 °C, or 1 °C, respectively, EET would be lowered 7 °C, 1.5 °C, or .5 °C.

Now, consider a pig in a group inside, where air temperature is 20 °C (thermoneutral for most growing swine); air speed at pig level .5 m/s; with concrete-slat flooring; and walls-ceiling surfaces average 3 °C cooler than air. That pig's EET would be 6.5 °C (that is, in the cold zone, not the thermoneutral zone): 20 °C – 7 °C – 5 °C – 1.5 °C = 6.5 °C.

Environmental and Nutritional Energetics

Environmental and nutritional energetics are closely related. Animal SMR, productive and reproductive rates, physical activity, and EHD are chief determinants of an animal's requirement for metabolizable energy (ME), which is derived from feedstuffs. As the environment turns cold, animals respond by taking in more feed or by diverting ME from productive processes (lower priority) to simply keeping the body warm (very high priority). Either way, feed conversion efficiency, productive rate, or both will be reduced. As the surroundings become hot, voluntary FI typically drops as the animal attempts to reduce internal heat load to reestablish heat balance. Here again, productive performance and feed-conversion efficiency will decrease.

Lower Critical Effective Environmental Temperature (LCT)

The lower critical EET (LCT) is the lower limit of the thermoneutral zone. It is the temperature below which an animal must increase HP above the minimal level at its current FI in order to effect heat balance. At the LCT, if the EHD (and therefore HL) rose further and the animal did not raise its HP, body core temperature would drop below normal, which is a sign of distress.

Moreover, the LCT is important to the economics of animal performance. When the EET drops below the LCT, the animal must divert ME from productive process(es) to generating heat simply to keep the body warm. This is a costly maintenance process, resulting in no additional productivity. Alternatively, depending on relative costs of the feed and the fuel being used, heat may be added to an environment to raise the EET above the LCT.

An animal's LCT is determined graphically by the intersection of the animal's thermoneutral HP and its maximal thermal insulation. So the lower these two parameters, the higher the LCT will be. Further, in general, as FI increases, the LCT decreases (and the animal becomes less vulnerable to cold); as cover or tissue insulation decreases, the LCT increases (and the animal becomes more vulnerable to cold); and, because they have higher surface:mass ratios, small animals have higher LCT.

Because many variables affect LCT, it is risky to list LCT values for various species. If certain assumptions are made and conditions met, however, first-approximation generalizations are possible (Table 9–2).

Cold Susceptibility of Young Animals

At birth or hatching, the newborn animal must abruptly cope with massive environmental changes, including new means and sources of nutrients, of respiratory-gas exchange, of heat, and of immunity. Very young animals are extremely vulnerable to becoming chilled due to their relatively high area:mass ratios; their relatively low insulation (and therefore high LCT); and a relatively weak, inexperienced metabolic response to cold.

Normal seasons of birth and maternal care-giving (discussed below) ordinarily compensate for these vulnerabilities. With the out-of-season births and hatchings now common in many industries, however, special attention to the thermal environments of young animals is necessary during cool or cold weather.

LIGHT ENVIRONMENT

Light cycles in the natural environment influence a variety of animal processes and traits—temperature, reproduction, cover loss, and general activity. They serve as time-givers, by which animals synchronize and integrate cyclic phenomena, as well as circulating concentrations of hormones and metabolites important in various processes. These effects generally are stronger in avian species than in mammalian.

TABLE 9-2

TYPICAL LOWER CRITICAL TEMPERATURE AT GIVEN CONDITIONS

Animal	Conditions	LCT, °C
Pig, 3 kg	Fed 1Xmaintenance	31
	Fed 3Xmaintenance	30
20 kg	Fed 1Xmaintenance	26
	Fed 3Xmaintenance	17
60 kg	Fed 1Xmaintenance	24
	Fed 3Xmaintenance	16
100 kg	Fed 1Xmaintenance	23
	Fed 3Xmaintenance	14
140 kg	Pregnant gilt, thin	
	Fed 1Xmaintenance	25
	Fed 2Xmaintenance	20
	Pregnant gilt, fat	
	Fed 1Xmaintenance	23
	Fed 2Xmaintenance	18
Beef cow	Fed 1Xmaintenance	−21
Dairy cow	Dry, pregnant	−14
	7 kg milk/day	−24
	30 kg milk/day	−40
Feeder cattle		−36
Sheep	Growing, 5-mm fleece	
	Fasting	31
	Fed 1Xmaintenance	25
	Fed 3Xmaintenance	18
	Growing, fed 1Xmaintenance	
	1-mm fleece	28
	5-mm fleece	25
	10-mm fleece	22
	50-mm fleece	9
	100-mm fleece	−3
Horse	Mature, fed 1Xmaintenance	
	Early winter	−1
	Late winter	−9
	Young or thin	22

Sources: S. E. Curtis (1983); National Research Council (1981).

Effects of Light on Reproduction

Reproductive processes and other productive functions are more or less responsive to the length of the daily light period (daylength or photoperiod), especially to changes in it. Animals respond to light in the red-orange part of the visible spectrum (wavelength .63 μm). Fluorescent tubes and incandescent lamps used in lighting programs need not necessarily yield a full-solar-spectrum, but care should be taken to ensure that their respective spectra do include the red-orange range.

The season when most mating occurs or when the animals are most fertile is synchronized, in view of gestation or incubation period, with season of birth or hatching to maximize thriftiness and survival of the young. The incubation period for chicken eggs averages 21 d, for example, so chickens are "long-day breeders," with reproductive development, egglaying, and broodiness being stimulated by either long or lengthening photoperiods. Sometimes, to control onset of egglaying, pullets are kept in light-proof houses to restrict reproductive development due to photostimulation until photoperiod is intentionally lengthened. The consequent photostimulation brings the pullets into lay.

Several lighting programs are used in the egg industry, the choice depending mainly on the pullets' genetic strain and season of hatching. Lighting programs for the rearing and laying phases must be compatible; photoperiod should be either constant or decreasing until pullets are 14 to 16 wk old, then either constant or increasing during the laying phase. Laying hens generally are photostimulated either by constant long photoperiods (such as 14 h/day) or by gradually increasing photoperiod (in the range 8 to 16 h/day). Light intensity (bright sunshine $\cong$ 1,000 lux) during the photoperiod (light) as low as <5 lux can stimulate ovarian function in hens if the intensity during the scotoperiod (dark) is even lower.

Ewes of many breeds (gestation period 5 mo) tend to be "short-day breeders," with peak estrous activity beginning in fall (say, October in the northern hemisphere), when natural daylength is shortening, so lambs will come in spring (say, April). The breeding season of ewes of breeds that are inherently strong short-day breeders may be modified to obtain "out-of-season" lambs by artificially shortening photoperiod in light-proof shelters. Light intensity of 30 lux usually suffices to modify reproduction in sheep. The reproductive functions of cows and sows are less influenced by light.

Effects of Light on Lactation and Growth

Livestock and poultry are ordinarily day-active animals, so when the environment is light part of the day (L) and dark the other part (D), most eating ordinarily takes place in the light. Numerous alternative lighting regimens—including intermittent photoperiods (such as repeated 1L:2D around the clock) as well as various intensities—have been tried in attempts to increase FI and thus growth rate, but none has been consistently effective. Most growing animals are subjected to natural light-dark cycles or, if artificial lighting is used, to continuous (or 23L:1D), low-intensity (<5 lux) lighting. The 23L:1D regimen, employed mostly with poultry, gives the animals regular experience with darkness; then, if the power fails and the lights go off, they will not be frightened and will not experience counterproductive behavioral (piling or smothering) and physiological (stress hormone secretion) reactions. There is some evidence that daily 16-h photoperiods (at intensity >100 lux) increase growth rate and alter carcass composition of cattle and sheep, apparently via endocrine mechanisms.

Artifically lengthening daily photoperiod (at intensity 100 to 200 lux) to 16 h seems to increase dairy cows' milk yield by as much as 10%. Lactation rate in sows can be likewise photostimulated. These responses probably are mediated by light effects on the neuroendocrine and endocrine systems.

Other Effects of Light

The nature of an animal's feathers or hair depends partly on photoperiod and partly on environmental temperature. The growth rate of feathers and hair is roughly constant around the calendar, but the rate of feather loss (molting) or hair loss (shedding) is lower in the fall and early winter as compared to other seasons. The growth of pinfeathers by poultry (which reduce carcass quality) is minimized by continuous or 23L:1D lighting.

Solar radiation can cause pathologic changes in animal skin. A severe inflammation of the eye in cattle ("cancer eye") results from exposure of the tissue surrounding the eyeball to the ultraviolet component of solar radiation. This effect is related directly to exposure time, and inversely to amount of eyelid pigmentation (even in light-skinned cattle).

Photosensitization occurs in animals when ultraviolet radiation acts on certain compounds (originating in certain feedstuffs, such as buckwheat and canola leaves) that may be present in the blood to form toxic substances. Dark skin and hair protect animals against these consequences of ultraviolet radiation.

ENVIRONMENTAL EFFECTS ON ANIMAL HEALTH

Frequency and severity of infectious disease is partly determined by an animal's environment. Infectious microbes threaten to infect the animal, sometimes leading to disease, and the animal in turn tries to resist these challenges. Whether infection and disease occur depends on the balance between these two opposing forces, both of which are influenced by environment.

Challenges by Infectious Microbes

The threshold challenge dose of a given infectious microbe that results in infection of an animal is called the infective dose. Microbic challenges invariably originate in the potential host animal's environment (in the air, excreta, surfaces, humans, insects, or other animals). The challenge dose therefore is related directly to environmental concentrations of viable microbes, which in turn is determined by microbic survival in the environment.

Sanitation

Biosecurity and sanitation procedures are crucial means of keeping the microbic challenge dose an animal experiences below the infective dose. These include: limiting contact between healthy animals and other animals (or humans) that may be carrying and shedding infectious microbes; quickly removing infective excreta and sick and dead animals from the environment; and various mechanical, physical, and chemical means of disinfection, while the facility is either occupied (concurrent sanitation) or empty (terminal sanitation).

When an animal house is occupied by a series of animal groups without thorough disinfection between groups (sanitation break), the frequency and severity of clinical and subclinical infectious disease typically rise over time (disease buildup). In the "old-house/new-house" phenomenon, antibiotics fed to minimize subclinical disease tend to enhance animal performance more in a relatively dirty "old house" than in a relatively clean "new house."

Defenses Against Infectious Microbes

An animal integrates its many defense mechanisms in response to microbic challenges. Primary defenses (such as bactericidal secretions at the skin or orifices) aim to prevent microbes from entering the body. Secondary defenses (such as immunoglobulins or phagocytic leukocytes) aim to prevent microbes that have already entered from infecting (that is, living or multiplying in) the body or to neutralize an infection that already has been established.

Specific defenses (such as immunoglobulins [antibodies]) impede infections by specific microbes. Nonspecific defenses (including innate traits rendering a body unreceptive to infection by certain pathogenic microbes) preclude or impede infection by several kinds of microbes.

Local defenses (such as leukocytic infiltration of an inflamed area) are effective only in that area. General defenses (such as macrophages fixed in certain organs) operate over a larger portion of the body.

Defense mechanisms may also be categorized as physical defenses (such as skin); chemical defenses (such as bactericidal secretions into gastrointestinal lumen); cellular defenses (such as circulating leukocytes); and humoral defenses (such as immunoglobulins). In turn, each of the various sorts of humoral immunity in animals can be categorized. There may be natural immunity, with no human involvement, or artificial immunity, in response to intentional exposure of an animal to an antigen. And there may be active immunity, with the subject itself synthesizing effective immunoglobulins, or passive immunity, where immunoglobulins were synthesized by another animal, then administered to subject.

Furthermore, defense mechanism categories may be combined to form new categories. For example, natural passive immunity results from absorption directly into the bloodstream of intact colostral antibodies by a newborn calf. Natural active immunity is due to a subject's own immunologic response to an antigen encountered in the environment. Artificial passive immunity owes to administration of hyperimmune serum, a biological product harvested from another animal previously inoculated with the antigen. Artificial active immunity is due to antibodies synthesized by a subject in response to an antigen to which it has been intentionally exposed.

Environmental stress generally impairs animal resistance to microbic infections. Given the presence of an infective dose of a given microbe, when an animal's defensive mechanisms become compromised, the chances that an infection will occur increase. The stressed animal today often will be the sick animal tomorrow.

AIR POLLUTION IN ANIMAL HOUSES

Contrary to conventional wisdom, the recommended ventilation rate for an animal house is based on neither maximizing "fresh air" nor minimizing "stale air," but instead on optimizing inside-air quality with respect to temperature during hot weather, and with respect to water-vapor content (relative humidity) during cold. When animals occupy closed and semiclosed shelters, the inside air will contain pollutants, which may affect animal health and performance. Air pollutants also may result in malodorous emissions into the surrounding atmosphere that may offend the general public. Air pollutants originate in the animals themselves, and tend to be problematic depending on the number of animals residing at one place, manure management practices, and other factors.

Malodorous gases and vapors emanate mostly from decomposing manure. The major inorganic fixed gases in the mix are ammonia and hydrogen sulfide. At aerial concentrations above 25 parts per million and 50 ppm, respectively, NH_3 and H_2S decrease FI and growth rate and impair respiratory-disease defenses. At slightly higher concentrations, H_2S is deadly. The dozens of malodorous volatile organic compounds also given off may mask pheromones, which serve as important cues between animals related to reproductive and aggressive behaviors. They also may impart "barny" or "cowy" off-flavor and -odor to milk. To reduce concentrations of air pollutants in animal living spaces, feces and urine should be removed from the house once daily and ventilation rate always should be at least 5 air changes/h.

Aerosols (such as droplets carrying dust and infectious microbes) also pollute animal-house air. Infectious droplets—especially those <5 μm in aerodynamic diameter (so small they can be inspired into the lungs)—transmit communicable respiratory infections among individuals. Many aerosolized microbes very quickly dry and consequently die in air at relative-humidity values between 50 and 60 percent. Increasing ventilation rate reduces aerial concentrations of infectious microbes by dilution.

The dust concentration in animal-house air may reach 15 mg/m³ (which, incidentally, is higher than ideal for human occupational hygiene). Origins of dust include the animals themselves (skin, hair, and feather debris), feed, and dried excreta. Airborne solid particles carry odorous gases as well as microbes, so with respect to odor management as well as health management it is desirable to minimize dust generation. Various means can reduce dust generation. These include managing ventilation rate to keep relative humidity no lower than 70%; applying oil mist on bedding or litter, other horizontal surfaces, and the animals themselves; and electrostatic precipitation.

EFFECTS ON HIGH ALTITUDE

As altitude above sea level increases, overall atmospheric pressure becomes progressively diminished. Partial pressure of oxygen (normally 20.95% of air) at altitudes of 0 (sea level), 1500, and 3000 m averages, respectively, 212, 177, and 147 millibars. Animals become chronically hypoxic (low oxygen concentration in blood) as a result of breathing air low in oxygen content. Effects of hypoxia can be enormous, affecting several organ-systems (including the respiratory, circulatory, nervous, and musculoskeletal systems). Cattle-grazing mountain pastures at altitudes of 2000 m or higher may adapt to low atmospheric oxygen, but in the process they may develop hypoxic pulmonary-arterial hypertension. Over time, this leads to bovine high-mountain ("brisket") disease, which in turn can lead to congestive right heart failure and death.

Hatchability of poultry eggs is reduced at high altitudes, so incubators and hatchers must be pressurized there.

ANIMAL-HUMAN INTERACTIONS

Animals are sentient creatures, and they have long memories of aversive events. Humans are regularly in the presence of agricultural animals during feeding and other caretaking chores. Moreover, most animals have to be handled several times in their lifetimes for procedures of a routine (processing, moving to market, hoof-trimming, and reproductive checks) or emergency nature (taking body temperature or medicine administration).

Stress associated with necessary procedures can be minimized if the animals are accustomed to having positive experiences with humans. Their productive performance reflects the level of fear or anxiety they experience when humans are close by. The reproductive performance of sows in terms of pigs weaned per year has been found to be inversely related to the fear the sows demonstrate when approached by a human. Similarly, the milk yield of dairy cows depends in significant part on the temperament of the humans caring for and milking them. Even broiler chickens respond positively in terms of health and performance to direct human attention and gentle care. Early experience is especially important. Pigs picked up and petted as little as 1 min/day prior to weaning behave more assertively in social contexts for the rest of their lives.

Most animals spend only a small fraction of their lifetime being transported from one place to another. These times nonetheless often constitute the most stressful experiences they ever have. The novelty of being handled and transported can cause anxiety, fear, and stress, making the animals more difficult to handle, and thus tempting handlers to become physically abusive (as often as not without the desired effect on animal motivation). Often in handling (local movement or restraint) and transportation (long-distance movement) the responsible humans do not own the animals, and thus have little or no economic incentive to handle them gently. In recent years there has been overall improvement in the conditions of handling and transportation in the animal industries. But there remains the need for handlers to use more "brain" and less "brawn," and for them to have a proper attitude about treatment of animals.

When moving livestock in groups, the handler should act like neither a predator chasing the animals nor a source of feed but rather as an unexcited, neutral person. Livestock movement should be at a slow walk, with handler movements keeping the animals moving in orderly fashion.

Design of milking centers affects dairy cow behavior at milking time. A powered crowd gate in the lead-up (holding) pen encourages cows to enter the milking center, but should not push or electrically shock them. Cows and handlers should be properly trained to the crowd gate.

Catching poultry reared on the floor at marketing time can be a stressful experience for both catchers and birds. With automatic catching machines, which minimize human contact, birds experience minimal injury and stress while being harvested.

Proper design of force (crowd) pens—used to organize a group of animals to enter a single-file chute—depends on species. Round crowd pens work well for all species, but the appropriate entrance to the chute differs. For cattle and sheep, a triangular (funnel-shaped) force area—one side straight, the other at a 30° angle—may be used. With pigs, to prevent jamming, an abrupt entrance must be used.

Sound design of facilities and equipment, as Temple Grandin (1993) points out, is but one critical factor in proper handling and transport. Others are trained handlers and progressive managers. Ample knowledge of principles of animal behavior and handling-facility design already exists. Persistent abuses and other problems, which both ignore moral imperatives and reduce business profits, owe to inadvertent or reckless neglect of that knowledge. Some principles are as simple as that, because livestock and poultry have memories, their treatment should be consistent, because inconsistent treatment causes anxiety.

ANIMAL ACCOMMODATIONS

In all animal industries, genetic strains especially adapted to particular production systems have been developed through selection and crossing. The environment must be designed to fit the animals, too. Designs of most contemporary accommodations have not had the benefit of enough scientific input. However, designs—traditionally done by innovative blacksmiths and farmers—are increasingly becoming based on scientific observations of animal needs in terms of size, behavior, and physiology.

Animal Equipment

Industry norms for designs of certain items of animal equipment—including cattle-restraint headgates and dairy-cow free stalls—are being revolutionized following introduction to the design process of pertinent behavioral, health, and productivity observations and principles.

Ragnar Tauson (1995) directly compared several commercial models of hen cage in terms of hen health, performance, and behavior and feed wastage. First, specific design features that contributed positively to cage performance were identified. Then these were combined in a series of experimental composite cages. Soon a new design of laying-hen cage had evolved. This new cage eliminated most of the problems (such as hen-trapping, injured feet, and feed wastage) characteristic of the traditional designs, and greatly reduced the rest of them.

Ian Taylor (1995) used various means—including high-speed cinematography and computer-assisted analysis of eating movements—to characterize a pig's use of three-dimensional space while eating. Most models of feeder on the commercial market provided the pig too little space for head and shoulders, resulting in feed wastage (5 to 10%) and injury. A fundamental feeder design was developed that could be used at all life-cycle stages and that resulted in negligible feed wastage and almost no injuries.

Primary Environmental Modifications

Primary environmental modifications are typically available to animals for their voluntary use in reducing stressful impacts of outdoor environments. A free-access shade reduces the impact of solar radiation, whereas a run-in shed reduces the impact of cold, windy, rainy weather. Other kinds of primary environmental modifications include wallows and other means of wetting, windbreaking, and snowbreaking.

Although they are relatively simple structures, for maximal effectiveness, these primary facilities must be designed carefully. Solar geometry, prevailing wind, wind-permeability of windbreak material, and snowbreak height and distance, among other factors, need to be considered. Even the appropriate height of a sunshade depends on local conditions. A shade roof should be high above the ground in dry, hot regions (so animals can expose themselves and lose heat by thermal radiation to the relatively cool clear sky). In tropical and subtropical regions, however, the roof should be low (to minimize animal exposure to relatively warm cloudy skies). Once properly designed and constructed, primary environmental modifications ordinarily require little attention from the manager.

Sometimes animals surprise us when, during periods of weather extremes, they choose not to take advantage of the primary shelters they have been provided. These instances provide evidence that animals' tolerances for weather extremes differ from humans' ("naked apes"), and that letting anthropomorphism serve as a guide in caring for animals can lead to wrong conclusions about animal state-of-being (Chapter 10).

Secondary Environmental Modifications

Secondary environmental modifications partly serve the same sheltering purpose as primary ones, but they go further. They are typically closed or semiclosed structures; the animals usually are confined to them; and attempts generally are made to regulate EET in all seasons. They make it possible to raise animals—even small and young animals—in temperate regions at all times of the year, minimizing seasonal production cycles common to outdoor production there. Additional benefits include ease of moving stored feedstuffs to the animals as well as economical use of caretaking labor.

As for disadvantages, in the typically limited living space, animals cannot freely move about. Also, animals' natural byproducts—such as respiratory gases, water vapor, heat, manure, manure-decomposition gases, and microbes—tend to accumulate inside these houses. All of them decrease environmental quality and must be continuously removed to ensure animal thriftiness. Closed and semiclosed houses therefore must be outfitted with special devices, processes, and structures for ventilation, heating, cooling, sanitation, and waste removal.

In contrast to primary shelters, construction of closed houses generally requires considerable capital expenditure. Moreover, both design and operation of such animal houses require careful attention to detail. A sophisticated, relatively high level of management skill is necessary to ensure success with these facilities.

Closed houses must be ventilated. Because ventilation rate is determined partly by thermal factors, in temperate regions, these structures also must be properly insulated. Additionally, heating systems (often unit heaters located throughout the house) and cooling systems (often evaporative-cooling in sidewalls or water drippers or sprayers throughout the living space) are employed when needed to keep the animals comfortable.

Animals continuously give off heat and water vapor, so air leaving a closed animal house is always both moister and warmer than as it entered. Ventilation systems are designed to control moisture buildup during cold weather, and heat buildup during hot. If these goals are achieved, air quality in terms of negligible pollutants and adequate oxygen will follow. Ventilation may be by mechanical or natural means.

Mechanical Ventilation

With most mechanical ventilation systems, exhaust fans create a partial vacuum (called negative "static pressure") inside the house. In particular, atmospheric pressure inside ideally will be around .3 millibar [around .12 inch water] below that outside in order to ensure adequate air velocity at inlets. At this static pressure, the slightly higher outside atmospheric pressure simply drives outdoor air through the inlets and into the house at a velocity of around .5 m/sec (around 1,000 ft/min). This is fast enough to keep primary air flow inside the house high enough above the floor to minimize drafts.

For a given total air-inlet area, increasing total air-exhaust rate increases the partial vacuum, causing air velocity through the inlet to increase (and vice versa). Likewise, for a given exhaust rate, increasing inlet area decreases the partial vacuum, causing inlet velocity to decrease (and vice versa).

To operate properly, a house's fans and inlets must be coordinated as to size. Moreover, both of these system components must be adjustable to achieve necessary static pressures and inlet-air velocities over a severalfold range in ventilation rate (low during cold weather, high during hot). The range is determined by certain thermodynamic properties of house structure and animals as well as expected weather conditions. Various control systems may be used.

For cold-weather operation, across the expected outdoor temperature range, the ventilation system should be designed to maintain relative humidity around 80%. Air moister than 80% RH leads to destructive condensation, and that drier than 80% RH to more dust generation and the need for more supplemental heat. In addition, to maintain acceptable indoor air quality, minimal design ventilation rate usually is set at around 5 air changes per hour (that is, the hourly exhaust of a volume of air equal to 5 times the volume of the house).

Maximal design ventilation rate can be estimated based on thermodynamic properties of air and, given an estimate of total animal-sensible HL, on limiting inlet-to-outlet rise in air temperature to 2 °C. If inside heat load due to animals exceeds the design estimate, ventilation rate will need to be increased, too (and vice versa).

In temperate regions, during fall and spring—the seasons of change—the outdoor atmosphere may be quite cool at night but quite warm in the afternoon, necessitating low (winter) ventilation rates at night and higher (summer) rates in the afternoon. When a higher rate is inadvertently left on overnight, a large amount of cool (dense) inlet air often will drop to the floor, so floor drafts frequently occur. These drafts, combined with falling inside air temperature, can chill the animals.

Natural Ventilation

Natural ventilation systems typically are less controllable than mechanical ones. But in many cases they create an indoor environment that is satisfactory for animals. Design rates and principles for natural ventilation are similar to those for mechanical ventilation. Air inlets in natural ventilation systems may be the same, too. But, instead of passing through exhaust fans, the air leaves the house through appropriately designed outlets (usually at the roof's ridge).

Drivers of air movement in natural ventilation systems are the air's thermal buoyancy and wind. As air moves through the house and becomes warmer, it also becomes less dense and more buoyant, and it tends to rise. The main determinant of natural ventilation rate is total outlet area at the ridge. Atmospheric wind moving over the outlet opening tends to increase ventilation rate via aspiration (Bernoulli's principle). Other rate-determining factors include vertical distance between inlets and outlets (the so-called stack effect, which may be intentionally exaggerated by chimneys) and the inside heat load due to animal-sensible HL.

ASSESSING ENVIRONMENTAL QUALITY

The quality of an animal environment is best evaluated in terms of animal state-of-being, which in turn reflects the numbers, kinds, and levels of adaptes the animal is invoking (Chapter 10). Nevertheless, it sometimes will be necessary to assess the environmental factors themselves. Several principles should be borne in mind during such troubleshooting:

The external environment consists of all external factors and conditions the animals experience.

The environmental complex acts as a whole on the animals, so additivities and interactions of single factors must be taken into account.

Environmental factors usually vary across space at any given time.

Environmental factors usually change over time at any given place.

The rate of environmental change an animal experiences may be critical.

Animals modify their own environments in several ways.

Often it is difficult to identify an accurate single index of the complex of multiple environmental stressors.

By their behavior and performance, animals give clues about their physical and psychological comfort.

Anthropomorphism is a common pitfall in assessing animal environments.

Environmental management handbooks and textbooks may be consulted for details about sampling approach (time and space considerations) and instrument choice for environmental measurement.

SUMMARY

Animal husbandry has to do with fulfilling an animal's needs. The animal needs space in which to live.

The necessary space allowance is determined by the quality of the space as well as the quantity. Space quality in turn depends on factors such as the location of vital resources, the shape of the space, and the presence of enriching features. The nature of the social interaction present also determines space requirement.

The animal also needs an acceptable thermal environment. After doing work in an animal, all energy, regardless of its origin, is dissipated to outer space in the form of heat. Agricultural animals are temperature regulators. Despite fluctuating external temperature, they maintain body-core temperature more or less constant over time. Temperature-regulating animals regulate body temperature by balancing heat losses, gains, and storage via altering the rates at which body heat is produced, gained, and lost. Various thermoregulatory mechanisms (including cardiovascular, panting, sweating, behavioral and postural responses, cover, and metabolic responses) are invoked in integrated fashion by signals originating in the hypothalamic thermoregulatory center, which receives temperature information from throughout the body.

Light cycles and intensities influence the body temperature, reproduction, cover loss, and general activity of an animal. Natural light cycles cause seasonal cycles in reproduction, aiming for births and hatchings to come at times supportive of survival of the young. These cycles can be artificially mimicked to manipulate reproductive seasons. Lactation and growth rate also may be influenced by the light environment.

The environment also affects an animal's health via the concentrations in the surroundings of infectious microbes and by supporting or impairing the animal's various general and specific defenses against microbic challenge.

The air pollution which may be present in animal houses has various effects on the animals. Special precautions must be taken when keeping animals at high altitudes.

Humans are in the presence of agricultural animals during caretaking chores and when handling them as a part of routine husbandry practices. Stress associated with such occasions can be minimized if the animals are accustomed to having positive experiences with humans.

The designs of animal equipment are being revolutionized following introduction to the design process of pertinent behavioral, health, and productivity observations and principles.

Animal accommodations may be of two general types. Primary environmental modifications—including shades, wallows, windbreaks, and snowbreaks—are for the animal's voluntary use in reducing stressful impacts of outdoor environments. Secondary environmental modifications partly serve the same purpose as primary ones, but are typically closed or semiclosed structures to which the animals are confined and where attempts are made to regulate environmental temperature in all seasons. This makes it possible to raise animals in temperate regions at all times of the year. Closed houses must be insulated and ventilated. Ventilation systems may be natural or mechanical.

The quality of an animal environment is best evaluated in terms of animal state-of-being. But it sometimes will be necessary to assess the environmental factors themselves. There are several principles that should be observed when doing so.

REFERENCES

Curtis, S. E. 1983. *Environmental Management in Animal Agriculture.* Ames, IA: Iowa State University Press.

Curtis, S. E. 1995. Ecological design: Philosophy and practice for animal systems. In *Animal Behavior and the Design of Livestock and Poultry Systems.* Northeast Regional Agricultural Engineering Service, Ithaca, New York.

Grandin, T. (Ed.). 1993. *Livestock Handling and Transport.* CAB International, Wallington, United Kingdom.

FASS, 1998. *Guide to the Care and Use of Agricultural Animals in Agricultural Research and Teaching* (2nd ed.). Federation of Animal Sciences Societies, Savoy, Illinois.

McDowell, R. E. 1972. *Improvement of Livestock Production in Warm Climates.* San Francisco: W. H. Freeman.

MWPS, 1987. *Structures and Environment Handbook.* Midwest Plan Service, Ames, Iowa.

MWPS 3–8, 1983–1995. *Housing and Equipment Handbooks* for beef cattle, dairy cattle, sheep, and swine, respectively. Midwest Plan Service, Ames, Iowa.

NPPC, 1992. *Swine Care Handbook.* National Pork Producers Council, Des Moines, Iowa.

NRC, 1981. *Effect of Environment on Nutrient Requirements of Domestic Animals.* National Academy Press, Washington, D.C.

NRC, 1996. *Guide for the Care and Use of Laboratory Animals.* National Academy Press, Washington, D.C.

NRAES, 1995. *Animal Behavior and the Design of Livestock and Poultry Systems.* Northeast Regional Agricultural Engineering Service, Ithaca, New York.

Tauson, R. K. 1995. Comparative evaluation and development of housing systems for laying hens. In *Animal Behavior and the Design of Livestock and Poultry Systems.* Northeast Regional Agricultural Engineering Service, Ithaca, New York.

Taylor, I. A. 1995. Designing equipment around behavior. In *Animal Behavior and the Design of Livestock and Poultry Systems.* Northeast Regional Agricultural Engineering Service, Ithaca, New York.

CHAPTER TEN
ANIMAL STATES-OF-BEING

S. E. CURTIS
UNIVERSITY OF ILLINOIS
URBANA, IL

DOMESTICATION AND ADAPTABILITY
MULTIFACETED INTERNAL AND EXTERNAL ENVIRONMENTS
ENVIRONMENTAL ADAPTABILITY
ANIMAL NEEDS
INEVITABLE COMPROMISES
A PUBLIC ISSUE: FARM-ANIMAL WELFARE
SUMMARY

DOMESTICATION AND ADAPTABILITY

Only a few of the animal species living on earth have ever been domesticated, and even fewer are being kept nowadays. Why did prehistoric humans abandon keeping raccoon, hyena, and ibex, and focus instead of cattle, chickens, sheep, swine, and the like, and continue hunting bison, deer, moose, and other wildlife?

Domestication of animals started around fifteen thousand years ago, at the start of the Neolithic Revolution. Humans evolved from being gatherers of wild plants and hunters of wild animals, to being farmers, relying for food on cultivated crops and domesticated livestock. Eventually, agriculture and pastoralism emerged, and both approaches to food production are being practiced to this day.

It has been said that domestication was a haphazard process, with many failed attempts. But Stephen Budiansky (1992) suggests that any notion that humans simply chose and set about domesticating certain animal species is giving our kind too much credit. He believes that humans and animals "cast their lot together ten thousand years ago"; that domestication was "the evolutionary product of a mutual strategy for survival"; that "in an evolutionary sense, domestical animals chose us as much as we chose them."

Anyway, for domestication to succeed, the animals had to fit with human cultures. Those dozen or so species we now keep as livestock and poultry differ markedly from their relatives we left in the wild, and they always have. They were special creatures all along in terms of environmental adaptability, having greater flexibility, range, resilience, and tolerance. They were up to the demands of domesticated life.

Even our agricultural animals have limits to their adaptability, though. They can become distressed, physiologically and psychologically. Their natures have largely resulted from intentional genetic selection and crossing to fulfill agricultural goals, so over the generations they have developed specific environmental niches. Care of these animals must be based on their unique needs, not on those of their wild progenitors or of humans. When livestock have difficulty adapting to their surroundings, their state-of-being and their performance—and the enterprise's profitability—usually deteriorate. Keepers of farm animals, in honoring agriculture's economic realities and moral imperatives, arrange husbandry regimens to minimize the occurrence of stressful occasions.

MULTIFACETED INTERNAL AND EXTERNAL ENVIRONMENTS

Any animal has to overcome its body's natural tendency to disintegrate. It has to maintain itself in order to survive. Next, it strives to thrive and reproduce. But the external surroundings usually are not optimal for the animals. They tend to fluctuate, so they continuously threaten to overwhelm the animal, which must adapt to changes in its external environment to achieve the essential steady states in its internal environment.

Internal Environment

The cells reside in the extracellular space, that is, in the animal's internal environment. By different but integrated components, processes, and responses, an animal ordinarily maintains steady states in dozens of internal traits—including temperature, pH, sodium concentration, osmotic pressure, and glucose concentration, to name a few—crucial to supporting all kinds of cellular processes.

HOMEOKINESIS AND NEGATIVE FEEDBACK. An animal continuously monitors its external and internal environments via peripheral and central sensation and perception components of its nervous system. When an unfavorable situation is recognized, the animal automatically and subconsciously responds with a set of neural, neuroendocrine, and endocrine output signals calling for appropriate adaptive responses by various organ-systems, often in distant parts of the body. In this way, the animal tries to neutralize a situation it perceives to be threatening. This constitutes negative feedback.

Dozens of negative-feedback control loops always stand ready to be engaged. They are responsible for homeokinesis, the phenomenon responsible for the essential, dynamic, steady internal state.

If a warm-blooded animal senses and perceives a slight decrease in skin temperature (as when environmental temperature falls), it may automatically and subconsciously decide the situation poses a threat to its state-of-being. Quickly, then, via one or more of its diverse behavioral, functional, immune, or structural reactions, the animal attempts to reestablish heat balance with its surroundings.

Notice that the animal does not have to wait for its body to be changed much at all before it responds. In fact, some of its sensory systems (such as hearing, smelling, and seeing) permit an alert animal to recognize the presence of a distant predator or weather system before it can cause injury or even threaten to do so. Perception and recognition of such potential harm occur at the input and decision stages of negative-feedback control loops (Figure 10-1). Avoidance or escape comprises output, the actual negative feedback aimed at neutralizing this particular threat.

External Environment

Around the world, animal agriculture is widely practiced in rainy tropical, wet and dry tropical, semiarid, desert, warm rainy, warm rainy (dry summer), and cold moist climes, but not in polar or icecap regions. Ultimately, agricultural strategies must accord with local climatic realities. Global distribution patterns of agricultural animals are correlated with local climates.

COMPLEXITY AND VARIETY. The environments inhabited by livestock and poultry are as complex as they are varied. Each has many features, each of which in turn varies over time and across space. When different environmental factors impinge simultaneously, the combined effect on animal performance ordinarily amounts to the sum of the factors' individual effects (additivity). But in some cases the combined effect differs from the sum of the single effects (interaction). Wind chill in cold, windy conditions is an example.

A further complication arises when, in some production environments, the animals

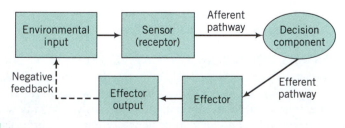

FIGURE 10-1

Perception and recognition of potentially harmful factors in the environment and negative feedback control loops.
Source: S. E. Curtis (1983).

can choose to reside in one place or another (for example, one end of the house or the other), and the available niches may differ in environmental quality. Inside a house in which draftiness varies horizontally, different spots on the floor will have different effective temperatures. Outdoors, solar radiation, wind, nearby structures, vegetation, and geologic features also may influence effective environmental temperature (Chapter 9).

To carefully evaluate a practical animal environment, analysis should focus first on animal state-of-being, and only later on environmental traits (Chapter 9). Then, as for environment, the focus should be on animal microenvironment; that is, the features with which the animal is actually interacting. During a winter storm in Minnesota, for instance, neither atmospheric temperature and wind speed outside a turkey house nor the temperature and air speed in the house's northwest corner are of any consequence to the birds that have been sensible enough to gather in the southeast corner, where the thermal microenvironment may be satisfactory.

NATURAL ENVIRONMENTS. Prior to domestication, progenitors of today's livestock and poultry had evolved for eons in a variety of outdoor environments. Their natural histories bore imprints of adaptations to the successions of climatic changes that took place where they lived. Worldwide, most agricultural animals still inhabit the natural outdoor environments—the deserts, pastures, plains, forests, savannas, wetlands, and mountain ranges—where little or no attempt is made to artificially modify the physical environment.

For an extensive agricultural system to be successful, however, the animals must possess traits favoring their "performance adaptability" to the natural environment, that is, environmental adaptability sufficient to permit productive and reproductive performance to flourish. Indigenous breeds, stocks, and strains may be genetically adapted to unusual thermal, vegetation-cycle, parasite, or cultural factors peculiar to a particular locale. Attempts to introduce genotypes that perform in superior fashion elsewhere often fail. For example, Holstein cows may be less resistant to parasites, and less tolerant of heat, and may require more and higher-quality feedstuffs to perform maximally than do indigenous zebu cows. Similarly, Scottish Highland cattle are more adaptable to cold climates than Holsteins or zebus. Hybrids of two genotypes or breeds sometimes prove useful, especially fifty-fifty crosses.

Production costs in extensive animal-agriculture tend to be relatively low. But, in most such systems, animals show marked seasonal differences in productive and reproductive performance. Various husbandry strategies are followed, depending on available resources. One is to modify the natural physical environment little or not at all. Where forageable vegetation of adequate nutritional quality is available the year around, no feedstuffs are stored. Alternatively, feedstuffs may be stored at their peak quality during the growing season(s), to be fed during the seasons that are slack for forageable vegetation: during winter in cold moist regions, when vegetation availability and quality decrease, or the rainy season in tropical locales, when the quality of natural vegetation typically deteriorates. Or the animals may be regularly moved, following available natural forage and shelter. Sheep and cattle may graze mountain pastures during summertime and river-valley meadows spring and fall, and then during winter be fed meadow hay, stored in the summer, in lots providing only natural topographical shelter.

ARTIFICIAL ENVIRONMENTS. In some climatic regions, agricultural animals need artificial shelter if they are to thrive the year around. In cold-moist Illinois or semiarid New Mexico, for example, nature does not provide enough protection from inclement weather at certain times of the year. Suitable shelters cover a wide range. Some are primary environmental modifications, others secondary (Chapter 9).

ENVIRONMENTAL ADAPTABILITY

Adaptation and Stress

A so-called environmental adaptation refers to any behavioral, functional, immune, or structural trait that favors an animal's fitness—that is, that favors its ability to survive and reproduce under given environmental conditions. An animal is said to be coping when, in the face of an adverse environment, it maintains or regains control of its body and psyche. The homeokinetic response required to cope depends on the animal's genetic adaptability, experiences, adaptation status, and unrealized adaptation potential.

ADAPTAGENTS AND ADAPTATES. Adaptagent is another word for stimulus. An environmental factor differs between a neutral situation and one that provokes a homeokinetic response, and that difference amounts to the adaptagent. For a piglet, if an environmental temperature of 25 °C were thermoneutral (comfortable) but one of 18 °C elicited heat-conserving and -producing responses (chilly), for example, then the difference (7 °C) would be the adaptagent. The impact on an animal of several minor adaptagents occurring simultaneously or sequentially may be as great as that of one major adaptagent.

An animal responds to an adaptagent by changing output(s) in one or more of its behavioral, functional, immune, or structural traits. These responses are called adaptates. For example, an animal may double its visits to the waterer in a hot environment; change secretion rates of reproductive hormones when daylength changes; increase circulating concentration of a specific immunoglobulin when confronted by an antigenic microbe; or increase its hair-coat depth as winter approaches.

Responses: Adaptive and Stress

When an animal successfully copes with one or more adaptagents, it is said to have adapted, and the adaptate is called an adaptive response. But the animal does not always cope. When its attempts to cope fail, the adaptate is called a stress response, and the adaptagent is said to be a stressor.

KINDS OF STRESS. An animal may experience stress in four categories, each having a different effect on its state-of-being. Understress occurs in simple artificial accommodations lacking key behavioral stimuli or resources that may result in sensory deprivation of the animal (see "Behavioral Needs," below). To compensate, an animal may engage in vices and other unusual behavior patterns. Eustress is associated with exciting but pleasurable experiences, positive emotions and feelings. Frolicking chicks well might be experiencing eustress. Overstress comes with unpleasant stimulation with which an animal is unable to cope. It may be accompanied by pain and emotional states such as anxiety, fear, or frustration. An animal residing in a cold accommodation may be overstressed. Distress, which is severe overstress, involves the mind as well as the body, and may be accompanied by extreme negative emotions, unpleasant feelings. An animal in the throes of heat death may be experiencing distress.

ADAPTATES AND PERFORMANCE. Animals ordinarily must deal with limits in their bodily and dietary resources. The more the resources that must be redirected to coping with environmental stimuli, the fewer that remain to support productive and reproductive processes. Responses to environmental stimuli affect animal performance—ordinarily negatively—both directly and indirectly by

Redirecting nutrients from synthetic processes to maintenance processes

Altering functions involved in both productive processes and homeokinetic responses

Intentionally reducing rates of productive processes (a heat-stressed broiler chicken reduces feed-intake rate to reduce heat-production rate, and consequently growth rate)

Increasing interindividual variation in performance (because different coping strategies employed by different individuals differentially draw on bodily and dietary resources)

Altering resistance against infectious diseases

The performance of a stressed animal will tend to be below normal. Within reasonable constraints of benefit:cost relationships, producers attempt to arrange husbandry regimens to minimize the total stress the animals will experience (see discussions of "inevitable compromises" and "individual state-of-being versus group profitability," below).

States-of-Being

Animal state-of-being is properly evaluated with respect to the numbers, kinds, and intensities of adaptates invoked in attempting to cope with present environmental conditions. When a few or no extraordinary homeokinetic responses must be invoked, the animal is said to be experiencing well-being. As the number or intensity of adaptagent(s) increases, the animal calls minor stress responses into play, and it is said to be experiencing fair-being. If adaptagent intensity continues to increase, the animal changes its adaptates accordingly, eventually reaching the limit of its adaptability. Beyond this, if adaptagent intensity increases still further, the animal is frankly stressed, and experiences ill-being. In the range of ill-being, maintenance (coping) requirements are extremely high, and the situation may quickly progress to the collapse and death of the animal.

Adverse external stimuli are a part of life, and their absence does not necessarily lead to animal comfort and well-being. The goal that a kept animal will experience well-being at all times may be admirable in terms of a keeper's moral responsibilities, but it is practically unrealistic. Animals are inherently prepared to cope with adverse surroundings. More reasonable goals are that agricultural animals will be well most of the time; fair occasionally; and ill infrequently. The challenge is to determine whether external stimuli are natural and unavoidable, on the one hand, or artifactual and avoidable, on the other, and then manage accordingly.

ANIMAL NEEDS

Needs motivate an animal to respond in some way. Animals prioritize fulfilling their needs as follows: first, physiological needs; then, safety needs; and finally, perhaps, behavioral needs.

Physiological Needs

A great deal is known about animals' physiological needs and how to fulfill them. Modern dietary formulations, for example, are possible because of our relatively vast knowledge of animals' nutritional needs (Chapter 8). Direct and indirect effects of physical, chemical, and biological aspects of the surroundings on animal health and productivity have been appreciated for decades. Research results have made it possible to improve thermal, light, air, microbic, and social aspects of the environment, too.

Animal health has been enhanced as nutritional and environmental care have improved and as health care has evolved from art to science. With intensification of production have come the diseases of multiple etiology (for example, chronic respiratory disease in poultry and environmental mastitis in dairy cows). Such "production diseases" typically result in high morbidity rates (reduced performance) but low mortality rates (death). Also, clinical manifestations of certain infectious diseases may be influenced by the animal microenvironment. Environmental design and management now take into account microbic challenges and animal defenses (Chapter 9).

Safety Needs

Safety needs are tended less diligently than physiological needs, although laxity may result in losses that actually are avoidable. In most cases, equipment and facilities could be further improved with respect to animal safety.

Animals living outdoors in temperate and mountainous regions may be hurt or killed in weather-related incidents. The number would be greater but for natural and artificial shelters (primary environmental modifications, Chapter 9) that offer protection from severe conditions. (Ironically, animals in closed houses [secondary environmental modifications] may succumb indirectly to storms, when power outages may cause prolonged ventilation failure.)

Predators still destroy millions of domestic animals yearly. Acceptable, effective methods of predator control are available. For example, an animal's chance of falling prey to feral or wild carnivores is usually decreased when it is shifted from an extensive production system to an intensive one.

Recent advances in enhancing safety include the design of cages that trap fewer laying hens; restraint headgates resulting in fewer cattle being choked or injured at the head, shoulder, or leg; and floor surfaces approaching the ideal of resilience and cleanability with a friction coefficient that minimizes slipping without abrasion (Chapter 9). Still, equipment and facilities could be further improved with respect to animal safety.

Behavioral Needs

Agricultural animals may have behavioral needs, but none have yet been determined. Before a behavior could be declared as needed, animals would have to be subjected to careful and thorough behavioral analysis in the specific environments of interest. Speculation about a reduced state-of-being under alleged behavioral deprivation has focused on animal emotions (discussed below).

A unitary model of behavioral motivation proposed in the 1970s by Barry Hughes provides one approach to determining behavioral needs. It involves three categories of animal motivation.

Category 1—External stimuli of animal behaviors are far more important than internal near one end of a continuum of the motivational mix.

Category 2—Both external and internal factors contribute to triggering behaviors in this motivational mid-range.

Category 3—Internal factors are chief releasers of behavior near the other end of the motivational-mix continuum.

Examples would be:

In hens—(1) escape behavior, (2) sexual-receptivity crouch, and (3) pecking

In sows—(1) mud-wallowing, (2) mating stance, and (3) maternal nest-building

In cows—(1) fly-swatting, (2) rumination, and (3) separation from herd prior to calving

Arguably, to ensure well-being, it is essential to accommodate any behavior pattern in category 3; that is, any behavior for which there is clear evidence of frustration (such as some stereotyped response) or pattern distortion if an animal tries to perform it in an unaccommodating environment. For example, a hen frustrated by the absence of a suitable nest may engage in stereotyped pacing before laying an egg. And phantom nest-building occurs in most sows within a day before parturition, regardless of environment. According to the theory, production environments should make it possible for animals to perform such behaviors.

Also, it would be reasonable to accommodate some of the behavioral patterns in category 2. In a hen, sexual crouch depends on an appropriate endocrine state, but ultimately it must be released by an external stimulus (namely, the presence of a male chicken), so it would not be considered a behavioral need. Dust-bathing, however, may be triggered by environmental stimuli (such as dusty air), although sometimes it occurs in a simple environment devoid of discernable external triggers, when internal factors appear to suffice to release the behavior. So dust-bathing would be considered a category-2 behavior that ought to be accommodated by the production environment.

PREFERENCES AND DEMANDS. An animal will express its preferences for environmental resources—such as among flooring and bedding types, between pens located adjacent to occupied or unoccupied pens, and among group and pen sizes. Relative strengths of preferences can be determined, too. For example, given the choice, pigs normally choose to reside in a pen next to an occupied pen. Their preference for a soil floor over a concrete floor counteracts this social preference, but that for straw bedding over woodshavings bedding does not. Similarly, hens may prefer an empty-feeder litter-floor cage to an empty-feeder wire-floor one, but a wire-floor cage furnished with a full feeder may be preferred over both.

Animals also readily learn to operate a switch for a reward of feed, heat, light, or water (operant conditioning). By increasing the number of switch responses required before a reward is delivered, and then observing how increasing this response:reward ratio affects animal activity, the relative strengths of motivations to gain different rewards may be gauged.

Interpretation of such preference and motivation results still remains a difficult task. Chosen resources or activities may actually cause harm. For example, hens choose to stand on flooring known to injure their feet over time; grazing animals sometimes choose to eat poisonous plants; and piglets suffering from diarrhea need an environment warmer than normal, but choose to reside where it is cooler than normal.

PERCEPTION AND COGNITION. Ian Duncan (1996) emphasizes that an animal's state-of-being has much to do with how that animal feels. Unfortunately, the limits of experiences that give an animal pleasure or displeasure, comfort or discomfort, pain or the absence thereof, remain unknown. There is evidence that what an animal perceives depends not only on the intensity and duration of the stimulus, but also on the animal's bodily and mental states at the time. For example, due to the phenomenon of alliesthesia, an animal that is experiencing heat stress finds great pleasure in exposure to the same cold air draft that it would find very unpleasant in a cool environment.

Future research on the cognitive processes (mental activity and intelligence) of livestock and poultry may provide insights into how the animals think, perceive, and feel, as well as permit more direct communication between humans and animals as we try to better understand their needs.

INHERENT EXPECTATIONS. Piet Wiepkema suggests that each animal has from birth an expectation of what constitutes a normal, comfortable, secure environment. Further, the animal continuously compares its actual environment of the moment against this expected environment. Discrepancy leads to environmental uncertainty; and the animal will work to bring its environment more in line with expectation. When the environment is more controllable—or at least more predictable—animals tend to feel more comfortable and more secure, even when facing stressors. Lack of either controllability or predictability may lead to anxiety, fear, and their consequences. It also is conceivable that the absence of environmental controllability or predictability will lead to learned helplessness, where the frustrated animal gives up trying to interact with its environment, and the quality of its life quickly deteriorates.

Clearly, variables such as these make it difficult to identify conditions that would ensure the well-being of a specific individual at a particular time, let alone all animals all the time.

ABNORMAL BEHAVIOR. An animal sometimes engages in behavior patterns that are not part of its healthy repertory as it tries to cope with an extreme environment. These "vices" include tail-biting in pigs, toe-pecking in chickens, wool-pulling in sheep, and intersucking in cattle. They typically are traumatic and do not enhance performance.

Many such anomalous behaviors are caused by stress due to frustration. Most behaviors are comprised of a series of preliminary (appetitive) patterns followed by a final (consummatory) act. For example, a hungry turkey, before it can actually swallow a bolus of feed, must walk to a feed trough, extend its neck, lower its head, open its beak, peck at and gather feed, move that feed back into the mouth, and mix it with saliva. If anything prevents the bird from completing any of these appetitive acts, it is frustrated in its attempt to eat. Common causes of frustration, in general, include blocking an original motivation to perform a behavior; restraint of movement; living in an environment that is either too exciting or too dull; or the absence of a key stimulus or needed resource. An animal may cope with frustration in four main ways:

1. It may repeatedly make the same preliminary acts, but never proceed to the final act, eventually developing stereotyped behavior (tic). A sow highly motivated to escape a tether may move its head stereotypically.

2. It may perform abnormal preliminary acts in trial-and-error fashion. A newly weaned lamb may try numerous openings in a fence as it searches for a way back to its dam.

3. It may direct the final act at an alternative target different from usual (redirection). A pig blocked in its drive to eat may redirect its bite at a waterer or a groupmate's tail.

4. It may change both preliminary and final behaviors by commencing an irrelevant activity (displacement). A hen frustrated in her search for a suitable nesting place may engage in displacement feather preening.

So it is that anomalous behavior patterns signal the possibility of a frustrating situation.

MALTREATMENT OF ANIMALS. Any instance of animal maltreatment falls into one of four categories—abuse, neglect, deprivation, and routinely inflicted pain (usually relatively minor and short-termed).

Outright abuse and ignorant neglect occur rarely—and should never occur—in respectable agricultural operations. They usually arise due to poor facility design or inadequately trained or supervised caretaker-handlers.

Deprivation—the form of maltreatment most difficult to assess—would involve denying the animal access to certain, often less vital environmental resources. Many alleged deprivations relate to possible behavioral needs (although no behavioral need has yet been ascertained, let alone characterized well enough to be useful in designing animal quarters). Any such need presumably would be signaled by demonstrations of an emotional state such as anxiety, discomfort, fear, frustration, or pain. Animal state-of-being is most controversial with respect to alleged deprivations, because animal feelings are not yet directly accessible by humans.

Inflicted pain refers to that associated with routine husbandry practices such as beak-trimming, branding, castration, dehorning, tail-docking, and nail-clipping. Questions today include: How should such a procedure be conducted to minimize trauma and pain at the time and inflammation and discomfort during recovery? Is the procedure justified in terms of trade-offs with benefits (see below)? Is there a suitable, less traumatic alternative?

ASSESSING ANIMAL STATE-OF-BEING. A thorough assessment of state-of-being ideally would reflect, at least in part, how the animal is feeling. Evaluation of conscious suffering cannot yet be included, however, because we still cannot know an animal's conscious activities. Instead, indirect clues—behavioral, physiological, immunological, anatomical, and performance indicators of stress and distress—must be detected and holistically interpreted. Overall health and performance are sensitive indicators of state-of-being, provided, of course, that the creature is constitutionally fit to be used agriculturally in the first place. A dairyman following cows' daily milk yields knows immediately that a particular cow is somehow not coping when her yield drops relative to herd average.

INEVITABLE COMPROMISES

Achieving complete, continuous animal well-being on farms remains a vague exercise. We have incomplete understanding of just what constitutes well-being; thus we are unable to accurately assess it. Also, compromise inevitably must be struck because animal agriculture is a business, and providing the best environment possible may be unprofitable.

Dennis Hardwick proposed the concept of a welfare plateau, according to which animals experience a satisfactory state-of-being over a range of conditions provided by various production systems. This plateau is not truly flat, however. Some improvement in state-of-being occurs as the environment is improved. But a production system located at any point on the welfare plateau is morally acceptable. In other words, animals are able to achieve well-being not only in one ideal set of circumstances. Moreover, on the welfare plateau, whereas a relatively small environmental change may subtly improve state-of-being, anywhere in this range, an animal is as *free of suffering* as possible.

Incidentally, because individual human preferences vary so much, even architects generally aim to achieve in facilities for use by humans the absence of discomfort as opposed to the presence of comfort.

A PUBLIC ISSUE: FARM-ANIMAL WELFARE

Ruth Harrison (1964), an English housewife, wrote *Animal Machines*. Her book criticized intensive systems of animal production as being fundamentally cruel. It aroused public interest and prompted the British Parliament to appoint a committee, chaired by F. W. R. Brambell (1965), to investigate Mrs. Harrison's expressed concerns. That committee's report stated (1) that animal welfare refers to "both physical and mental well-being"; (2) that its assessment must involve "scientific evidence available concerning the feelings of the animals that can be derived from their structure and function and also from their behavior"; and (3) that there are sound reasons for assuming that sensations and emotional states are substantial in animals and should be considered.

That report also established *a priori* "five freedoms," holding that an animal should at least be able, without difficulty, to turn around; groom itself; get up; lie down; and stretch its limbs. Of course, some intensive production systems widely used even today do not meet all of these criteria. Nevertheless, subsequent attempts to establish meaningful assessment of overall state-of-being of individual animals in agricultural production settings have sprung from this framework, which was set over 30 years ago and was based more on anthropomorphism (humanization of animal experiences) than on scientific knowledge of animal needs at that time.

Since the mid-1970s, "farm-animal welfare" has been a public issue across the Western hemisphere. It is destined to remain a smoldering issue on state and national political agendas into the foreseeable future.

Philosophical Considerations

Philosophers have been debating the general concepts of rights and welfare, respectively, for at least 3000 years. But for a couple of decades after farm-animal welfare emerged as a public issue in the mid-1970s, animal agriculture was unprepared to fully participate in the public debate, which has strong philosophical roots. For one thing, the very terms "right" and "welfare," which have various but nonetheless tight meanings for philosophers, tend to be used loosely by agriculturists and the agricultural trade press. Given the different interests of various segments of pluralistic societies, much of the tension that has attended and still attends farm-animal issues owes simply to confusion over terminology.

Hundreds of philosophical books, articles, and essays have been written and speeches given in recent decades on the topics of animal rights and animal welfare. Prominent thinkers on farm-animal issues in particular have included R. G. Frey, Tom Regan, Bernard Rollin, James Serpell, and Peter Singer, each taking a unique philosophical tack. Unfortunately, their offerings are generally inaccessible by most agriculturists because they are difficult to comprehend for those of us not trained in scholarly philosophical argument and discussion. Singer's *Animal Liberation*, first published in 1975, was, nevertheless, pivotal in engaging North American public interest in farm-animal welfare.

WELFARE (TRADES) VERSUS RIGHTS (TRUMPS). Measurement of welfare (state-of-being) of animals, as Paul Thompson has written, is still as contentious an exercise as that of humans. If and when consensus on definitions emerges, then the goal will be to identify ways and means of optimizing animal state-of-being. Of course, this ordinarily entails cost, so an important consideration inevitably is the benefit:cost ratio of pertinent public policy. In other words, trades (trade-offs) between costs and benefits are examined and a decision is made about "where to draw the line." Here the criteria become vexed because costs to one group (such as farmers) have to be weighed against benefits to another (such as consumers). A further complication is that the animals themselves comprise a third group across which benefits and costs have to be distributed.

The term "rights" has several meanings, and this also has caused confusion. Its core meaning depends on claims that can be made by or on behalf of one party against another party. Criteria for validating such claims depend on frame of reference. If a claim can be validated through action in a court of law, it represents a legal right; if by general principles of ethics and morality, a moral right; and if by custom or etiquette, an informal right.

Existence of a right in one context does not necessarily guarantee its existence in another. Neither does existence of a right necessarily imply existence of any supporting rights. A claim that an animal has a right not to be mistreated that has been validated by custom (informal right) or by law (legal right) need not imply that the animal has a moral right not to be used for human food. Neither does it necessarily validate all of the claims made by certain animal activists. So animals may be granted limited legal and customary rights without implying commitment to all of the extensive changes in agricultural production systems sought by some activists.

Use of the term "rights" also may indicate rejection of an evaluation process emphasizing trades (drawing the welfare line to optimize benefit:cost ratio), and the concept of trumps can explain this aspect of rights.

The process of examining trades (optimizing benefit:cost ratio) is constrained by rights. Trades that would violate individual rights are trumped by those individuals' valid rights claims. Similarly, welfare and rights can be opposing concepts in a variety of ethical, legal, and political controversies. Those who believe that lowering prices of animal-origin foods for consumers or raising profits for farmers is more important than certain perceived animal interests would be inclined to emphasize achieving a common good through a trades (welfare) approach. But those who find that important animal interests are about to be sacrificed would attempt to trump the welfare argument by insisting that valid animal rights would be violated.

Economic Policy Considerations

As Harold Guither has written, farmers adopted intensive animal-production systems because they allowed them to produce more product by substituting capital for labor and to achieve lower cost per unit of product. Clearly, intensive production has economic advantages. In the meantime, however, some of these methods have been severely criticized by animal activists. In terms of public policy, at least four alternative approaches to resolving these differences exist.

1. Pass laws requiring changes in production methods that activists allege cause animal suffering.
2. Pass laws requiring changes in production methods documented through science to cause animal suffering.
3. Encourage production systems that are intensive and at the same time engender animal well-being, because efficient food-production systems will be needed to supply growing worldwide demand.
4. Give consumers a choice among foods labeled as originating respectfully in animals kept in a variety of production systems that have been well-characterized regarding the animal state-of-being they engender.

How animals are treated and used in the future will depend mostly on public attitudes and ethical and social values, all of which probably will continuously change. In the current era, agriculturists can expect that, step by step, ethical values will foment and influence change in animal-production systems. But those changes probably will not come quickly, because farm-animal welfare probably will not be in the forefront for either state or federal legislative action.

Legal Considerations

As Jake Looney has written, up to now, the legal framework regarding animals in the United States has focused on concerns that they be treated humanely. Concerns related to the moral rights of animals, on the other hand, generally have not been recognized and validated as legal rights. Such legal rights probably will not soon be granted in the United States because they presumably would include the right not to be used for human purposes, which would run counter to strong cultural traditions and values.

Most states have anticruelty laws designed to prohibit gross mistreatment of animals in general. Some states' legislation, however, excludes agricultural animals altogether, and other legislation is limited to situations besides those considered standard farming practices. Only limited federal legislation exists related to the humane treatment of farm animals, and that has to do with very specific situations (such as "soring" of show horses, livestock transportation, and humane slaughter), some of which is specifically related to agricultural production.

The current situation in Europe differs considerably from that in the United States. Animal-protection laws pertaining to many farming practices already have been enacted in several nation states, although some soon turned out to be ill-founded and have been rescinded. Attempts at achieving trans-European consensus have been active for decades, but so far harmonization has been slow in coming there due to the complicated international politics of Europe.

Political Considerations

The public issue of farm-animal welfare has become more polarized in the United States than anywhere else. The issue's primary contending stakeholders—animal activists and agriculturists—will continue into the foreseeable future to tenaciously hold strong respective positions.

POLITICAL ACTIVISM IN THE UNITED STATES. For agriculture, animal-protection activist groups are a force to be dealt with. They have struck a sympathetic chord with a considerable part of the citizenry, and have generally been successful in garnering substantial financial contributions from their followers. As a whole, much of this money has been dedicated to political activism in Washington and in statehouses across the land. Overall, probably because many animal-protection organizations in this country enjoy much financial security, they have not been as willing to seek the progress toward their goals that could have been made by negotiating political resolutions with agricultural interests. The result of much of the humane community's inflexible, all-or-nothing approach so far has been that neither any state legislature nor the federal Congress has become engaged in the farm-animal welfare issue on a sustained basis.

Animal-protection organizations operate over a wide ideological front. With respect to farm-animal issues, some of the more moderate groups condone use of animals as human food, but are simply intent upon doing what they can—recently including networking with mainstream agricultural organizations—to ensure that farm animals will be treated humanely. Fervent activist organizations at the other end of the ideological spectrum, however, hold to strict moral-vegetarian views, and aim to see their radical notions of animal suffering and its causes become the law of the land, even to the point of abolishing animal agriculture.

Interestingly, Ruth Harrison, the woman who first wrote about farm-animal welfare several decades ago, more recently has said that, in the meantime, she has become more knowledgeable about farm-animal husbandry and also has learned to be more patient. She prefers not to be referred to as an animal activist, and emphasizes that the issue is more one of human responsibilities to animals than of animal rights versus human rights. Mrs. Harrison participated for many years as a constructive member of the official Farm Animal Welfare Council, advisory to the Ministry of Agriculture, Fisheries, and Food in the United Kingdom. She raised an important public issue in the early 1960s, and went on to serve as an excellent role model for concerned citizens. In her own quiet but persevering way, she has made a difference.

POSITIONS OF AGRICULTURE IN THE UNITED STATES. Agricultural organizations in the United States have invariably opposed legislative initiatives aimed at state or federal regulation of animal care on farms and ranches and in commercial channels.

Already in the early 1980s, however, many animal-agricultural organizations, together with ancillary support industry associations and professional and scientific societies, established the Farm Animal Welfare Coalition (FAWC). The coalition's purpose is to enhance communications on farm-animal welfare issues among agricultural stakeholders and to facilitate organization of initiatives and responses on the public-education and political fronts. The FAWC played a key role in orchestrating agriculture's participation in a congressional hearing on veal calf husbandry in the late 1980s. In the early 1990s, FAWC member organizations joined forces with the federal government to deal effectively with the controversial issue of "downer animals" (animals that arrive at markets or abattoirs in nonambulatory condition [unable to walk]). They oversaw agriculture's input at a hearing on this matter in the House of Representatives.

Also, in the 1990s, many national commodity organizations, of their own volition, appointed and staffed animal care committees (mostly comprised of producers) and commissioned task forces (mostly comprised of animal scientists, veterinarians, and producers) to develop guidelines for farm-animal care. These subsequently have been published and made available to producers nationwide.

Despite the fact that no new governmental regulations have been promulgated, treatment of farm animals on farms and in commercial channels in the United States has become more humane in recent years. This has been so especially with regard to the so-called abusive form of cruelty. Alleged deprivation of animals in terms of suggested behavioral needs remains a highly contentious issue between agriculturists and humane activists. Constructive discussion, negotiation, and compromise between these primary contending stakeholders have not yet occurred. Still, activists have demonstrated their ability to influence consumer demand for specific commodities of animal origin (for example, causing a reduction in the domestic demand for "special-fed" veal), at least in the short term, and thereby they have been successful in raising agriculture's attention to humane matters.

INDIVIDUAL STATE-OF-BEING VERSUS GROUP PROFITABILITY. There is another perennial source of debate between the two major sides in the farm-animal issue that is not likely to be resolved soon; namely, the common discrepancy between individual biological performance and returns to invested capital in production systems where animals are being kept at very low space allowances. Laying hens, for example, often are better off in terms of individual egglaying performance at space allowances greater than those at which profitability indices for an entire flock are maximal. The industry continues to keep laying hens at the more profitable, lower space allowance. The humane community continues to point out that, with such crowding, a hen is so distressed that her individual productive performance is subnormal.

Any change in position on this matter by either of the primary contending stakeholders would signal a breakthrough in depolarizing the farm-animal welfare issue.

SUMMARY

The animals we keep as livestock and poultry differ from their relatives we left in the wild. They are special in terms of environmental adaptability, having greater flexibility, range, resilience, and tolerance. But they do have limits to their adaptability, and can become distressed, physiologically and psychologically. When this occurs, the animal's state-of-being and performance usually deteriorate.

The cells reside in the animal's internal environment. Dozens of internal bodily traits ordinarily are maintained in steady states (homeokinesis) via scores of negative-feedback control loops. Quickly and automatically, via one or more diverse behavioral, functional, immune, or structural adaptive reactions, the animal attempts to maintain steady internal states in the face of changing and threatening external factors.

The external environments inhabited by livestock and poultry are complex and varied. To carefully evaluate practical animal environments, analyses should focus first on animal state-of-being, later on environmental traits. Agricultural animals may be produced in natural environments or artificial ones. Indeed, in some climatic regions, the animals need artificial shelter if they are to thrive the year round.

Environmental adaptation refers to any behavioral, functional, immune, or structural trait that favors an animal's fitness (its ability to survive and reproduce under given conditions). When an animal successfully copes with one or more threatening environmental factors, its response is an adaptive response, and it is said to have adapted. But when attempts to cope fail, the response is a stress response, and the environmental factor is called a stressor. There are four kinds of stress: understress (as in a barren environment); eustress (exciting but pleasurable experiences); overstress (unpleasant stimulation with which the animal cannot cope); and distress (severe overstress). Responses to environmental factors affect animal performance, ordinarily negatively, both directly and indirectly.

Animal state-of-being is best evaluated with respect to the numbers, kinds, and intensities of homeokinetic responses invoked in attempting to cope with present conditions. With a few or no responses, the animal is experiencing well-being; with minor stress responses, it experiences fair-being; and beyond its limit of adaptability, it experiences ill-being.

Needs motivate an animal to respond. In responding, animals prioritize their needs as follows: first, physiological needs; then, safety needs; and finally, perhaps, behavioral needs. Needs in the first two categories ordinarily are well-met in livestock and poultry operations.

Although no behavioral need has yet been certainly determined, it has been suggested that behavior patterns for which the chief releasers are internal should be accommodated by the environment. For example, it may be that maternal nest-building in the sow is triggered solely by internal hormonal events. If so, the environment in which sows about to farrow are kept should make it possible for the sow to engage in nest-building behavior. Otherwise, the sow would be frustrated in performing an internally driven behavior, and may experience the negative performance consequences that usually accompany frustration (including those due to "vices").

It may well be that an animal's state-of-being has much to do with how it feels, so an assessment of animal state-of-being ideally would reflect how the animal is feeling. Unfortunately, we still have little knowledge of animals' perceptions, feelings, or other cognitive experiences, so indirect clues must be detected and interpreted. Overall health and performance are sensitive indicators of state-of-being, provided the creature is constitutionally fit to be used agriculturally in the first place. Achieving complete, continuous animal well-being on farms remains a vague exercise.

Farm-animal welfare has been a public issue for over three decades. It is a multifaceted issue, and has philosophical, public-policy and political, and legal considerations in addition to biological aspects. An example of its complexity is the long-standing debate about individual-animal state-of-being versus animal-group profitability.

REFERENCES

Bowman, J. C. 1977. *Animals for Man.* London: Edward Arnold.

Brambell, F. W. R. 1965. Report of technical committee to enquire into the welfare of animals kept under intensive husbandry systems. Command Paper 2836. H. M. Stationery Office, London.

Broom, D. M., and Johnson, K. G. 1993. *Stress and Animal Welfare.* New York: Chapman & Hall.

Budiansky, S. R. 1992. *The Covenant of the Wild: Why Animals Chose Domestication.* New York: William Morrow.

CAST, 1997. *The Well-Being of Agricultural Animals.* Council for Agricultural Science and Technology. Ames, IA: Iowa State University Press.

Curtis, S. E. 1983. *Environmental Management in Animal Agriculture.* Ames, Iowa: Iowa State University Press.

Curtis, S. E. 1995. Ecological design: Philosophy and practice for animal systems. In *Animal Behavior and the Design of Livestock and Poultry Systems.* Northeast Regional Agricultural Engineering Service, Ithaca, New York.

Curtis, S. E., and Stricklin, W. R. The importance of animal cognition in agricultural animal production systems: An overview. *J. Anim. Sci.,* 69: 5001–5007.

Dawkins, M. S. 1993. Through Our Eyes Only?: The Search for Animal Consciousness. New York: Oxford University Press.

Duncan, I. J. H. 1987. The welfare of farm animals: An ethological approach. *Sci. Prog.,* 71: 317–326.

Duncan, I. J. H. 1996. Animal welfare defined in terms of feelings. *Acta Agric. Scand., Sec. A, Anim. Sci., Suppl.,* 27: 29–35.

Duncan, I. J. H., and Petherick, J. C. 1991. The implications of cognitive processes for animal welfare. *J. Anim. Sci.,* 69: 5017–5052.

FASS, 1998. *Guide to the Care and Use of Agricultural Animals in Agricultural Research and Teaching* (2nd ed.). Federation of Animal Sciences Societies, Savoy, Illinois.

Harrison, R. 1964. *Animal Machines.* London: Vincent Stuart.

Hemsworth, P. H., and Coleman, G. J. 1998. *Human-Livestock Interaction: The Stockperson and the Productivity and Welfare of Intensively Farmed Animals.* CAB International, Wallingford, United Kingdom.

Houpt, K. A. 1998. *Domestic Animal Behavior.* Ames, IA: Iowa State University Press.

Manning, A., and Dawkins, M. S. 1992. *An Introduction to Animal Behaviour* (4th ed.). Cambridge University Press, Cambridge.

McDowell, R. E. 1972. *Improvement of Livestock Production in Warm Climates.* San Francisco: W. H. Freeman.

Moberg, G. P. (Ed.), 1985. *Animal Stress.* Bethesda, MD: American Physiological Society.

NPPC, 1992. *Swine Care Handbook.* National Pork Producers Council, Des Moines, Iowa.

NRAES, 1995. *Animal Behavior and the Design of Livestock and Poultry Systems.* Northeast Regional Agricultural Engineering Service, Ithaca, New York.

NRC, 1996. *Guide of the Care and Use of Laboratory Animals.* National Academy Press, Washington, D.C.

Smidt, D. (Ed.). 1985. *Indicators of Welfare in Farm Animals.* Boston: Martinus Nijhoff.

Tauson, R. K. 1995. Comparative evaluation and development of housing systems for laying hens. In *Animal Behavior and the Design of Livestock and Poultry Systems.* Northeast Regional Agricultural Engineering Service, Ithaca, New York.

Taylor, I. A. 1995. Designing equipment around behavior. In *Animal Behavior and the Design of Livestock and Poultry Systems.* Northeast Regional Agricultural Engineering Service, Ithaca, New York.

USDA and Purdue University. 1993. Food animal wellbeing. *Conference Proceedings and Deliberations.* Purdue University, West Lafayette, Indiana.

Yousef, M. K. (Ed.). 1989. *Stress Physiology in Livestock,* Volumes I, II, and III. Boca Raton, FL: CRC Press.

CHAPTER ELEVEN
NEW AND EMERGING ISSUES

How will animals contribute to feeding the 8 to 10 billion people expected to inhabit the planet fifty or one hundred years from now? Most experts agree that this major challenge—perhaps the largest facing society in the next generation—will be met by ensuring the stewardship needed for a sustainable animal agriculture. The term sustainable animal agriculture refers to the pursuit of the principle that animal production specifically, and agricultural systems in general, must be environmentally, economically, and socially sound. This chapter examines some of the issues related to the future role of animals in meeting the challenge of producing an adequate food supply while, at the same time, adhering to the wise and prudent use of science and technology, and safeguarding environmental stability, biological diversity, food safety, and overall quality of life. Most students in animal science classes in colleges and universities in the United States no longer come from farms. The field of animal production has broadened to include not only the traditional farm animals—beef cattle, dairy cattle, swine, sheep, poultry, horses—but dogs, cats, other animals, birds, and aquatic species. Because of the broadened scope of animal production and its changing structure, many new issues have emerged. Some of these issues, acknowledged by contemporary society to be critical, are addressed in this chapter. As an important component of introducing students to animal production, some of these same issues are included in succeeding chapters on animals and their products and functions. The issues addressed do not necessarily offer solutions, but describe the challenges, options, and opportunities associated with them. We are grateful to Duane E. Ullrey, Professor of Animal Science Emeritus, Michigan State University and Daniel G. Sisler, Liberty Hyde Bailey Professor of Agricultural Economics, Cornell University for identifying and elucidating some of the issues addressed.

PLANT-ANIMAL ECOSYSTEMS

The total food production enterprise, on a global scale, involves a complex of plant and animal ecosystems, of which domesticated plants and animals are a major component, functioning symbiotically. A challenge to animal agriculture is to practice the stewardship needed to sustain balanced ecology and environmental stability while producing sufficient food, fiber, and other products to ensure adequate food and high quality of life in a world projected to double in population by the mid-twenty-first century. Some of the factors associated with a stable plant-animal ecosystem are briefly addressed here.

Cereal Grains, Oil Seeds, Crop Residues, and Their Byproducts

World grain production has increased nearly 300% in the last 50 years (from 631 million tons in 1950 to more than 1800 million tons in 1999). However, human population has increased faster, so that the amount available per capita has been declining since 1980, despite a steady increase in grain yield per acre. Nevertheless, World Bank estimated that the total world demand for cereal grains will double between 1992 and 2030 and that a major portion of that increase will be for the production of food animals. A large array of food processing byproducts and inedible food wastes from these cereal grains and from oil seeds and other crops are used for livestock feeding. Such resources include milling, distillery, and brewery byproducts, oil seed meals, and low-grade cereal grains and seed legumes declared substandard for human consumption. These products, were they not utilized for animal feed, would contribute to disposal problems and environmental pollution. This outlet for such resources reduces costs of meat, milk, and egg production while providing a market for byproducts of grain and seed legume processing.

Grazing Public and Private Rangelands and Pastures

Worldwide, ruminant animals (beef cattle, dairy cattle, sheep, goats, water buffalo, and other species) consume enormous quantities of harvested and grazed forage. Most of this animal feed is neither palatable nor of significant nutritional value to humans. Livestock use a sizeable portion of the total land base of little economic value for other agricultural uses (one-third or 704 million acres in the United States) for grazing, in addition to post-harvest grazing of cropland. Cultural practices such as overgrazing of rangelands and deforestation, which lead to decreases in biological diversity, and to soil erosion and im-balanced ecological systems, clearly are detrimental, but wisely planned and monitored plant-animal production systems that maintain a stable environment and balanced ecol-ogy seem attainable despite concerns to the contrary.

Approximately 262 million acres of public land in the western United States are grazed by livestock. For many years during the early settlement of the United States, western range-lands were not well managed and most were overgrazed. Livestock grazing in the United States was regulated first in 1897 on public forest reserves and in 1934 on the rest of the public rangelands. It is estimated that U.S. rangelands, with some exceptions, are currently in their best condition of the twentieth century as we enter the new millennium. Effective range management worldwide, on a par with that now practiced in the United States, should encourage long-term ecological balance needed for a stable global environment.

ECOLOGICAL BALANCE AND ENVIRONMENTAL QUALITY

Animal agriculture practiced in its most intense form has the potential for a serious nega-tive impact on the environment. Some of the factors associated with this concern are briefly discussed here.

Competition for Land Use

As human land use encroaches on agricultural land use, odors from livestock production units (farms) become a problem. Regulation must ensure that human housing and new animal production operations are not in juxtaposition. Continuing loss of highly produc-tive land to housing developments, shopping malls, roads, and other human activities as-sociated with an expanding population highlights the need for policies to encourage the preservation of these valuable acres for agriculture.

INCREASING EFFICIENCY OF ANIMAL AND CROP PRODUCTION. Improve-ment in animal production efficiency will reduce the number of animals necessary to pro-duce the same amount of product, just as increases in crop yields per acre will increase total food from plants available from the same land base. To meet future food needs, improved ef-ficiency of food production from both animals and crops will be required, while maintaining food production systems that will ensure ecological balance and environmental quality.

Water Quality and Use

Wastes from intense animal production facilities can pollute streams, surface water, and ground water. The greatest impact on water quality probably comes from the intense use of fertilizers (including manure and human sewage), herbicides, and pesticides. Systems of sustainable agriculture are being devised that will minimize the use of these agents and continue high productivity. Tillage and irrigation practices contribute to soil erosion, water pollution, and a conflict for water resources between use in agriculture and use for other purposes. These complex challenges are being addressed by agriculturalists and others working in interdisciplinary research and technology.

Future of Irrigated Agriculture

Irrigation dates back to Biblical times and has been a crucial factor for centuries in promoting food production throughout the world. The use of irrigation in intensive crop production in the United States is increasingly scrutinized as demands grow for water in nonagricultural uses. A Task Force Report (CAST, 1996) summarizes the future of irrigated agriculture in the western United States as follows:

> Irrigated agriculture in the western United States is faced with a confluence of change. Competition for increasingly scarce water supplies to serve growing urban and environmental needs means that water will become less generally available for irrigation. Ground water overdraft, which occurs in many locales throughout the West, cannot be sustained indefinitely, and some irrigated acreage ultimately will disappear as a result. Historically, federal water and agricultural policies have been very supportive of irrigated agriculture. Future policies will be less favorable as the federal government continues to transfer responsibility for water management to the states and as agricultural commodity programs and other agricultural support programs are curtailed or phased out. Environmental policies undoubtedly will require irrigated agriculture to economize on the use of natural resources and to minimize its contribution to environmental degradation. Simultaneously, the economic circumstances of western agriculture will become more demanding as markets for food and fiber become increasingly globalized.
>
> Change will not affect all regions of the West equally. Ground water overdraft is the most severe on the southern Great Plains but is also significant in Arizona and California. Rapidly growing urban areas will compete with irrigated agriculture for relatively fixed supplies in California and Arizona. Competition from environmental and instream uses will be pervasive but most intense in the Pacific Northwest where additional instream flows may be required to support anadromous fish, hydroelectric power generation, and navigation. . . .
>
> Historically, western growers generally have been both adaptive and innovative and thus have been able to adjust to change successfully. Many strategies are available to growers attempting to adapt to the future. These strategies include altering the crop mix to emphasize high-value fruits and vegetables; employing sophisticated technology and management schemes in managing water at the field level; and investing in research to develop improved crops, cultivation methods, and irrigation-

water management techniques. New and emerging means of adaptation will continue to evolve. Technologies permitting automation of irrigation systems and allowing water to be managed more precisely are developing. The advent of biotechnology adds greatly to the possibilities of developing new varieties of crops that are cheaper to produce probably because they require less water and other inputs but also yield products of superior quality. Innovations in the management of farming operations also should allow growers to adapt to changing and less favorable circumstances.

One of the largest reservoirs of underground irrigation water in the United States is the Ogallala Aquifer, which extends from Nebraska to Texas and provides water for intensive agriculture in these formerly arid regions of the Great Plains. There is concern that overdrafts of water removed from this aquifer through irrigation will force reductions in the production of grains, soybeans, and forages in this highly productive area.

Worldwide area of irrigation has increased steadily from 348 million acres in 1962 to 615 million acres in 1994. Concerns regarding irrigation in the United States are parallel to those in many other parts of the world. Policies to provide solutions to the problems of water scarcity for agriculture as world population increases will be needed everywhere.

Global Climate Change

Increases in the concentrations of carbon dioxide, methane, and nitrous oxide in the atmosphere (called greenhouse gases because they reduce the heat radiated away from the earth) enhance the likelihood of global warming. Agriculture accounts for only a small fraction of the contributions of greenhouse gases to the atmosphere. To compare the contribution of different activities to climate change requires a single measure called climate forcing. It combines the estimates of emissions of the various gases by each activity with the absorption of long-wave radiation from the earth and the estimated lifetime in the atmosphere of each gas.

Emissions of carbon dioxide from the globe are about 57% of all forcing (carbon dioxide from U.S. agriculture is about 0.3% of all forcing). Emissions from methane from the globe are 27% of all forcing (methane from U.S. agriculture is 0.4% of all forcing). Corresponding figures for nitrous oxide emissions are 17% and 0.4%, respectively.

Through photosynthesis, agriculture and forestry take in large amounts of carbon dioxide and store the carbon in crops and trees. In addition, much carbon is stored in timber, cotton, and other organic matter in the soil. Thus, agriculture and forestry sequester carbon in crops and timber. Increased crop and timber yields not only provide more food and forest products, but stash more atmospheric carbon dioxide.

Methane gas is produced by microorganisms in the digestive tracts of animals, particularly in the rumen of cattle, sheep, and wild ruminants, as a means of breaking down dietary fiber (grasses and other forages) to provide energy to the host animal. Methane constitutes up to 10% of the total energy released by fiber breakdown by these symbiotic microflora. It is lost from the animal into the atmosphere. Scientists are searching for ways to reduce this methane loss in food animals so as to decrease atmospheric methane and improve efficiency of energy use from fibrous feeds. Although methane emission from U.S. agriculture is only 0.4% of all forcing, any reduction in methane emission from animals would be a positive contribution. Domestic and wild ruminants contribute about 15% (mostly from the latter) of the total global methane production, one of the contributors to the potential for global warming.

World carbon emissions from the burning of fossil fuels reached a high in 1996, raising prospects for climate changes. A doubling in atmospheric concentrations of greenhouse gases is predicted to increase global temperature by 1 to 3.5 °C by the year 2100, causing environmental dislocation and adversely affecting agricultural production. A Task Force of the Council for Agricultural Science and Technology (CAST, 1996) addressed the question, "For a warmer climate with more people, more trade, and more carbon dioxide in the air, can U.S. farming and forestry within a few decades sustain more production while emitting less and stashing away more greenhouse gases?" The Task Force defined several policy steps needed to prepare for climate change. These included:

- Encourage flexible land use.
- Change institutions to encourage more prudent use of water.
- Raise the value of crop produced per volume of water consumed.
- Improve the efficiency of energy conversion in food production.
- Explore new biological fuels and ways to stash more carbon in trees and soil.
- Assemble, preserve, and characterize plant and animal genes.
- Conduct research on alternative crops and animals.
- Broaden research agenda to encompass adaptation to climate change.
- Encourage private research on adaptation.
- Make flexible skills the hallmark of agriculture's human resources.
- Promote freer trade and avoid protectionism.

The broad challenge to achieving ways to maintain ecological balance and environmental quality is to implement technologies and policies to accommodate long-term implications, rather than the short-term economics, of agricultural practices. Food animal production will continue because in many cultures animal products are desired and are more in demand as economic status improves. On a local or global scale, an urgent challenge is to factor the environmental impact of animal agriculture into decisions regarding the practices used, the size and intensity of the production units, and their locations relative to human population centers. Food animal production, to contribute most fully to human nutrition and well-being, must use strategies to change animal product composition in accordance with currently understood nutritional requirements and preferences and must adjust production practices as needed to sustain environmental quality.

ANIMAL WELL-BEING

Animal welfare has become an increasingly great issue during the past decade. Farm-animal care throughout history was left to the individual farmer. There has always been a built-in economic incentive to provide for the comfort and well-being of the animal to ensure maximum productivity of individual animals and therefore profitability of the enterprise. Good husbandry, which includes adequate shelter, nutrition, health care, sanitation, and other practices amenable to high productivity, remains a fundamental goal of most farm-animal producers. Opponents of food-animal production maintain that high productivity of animals is not synonymous with animal well-being. Specific husbandry practices, for example, standard veal calf management and use of crates for sows at parturition to minimize piglet deaths, have been cited as inhumane. The factors associated with good husbandry and with animal well-being are discussed in Chapters 9 and 10. The subject of animal well-being has become a critical issue of concern to society and particularly to animal agriculture. The Council for Agricultural Science and Technology addressed the issue in a comprehensive Task Force Report (CAST, 1997). The purposes of the report were to (1) outline philosophical, policy, and legal aspects of the public issues concerning the well-being of farm animals, (2) describe scientific approaches to assess their well-being, and (3) identify areas in which additional scientific insight would help ensure that they do experience well-being. The following subsections contain paragraphs that are quoted from the Interpretive Summary of that Task Force Report:

Philosophical Aspects

Welfare and rights can be opposing concepts in a variety of ethical, legal, and political controversies. The utilitarian strategy considers an action or policy justified in light of its cumulative consequences to all affected parties whereas the rights strategy states that certain traits (rights) must be protected and the morality of an act judged according to whether it respects the rights of other individuals.

Economic and Policy Aspects

Extreme animal-rights advocates call for the end of raising animals for food and co-products. Changes in how animals are treated could affect what is eaten and worn and what medicines remain available. Recent legislation in western Europe outlawed certain production systems and led to the collapse of affected agricultural sectors as well as to the importation of foods originating in production systems similar to those forbidden. Many of these laws since have been modified or rescinded as citizens have come to recognize domestic economic realities and the inevitability of undesirable events cascading from them. Judging from the western Europe experience, U.S. animal producers can expect ethical values to influence changes in animal care practices.

Legal Aspects

Concerns related to the ethical rights of animals generally have not been recognized as legal rights. In the United States, most states have anticruelty legislation to prohibit gross mistreatment of animals, but they often are criticized as ineffective, in part because of apathetic enforcement. Some state legislation excludes agricultural animals altogether whereas application of other statutes is limited to practices other than those customary in farming. Still other legislation applies only to unjustifiable actions or practices. No federal legislation exists related to the well-being of animals residing on farms.

Scientific Aspects of the Well-Being of Agricultural Animals

Although many of the issues of agricultural animal well-being probably will be resolved politically, for several reasons the scientific assessment of animal well-being is needed. Specific recommendations follow:

- Producers should continue to adopt scientifically based practices.
- Voluntary animal-care guidelines published by producer organizations have been based on scientific assessment of husbandry practices and should be consulted.
- Education of the general citizenry should be based on scientific assessment of animal well-being.
- The Congress of the United States should continue to consider scientific assessment and opinion seriously when addressing specific issues.
- The public should consider requesting scientific assessment of (1) the actual need to alleviate animal suffering and (2) the degree to which proposed alternative practices would alleviate any suffering.
- Future designs of animal accommodations and practices should reflect the results of scientific assessment.

Approaches to Scientific Assessment

Several proposals for assessing animal well-being have emerged. The report of a special committee to the British Parliament in 1965 constitutes the first attempt at addressing the issue. That report stated (1) that *welfare* refers to both physical and mental well-being. (2) that its assessment must involve "scientific evidence available concerning the feelings of the animals that can be derived from their structure and functions and also from their behavior," and (3) that there are sound reasons for assuming that sensations and emotional states are substantial in animals and should not be disregarded.

The report also established "five freedoms: an animal should at least be able without difficulty, to turn around, groom itself, get up, lie down and stretch its limbs." In the main, subsequent attempts to establish meaningful assessment of the overall well-being of individual animals have sprung from that framework.

Scientific Insight and Recommended Approaches

Animal scientists and others in agriculture have identified and prioritized six researchable areas that address questions of animal well-being (CAST, 1997). The six research areas are (1) bioethics and conflict resolution, (2) responses of individual animals to the production environment, (3) stress, (4) social behavior and space requirements, (5) recognition, and (6) alternative production practices and systems. Concurrent with the ongoing pursuit of these six areas identified for research focus, an approach recommended by the CAST Task Force of 14 scientists (CAST, 1997) would involve assembling a multidisciplinary team of expert scientists to assemble a worldwide database of reliable information on matters of farm animal well-being. Using the database, the team would employ appropriate statistical methods to elucidate indices of well-being in farm animals.

Animal well-being concerns are pervasive in contemporary society, and satisfactory progress in improving real and perceived deficiencies in animal care will require sustained long-term research and public education and support. The future of animal agriculture will be shaped to a large degree by the success with which those involved in the production of animals are perceived as upholding high standards of animal care and well-being. The 1997 CAST Task Force Report on the Well-being of Agricultural Animals addresses the issue objectively and its conclusions and recommendations represent a framework of action to achieve common ground between animal agriculture and contemporary urban society on the animal well-being issue in the new millennium.

BIOLOGICAL DIVERSITY

Creation of life was followed by great diversity of plant and animal species during the ongoing evolutionary process. This biological diversity is of importance in both animal and crop production. Countless species of plant and animal life inhabit the planet, from single-cell organisms to the most complex organisms. Stewardship of this vast array of living organisms is an increasing challenge as population pressure mounts. The focus here is mainly on the animals and plants that contribute most prominently to food and fiber, recognizing the inherent interdependence of life at all levels.

Animals

Of the hundreds of species of mammals and birds in nature, only about 30 have been domesticated. The characteristics and production of many of these species are described in individual chapters of this book. Now there is a modest understanding of the biology, nutrient needs, and husbandry requirements of most of these species. That understanding is restricted to a narrowly defined set of environmental circumstances, using a limited range of dietary ingredients to meet the needs of animals whose genetic diversity is markedly restricted. This is an issue of concern, should our present breeds be unable to adjust to unforeseen environmental change. Agronomists have prepared for this by establishing "banks" containing seeds from plants of many species from many parts of the planet. Seed banks for animals are more difficult to establish and maintain because, although semen and embryos of some species have been preserved by freezing, preservation technology for most species has not been developed, and tissue viability depends upon expensive freezers, an uninterrupted power supply, and suitable female recipients.

It is ironic that the need for diversity in wild ecosystems is widely recognized in the scientific community, yet dozens of livestock breeds have been abandoned. Most breeds were developed by physical isolation and genetic divergence of traits that made them especially suitable for specific environments (for example, one sheep breed is metabolically unique in its tolerance of the high copper concentrations found in plants growing within the region where the breed evolved). Emerging biotechnology (see next section) may be used as a tool in the future to retain biological diversity in animals. The genome of a rare breed of cattle in New Zealand has been saved recently by producing a clone of the last survivor using modern cloning technology.

Those livestock breeds that predominate in animal agriculture do so because they have been selected for productive traits judged to be of high economic importance. If the adaptive traits of a favored breed do not match the natural environment in which the breed lives, that environment may be altered to accommodate the favored breed. This involves advanced technology and costly inputs, often associated with increased dependence on nonrenewable resources.

As the human population continues to grow, there is increasing concern that nonrenewable resources will be exhausted before alternatives can be found. A preview of what can happen when resources are suddenly reduced was experienced in the United States in the early 1970s. Shortages of petroleum products associated with curtailed imports forced severe conservation of energy, nitrogen, and phosphorus, and agronomic practices were modified to minimize fuel use. The resulting reduced supplies and increased costs of feedstuffs needed for intensive animal agriculture, in turn, forced changes in animal diet composition and shifted husbandry toward greater use of forage.

If similar or more serious crises recur, it is possible that livestock breeds and animal species other than those currently favored in the United States may become more important in meeting our needs. Some alternative breeds or species could be of use now in developing regions where financial resources and natural environments are significantly different from our own. Although some breeds are already extinct, the American Livestock Breeds Conservatory (P.O. Box 477, Pittsboro, NC) is leading preservation of the remainder. Breeds with numbers classified as critical have fewer than 200 annual registrations in North America and an estimated global population less than 2,000. Breeds classified as rare have fewer than 1,000 annual registrations in North America and less than 5,000 in the global population. Examples of the latter include: Dexter cattle, Nigerian Dwarf goats, Clydesdale horses, Karakul sheep, and Hereford swine. Breeds on the watch list have fewer than 2,500 annual North American registrations and global populations less than 10,000. Examples in this category include Ayrshire, Guernsey, Highland, Milking Shorthorn, and Red Poll cattle, and Tamworth swine.

One can argue whether the loss of any of the breeds on the critical, rare, or watch lists would result in irreparable damage to humans, just as one can argue whether the loss of an endangered species, such as the greater panda, is important. The underlying causes for the loss of breeds or species may differ, but extinction of animal species or breeds within species represents the loss forever of potentially useful genes.

Generous support from private industry in the 1950s and 1960s, when Clydesdale horses were near extinction, saved this beautiful breed. But as pleasing as Clydesdale horses are to look at, there are more practical reasons why breed conservation may be important. Clydesdale, Belgian, and other breeds of draft horses are still widely used for farm work in many cultures. For example, Amish and Mennonite farmers in several areas of the United States use these large horses in preference to mechanized equipment for planting, cultivating, and harvesting crops. Meishan sows from China, in comparison with contemporary U.S. and European breeds of sows, have a shorter farrowing interval and farrow and raise larger litters of pigs. Thus, while contemporary Western breeds of pigs are highly favored in the United States for their rapid growth and lean carcasses, genetic contributions from the Meishan and other Asian breeds might improve fecundity and enhance profitability.

Several species have characteristics so unique, it is surprising they have not been domesticated previously. One of these is the babirusa (Babyrousa babyrussa), a piglike mammal native to a few islands in eastern Indonesia. It probably was introduced into the Sula and Buru Islands by prehistoric peoples. It is easily tamed, and the young have been caught and raised for meat. One of the features that makes this species so unique and potentially useful is its compound stomach, similar to that of the sheep. Babirusas consume leaves, fruit, roots, and grubs, but do little rooting, unlike pigs. Although the babirusa's ability to use fiber through microbial fermentation is still uncertain, the morphology of its gastrointestinal tract is consistent with that possibility. If efficient utilization of dietary fiber can be demonstrated, the babirusa would be particularly useful in circumstances in which forage is abundant but concentrates are in short supply.

Plants

As in the case of animals, a relatively small number of plant species are used as crops for human food and animal feedstuffs worldwide. In the United States, the major crops include corn, cereal grains, soybeans (and other seed legumes), root crops, tubers, grass and legume forages, and an array of fruits and vegetables. Almost all of these crops were introduced into North America from other continents. Through the process of new crop introduction, testing, and acceptance or rejection by farmers and consumers, U.S. agriculture has become based on a relatively narrow spectrum of crops. Nearly 80% of the annual acreage of row-crops in the United States is planted to corn, wheat, and soybeans. The result is that many growers have few alternatives, and low and fluctuating prices have serious economic consequences. The Council for Agricultural Science and Technology has recommended that an initiative be funded for diversification of crops in the United

States through new crop development. High-potential crops that have existed here, but are not widely used, have been identified for attention as alternative crops because of their special characteristics. These crops include kenaf (a fiber source for industrial use), pistachio (edible nut), quinoa (unique starch properties for industrial uses), meadowform (seed oil has unique properties for derivatives), milkweed (nonallergenic filler for pillows and jackets), and a tree, Taxus brevifolia, the bark of which contains an anti-cancer substance.

Plant breeding programs have emphasized economically important production traits such as yield and resistance to specific pathogens; this has resulted in a narrow genetic diversity within a particular crop. The consequent vulnerability to disastrous crop failure due to a plant disease epidemic could threaten the demise of a highly productive strain of that plant species and lead to a serious food shortage. The historic Irish potato famine is a graphic example of the impact of a failure of a specific staple food crop. There is a recognized need for preserving plant germ plasm for future potential use. Seeds from many species of plants collected from around the world are now stored in "seed banks" as a means of sustaining biological diversity for the future.

Research is underway on several fronts to develop strains of specific crops with resistance to drought, specific pathogens, or insect pests, or having particular characteristics related to harvestability (e.g., short-stemmed wheat) or pest palatability (e.g., high tannin grain sorghum for bird resistance).

Plant biodiversity has made giant steps through the efforts of geneticists using gene-transfer techniques to introduce traits of particular importance such as yield, nutrient content, disease resistance, shelf-life, or general consumer acceptance of the commodity. These "designer crops" run the gamut from corn, grains, soybeans, and forages to fruits and vegetables. This breakthrough in crops has its counterpart in animals, discussed as a separate issue under biotechnology.

BIOTECHNOLOGY

Biotechnology, broadly defined, includes any technique that uses living organisms or processes to make or modify products, to improve plants or animals, or to develop microorganisms for specific purposes. The rapidly developing field of biotechnology has created many new opportunities in agricultural and medical science. Much of the new knowledge is quickly being applied. Some of the emerging technologies raise ethical and moral issues that society must ultimately address. Biotechnology focuses on two powerful molecular genetic techniques, recombinant deoxyribonucleic acid (rDNA) and cell-fusion technologies. We focus here on four interrelated aspects of biotechnology: recombinant DNA technology, transgenic animals, cloning animals, and xenotransplantation.

Recombinant DNA Technology

A major contribution of recombinant DNA (gene-splicing) technology is the reality of producing mass quantities of hormones, enzymes, amino acids, and other proteins in microorganisms. Growth hormone, insulin, insulin-like growth factors (IGFs), and other hormones used in human medicine and, more recently, in animal production are now available for widespread use, whereas previously the only source was from animal organs; the supply was limited and the cost was often prohibitive. The amino acids lysine, threonine, and tryptophan, present in inadequate amounts in most plant feedstuffs for normal animal growth, are now produced in microorganisms by gene-splicing technology and can be supplemented in pure form in animal diets, thereby reducing protein supplements and diet costs. Enzymes such as phytases, not produced by animal cells, are now available from microbes produced by gene splicing, allowing more efficient utilization of phosphorus in pig and poultry diets and reducing environmental phosphorus overloading. Vaccines for infectious disease control also are produced by recombinant DNA technology. These products and other pharmaceuticals are now in use commercially and many more are likely to follow, contributing enormously to animal production efficiency and human health. Numerous examples of applications of recombinant DNA technology could be cited in crop production. The animals or plants administered these biological products are not altered genetically, so the effects are not passed to their progeny.

Transgenic Animals

Transgenic farm animals have been produced in research laboratories to investigate the possibility of improving production traits such as growth rate and milk production, to increase resistance to infectious disease, and most recently, to secrete specific products into the milk of transgenic sheep for potential use in human medicine (in this case, Human Factor IX, a blood-clotting factor, for clinical use in hemophiliac patients). The main method of producing transgenic animals is to microinject DNA into the pronucleus of fertilized oocytes. Briefly, ova are placed in an injection medium and under a microscope, and DNA is injected through the zona pellucida (membrane surrounding the oocyte) into the pronucleus of the ovum. The injected ova are cultured a few hours and then transferred directly into the oviduct of the time-matched host female.

Transgenic pigs that have high blood levels of growth hormone (GH) have been produced. The transfer of the GH gene has been accomplished using a fusion gene[1] produced by fusing the regulatory region of the metallothionein gene (MT), which causes MT synthesis in liver, kidney, and other tissues, with the structural region of the growth hormone gene (GH). Thus, when the MT-GH fusion gene is introduced into the fertilized pig ovum, the resulting transgenic pigs express the GH gene not only in the pituitary gland (the normal source of GH), but also in several other tissues in the body as a result of the presence of the regulatory region of the MT gene. Since the original research with MT-GH fusion gene, many other fusion genes have been studied to improve GH expression in transgenic pigs.

---

[1]A gene is composed of two major regions, structural and regulatory. The structural component contains the DNA coding sequences that determine the structure of the messenger RNA. The regulatory component contains the DNA coding sequences that control the timing, location, and amount of messenger RNA produced by the structural component. See Chapter 6 for greater detail.

Most of the transgenic animals produced to date are mice. Transgenic mice have been used as a research tool to determine the effects of deletion of functional genes (knockout mice). This approach is a powerful tool to elucidate many metabolic phenomena in laboratory animals and potentially in other animals and humans. The concept of gene therapy in humans to correct metabolic defects causing chronic degenerative diseases (e.g., abnormal liver lipoprotein metabolism leading to atherosclerosis) is receiving major attention in biomedicine.

Cloning Animals

Cloning may be defined as the creation of a genetic duplicate of an individual organism through asexual reproduction, as by stimulating a single cell. When Dolly, a Finn-Dorset lamb (referred to in Chapter 6), was successfully cloned from mammary tissue of a 6-year-old ewe, scientists and the public alike were excited by the prospect of other applications. Differentiated cells, such as those in mammary tissue, contain an animal's entire genetic blueprint, but genes permitting differentiation into other cell types are normally turned off. Remarkably, in this research, scientists were able to turn on all genes as they would in an undifferentiated embryo. Several laboratories worldwide are working on cloning in livestock. Most are using fetal cells rather than undifferentiated cells, and sheep, cows, and other species have now been cloned in this way. The same group that produced Dolly have now cloned sheep carrying foreign genes. They produced six live transgenic lambs by nuclear transfer of ovine primary fetal fibroblasts tranvected with a gene marker and a human coagulation factor IX gene construct designed for expression of the coagulation factor in sheep milk. Of the six transgenic lambs, three contained the factor IX. This breakthrough research demonstrated that somatic cells can be subjected to genetic manipulation in vitro and produce viable animals by nuclear transfer rather than by the earlier method involving pronuclear injection. The door is now open not only for eventual production of transgenic populations of sheep to supply a source of factor IX for use in clinical medicine, but for the potential of transgenic animals produced by nuclear transfer for use as organ donors, and for improved production traits (e.g., faster growth, increased disease resistance, leaner meat, greater reproductive efficiency). Studies are in progress involving production of blood-clotting factors in transgenic pigs and of a protease inhibitor in sheep. At least two compounds are now in clinical trials with humans.

The production of a Holstein calf by cloning a stem cell from a 30-day-old calf fetus demonstrated that this procedure can be used to produce a whole animal. Stem cells are the relatively unspecialized embryonic cells that differentiate into a variety of cell types making up the entire body. Stem cells are being cultured to learn more about factors controlling differentiation in the hope that means will be found to direct differentiation into development of particular tissues such as skin, heart, liver, or nerve that might ultimately be used for grafts or transplants. Two U.S.-based companies have joined forces to produce cloned cattle that would produce milk containing human proteins. Plans are to introduce the appropriate human gene into newly fertilized cells. The cells in which gene transfer is successful will be cloned to produce a herd of identical cows with human protein-synthesizing ability. The objective is to provide an alternative source of human albumin that is currently derived from human plasma. Worldwide use of this protein is currently 440 metric tons per year with a value of $1.5 billion.

It has become clear that the ability to turn genes on and off (as demonstrated in the Dolly cloning study) could be very important to the repair and replacement of defective body parts. For example, if scientists could control gene-regulating substances that influence cellular differentiation, they may be able to stimulate regrowth of nerve cells which do not normally regenerate after spinal cord injury, or they may be able to produce new skin for burn victims or new bone marrow for leukemia patients.

There is speculation in the media about cloning humans, stirring debates concerning the ethics of cloning procedures. Some countries have already banned human cloning, and this profound ethical and religious issue most certainly will challenge society for the foreseeable future.

Xenotransplantation

The use of animal organs to replace diseased or defective organs in humans is an active field of research. Recent advances in dealing with immunological rejection of donor organs by the recipient and improved surgical techniques have brought the prospects of the widespread use of xenotransplantation near the horizon. There are several potential benefits of using animal organs instead of human organs for transplantation. The number of human organ donors has not kept pace with the increasing demand. The use of animal organs for transplantation (xenografts) would relieve this organ shortage. Through the use of transgenic animals, a xenograft donor might provide organs to serve as delivery vehicles for gene therapy in appropriate cases. The pig has emerged as the animal of choice for use in xenotransplantation, even though nonhuman primates might intuitively be regarded as the ideal choice. Reasons for this include: pigs are available in large numbers; the size of pig organs is appropriate for human recipients; pigs are easier to breed and are more prolific; pigs are less likely to harbor infectious diseases that might be transmitted to the recipient; technologies for genetic engineering of pigs to provide organs for xenotransplantation are for practical reasons more applicable than for nonhuman primates. Assuming that the immunological hurdles to xenotransplantation of pig organs to humans (i.e., hyperacute rejection, acute vascular rejection, cellular rejection, and chronic rejection) can be overcome during the near future, as predicted by researchers in the field, the use of this technology in human clinical medicine may be at hand early in the twenty-first century.

FOOD SAFETY

Throughout human history, food has been a source of contamination with pathogenic organisms and other toxicants. Cooking animal products before eating them has probably been practiced for as long as fire has been harnessed. Yet, as the twenty-first century begins, the issue of food safety looms as a major public concern. In addition to the threat of food poisoning by microorganisms, there has long been concern about chemical residues from pesticides and other environmental contaminants and about tissue residues of feed additives and antibiotics fed to animals. For many years, the U.S. Food and Drug Administration (FDA) has monitored the animal feed and human food supplies in accordance with federal laws passed to ensure a safe and wholesome food supply in the United States. Federal laws are bolstered by state and local laws and regulations related to a safe food supply.

Forces driving change in food safety in the United States in the twenty-first century described in a special publication of the Council for Agricultural Science and Technology (CAST, 1998) are:

1. Globalization of the food supply through increased international trade of animal and plant food products

2. A shift from a major focus on chemical residues to microbial pathogens

3. Development of a conceptual framework of food safety in regulatory agencies around the world, culminating in the emergence of systematic monitoring and control of food safety through a program called Hazardous Analysis Critical Control Point (HACCP)

The future of food quality and safety is characterized by three trends (CAST, 1998): (1) greater reliance on "systems" approaches, (2) proliferation of food safety standards, and (3) greater application of scientific and technological solutions to food safety problems, for example, wider use of pasteurization and greater acceptance by the public of food irradiation as an effective and safe method of food preservation.

Chemical Residues in Animal Tissues and Products

Tissue residues of antibiotics, hormones, feed additives, and toxic chemicals in animal products used for human consumption are rarely present, thanks to careful monitoring and inspection practices. When violations are discovered, federal and state regulators act quickly to minimize the dissemination of the contaminated product. The public concern about the safety of animal products with regard to tissue residues is appreciated by the food industry and continuous monitoring of the safety of the food supply ensures minimum risk.

Pathogenic Organisms in Food

Of greater concern than that of residues of environmental contaminants and feed additives in the tissues of animals or in milk and eggs, to most Americans, is that of pathogenic organisms. Ingestion of pathogenic strains of Salmonella, *Escherichia coli,* and Campylobacter and other microbes has been responsible for sporadic outbreaks of serious food poisoning in several locations in the United States in recent years. Pathogens can be present in almost any food. Animal products, including meat, milk, and eggs, are all potential sources of these pathogens. Hamburger is a favorite American food, served every day at backyard cookouts and countless fast-food restaurants. In years past, local butcher shops would grind hamburger fresh from less-expensive cuts of beef. At that time, beef carcasses were delivered in halves to the butcher shop and would be broken down there into retail cuts. Now, to improve efficiency, meat distributors commonly prepare retail cuts and grind hamburger at a central processing facility. This extends the time between processing and consumption, and allows contaminating organisms more time to multiply. Because such organisms are most likely to contaminate the external surfaces of the carcass, steaks and roasts are least likely to constitute a hazard. However, grinding incorporates external surfaces throughout the hamburger and, if improperly handled or stored, multiplication of contaminating organisms will be favored. Thorough cooking normally eliminates the hazard but, as news reports attest, not everyone consumes thoroughly cooked meat.

A variant of *Escherichia coli,* O157:H7, is a particularly dangerous contaminant, causing severe gastrointestinal cramps and blood diarrhea, and can be fatal to children, geriatric patients, and others with compromised immune systems. Although *E. coli* O157:H7 is not restricted to hamburger, and there are contaminants in other food products (including fruits and vegetables), this organism has caused the recall of millions of pounds of hamburger. These incidents and others have led to a reevaluation of the U.S. meat inspection system, and new procedures have been put in place to provide greater assurance of product quality. These improvements can now be reinforced by irradiation of meat with gamma rays prior to sale, a safe and effective tool just approved for use. Irradiation does not cause the meat to become radioactive, nor does it alter its nutritional value. It appears that the appropriate use of this and related technologies will protect the public health and enlarge the opportunity to process and prepare meat in ways that are affordable, yet preserve the meat's taste appeal.

Mad Cow Disease (Bovine Spongioform Encephalopathy, BSE)

A recent addition to the list of concerns about food safety is the possible association between a neurological disease of cattle, bovine spongioform encephalopathy (BSE), sometimes called mad cow disease, and Creutzfeldt-Jakob disease (CJD), a fatal neurological affliction of humans. BSE was first identified in Great Britain in 1986. The disease is caused by a prion, a small protein that is a member of a new class of infective agents (it is not a bacteria or other microbe). As a consequence, there is great concern about cross-species transmission of this prion to humans from consumption of infected beef products, particularly nervous system tissues that contain the prion. The result has been to disrupt the market for beef in the European Economic Community and to essentially eliminate Britain's cattle herds from that and other markets.

BSE is difficult to study because of the prolonged incubation period (the interval between infection and signs of illness). Although BSE has not been found in the United States, the possibility that byproducts such as meat and bone meal from ruminants might serve as a carrier of the disease when fed to other ruminants has led to an FDA ban on this practice. The progressive brain disease of sheep, called scrapie, is also caused by a prion, but there is no evidence that scrapie causes CJD in humans. The prion protein of scrapie is different from that of BSE.

Whenever public confidence is shaken by reports of a health problem with a food, the economic impact is serious. When a Chicago radio station reported the death of an Indiana resident from CJD and implied a connection to cattle, market prices of grain and cattle went into free-fall. Fortunately, there was no evidence of the involvement of BSE. To avoid a future problem, importation into the United States of ruminants and ruminant animal products has been banned from countries where BSE is present and from a number of countries where it may be present. In addition, a cooperative federal-state BSE surveillance program has been started. As a further precaution, meat and bone meal from ruminant animals cannot be fed to ruminants in the United States. To date, no BSE has been found in the United States.

Naturally Occurring Antimicrobial Agents in Animals and Plants

It is increasingly perceived by the consumer that food antimicrobials that are industrially synthesized may be associated somehow with toxicity or inferiority (akin to the incorrect assertion that "natural" vitamins are somehow superior to synthetic vitamins). Thus, interest has been generated in the food industry for the use of naturally occurring agents for food preservation and safety.

Many naturally occurring antimicrobial agents exist in animal and plant tissues, where they probably evolved to protect the host against invasion by microbes (CAST, 1998). Naturally occurring antimicrobials can be obtained from plant leaves, flowers, stems, and fruit and from various animal tissues and products. Examples of antimicrobials found in plant and animal products are citric, benzoic, and ascorbic acid from many fruits and vegetables, cinnamon from tree bark, thymol from the herbs sage and mint, lysozyme from egg white, and lactoferrin from milk. This list represents only a small fraction of naturally occurring substances with antimicrobial activity. In light of consumer demands for minimally processed and safe foods and the projected continued growth of the world population, there is an incentive for expanded use of these natural products. However, their increased use will depend on adequate research, commercial development, and assured safety and sensory acceptability. Genetic manipulation of plants and animals to enhance the production of some of these antimicrobials also may be a possibility.

ECONOMIC SUPPORT FOR AGRICULTURE

The future of food production depends on sound research, education, and technology transfer of new knowledge. Renner (1997), in summarizing the conclusions of the National Science Board (1996), stated, "It is widely accepted in modern societies that investing in research and development (R&D) programs in such varied areas as product innovation, productivity and competitiveness, health care, food grain yields, protection of the environment, and national defense is essential to the welfare of a society."

Economic development in a particular country has historically been driven by a strong agriculture. The unprecedented growth of the U.S. economy over the past century depended to a major degree on the strong support provided through federal, state, and local funds for education (primary, secondary, and college), research, and extension. The establishment of Land Grant Colleges and Universities in each state and of the Federal and State Extension Services to enable the transfer of research findings directly to farmers for immediate application proved to be the engine that drove the agricultural economy forward during a time when most of the U.S. population was engaged in farming. Support for agriculture is more critical now than ever before because of the rapidly growing world population and the finite land, water, and other natural resources available. Global agriculture requires global efforts for support. This brief summary of current sources of economic support for agriculture is intended to engender an appreciation of the scope and importance of this issue in the context of the massive increases in food production needed over the next century and beyond. Among Organization for Economic Cooperation and Development (OECD) countries (representing mostly developed countries and accounting for most of R&D expenditures), governments are contributing about one-third of R&D funds, industry about 60%, and universities and other nongovernment groups the remaining 6 or 7% (Renner, 1997).

The world economy is growing rapidly. Total output of goods and services increased by nearly 4% annually during the mid-to-late 1990s, resulting in an annual gross world product near $30 trillion in recent years. Developing countries grew at more than twice the rate of the developed (industrialized) countries (more than 6% vs. less than 3% annually). The most rapid growth occurred in Asia (e.g., China and Viet Nam). Long-term trends are always subject to fluctuations, as exemplified by the economic crises in Asia in 1998, which had a negative impact on the world economy. The long-term increased buying power in developing countries has resulted in substantial increases in per-capita meat consumption in these countries. Total world meat production reached a level of 195 million tons in 1996 (compared with 112 and 152 million tons in 1976 and 1986, respectively) and continues to expand. The increased meat consumption has been accompanied by similar increases in world grain and soybean harvests. Of concern is the ability of agriculture to continue to increase food production at a rate fast enough to keep up with the increasing demands in a world of shrinking available land for food production.

Economic support for agriculture has been vital in the past and will be increasingly vital. Public funding sources include tax revenues of individual governments (in the United States, by federal and state appropriations), and such international agencies as the Food and Agriculture Organization (FAO) of the United Nations (UN), International Monetary Fund (IMF), Organization for Economic Cooperation and Development (OEDC), and World Bank. Many international centers for research in plants and animals have been developed and consortia formed to implement their cooperation and efficiency. Private sources include foundations such as Rockefeller, Ford, Kellogg, and many others; charities such as Heifer Project International; cooperatives involving a range of plant and animal commodities; and private industry (farm equipment, feed/fertilizer, pharmaceuticals). Economic support from private industry comes in the form of goods and services which spur the farm economy directly and indirectly and in the form of research support for specific topics related to their specific needs and interests. Recently, collaborative arrangements between private industries and universities and/or government as two- or three-way partnerships have evolved as a means of improving cost effectiveness, output, and utilization of research results.

In the United States, joint efforts of commodity groups and of professional societies have been successful in developing congressional appropriations for competitive research funding among scientists in universities, government, and private industry. An example is the National Research Initiative (NRI) Competitive Grants Program sponsored by the Agricultural Research Service of the U.S. Department of Agriculture. This program funds several million dollars annually to scientists in many areas of animal and plant biology to address researchable areas aimed at increasing efficiency and productivity of agriculture. Other countries have similar research support programs.

Economic support for agriculture will be generated at an adequate level only if consumers and consumer groups understand that sustained food production and an acceptable standard of living require their support.

CHALLENGES AND OPPORTUNITIES FOR ANIMAL SCIENCE GRADUATES IN THE TWENTY-FIRST CENTURY

This final issue is the most significant of all those addressed in this chapter because it involves humans, the most valuable resource of all. Today's students of animal science will play a large part in shaping the future of animal agriculture and society. With only a small minority of today's students having grown up on a farm or even having had more than a cursory exposure to farm life, the animal industry of the future will be in the hands of highly trained and able leaders whose experiences will differ greatly from those of the farm-reared majority of a generation or two ago.

The many and varied opportunities awaiting those with training in animal science include farming and ranching, agribusiness, banking, teaching, extension work, research, and many types of technical service in private industry and government. For those who complete advanced training, positions are available for graduates in university teaching, research and extension, government research, or administrative and technical responsibilities in regulatory agencies. The rapidly developing field of biotechnology offers new opportunities. The exciting activities recounted above (in the section on biotechnology) illustrate the dynamism of biology, of which animal science is a part. Animals will continue to be important sources of food and recreation, and their contributions to biomedicine in the twenty-first century may be significant. The specialized nature of the new technologies will require that animal scientists be very well trained, and scientists and technologists with different specialties will have to work together.

Agriculture is a growth industry and students with training in animal science will find challenging and rewarding positions in the United States and in international settings. The broad field of production agriculture runs the gamut from farm or ranch ownership through the many allied industries that provide the goods and services required by farmers and ranchers, such as feed, fertilizer, farm equipment, meat, milk, poultry and egg processing and marketing, and many more. For those interested in companion animals, opportunities also exist in breeding enterprises, kennels, racetracks, animal training, zoos, and more.

Students who are motivated for more training in animal science after completing the introductory course are encouraged to explore additional animal science courses, but also to sample other areas of science, economics, and business that might complement their animal science training in career preparation. Whatever their area of specialization, those with training in animal science will be participating in the greatest societal challenge of the twenty-first century—feeding and improving the quality of life of this and future generations.

SUMMARY

With a rapidly expanding human population living on a planet with finite space and resources, many issues are emerging related to food production, including the role of animals in the food and fiber supply. In this chapter, some of the most overriding concerns facing agriculture and society as a whole are briefly addressed. The subject is introduced at this juncture to emphasize the need for viewing agriculture and food production as a complex system critical to society. The technical nature of animal production and the use of products of animals is the theme of the chapters that follow, but in mastering the fundamental principles and practices of the animal industry, it is important to understand and appreciate the complexities of animals and the societal issues associated with them. In this context, the concepts and importance of plant-animal ecosystems, ecological balance, environmental quality, biological diversity (both animals and plants), biotechnology, food safety, and economic support for agriculture are addressed. Finally, the challenges and opportunities for animal science graduates are discussed. Animal science students of today will play a major role in shaping the future of animal agriculture and society. The field is broad and demanding and those who pursue careers in animal agriculture must not only be technically well prepared, but must be participants in finding creative solutions to issues facing animal agriculture.

REFERENCES AND FURTHER READING

Plant-Animal Ecosystems

Brown, L. R. 1990. The illusion of progress. In L. R. Brown et al., (eds.), *State of the World*. Worldwatch Institute Report on Progress Toward a Sustainable Society. New York: Norton, pp. 3–16.

Brown, L. R. et al. 1997. *Vital Signs*. Worldwatch Institute. New York: Norton.

CAST. 1996. *Grazing on Public Lands*. Task Force Report No. 129, Council for Agricultural Science and Technology, Ames, IA.

Crosson, P., and Anderson, J. R. 1992. *Resources and Global Food Prospects: Supply and Demand for Cereals to 2030*. Washington, D.C.: The World Bank.

Durning, A. B. 1992. Reforming the livestock economy. In L. R. Brown et al., (eds.), *State of the World.* Worldwatch Institute Report on Progress Toward a Sustainable Society. New York: Norton, pp. 66–82.

FASFAS. 1993. Linking science and technology to societal benefits. *FAIR '95, Federation of American Societies of Food Animal Science,* Champaigne, IL, pp. 1–17.

Ecological Balance and Environmental Quality

Cheeke, P. R. 1993. *Impacts of Livestock Production on Society, Diet/Health and the Environment.* Danville, IL: Interstate Publishers.

CAST. 1978. *Forages: Resources for the Future.* Task Force Report No. 108, Council for Agricultural Science and Technology, Ames, IA.

CAST. 1988. *Integrated Animal Waste Management.* Task Force Report No. 128, Council for Agricultural Science and Technology, Ames, IA.

CAST. 1995. *Water Quality: Agriculture's Role.* Task Force Report No. 120, Council for Agricultural Science and Technology, Ames, IA.

CAST. 1996. *Future of Irrigated Agriculture.* Task Force Report No. 127, Council for Agricultural Science and Technology, Ames, IA.

CAST. 1996. *Preparing U.S. Agriculture for Global Climate Change.* Task Force Report No. 119, Council for Agricultural Science and Technology, Ames, IA.

CAST. 1996. *Waste Management and Utilization in Food Production and Processing.* Task Force Report No. 124, Council for Agricultural Science and Technology, Ames, IA.

Gardner, G. 1997. In L. R. Brown et al., (eds.), *Vital Signs.* New York: Norton.

National Research Council. 1978. Plant and animal products in the U.S. food system. Washington, D.C.: National Acad. Sci. Printing and Publishing Office.

National Research Council. 1988. Designing foods: Animal product options in the marketplace. Washington, D.C.: National Academy Press.

Northeast Regional Agricultural Engineering Service. 1996. Animal agriculture and the environment. NRAES-96. Ithaca, NY: Riley-Robb Hall, Cornell University.

Pond, W. G., and Mersmann, H. J. 1994. The challenge: Animal production for human needs. In *Proc.*

XVth International Congress of Nutrition, Smith-Gordon, United Kingdom.

Postel, S. 1990. Saving water for agriculture. In L. R. Brown et al. (eds.), *State of the World,* A Worldwatch Institute Report on Progress toward a Sustainable Society. New York: Norton.

Reganold, J. P., Papendick, R. I., and Parr, J. F. 1990. Sustainable agriculture. *Scientific American* 262: 112–120.

Vavra, M., Laycock, W. A., and Pieper, R. D. 1994. *Ecological Implications of Livestock Herbivory in the West.* Society for Range Management, Denver, CO.

Animal Well-Being

American Veal Association. 1994. *Guide for the Care and Production of Veal Calves.* American Veal Association, Harrisburg, PA, 28 pp.

American Welfare Institute. 1990. *Animals and Their Legal Rights* (4th ed.). Animal Welfare Institute, Washington, D.C., 441 pp.

Brambell, F. W. R. 1965. *Report of Technical Committee to Enquire into the Welfare of Animals Kept Under Intensive Husbandry Systems.* Command Paper 2836. HM Stationery Office, London.

Broom, D. M. 1991. Animal welfare: Concepts and measurement. *J. Anim. Sci.,* 69: 4167–4175.

Broom, D. M., and Johnson, K. G. 1993. *Stress and Animal Welfare.* New York: Chapman and Hall, 211 pp.

CAST. 1997. *The Well-Being of Agricultural Animals.* Task Force Report No. 130, Council for Agricultural Science and Technology, Ames, IA.

Curtis, S. E. 1993. Variations in U.S. animal production systems: Current trends and their impacts on animal well-being and the economics of production. In S. E. Curtis (ed.), *Food Animal Well-Being,* pp. 55–61. W. Lafayette, IN: Purdue University.

Duncan, I. J. H. 1993. Welfare is to do with what animals feel. *J. Agric. Environ. Ethics,* 6 (Special ed., vol. 2): 8–14.

Ewing, S. A., Lay, D. C., Jr. 1998. *Farm Animal Well-Being.* Upper Saddle River, NJ: Prentice-Hall.

Farm Animal Welfare Council. 1993. *Second Report on Priorities for Research and Development in Farm Animal Welfare.* Ministry of Agriculture, Food and Fisheries, Tolworth, London.

Gonyou, H. W. 1994. Why the study of animal behavior is associated with the animal welfare issue. *J. Anim. Sci.,* 72: 2171–2177.

Grandin, T. 1994. Farm animal welfare during handling, transport and slaughter. *J. Amer. Vet. Med. Assoc.,* 204: 372–377.

FASFAS. 1997. *Guide for the Care and Use of Agricultural Animals in Agricultural Research and Teaching* (2nd ed.). Savoy, IL: Federation of American Societies of Food Animal Sciences.

Hemsworth, P. H., Barnett, J. L., and Coleman, G. J. 1993. The human-animal relationship in agriculture and its consequences for the animal. *Anim. Welfare,* 2: 33–51.

Houpt, K. A. 1998. *Domestic Animal Behavior for Veterinarians and Animal Scientists* (3rd ed). Ames, IA: Iowa State University Press.

Hurnik, J. F., Webster, A. B., and Siegel, P. B. 1995. *Dictionary of Farm Animal Behavior* (2nd ed). Ames, IA: Iowa State University Press.

Northeast Regional Agricultural Engineering Service. 1995. Animal behavior and the design of livestock and poultry systems. NRAES-84. Ithaca, NY: Riley-Robb Hall, Cornell University.

Rachels, J. 1993. *The Elements of Moral Philosophy* (2nd ed). New York: McGraw-Hill.

Rollin, B. E. 1995. *Farm Animal Welfare: Social, Bioethical, and Research Issues.* Ames, IA: Iowa State University Press.

Rowan, A. N. 1993. Animal well-being: Key philosophical, ethical, political, and public issues affecting food animal agriculture. In *Food Animal Well-Being.* W. Lafayette, IN: Purdue University, pp. 23–25.

Siegel, P. B. 1993. Opportunities for science and technology to improve production systems to assure animal well-being and economic viability. In *Food Animal Well-Being.* W. Lafayette, IN: Purdue University, pp. 79–88.

Taylor, I. A. 1993. Designing equipment around behavior. In *Animal Behavior and the Design of Livestock and Poultry Systems,* Northeast Regional Agricultural Engineering Service, Ithaca, NY, pp. 94–103.

Biological Diversity

CAST. 1996. *Diversifying U.S. Crop Production.* Issues Paper No. 6, Council for Agricultural Science and Technology, Ames, IA.

Leonard, J. N. 1973. *The Emergence of Man: The First Farmers.* New York: Time-Life Books.

National Research Council. 1983. *Little-Known Asian Animals with a Promising Economic Future.* Washington, D.C.: National Acad. Press.

National Research Council. 1991. *Micro Livestock.* Washington, D.C.: National Academy Press.

Biotechnology

Campbell, K. H. S. et al. 1996. *Nature,* 380: 64.

Gasser, C. S., and Frayley, R. T. 1997. *Science,* 244: 1293–1299.

Gonzalez-Stawinski et al. 1998. In W. G. Pond and H. J. Mersmann (eds.), *Biology of the Domestic Pig.* Ithaca, NY: Cornell University Press, Chapter 17.

Hamer, R. E. et al. 1985. *Nature,* 315: 680.

Koshland, D. E. 1997. *Science,* 244: 1233.

Kreeger, K. Y. 1997. *The Scientist,* 11 (15): 11, 14 (July 21).

Lewis, R. 1997. *The Scientist,* 11: 1, 4.

Lin, S. S., and Platt, J. L. 1996. Immunological advances towards clinical xenotransplantation. In M. E. Tumbleson and L. B. Schook, (eds.), *Advances in Swine in Biomedical Research,* Vol. 1. New York: Plenum Press, Chapter 16.

News Report. 1997. *Large Animal Practice,* Nov/Dec, p. 6.

Office of Technology Assessment (OTA). 1986. Technology, public policy, and the changing structure of American agriculture. Volume II—Background papers. OTA, Congress of the United States, Washington, D.C.

Pennisi, E. 1997. *Science,* 278: 2038–2039.

Pursel, V. G. et al. 1996. Genetic engineering of swine. In M. E. Tumbleson and L. B. Schook, (eds.), *Advances in Swine in Biomedical Research,* Vol. 1. New York: Plenum Press, Chapter 19.

Pursel, V. G. et al. 1997. *Science,* 244: 1281–1288.

Schnieke, A. E. et al. 1997. *Science,* 278: 2130–2133.

Wall, R. G., and Seidel, G. E. 1992. *Theriogenology,* 38: 337.

Wells, D. N., et al. 1997. *Biol. Reprod.,* 57: 385.

Wilmut, I., et al. 1997. *Nature,* 385: 810.

Food Safety

Associated Press. 1997. FDA approves bacteria-killing irradiation of beef. *Ft. Meyers News-Press,* p. 7A, (Wed., Dec. 3).

CAST. 1998. *Food Safety, Sufficiency, and Security.* Special Publication No. 21, Council for Agricultural Science and Technology, Ames, IA.

CAST. 1998. *Naturally Occurring Antimicrobials in Food.* Task Force Report No. 132, Council for Agricultural Science and Technology, Ames, IA.

House, C. 1997. *Feedstuffs,* 69(16): 9.

Morganthau, T. 1997. *E. coli.* alert. *Newsweek,* pp. 26–32, (Sept. 1).

Zottola, E. A., and Smith, L. B. 1990. In A. M. Pearson and T. R. Dutson, (eds.), *Meat and Health—Advances in Meat Research,* Vol. 6. New York: Elsevier Applied Science, Chapter 7.

Economic Support for Agriculture

Brown, L. R. 1997. Food trends. In *Vital Signs.* New York: Norton.

National Science Board (NSB). 1996. *Science and Engineering Indicators 1996.* Washington, D.C.: U.S. Government Printing Office.

Renner, M. 1997. R&D spending levels off. In *Vital Signs.* New York: Norton.

Challenges and Opportunities for Animal Science Graduates in the Twenty-First Century

Taylor, R. E. 1998. Careers and career preparation in the animal sciences. In *Scientific Farm Animal Production* (6th ed.). Upper Saddle River, NJ: Prentice Hall.

CHAPTER TWELVE

LIVE ANIMAL EVALUATION: BEEF CATTLE, SHEEP, AND SWINE

S. P. JACKSON
TEXAS TECH UNIVERSITY,
LUBBOCK, TX

In this chapter we specifically address the evaluation of beef cattle, sheep, and swine. It must be recognized that selection and evaluation of animals, both agricultural and companion animals, is an integral part of their respective niches in animal production. Local, national, and international fairs, shows, and expositions attest to the efforts devoted to live animal evaluation and appraisal. The social and festive features of these events continue to be a central part of livestock shows and expositions. In modern urban society, livestock shows play a role in encouraging interest in and support for animal agriculture and its products. The continuance of such traditions in the United States and around the world speaks to the strong link between grassroots agriculture and urban society. Experienced judges evaluate livestock, including dairy cattle, horses, poultry, and other farm animals, as well as companion animals, at such events. The ranking of animals in these contests and clinics has an important bearing on the future direction of each animal industry.

The criteria for selection and evaluation and the scoring systems, of course, differ. For example, pleasure horse evaluation is based on such factors as hoof and leg soundness, correctness of movement, and conformational characteristics scored against some ideal standard. Evaluation and selection of other companion animals are also based on specific "standards of perfection" for individual breeds and types, and the ideals change over time. This broad concept of the evaluation of live animals should be acknowledged as the student considers the information presented in this chapter on live animal evaluation.

LIVE ANIMAL EVALUATION: PAST AND PRESENT

The evaluation of livestock has been practiced for centuries by cultures on all continents. The Bible refers to the "fatted calf" as a special animal that was to be slaughtered only on special or sacred occasions. Selection of livestock based on visual appraisal was the first step toward the improvement of domesticated farm animals. The art of livestock selection has been cultivated through many years and passed on through many generations. Many of the great animal breeders of the past were excellent evaluators of livestock. The skills of the early livestock evaluators have greatly contributed to the breeds of livestock that we recognize today.

In the livestock industry of the twenty-first century, live animal evaluation by visual appraisal is still an important tool used for predicting the value of slaughter animals as well as for selecting breeding stock. Modern technology has provided more objective estimates of body composition and carcass leanness in live animals destined for use as breeding stock or for food. Methods now in use for predicting body fat and lean in food animals include ultrasonics[1] and whole-body counting of Potassium-40 (body potassium content is closely related to body protein content).

Slaughter Animals

The ultimate goal of an evaluator of live slaughter animals is to accurately predict the composition as well as the eating quality of livestock. If the evaluation is adequate, the buyer or seller of the livestock has an accurate estimation of the value of the livestock before it is bought or sold. Therefore, in the livestock and meat trading business, the accuracy of prediction can be the difference between a profit or loss. When livestock are evaluated for slaughter, dressing percentage, cutability, and quality grade should be accurately assessed in order to predict ultimate carcass value.

---

[1]Ultrasonic measurement of carcass leanness in cattle and swine is used by breeders and in commercial slaughter plants in the United States and elsewhere. Other potentially useful tools include computerized tomography (computation of an image from X-ray transmission data obtained in many different locations through a prescribed plane) and electronic whole-body measurement equipment.

Breeding Animals

Livestock producers have many tools at their disposal to aid them in the selection of breeding stock. Visual appraisal is still one of the important tools used in the selection of animals. One of the major factors for many livestock producers is the phenotypic appearance of the selected animals. Therefore, the skill of the evaluator is related to the success of the breeding program. Visual appraisal is the only method for determining such traits as structural soundness, balance, femininity, masculinity, body capacity, correctness in movement, and others.

BEEF CATTLE EVALUATION

Breeding Cattle Type

Breeding cattle type (size and conformation) in the United States has changed significantly over the past forty years. In the 1950s, cattle were short-legged and compact in appearance. The cattle of the 1950s and 1960s were predominantly British breeds that were fat and small-framed. The cattle of the late 1960s and early 1970s were influenced by exotic breeds of cattle that were imported from Europe and India. The trend in the 1970s and 1980s was to increase the frame size and weight of cattle. Breeders during this period changed cattle size to the point that cattle became too large to be functionally efficient in many environments. The carcass weights of slaughter animals from these large-framed cows were too large to fit the beef industry's marketing schemes. In the early 1990s, the beef industry began to decrease the size of cattle and select for "moderate" frame size. The downsizing of cattle in the United States has been driven by two distinctly different forces. One reason for downsizing was the need to improve the efficiency of commercial cowherds. Smaller cows survive on limited feed resources and are cheaper to maintain during times of drought than large-framed cows. Another driving force was the need to maintain slaughter cattle with carcass weights that fit the specifications of the retail beef industry. The ideal slaughter weight of cattle is determined by the price premiums or discounts that are offered by beef packing companies. Most packers prefer carcass weights of 600 to 950 pounds. Significant discounts are applied to carcasses that weigh less than 600 pounds or more than 1,000 pounds. Retail cuts from cattle with carcasses weighing below or above this weight range are not well accepted in most retail markets.

Structural Correctness

Structural correctness (soundness) in beef cattle is paramount to their survival in range-grazing conditions. Cows are expected to be functional in many different types of rough terrain. The ability of a cow to perform in adverse terrains is dependent upon her structural correctness and skeletal durability. Cows must have adequate angle in their hocks and slope of shoulder in order to travel countless miles in their lifetime. Structural correctness in the bull is perhaps even more important because of the stress that is applied to his hocks during the breeding process. A large proportion of the weight of the bull is on the hocks during copulation. Bulls must have adequate angle in the hocks in order to mount and thrust during breeding. Many bulls with hocks that are too straight or "post-legged" become arthritic in their hock joints and are unable to successfully breed cows because of the pain experienced during the breeding process. The older and heavier these bulls are, the more severe the hock inflammation and joint damage becomes.

Sheath and Navel

Many breeds of cattle (especially Bos indicus breeds) have loose skin in the sheath or navel area of the body. This extra skin improves the evaporative cooling of cattle in hot climates. However, if cattle have excessive loose skin, it can be detrimental to their overall productivity. The most common problem associated with this loose skin is the damaged prepuce of bulls. Bulls with very pendulous sheaths and large prepucial openings are predisposed to injury. The most common injuries occur when the sheath is stepped on or injured by thorns or brush. This type of injury is common in the southern part of the United States, where many cattle have a high percentage of Bos indicus breeding and are raised in an environment where thorny plants and brush are prevalent vegetation. Selection of heifers and bulls with clean navels tends to produce offspring with cleaner sheaths and therefore less prone to injury than their heavy-sheathed contemporaries. Feedlot steers with pendulous sheaths are prone to sheath injuries that can lead to urinary calculi or an obstructed urethra, reduced performance, and even death.

Several breed associations have sheath and naval scoring systems that allow bulls and heifers to be scored for culling purposes. Figure 12-1 is an example of the scoring system that is utilized by the Beefmaster Breeders Universal Association. Similar systems are used by many of the Bos indicus–based breed associations in the United States.

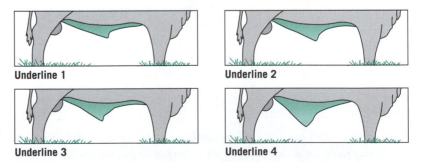

FIGURE 12-1.

Beefmaster Breeders Universal sheath scoring system. These drawings show the maximum amount of underline allowable to receive a particular sheath score. Bulls with sheaths that are more pendulous than drawing #4 are disqualified from registration in Beefmaster Universal. (Drawings courtesy of Beefmaster Breeders Universal.)

Udder Quality

The lifetime productivity of a female is limited in part by her ability to nourish her offspring. Udder damage by either bacterial or physical means is a major factor affecting the culling rate of breeding females. Selection of females with well-attached and properly shaped udders can increase the length of time the udder will be functional. Udders should be attached high in the rear udder attachment and attached well forward in the fore udder attachment. Ideally, the mammary glands (four glands in cattle, two in sheep and goats) of the udder should be uniform in size and the teats should come from the center of each gland. The size and shape of teats also has a profound effect on the lifetime productivity of the female. Cows with large teats tend to be less profitable than those with smaller, more refined teats. It is extremely difficult for newborn calves to nurse a teat that is too large to grasp. If the offspring is not assisted by the attendant, starvation and death may result. Females with large teats can usually be milked out several times until the teats are small enough for the offspring to nurse, but this is a very labor- and time-intensive task that can be avoided through the selection of females with excellent udder quality. Examples of good and poor udder quality in cows are illustrated in Figure 12-2.

Visual Appraisal of Live Cattle Composition

In order to determine by visual appraisal the composition of a beef animal, one must establish reference points to evaluate for muscle and fat. In determining composition, the evaluator is concerned with fat, muscle, and bone. Of these three tissues, bone is the most constant from animal to animal. This simply means that if animals are similar in weight, the amount of bone in those animals will remain fairly constant and is therefore not an important variable in the evaluation of cattle. The skeletal design of all cattle is also very

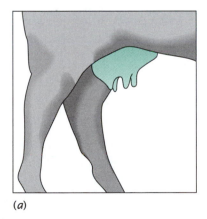
(a)

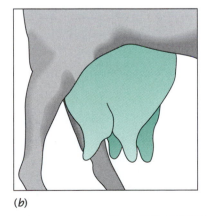
(b)

FIGURE 12-2

Drawings of udders showing (a) good and (b) poor quality udders. (Drawings courtesy of the International Brangus Breeders Association.)

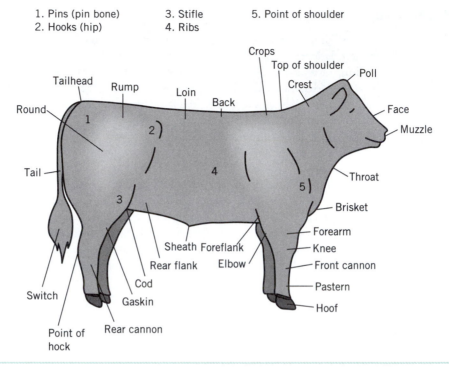

1. Pins (pin bone) 3. Stifle   5. Point of shoulder
2. Hooks (hip)   4. Ribs

FIGURE 12-3

Parts of a beef steer.

similar. This skeletal similarity in all cattle allows us to look at skeletal reference points in determining fat measurements. We also know that all beef cattle have exactly the same number of muscles that are in the same physical location. This concept also aids us in evaluating muscularity in beef cattle. The following are reference points that can be used for fat determination in slaughter cattle that are haltered (Figure 12-3).

The point of the shoulder. The main tissues that cover the point of the shoulder are fat and hide. This allows us to handle a steer with our fingertips to decide how much fat covers the bone.

Over the ribs. This reference point is also covered mainly with fat and hide so it is also a valuable point to handle for fat.

Down the topline. By handling cattle down the topline, the tips of the spinous processes can be palpated in order to determine fat cover.

Besides these palpable reference points, several visual reference points can also be used to estimate fat. Cattle should be evaluated in the brisket, rear flank, cod, udder, tailhead (pones), and for overall smoothness and width down the top. Fat cattle are full (deep and wide) in the brisket because the brisket contains very little muscle and, when it increases in size, its growth is due to fat deposition. The rear flank area is also an area that contains very little muscle and some connective tissue. Therefore, when cattle fatten, they deposit fat in this area and become deep and full in the flank. Many people erroneously believe that depth of rear flank is an indicator of body capacity, but in reality, flank depth has no bearing on body capacity. Fat cattle also deposit fat in their cod (scrotal remains) in steers or udder in females, and around their tailheads. Overall, fat cattle are smooth in appearance and are wide down the top and square over the loin edge. In summary, fat will always make animals appear deep, smooth, and square. Lean, muscular cattle are rounder and more chiseled in appearance and have shallow flanks and a trim brisket.

The estimation of muscle also centers on the evaluation of cattle at specific anatomical locations. Market animals should be evaluated for muscling through the stifle (lower quarter), forearm, loin and top, and in the shoulder. Muscular animals are wide and expressive in these areas. Muscular animals also tend to stand and travel with width between their legs. The width of stance is caused by muscle occupying space and forcing the animal to stand and move wide due to muscle-to-muscle contact. It is important to remember that muscles are round and therefore roundness or "shape" is indicative of muscular animals, whereas flat, smooth, and square animals may be fat and light-muscled (Figure 12-3).

Beef Cattle Grading

Because so much meat is bought and sold each day, the industry needs a system that allows the orderly exchange of meat between seller and buyer. The most-used system is the federal meat grading system. Federal beef grades are a two-faceted system—quality grades, implemented in 1925, and yield grades, implemented in 1965. The two grades may be used together or separately and are optional for packers to use. Quality grades estimate the consumer acceptability of the product at the dinner table, and yield grades estimate the cutability of the carcass.

Most of the slaughter cattle marketed in the United States are purchased on the basis of their predicted quality grade. If buyers and sellers of slaughter cattle are accurate in predicting the quality grade of cattle, the actual value of the cattle will be more accurately calculated. However, the accuracy of predicting the quality grade of live cattle by visual appraisal is very low. Many evaluators of livestock claim to be able to accurately predict quality grade. In reality, without knowledge about the genetics of the cattle or their nutritional background, prediction of quality grade is little more than a guess.

The purpose of carcass grading systems is to sort carcasses within classes into groups similar in value. Calves are classed as veal (up to about 3 months of age) and calf (from 3 to 12 months). Classes of beef carcasses from cattle over about a year of age are steers, heifers, bullocks, bulls, and cows. Classes are determined by age, sex, and reproductive status. About 80% of our domestic beef supply is obtained from steer and heifer carcasses. Most bull and cow beef is used as grinding meat for sausage manufacture because of its lack of tenderness.

The Standardization and Grading Branch of the Livestock Division of the Food Safety and Quality Service (FSIS) of the USDA develops grading standards, trains federal graders, and provides the grading service that costs about 1/20 cent per pound. Packers who use this service must pay for it on an hourly basis.

BEEF QUALITY GRADES. The eight quality (or carcass) grades for beef carcasses are Prime, Choice, Select, Standard, Commercial, Utility, Cutter, and Canner. The first four grades are primarily used for carcasses from cattle under 42 months of age and the last four are for cattle over 42 months of age. Most Prime grade beef is bought by restaurants or exported to the Far East, Japan, and Korea. The large majority of steer and heifer carcasses grade either Choice, 45–55% or Select, 35–45%, the grades of beef most likely to be found in supermarket display cases. The National Beef Quality Audit in 1995 showed that about 47% of steers and heifers graded Choice, 47% Select, 1% Prime, and 5% Standard. Thus, about 94% of the carcasses graded Choice and Select. These figures illustrate that most steers and heifers are fed until the feedlot manager believes that the majority of them will grade Choice. The length of feeding period will depend in part on the price spread between Select and Choice grade carcasses, which was about $7 per hundredweight in the mid-1990s. If the price spread is wider, more will be fed to the Choice grade, but their yield grade will be less desirable. Because animals genetically differ in their ability to marble, the percentage of a pen of cattle that will grade Choice varies widely.

Maturity and quality-indicating characteristics are assessed to determine the final beef quality grade. Maturities (age of the animal in months) are A, B, C, D, and E and can be quoted as the percentage across that maturity. For example, A^{90} would be 90% of the width of the A maturity (almost a B maturity). The A maturity carcasses range from about 12 to 30 months of chronological age, B from 30 to 42, C from 42 to 72, D from 72 to 96, and E more than 96 months. As animals become older their meat becomes tougher. The connective tissue that surrounds each muscle becomes less soluble to the heat of cooking and makes the meat tougher. However, considerable overlap exists in chronological age among maturities (i.e., chronological age and physiological maturity are different in many cases). Some animals, particularly those that will be lighter in weight at maturity, mature more quickly than larger ones. Maturity score is determined from the amount of bone ossification (converting cartilage to bone) and muscle color and texture. Major emphasis is placed on the amount of cartilage at the tips of the spinous processes of the vertebrae. Younger carcasses show more cartilage than older cattle. Ossification proceeds from the posterior to the anterior parts of the vertebral column. Increased maturity is accompanied by flattening, whitening, and hardening of ribs, a darker muscle color, and a coarser muscle texture. Desirable beef muscle color is bright cherry red, and desirable texture is smooth and velvety. Firmer muscle and fat also are desirable. These quality factors help determine sales appeal of the meat in the retail showcase but have little relation to eating quality of beef.

Quality is principally determined by the amount of marbling (visible specks of fat within muscles) in the ribeye (longissimus muscle cross section between the 12th and 13th ribs), which is the location of ribbing (dividing the carcass side into forequarters and hind quarters for ease of handling). Six of the ten marbling scores are illustrated in Figure 12-4. Marbling scores can be designated by the distance across the score such as

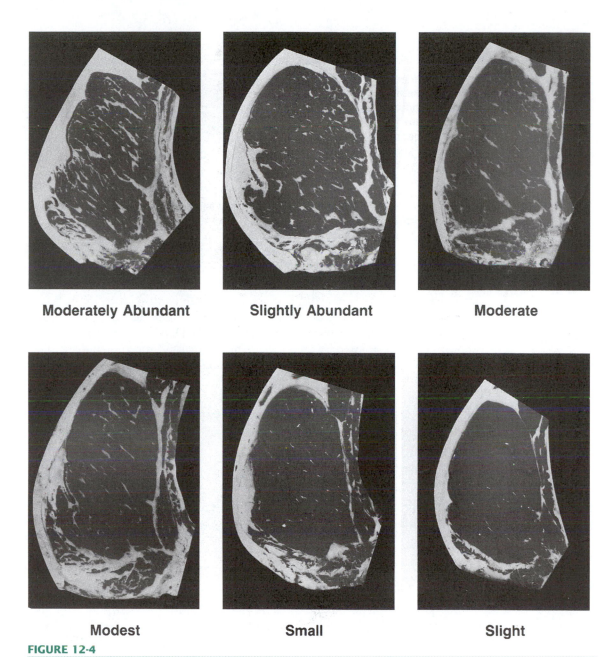

Moderately Abundant   **Slightly Abundant**   **Moderate**

Modest   **Small**   **Slight**

FIGURE 12-4

Official USDA marbling photographs. Not shown are: Abundant, Traces, Practically Devoid, and Devoid.

Source: Meat Evaluation Handbook. National Live Stock and Meat Board.

Small[50] (the middle of the Small score). More marbling produces a higher carcass grade, and it has much more influence on grade than any other single grading factor. Over 80% of the variation in final quality grade is associated with marbling score. Animals tend to deposit more marbling as they fatten, but some carry genes to marble with little subcutaneous fat. The beef quality factors are intended to reflect the palatability (tenderness, juiciness, and flavor) of the meat. However, a high carcass grade is no assurance of desirable eating quality. Higher grading carcasses tend to have superior eating quality, but a large overlap exists among grades. For example, some Select grade carcasses have eating quality as desirable as some Prime, but consumers' chances of eating tender, juicy, and flavorful beef increase if they purchase retail cuts with a higher grade. A consumer purchasing a Prime steak is likely to experience eating satisfaction 95% of the time; however, a consumer purchasing Standard beef may be dissatisfied 59% of the time (Figure 12-4).

After maturity and quality have been assessed, these factors are combined to provide the final grade. Figure 12-5 shows the relationship between maturity and marbling scores. For example, A maturity and Small marbling correspond to a Choice quality grade. However, if the marbling score is only Slight, the quality grade (with A maturity) is Select. Therefore, more marbling produces a higher-quality grade. More marbling is needed to give the same quality grade if maturity is increased in B, C, D, or E maturities. Note that carcasses with C, D, or E maturity cannot grade higher than Commercial and are called "hard-boned" because their cartilage has ossified to bone (Figure 12-5).

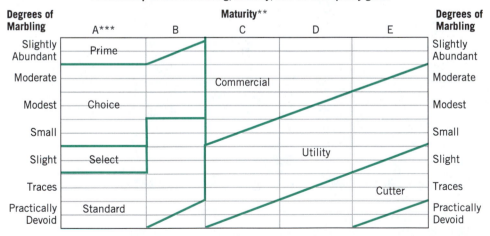

Relationship between marbling, maturity, and carcass quality grade*

*Assumes that firmness is comparably developed with the degree of marbling and that the carcass is not a "dark cutter".
**Maturity increases from left to right (A through E).
***The A maturity portion of the Figure is the only portion applicable to bullock carcasses.

FIGURE 12-5

Relationship between marbling, maturity, and carcass quality grade in cattle carcasses.

Source: Meat Evaluation Handbook.

BEEF YIELD GRADES. Yield grades (YG) estimate the percentage of retail cuts in a carcass. Specifically, YG estimates the percentage of cold carcass weight in boneless, closely trimmed retail cuts in the round, loin, rib, and chuck (the four thick or major wholesale cuts in the back region of a carcass). The YGs are 1, 2, 3, 4, and 5. A YG1 carcass has the least fat, most muscle, the highest cutout of retail cuts, and is most desirable and valuable. A YG5 is fattest and least desirable.

The National Beef Quality Audit in 1995 (Figure 12-6) showed that about 45% of carcasses of steers and heifers were YG2, 34% YG3, 13% YG1, 7% YG4, and <1% YG5. Thus, almost 80% of the carcasses were YG2 and 3. Fewer YG4 and 5 carcasses are in the population today because they are severely penalized in price due to their excessive fatness. This penalty is reflected in the changes that occurred in percentages in each YG in the 1991 audit. In four years, a considerable shift from the fatter to the leaner grades occurred (Figure 12-6).

YGs are easier to determine in carcasses than in live cattle because only one of the four factors needed to determine the YG needs to be estimated. The other three can be measured. In live animals, all four factors must be estimated. The four factors needed to determine YG and the effect of each on the YG and cutout of retail cuts are:

1. Fat thickness (FT) over the ribeye—measured with a ruler at a point three-fourths of the distance across the ribeye muscle from the chine or medial end between the twelfth and thirteenth ribs. FT has the most influence on YG— a .1-inch change in FT changes YG .25. A thicker fat cover increases YG but decreases cutout because more fat must be trimmed during fabrication of retail cuts.

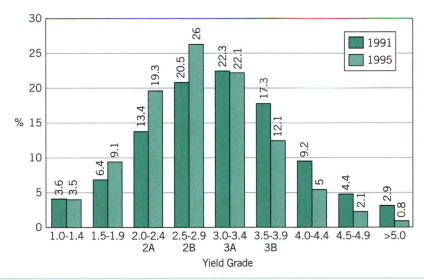

FIGURE 12-6

Percentage distribution of yield grades in beef cattle.

Source: The National Beef Quality Audit, 1995.

2. Ribeye area (REA)—measured between the twelfth and thirteenth ribs with a plastic grid of .1-inch^2 squares. A 1-inch^2 change in REA changes YG .3. A larger REA decreases YG but increases cutout because REA is a muscling indicator and more muscle is desirable.

3. Kidney, pelvic, and heart fat (KPHF) percentage—determined by estimating the pounds of fat in the kidney knob, pelvic cavity, and heart region and dividing by carcass weight. A 1% change in KPHF changes YG .2. A greater percentage of KPHF increases YG but decreases cutout because this fat is trimmed during fabrication of retail cuts.

4. Hot carcass weight (HCW)—obtained from the carcass tag. A 1-lb change in HCW changes YG .004 or a 25-lb change in HCW changes YG .1. A heavier HCW increases YG but decreases cutout because heavier carcasses tend to be fatter.

To determine YG:

1. Find the preliminary YG (PYG) using FT over the ribeye muscle:

FT, inch	PYG
.0	2.00
.1	2.25
.2	2.50
.3	2.75
.4	3.00
.5	3.25
.6	3.50
.7	3.75

2. Subtract the REA from 11.00 and multiply by .3. Be sure to retain the sign (+ or −).

3. Subtract 3.5 from the KPHF% and multiply by .2.

4. Subtract 600 from the HCW and multiply by .004.

5. Add or subtract (as the sign indicates) each from the preliminary YG to obtain the final YG.

SHEEP EVALUATION

Market Lambs

WEIGHT. Traditionally, market lambs weigh between 100 and 140 pounds at slaughter to fit into the U.S. lamb marketing system. The ideal market weight of each breed will differ because of differences in mature weight and how heavy lambs are when they reach an optimum degree of finish. Smaller breeds such as Southdowns and Cheviots as well as fine wool breeds should be slaughtered at lighter weights to avoid becoming excessively fat. Larger terminal sire breeds such as the Hampshire and Suffolk can be fed to much heavier weights and still maintain an acceptable ratio of muscle to fat. Weight alone is a poor indicator of the value of lambs. However, weight is important because of discounts that occur during certain seasons of the year. It is difficult to describe the weight of the ideal market lamb because the preferred weight of lambs deviates significantly during the course of a year. In the fall, prices tend to favor heavy lambs that may have a live weight of 130 to 140 pounds. However, in the spring, lambs in the same weight range may be discounted by the same buyer that had offered a premium for heavy lambs in the fall. This seasonal effect on lamb pricing makes it difficult for sheep breeders to target a particular weight goal in their breeding programs. The U.S. lamb marketing system prefers a larger lamb than most foreign producers can supply.

FINISH. Overly fat lamb carcasses are associated with reduced profitability to the producer because of higher feed costs of depositing the extra body fat. Furthermore, overly fat lamb is not preferred by the consumer. Excessive fat must be trimmed off at the retail level and thrown away before retail cuts are sold to consumers.

External finish (fatness) of lambs is determined by visual evaluation of fat deposition sites as well as by handling skeletal reference points (Figure 12-7). Lambs should be manually handled over the ribs, down the spine, and around the dock to estimate subcutaneous fat levels. Lambs deposit fat over the forerib and dock as well as in the breast, flank, and crotch. As lambs fatten they tend to become smooth in appearance. Fat is deposited in the seams between muscles and tends to hide the muscle definition that is apparent in lean lambs. A fat lamb tends to be wider in the center part of the body and tapers toward each end. Fat, lightly muscled lambs tend to resemble a canoe when viewed down the top. Lean, muscular lambs should have the largest part of the body in the rump and leg and the smallest part in the shoulders. Market lambs should have at least .1 inch of backfat over the twelfth and thirteenth rib in order to prevent cold shrink and dehydration of the carcass during chilling and transportation of the carcass. Most lambs are raised and slaughtered in the center of the United States and are shipped under refrigeration to the east and west coasts. Carcasses without adequate finish can be damaged during this shipping period. Lamb carcasses also need some level of body fat to maintain good flavor and acceptable eating quality. Lambs should have no more than .25 inch of backfat to maintain an acceptable level of cutability. Lambs with .25 inch of backfat are still graded as a USDA number-2 carcass and will fit lamb retailer specifications of .25-inch trim without much additional trimming. Lambs with over .25 inch of external fat are excessively fat and will have significant trim losses at the retail level.

MUSCLE. Muscle is the other tissue besides fat that influences the composition of lamb carcasses. Obviously, selection for muscle is very important since it is the primary tissue consumed from lamb carcasses. When evaluating lambs for muscle, the most important muscle indicator is the rear leg. The size of the leg is the most accurate live indicator of muscle because it is one of the last sites for fat deposition on the lamb carcass. Evaluation of muscle down the top of a lamb is less accurate because of the large amount of fat that is deposited in this area. It is difficult at times to decide how much of the width of the rack

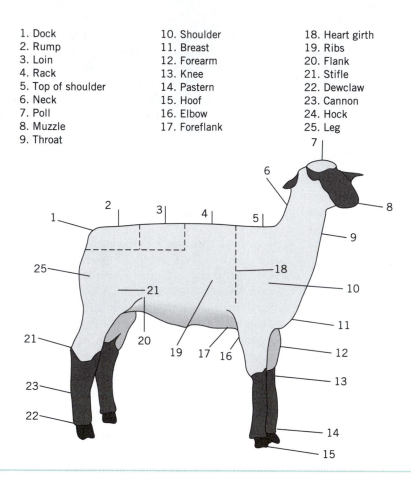

1. Dock	10. Shoulder	18. Heart girth
2. Rump	11. Breast	19. Ribs
3. Loin	12. Forearm	20. Flank
4. Rack	13. Knee	21. Stifle
5. Top of shoulder	14. Pastern	22. Dewclaw
6. Neck	15. Hoof	23. Cannon
7. Poll	16. Elbow	24. Hock
8. Muzzle	17. Foreflank	25. Leg
9. Throat		

FIGURE 12-7

Parts of a lamb.

and loin is due to muscle or fat. Ideally, evaluators determine the muscularity of lambs by evaluating many muscle groups and by using all of the indicators together will form an opinion of the total muscularity of the lamb. Muscular lambs will have a large leg, be expressively muscled in the rack and loin, have large forearms, and have proportionally sized shoulders. The widest part of a muscular lamb will be through the center part of the leg. Muscular lambs tend to stand with their rear legs wide apart and travel with width at the hocks. Light-muscled lambs tend to stand with their rear legs close together and travel narrowly at the hocks. Figure 12-8 shows examples of market lambs of high and low muscularity.

Lamb Carcass Grading

Quality grades sort lamb carcasses into groups that are similar in acceptability as retail cuts at the dinner table. The beef and lamb grading systems are similar in principle, with

FIGURE 12-8

Examples of market lambs of high and low muscularity.

more fatness associated with a more desirable quality grade but a less desirable yield grade. The quality (or carcass) grades are Prime, Choice, Good, Utility, and Cull. Characteristics indicating conformation, maturity, and quality are combined to determine the final grade.

Conformation refers to the shape of the carcass. Carcasses with superior conformation are thickly muscled, implying a high proportion of meat to bone, with much fullness and thickness in relation to their length. They have a plump, full, and well-rounded appearance. However, research has shown that fatter carcasses tend to receive higher conformation grades and conformation is not related to eating quality of the meat. Conformation is designated in the same manner as the final grade (i.e., Prime, Choice, Good, Utility, or Cull).

Maturity in lamb carcasses is designated as A (young) or B (mature). Carcasses designated as lamb usually are less than 12 months of age, and they always have at least one break joint on their foreshanks. The A maturity carcasses have moderately narrow and slightly flat ribs, moderately red, moist, and porous break joints, and a slightly dark-pink lean color. B maturity carcasses have slightly wide and moderately flat ribs, slightly red, dry, and hard break joints, and a light-red lean color. Because lamb carcasses are light in weight and are not split into sides as are beef carcasses, the amount of cartilage on the spinous processes of the vertebral column cannot be viewed. Increased maturity is accompanied by flattening, whitening, and hardening of bones and a darkening of muscle color and coarsening of muscle texture.

Yearling mutton carcasses are obtained from animals that usually are between 12 and

20 months of age. They may have either break or spool joints on their foreshanks. Such carcasses have moderately wide ribs, which tend to be flat, a slightly dark-red lean color, and slightly coarse lean texture. The latter two traits aid in distinguishing yearling mutton from lamb carcasses.

Mutton carcasses are obtained from sheep over 20 months of age. Such carcasses have wide, flat ribs, a dark-red lean color, and a coarse lean texture. They always have spool joints on their foreshanks. Most of the meat from mutton carcasses is used in processed meats because of its strong flavor and usual lack of tenderness. The meat flavor becomes stronger and generally is less desirable as the sheep increases in age. Therefore, lamb carcasses are more valuable than mutton carcasses.

The quality-indicating factor used in lamb grading is flank streaking, which tends to increase as an animal fattens. Therefore, a lamb that is fatter or has been fed longer tends to grade higher in quality (but have a poorer yield grade). Because lamb carcasses are not ribbed, the loineye muscle is not exposed and the amount of marbling cannot be determined as is done with beef carcasses. Flank streakings are an indicator of marbling in the muscles. More streaking of fat on the surface of the flank muscles is equated with higher quality and more juiciness at the dinner table.

When conformation, maturity, and quality have been assessed, these factors are combined to determine the final grade. Figure 12-9 shows the relationship between maturity and quality for lamb carcasses. For example, a young (A-maturity) lamb carcass with

Relationship between flank fat streakings, maturity and quality

In addition, a minimum degree of lean and external fat firmness is specified for each grade, regardless of maturity. These are: Prime-tends to be moderatley firm; Choice-tends to be slightly firm; Good-Slightly soft; and Utility(mutton only)-soft. These requirements are applicable only to the quality aspects of the grade and do not reflect any comparisons for superior or inferior conformation.

FIGURE 12-9

Relationship between flank streakings, maturity, and quality in sheep carcasses.

Source: Meat Evaluation Handbook.

Slight$^+$ flank streakings would have Choice$^+$ quality. The last step in grading is to combine the quality and conformation to obtain the final carcass grade. In each grade, superior quality compensates for inferior conformation on an equal basis (i.e., midpoint Choice quality and Good$^+$ conformation provide a Choice$^-$ final grade). However, a carcass cannot grade Prime unless it has at least Choice$^-$ conformation, and it cannot grade Prime unless it has at least Prime$^-$ quality.

About three-fourths of all lamb carcasses in the United States are quality graded. Of these, less than 10% are Prime, about 90% are Choice, about 1% are Good, and about .25% are Utility. Those that would grade Cull are extremely rare.

Lamb Yield Grading

The USDA lamb yield grades (YG) are 1, 2, 3, 4, and 5, the same grades as for beef carcasses. They estimate the percentage of retail cuts in a carcass. Specifically, YGs estimate the percentage of cold carcass weight in boneless, closely trimmed retail cuts from the four major (or thick) wholesale cuts—leg, loin, rib, and shoulder. A lower-numbered YG (more toward a 1) has a higher cutout of retail cuts. YGs are easier to determine in carcasses than in live sheep because wool and skin do not mask the carcass.

In 1992, a revised yield grading system was adopted by the USDA. Only fat thickness between the last two ribs (12th and 13th) now is used to determine yield grade. The relationship between yield grade and fat thickness (FT) is:

FT, inch	YG
.00−.15	1
.16−.25	2
.26−.35	3
.36−.45	4
.46+	5

To determine the yield grade, multiply the fat thickness by 10 and add .4. For example, a carcass with .15 inch of FT would have a YG of 1.9 [(.15 × 10) + .4 = 1.9]. The present lamb yield grading system does not account for muscling because of the extreme variation in external fat. The KPHF percentage is rarely used because it is removed at slaughter. When the lamb industry reduces the amount of fat variation then the importance of muscle will be reevaluated in USDA lamb yield grades.

Selection of Breeding Sheep

When selecting breeding sheep it is important to realize the purpose for which the sheep will be used. Many breeds of sheep have been selected for generations for the production of wool, whereas other breeds have been selected for growth rate and carcass merit. Sheep breeds and other aspects of sheep production are covered in Chapter 18. This discussion addresses traits related to feed resources and carcass merit.

SHEEP SIZE AND FEED RESOURCES. Sheep must be productive in whatever environment they are raised. Therefore, the optimum size of breeding sheep is dependent on the feed resources available in a given environment. Sheep raised under range conditions in the southwestern region of the United States must be moderate in frame size and weight because of the limited feed resources available in the semi-arid environment. Smaller sheep have an advantage over large sheep in this environment because they have a lower maintenance requirement. In other areas of the country, large sheep are preferred because of their advantage in growth rate and gain efficiency. Because of the vast differences in forage availability, the best advice for size selection for breeding stock is to select animals that can function best in the particular environment in which they are raised.

Breeding males and females should have well-developed secondary sex characteristics. Fertility tends to be higher in sheep that have well-developed genitalia and prominent secondary sex characteristics. Rams should be masculine in appearance with larger, more rugged bones, heads, and shoulders than females. Rams should have two well-developed testicles that measure at least 28 cm in diameter at one year of age. Ewes should appear feminine, with refined muzzles, refined, smooth shoulders, and bones that are smaller with smoother joints than rams. Ewes should have udder development and well-developed external genitalia.

MUSCLE. The amount of muscle that is desired in a breeding sheep is dependent on the sex of the sheep and the production purpose. Ewes need to have adequate muscling. However, ewes with too much muscle expression may be infertile or have dystocia problems when lambing. Muscle is very important in the selection of rams that will be used in terminal crossbreeding programs. Rams should be very muscular in their rear legs and thick and muscular through the loin and rack.

SWINE EVALUATION

Slaughter Hogs

To accurately evaluate the composition of market hogs, one must know where the major fat deposition occurs and where the major muscle groups are located. Accurate estimation of the amount of muscle and fat in a market hog allows one to predict the body composition. Parts of a hog are illustrated in Figure 12-10.

FAT. At body temperature, fat is less firm than it is in the chilled carcass. The lower third of the body in a fat hog is loose and flabby because the fat in this area is not supported by strong musculature. The jowl, belly, flank, and crotch will all be filled with sloppy fat in a fat hog. The shape of the top is also a primary site to evaluate fat in market hogs. Subcutaneous back fat is a major site of fat deposition in swine. A lean, muscular hog viewed over the top is wider at the shoulders and ham and trim through the middle part of the body. The ham-loin junction should be clean and the ham should

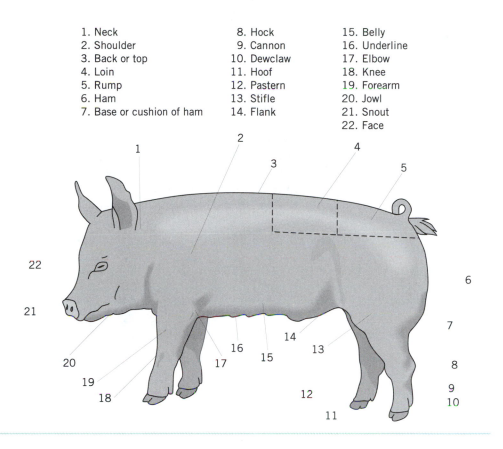

1. Neck
2. Shoulder
3. Back or top
4. Loin
5. Rump
6. Ham
7. Base or cushion of ham

8. Hock
9. Cannon
10. Dewclaw
11. Hoof
12. Pastern
13. Stifle
14. Flank

15. Belly
16. Underline
17. Elbow
18. Knee
19. Forearm
20. Jowl
21. Snout
22. Face

FIGURE 12-10

Parts of a hog.

flare out and be the widest part of the body. In contrast, a fat hog appears smooth down the top and more square in shape. The shoulder pocket and the ham-loin junction are filled with fat and the body contours are lost as fattening progresses. Hogs should also be evaluated for fat while they move. The movement of the shoulder blades can be seen more easily in a lean hog because the blades of a fat hog are covered with a thick fat layer.

MUSCLE. The major locations to evaluate muscle in a market hog are the ham, shoulder, forearm, and loin. The ham is the best indicator of muscle followed by the shoulder, forearm, and then the top (loin). The top is the least accurate location for muscle determination because the width of the top can be significantly affected by the amount of back fat. Fat can cause a hog to be wide down the top and can confuse evaluators when they are trying to distinguish between fat and muscle. Because of the difficulty in distinguishing muscle from fat down the top, it is best for beginning evaluators to assess muscle using the ham, shoulder, and forearm.

Evaluation of Breeding Swine

A current need in the swine industry is to produce an extremely lean, muscular market hog that has the ability to reach a market weight of 220 to 270 pounds on full feed and still retain acceptable body composition. To produce such a market hog, breeding stock must have the genetic potential to meet this goal. Pork producers strive to produce market hogs that excel in carcass composition, yet retain production characteristics and longevity in breeding animals housed in a physically restricted confinement environment. Females must also be able to reproduce and raise litters efficiently over several parities. To attain longevity in a rigorous confinement environment, boars and gilts must be structurally correct. Breeding stock with desirable and undesirable skeletal structure is depicted in Figure 12-11a and b. The steep rump and straight pasterns shown in Figure

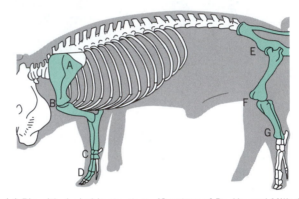

(*a*) Pig with desirable structure. (Courtesy of Dr. Howard Miller)

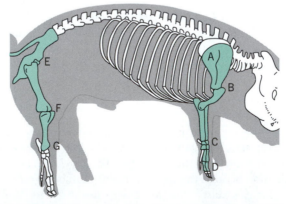

(*b*) Pig with undesirable structure. (Courtesy of Dr. Howard Miller)

FIGURE 12-11

(a) Pig with desirable skeletal structure; (b) pig with undesirable skeletal structure. (Courtesy of Dr. Howard Miller.)

12-11b may be associated with development of lameness, inability to mate successfully, and bone anomalies in later life.

In order to produce fast-growing, lean, and muscular offspring, sows must also be big, muscular, and lean. The commercial swine industry has moved toward using sows selected with productivity and longevity mated to boars selected with growth rate and carcass composition as the major selection criteria. This crossbreeding scheme has allowed breeders to capitalize on improved genetics in their selection of both boars and sows.

Ultrasonic measurement is now used by swine breeders to estimate backfat thickness and muscularity in the live animal. Figure 12-12a shows the measurement of backfat and loin muscle in a live pig and Figure 12-12b shows the procedure on a hog carcass. Ultrasonic measurement of pork carcasses in slaughter plants is now a commercial reality.

Pork Carcass Evaluation

The most accurate method for determining value of any kind of carcass is to calculate the total value (weight × selling price/lb) of all wholesale cuts. However, this method of evaluation usually is not used because the carcass must be fabricated into these cuts and weighed, requiring too much time and effort. When carcasses are not broken into wholesale cuts, other methods of quantity evaluation must be used. Estimates of cutability of intact carcasses are made by such measurements as carcass length, average backfat thickness, loineye area, carcass weight, and muscling score. Two such methods have been developed by the USDA and the University of Wisconsin. They are described below.

USDA GRADES. A grading system for both live hogs and pork carcasses was developed by the USDA. All factors needed to determine carcass grades can be measured without altering the split carcass, an advantage over most other methods of carcass evaluation. These grades are widely used in buying live hogs but are less used for carcasses because most pork carcasses are fabricated into wholesale cuts in the plant in which the live hogs are slaughtered. Some large commercial hog slaughter facilities now use ultrasonic measurement of fat and lean in pork carcasses on the slaughter floor to establish the value of individual carcasses. This method of pricing hogs based on carcass measurements of leanness is used in Canada and other countries and is of increasing importance in the United States. Even so, only a small percentage of pork in the United States is sold as carcasses and the grade usually is not shown on wholesale and retail pork cuts as it is on beef and lamb carcasses and cuts. However, the USDA carcass grades are acceptable as evaluators of carcass merit. Pork grades differ from those of beef and lamb carcasses because they consider both muscle quality and muscle quantity in the same grading system.

The five pork carcass grades are U.S. No. 1, 2, 3, 4, and Utility (Table 12-1). The grades are determined from two general considerations: (1) quality-indicating characteristics of the lean meat and fat, and (2) expected combined yields of the four lean cuts—ham, loin, picnic shoulder, and Boston shoulder. Two quality levels are considered. One level is for carcasses of acceptable quality. These carcasses will have fat that is at least slightly firm, muscle (or lean) that is at least slightly firm and grayish-pink to moderately dark-red in color, and bacon that is at least slightly thick (at least .6 in. thick at the

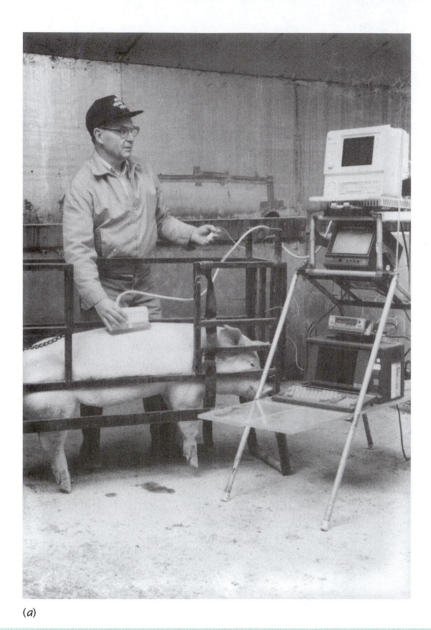

(a)

FIGURE 12-12

Ultrasonic measurement of backfat thickness and loineye (longissimus muscle) in swine. Cross-sectional area in (a) live animal; (b) carcass. (Photos courtesy of J. R. Stouffer, Animal Ultrasound Services, Inc., Ithaca, NY.)

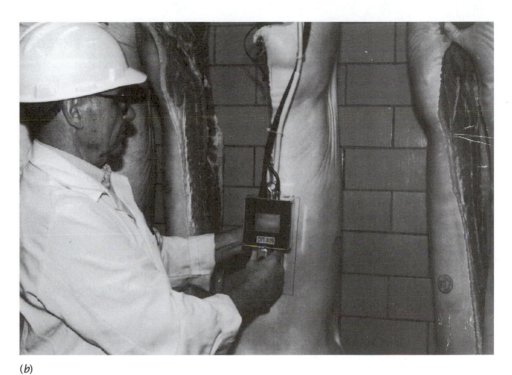

(b)

FIGURE 12-12 (continued)

thinnest point). These carcasses of acceptable quality will grade either U.S. No. 1, 2, 3, or 4, depending on their last rib backfat thickness (LRBF) and thickness of muscling. Carcasses having less than acceptable quality will always grade U.S. Utility, whatever their fatness or muscularity. Very few carcasses grade Utility.

If a carcass has acceptable quality, the grade is determined with the aid of information in Table 12-1. Only the backfat thickness (including the skin) opposite the last rib is used to estimate fatness. If the muscling is "average," the LRBF determines the grade. If muscling is "thin," the grade is lowered (toward a 4), and if muscling is "thick," the grade is raised (toward a 1). However, if the LRBF is over 1.75 inch, the carcass is graded a 4 despite any superiority in muscling.

WISCONSIN GRADES. A method of carcass evaluation, developed by University of Wisconsin researchers, estimates pounds (or percentage) of carcass muscle containing about 10% fat. This method requires hot carcass weight (HCW), loineye area (LEA) at the tenth rib, and fat thickness (FT) over the loineye at a point three-fourths of the distance across the muscle at the tenth rib. A heavier carcass weight and a larger loineye muscle produce more muscle, while a thicker fat layer is associated with less muscle because fat has to be trimmed during cutting operations.

TABLE 12-1

LAST RIB BACKFAT THICKNESS (LRBF) AND EXPECTED YIELD OF LEAN CUTS FOR MARKET HOGS BY GRADE

USDA Grade	Four Lean Cuts, %[a]	Last Rib Backfat Thickness, in.
1	60.4 and more	< 1.0
2	57.4 to 60.3	1.00 to 1.25
3	54.4 to 57.3	1.25 to 1.50
4	54.3 and less	> 1.50
Utility[b]	Variable	Variable

[a]Percentage of chilled carcass weight.
[b]Belly less than .6 inch thick at some point and/or muscle and fat are soft and/or off-color.

To determine the amount of muscle:

1. Find the preliminary amount of muscle from the listing below using FT over the loineye:

FT, inch	Preliminary amount of muscle, lb
.5	92.9
.6	91.8
.7	90.7
.8	89.6
.9	88.5
1.0	87.4
1.1	86.3
1.2	85.2
1.3	84.1
1.4	83.0
1.5	81.9

Each .1-inch change in FT over the loineye changes amount of muscle 1.1 lb—more fat, less muscle.

2. Subtract 165 from the HCW and multiply by .45. Each 1-lb change in HCW changes amount of muscle .45 lb—more weight, more muscle. Retain the sign (+ or −).

3. Subtract 4.5 from the LEA and multiply by 5. Each 1-inch^2 change in LEA changes amount of muscle 5 lb—more LEA, more muscle. Add or subtract (as

the sign indicates) each from the preliminary amount to obtain the estimated pounds of muscle.

The packing industry purchases carcasses and live animals based on instrumental assessment of each carcass. These measures are taken by utilizing such commercially available ultrasonic instruments as a fat-o-meter, which measures fat thickness at the tenth rib and loineye depth. These measures along with carcass weight may be used to predict the percentage lean in the carcass. Packers purchase pork carcasses based on the percentage lean. In the future, pork quality will also be used to determine carcass value.

SUMMARY

The evaluation of livestock has been practiced for centuries by cultures on all continents. This practice has significantly contributed to the diversification and improvement of present breeds and types. The chapter specifically addresses the evaluation and grading of beef cattle, sheep, and swine. Selection and evaluation of animals, both agricultural and companion, is an integral part of the respective niches of each type of animal in agriculture and society. Fairs, shows, and expositions, in which animals are exhibited and judged locally, nationally, and internationally attest to the importance and effort devoted to live animal appraisal and evaluation. Beef cattle, sheep, and swine selection includes live animal and carcass evaluation. The visual appraisal of the live animal is often the basis of breeding stock selection. To the extent that carcass measurements (lean and fat composition and meat quality factors) are related to visual appraisal of the live animal, changes in size, shape, and other characteristics of a breed or type of livestock can be achieved. The principles of animal evaluation and the grading and scoring systems in use by the meat industry in the United States are described. The broad concept of the evaluation of live animals, including farm animals and companion animals, should be acknowledged as the student considers the information presented in this chapter on meat animal evaluation.

GLOSSARY

Balance The overall blending of animal parts; determined by length of body relative to depth of body, structural correctness, muscularity, levelness of topline and length of neck.

Break joint The nonossified joint between the foot and pastern on a lamb carcass.

Bullock Young bull under two years of age.

Composition Relative amounts of muscle, fat, and bone that make up an animal or carcass.

Cutability Percentage of the carcass made up of closely trimmed (0.25 inches of fat) retail cuts after carcass fabrication. For example, a YG1 carcass would have high cutability, while a YG5 carcass would have a low cutability.

Dressing percentage   The relationship of carcass weight to live animal weight: (chilled carcass weight / live slaughter weight) × 100 = dressing percentage.

Mastitis   Inflammation of the mammary gland.

Navel   The loose skin on the belly of a heifer or cow marking where the umbilical cord was attached prenatally.

Phenotypic   The visual appearance of an animal.

Pones   Subcutaneous fat deposits that form on both sides of the tailhead in cattle and sheep.

Prepuce   The opening in the sheath of a bull from which the penis extends.

Sheath   The loose skin on the belly of a bull through which the penis extends.

Spool joint   The ossified joint on the end of the foreshank of a mutton carcass.

Urinary calculi   Mineral crystals that form in the urethra or bladder of male sheep and cattle because of injury to the urethra and/or imbalance of calcium and phosphorus in the diet. Calculi can block the urinary tract, prevent urination, and lead to death if the affected animal is not treated promptly.

CHAPTER THIRTEEN
DAIRY CATTLE

**L. E. CHASE
CORNELL UNIVERSITY,
ITHACA, NY**

CHANGES AND TRENDS IN THE DAIRY INDUSTRY
DAIRY CATTLE BREEDS
MILK MARKETING
GENETIC IMPROVEMENT
HOUSING SYSTEMS
HERD HEALTH
NUTRITION AND FEEDING
REPRODUCTIVE MANAGEMENT
DAIRY REPLACEMENTS
ECONOMICS
SUMMARY

The dairy industry has a key role in providing consumers with fresh, nutritious, and safe dairy products. Dairy products are valuable sources of nutrients, including protein and calcium, for humans. The dairy cow has the ability to convert a wide variety of feeds into milk. Many of these feeds could not be used directly in the human diet. Thus, the dairy cow is a key link in the total food and environmental recycling chain. The type and diversity of products in the dairy case of today's supermarket is truly amazing. New dairy products are continually being introduced by the dairy industry. In addition, dairy products are ingredients in many other items in the grocery store (see Chapter 23). The challenge for the dairy industry is to continue to economically and efficiently provide the high-quality dairy products desired by the public. This must be done in an environmentally responsible manner while providing profitability for the dairy producer.

CHANGES AND TRENDS IN THE DAIRY INDUSTRY

The dairy industry in the United States continues to change in terms of cow numbers, farm numbers, and milk production per cow. Dairy cattle were first imported to the Jamestown Colony in 1611. Since that time, the industry has undergone many changes. Figure 13-1 contains changes in numbers of dairy cattle and dairy farms since 1955. Note that significant reductions in both variables have taken place over this time period. However, during this same period, both milk/cow and total milk production have greatly increased. Total yearly milk production and consumption is given in Figure 13-2. The shifts in milk per cow for all cows and those enrolled in Dairy Herd Improvement Association (DHIA) testing programs are shown in Figure 13-3. In January 1997, 48% of the cows in the United States were enrolled in DHIA testing programs. The annual increase in milk/cow over this time period is 265 pounds for all cows.

The dairy industry has also experienced significant structural shifts in terms of where milk is produced. In 1889, the top five milk-producing states were New York, Iowa, Illinois, Pennsylvania, and Ohio. Wisconsin was the leading dairy state in 1950, followed by

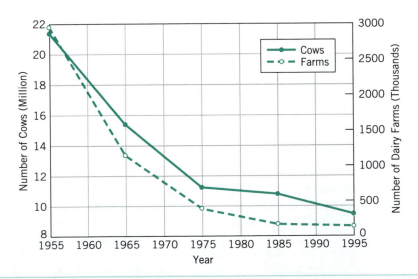

FIGURE 13-1

Number of dairy cows and dairy farms in the United States.

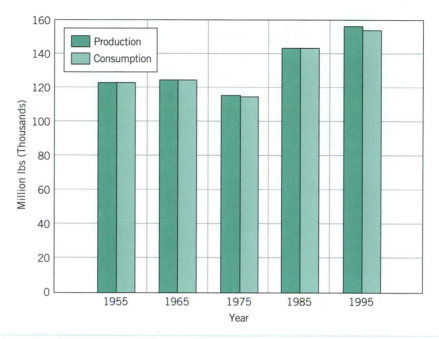

FIGURE 13-2

Annual total milk production and consumption in the United States.

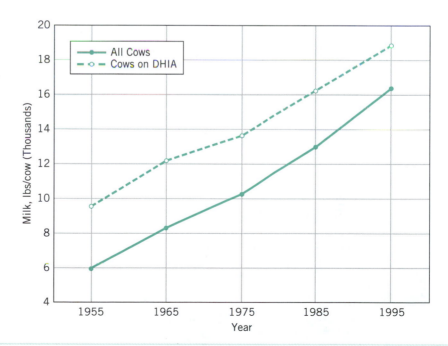

FIGURE 13-3

Lactation milk production for all cows and cows on DHIA testing programs.

TABLE 13-1
TOP 10 DAIRY STATES—1997

State	Farms	Milk Cows (1,000)	Milk/Cow (lbs)	Total Milk (Million lbs)	Cows/Farm
California	2,324	1,325	20,851	27,628	570
Wisconsin	23,890	1,393	16,057	22,638	58
New York	8,426	699	16,519	11,547	83
Pennsylvania	11,300	639	16,811	10,742	57
Minnesota	10,085	583	15,798	9,210	58
Texas	1,518	385	14,982	5,768	254
Michigan	4,039	306	17,680	5,410	76
Washington	868	264	20,095	5,305	304
Idaho	1,054	272	19,092	5,193	258
Ohio	5160	280	15,768	4,415	54

Source: USDA-NASS (1997).

New York and Minnesota. Table 13-1 contains the top 10 dairy states in 1997. California, Wisconsin, and New York are the top three states. These top 10 states account for about 68% of the total U.S. production.

Herd Size

Significant differences also exist in the number of cows per dairy herd in the United States. Cows per herd range from <29 to >8,000. Table 13-2 contains the distribution of cows by herd size for the three leading dairy states. California has very few herds with <100 cows while Wisconsin has few herds with >200 cows. However, the shifting industry in the upper Midwest and Northeast regions is moving toward larger herds. Dairy herds in both Wisconsin and New York tend to include cropping and dairy replacement enterprises in addition to the milking cows. California herds tend to be more specialized and concentrate primarily on milking cows. These herds tend to purchase all of their feed needs and many do not raise dairy replacements.

TABLE 13-2
DISTRIBUTION OF COWS BY HERD SIZE—1996

Cows/Herd	California	New York	Wisconsin
		(% of herds)	
1–29	0.1	2.7	5.1
30–49	0.3	11.3	26.0
50–99	0.8	37.0	41.0
100–199	3.8	28.0	21.0
> 200	95.0	21.0	6.9

Source: USDA-NASS (1997).

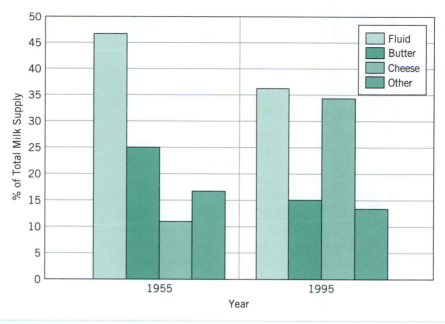

FIGURE 13-4

Milk use by product class.

Consumption of Dairy Products

The consumption of dairy products has also shifted. Figure 13-4 contains the distribution of the milk production by product class in 1955 and 1995. Per-capita consumption of dairy products is in Table 13-3. The decline in fluid milk consumption over this period was 37 lbs/person. Cheese consumption increased by 13 lbs, which is equivalent to 130 lbs of fluid milk. There has also been a shift in product consumption within the fluid

TABLE 13-3

Year	Fluid Milk	Cheese	Butter
CONSUMPTION OF DAIRY PRODUCTS IN THE UNITED STATES			
		(lbs/capita)	
1975	246	14.3	4.7
1985	227	22.6	4.9
1995	209	27.3	4.5
1997	206	28.1	4.1
% Change[a]	−16.3	+96.5	−12.8

[a]1997 as % of 1975.
Source: USDA/ERS Situation and Outlook (1997).

milk category. In 1975, per-capita consumption of whole milk was 168 lbs while lowfat milk was 53.2 lbs. Whole milk consumption in 1995 was 71.3 lbs/person while low-fat had increased to 92.5 lbs.

DAIRY CATTLE BREEDS

Dairy cattle in the United States are from several European breeds. Holsteins are (Figure 13-5) the most popular breed and represent about 93.7% of the total dairy cattle population. The other breeds are Jersey (4%), Ayrshire (0.4%), Guernsey (0.8%), and Brown Swiss (0.5%). Milking Shorthorns are also used for milk production but probably represent <0.5% of the total dairy cow population.

The breeds vary in size, coat color, milk production, and milk composition. Table 13-4 contains milk production and milk composition data for these breeds. The Holstein breed has the highest average milk production and the lowest concentration of fat and protein in the milk. The Jersey breed normally produces milk with the highest concentration of both fat and protein.

MILK MARKETING

Milk is a perishable product which must be moved quickly from the farm to the processing plant. Milk is stored on dairy farms in refrigerated tanks until picked up for processing. Typically, milk is picked up at the farm on a daily or every-other-day basis.

FIGURE 13-5

Holstein cows grazing pasture in the Finger Lakes region of New York state.

TABLE 13-4

AVERAGE MILK COMPOSITION BY BREED

Breed	Milk (lbs)	Milk Fat (lbs)	Milk Fat (%)	Milk Protein (lbs)	Milk Protein (%)
Ayrshire	14,815	581	3.92	496	3.35
Guernsey	13,714	621	4.53	485	3.54
Holstein	19,892	728	3.66	636	3.20
Jersey	14,049	659	4.69	526	3.75
Brown Swiss	16,032	651	4.06	572	3.57

Source: USDA-NCDHIP (1997).

The majority of milk is marketed by farmer-owned cooperatives. In 1997, about 120 billion pounds of milk from 71,000 farms was handled by the 50 largest cooperatives. This represents about 77% of the total milk marketed. The largest cooperative, Dairy Farmers of America, handled about 20% of the total milk produced in the United States. This cooperative represents about 18,500 members.

Milk market regulation has been a mixture of both federal and state marketing orders. The price paid to dairy producers is determined monthly by the market administrator. This determination is based on the end use of the milk shipped to plants within the order area. The milk supplied is divided into classes defined within the marketing order. General classes are:

1. Whole milk, lowfat milk, skim milk
2. Cream, soft products (cottage cheese, yogurt, frozen desserts)
3. Hard products (cheese, butter, dried milk)
3A. Nonfat dry milk (only in some marketing orders)

The minimum blend price received by dairy producers is established monthly by the market administrator. This price is based on the use of milk within the order. As an example, Class 1, 2, and 3 prices are $15.50, $13.50, and $12 per 100 lbs. The utilization in the market is 45% in Class 1, 15% in Class 2, and 40% in Class 3. The calculated blend price would be:

$$\text{Class 1} = .45 \times \$15.50 = 6.98$$
$$\text{Class 2} = .15 \times \$13.50 = 2.02$$
$$\text{Class 3} = .40 \times \$12.00 = 4.80$$
$$\text{Blend price} = \$13.80/100 \text{ lbs}$$

The calculated blend price (basic formula price) will vary in each of the 32 federal orders. This variation is related to differences in the proportion of the milk used in each class. The value of the milk in each class can also vary between orders. The blend price for

August 1996 was $14.92 in the Chicago regional order. However, it was $17.50 in the Tampa Bay order for the same time period. The USDA is also in the process of restructuring the federal order system and reducing the number of federal orders to from 10 to 12.

An additional change has been a shift to futures and options markets. The Coffee, Sugar and Cocoa Exchange (CSCE) introduced the use of futures and options for cheddar cheese and nonfat dry milk in June 1993. Grade A milk futures and options were initiated in December 1995 by the CSCE. The Chicago Mercantile Exchange (CME) began trading Grade A milk futures and options in January 1996. These changes offer opportunities for the dairy industry but it will take some time for all segments to gain a better understanding of the associated risks and benefits.

The actual price paid to an individual dairy producer will vary from the calculated blend price. One variable that alters price can be the distance from the major processing or consumption center within the market. Farms further from this center receive less for their milk due to the higher transportation cost. There may also be differences between producers in cooperative dues, premiums, milk composition, milk quality, or volume shipped. All of these impact an individual producer's price.

Milk pricing systems also vary between federal orders. In 1997, 13 orders used combinations of fat, protein, solids, nonfat or other solids to price milk. The remaining orders used fat and skim milk value.

Several changes have taken place in milk pricing systems in the United States. The M-W (Minnesota-Wisconsin) pricing plan, which had been in effect since 1961, was replaced by the BFP (basic formula price) in June 1995. The BFP is determined monthly and is the average value for Grade B milk converted into cheese, butter, and nonfat dry milk in Minnesota and Wisconsin.

GENETIC IMPROVEMENT

Genetics provide the foundation for efficient, profitable dairy cattle. A major contributor to the increased genetic potential in U.S. dairy cows has been progeny testing programs. These programs are conducted by the artificial insemination (AI) industry. Programs for progeny-testing young sires have been used since the early 1970s.

Heritability and Repeatability

The population must contain variation in the traits of interest if genetic improvement is to be made. The standard deviation for milk production in Holsteins is about 2,500 lbs of milk per lactation. Repeatability and heritability of traits are also important. Repeatability is a term describing how multiple measurements repeat. What is the repeatability of milk yield/day within a cow if we measure milk yields daily? Even though there is some variation in production between days, repeatability of daily milk yield is normally >.85.

Sire proofs available in the United States include reliability to provide an index of accuracy. Reliability is calculated based on a combination of number of daughters and the number of herds in which they are located. A sire with 50 daughters in 1 herd has a reliability of 29% (VanVleck, 1992). The reliability is 74% for a sire with 2 daughters in each of 25 herds. A higher reliability indicates that more confidence can be placed on the proof.

Heritability is the proportion of the total variation for a trait attributable to genetics. The heritability for milk, fat, and protein yield is about .3. Milk fat and protein content have a heritability about .5. Conception rate and calving interval have heritabilities in the range of .1.

Changes in milk production in a herd are due to both genetic and management (environmental) components. Milk production per cow in the United States increased about 5500 lbs between 1960 and 1986 (Norman and Powell, 1992). Genetic improvement accounted for about 2,000 lbs (36% of this total). The remaining portion is attributed to changes in management. A selection trial to evaluate genetic progress was initiated at Iowa State in 1968 (Freeman, 1992). One group of cows was bred to average predicted difference (PD) sires. The second group was bred to high PD sires. The cows bred to high PD sires have an average milk production per lactation of 21,529 lbs of milk in 1991. The average production for the cow bred to average PD sires was 18,149 lbs. Since these animals were similarly housed and managed, this difference of 3,380 lbs of milk is due only to genetics as the result of the selection program.

The foundation for genetic improvement programs in the United States is progeny-testing programs based on young sire sampling. In this program, the top 1 to 3% of the cows are bred to the best bulls. The males from these matings have semen collected when they are 12 to 15 months of age. This semen is used to breed a few hundred cows in a number of herds. Milk production of these daughters is used to evaluate the young sire. Usually, about 10 to 20% of the young sires are selected for inclusion in future breeding programs. A report by Ferris (1996) indicated that a higher annual income occurs in herds using AI versus non-AI bulls. This was about $110/cow in a 200-cow herd.

Sire Evaluation

A major change in sire evaluation was introduced in 1989. This is termed the animal model and is now routinely used in evaluating both cows and sires (VanVleck, 1992). The animal model is a more accurate evaluation system since it incorporates three key improvements:

1. All available information on an animal's relatives is used in this evaluation. This includes both male and female relatives.

2. An adjustment is made for the genetic merit of the other parent when evaluating progeny. This is designed to account for situations in which one bull is mated to high-genetic-potential cows while another bull may be bred to lower-genetic-potential cows.

3. A number of changes were made to refine the evaluations. These included dividing animals into registered and grade groups.

A new term, predicted transmitting ability (PTA), is used to estimate genetic merit. This value is one-half of the genetic breeding value. The following data are from three Holstein sires in the February 1997 sire summary. This sire summary was provided by the National Association of Animal Breeders.

	Bull A	Bull B	Bull C
PTA, milk, lbs	+2845	+912	−464
PTA, fat, lbs	+ 101	+ 31	− 3
PTA, protein, lbs	+ 77	+ 34	− 12
Reliability, %	74	99	99
MFP, $	323	121	− 41

The MFP is a calculation of the dollar value of the milk, fat, and protein PTAs. The accuracy of the PTAs is indicated by reliability. Reliabilities are higher as more daughters are included in the evaluation. There is less chance of the PTAs changing with higher reliability values.

HOUSING SYSTEMS

A housing system should provide a clean, dry, and comfortable living area for cows. This system should also be designed to be labor efficient and a safe environment for farm employees.

The types of facilities used to house dairy cows vary greatly throughout the United States. Dairy cows in the Midwest and Northeast are primarily housed in tie-stall or free-stall barns. In parts of the Southeast and Southwest, cows are often housed in open corrals with sunshades. A 1995 survey of 2,500 dairy farms by USDA:APHIS reported that 24.4% of the operations used free-stalls. Tie-stall or stanchion facilities were used on 61.4% of the operations. Dry-lot housing was reported on 47.2% of operations surveyed.

Herd size is an additional factor related to the type of housing system used. Tie-stall barns are the most common housing system for herds <100 to 150 cows. As herds get larger, free-stalls or corrals become more prevalent. The average number of cows per worker for tie-stall barns ranged between 24 and 29 cows in the 1997 New York Dairy Farm Business Summary. Cows per worker in free-stall barns averaged 33 for herds <150 cows to 45 for herds >300 cows. In some of the newer free-stall systems, cows per worker can be in the range of 60 to 80. Free-stall barns also tend to be less expensive to build. Cows per worker can exceed 100 in specialized dairy herds. These herds would concentrate on milking cows and not raise either crops or dairy replacements.

HERD HEALTH

Noninfectious diseases

A number of noninfectious diseases can impair productivity in the dairy cow. Table 13-5 contains incidence rates for some of these from three recent surveys. These diseases are related to nutritional imbalances or alterations in metabolism. An estimate of the cost associated with them is in Table 13-6.

These diseases primarily occur at the critical period around calving time. During this time a large number of metabolic and hormonal shifts occur in the cow as she goes from a nonlactating to a lactating state. A cow may be dry today, calve tomorrow, and be producing 50 to 80 lbs of milk in 2 to 3 days. This is a period of high stress for the cow and the immune system may be compromised in many cases. It has also been reported that a cow that experiences one disorder has a higher probability of a second disorder occurring.

It is beyond the scope of this chapter to provide in-depth information for each disorder. A brief synopsis of each disease is given:

KETOSIS

- May be primary or secondary (associated with other disorders such as retained placenta or metritis).
- Primary symptoms are loss of appetite, decreased milk production, and increased bodyweight loss.
- Related primarily to a glucose (energy) shortage.
- Elevated levels of ketone bodies in blood, urine, and milk.
- Treatments are to provide glucose or glucose precursors. A common treatment is an intravenous dextrose solution.
- Dry-matter intake must also be restored.

TABLE 13-5

INCIDENCE OF METABOLIC AND REPRODUCTIVE DISORDERS

Disorder	New York[a]	Michigan[b]	U.S. Survey[c]
	(% of cows)		
Retained placenta	7.4	12.0	9
Milk fever	1.6	5.8	7.2
Ketosis	4.6	11.8	3.7
Displaced abomasum	6.3	5.8	3.3

[a]*Source:* Grohn, et al. (1995).

[b]*Source:* Dyk and Emery (1996).

[c]*Source:* Jordan and Fourdraine (1993).

TABLE 13-6

COST OF CALVING TIME DISORDERS

Disorder	%[a] Deaths	%[a] Culled	Days Open	Increased Milk Loss, lbs	Average Cost/Case, $
Milk fever	8	12	5	1100	334
Ketosis	1	5	—	440	145
Retained placenta	1	18	19	450	285
Displaced abomasum	2	10	6	840	340

[a]% of cows with the listed disorder.
Source: Guard (1996).

MILK FEVER

▢ Occurs in the first few days postcalving.

▢ Incidence is higher in older cows.

▢ Symptoms include loss of appetite, sluggish digestive tract, and inability to get up.

▢ Thought to be related primarily to a shortage of calcium in the bloodstream. Recent research indicates that high potassium may also be a predisposing factor in milk fever.

▢ The most common treatment is intravenous calcium.

DISPLACED ABOMASUM

▢ Normally occurs in the first few weeks postpartum.

▢ The abomasum may twist to either the left (about 90% of the cases) or the right.

▢ Symptoms include cows going off-feed, decreased rumen contractions, dry, pasty feces, and an accumulation of fluid and gas in the abomasum.

▢ Exact cause is not well defined. Increased risk in any cow with a disorder or disease which decreases feed intake.

▢ The most common treatment is surgery. In some cases, rolling the animal may help.

FATTY LIVER

▢ Is the result of an accumulation of fat in the liver. Usually occurs at or within a few days of calving.

▢ Symptoms include low feed intake, increased incidence of other disorders, poor response to treatment, and depressed immune system function.

Treatments have limited success. Niacin or methionine can be fed to assist with mobilizing fat out of the liver.

The common thread in all of these disorders are the many changes, both metabolic and hormonal, which occur around calving. In addition, cows are often moved to a new environment and switched to new feeds at the same time. All of these changes tend to increase stress on the animal and have the potential to depress feed intake.

The best approach to minimizing the incidence of these diseases is to provide balanced rations for both dry and fresh cows. Diet formulation guidelines are given in Tables 13-7 and 13-8. This is also the time during the lactation cycle at which these cows need to be intensively monitored for general appearance, temperature, rumen contractions, and dry-matter intake. Any shifts in these should be a sign for initiation of treatment. This is also the period in which the manager should do everything possible to

TABLE 13-7

SPECIFICATIONS FOR DRY COW DIETS

Item	Early Dry Cow	Close-Up Dry Cow
Expected DMI, % of BW	1.9–2.1	1.6–1.8
Crude protein, % of DM	12–13	14–15
Soluble intake protein, % of CP	30–40	25–35
Degraded intake protein, % of CP	65–70	62–67
Undegraded intake protein, % of CP	30–35	33–38
NE_1, Mcal/lb DM	0.55–0.64	0.69–0.74
ADF[a], % of DM (minimum)	30–35	21
NDF[b], % of DM (minimum)	35–40	31
Ca, % of DM	0.5–0.7	0.6–0.7
P, % of DM	0.25–0.3	0.3–0.35
Mg, % of DM	0.2–0.25	0.25–0.3
K, % of DM	<1.5	<1.3
Na, % of DM	0.10–0.15	0.10–0.15
Cl, % of DM	0.20–0.25	0.20–0.25
S, % of DM	0.16–0.2	0.2–0.25
Fe, ppm	50–100	50–100
Mn, ppm	60–80	40–50
Zn, ppm	60–80	60–80
Cu, ppm	10–20	10–20
Co, ppm	0.1–0.3	0.1–0.3
I, ppm	0.4–0.6	0.5–0.7
Se, ppm	0.3	0.3
Vit. A, IU/lb	3,000–3,500	4,000–4,500
Vit. D, IU/lb	700–1000	1,000–1,500
Vit. E., IU/lb	20–30	35–45

[a]ADF = acid detergent fiber.

[b]NDF = neutral detergent fiber.

TABLE 13-8

SPECIFICATIONS FOR LACTATING DAIRY COW DIETS

Item	Stage of Lactation		
	Early	Mid	Late
Estimated DMI, % of BW	>4	3.5–4.0	3–3.5
CP, % of DM	17–18	16–17	14–16
SIP, % of CP	30–35	35–40	35–40
DIP, % of CP	60–65	60–65	60–65
UIP, % of CP	35–40	35–40	35–40
NE_1, Mcal/lb DM	0.75–0.80	0.72–0.75	0.69–0.72
ADF, % of DM	18–20	21–23	22–24
NDF, % of DM	26–30	32–34	34–36
Forage NDF, % of DM	20–22	23–25	25–27
NSC, % of DM	35–40	35–40	35–40
Fat, maximum, % of DM	5–7	4–6	4–5
Ca, % of DM	0.7–0.9	0.65–0.75	0.6–0.7
P, % of DM	0.40–0.45	0.35–0.40	0.33–0.38
Mg, % of DM	0.25–0.30	0.25–0.30	0.2–0.25
K, % of DM	1.0–1.5	1.0–1.5	1.0–1.5
Na, % of DM	0.2–0.25	0.2–0.25	0.2–0.25
Cl, % of DM	0.25–0.30	0.25–0.30	0.25–0.30
S, % of DM	0.24–0.28	0.22–0.24	0.20–0.24
Fe, ppm	50–100	50–100	50–100
Mn, ppm	60–80	60–80	60–80
Cu, ppm	10–20	10–20	10–20
Zn, ppm	70–80	70–80	70–80
I, ppm	0.6	0.6	0.6
Co, ppm	0.1–0.2	0.1–0.2	0.1–0.2
Se, added, ppm	0.3	0.3	0.3
Vit. A, IU/lb DM	1500–2500	1500–2500	1500–2500
Vit. D, IU/lb DM	600–800	600–800	600–800
Vit. E, IU/lb DM	10–20	10–20	10–20

minimize stress on the animal. The combination of these factors will be major steps in reducing the incidence of these disorders.

Infectious Diseases

MASTITIS. Mastitis is an inflammation of the udder which can be caused by many factors. A bacterial infection is the cause in most cases. It has been estimated that the average case costs about $170–$190. This figure encompasses losses in milk production, discarded milk, and treatment costs.

The severity of mastitis varies due to the type of infection and the degree of inflammation. Basic types of mastitis are:

1. Clinical
   —Visible changes in the milk (flakes, clots, discoloration)
   —Individual quarters may or may not be swollen
2. Acute
   —Abnormal milk
   —Cow may have a fever and poor appetite
3. Subclinical
   —Milk appears normal
   —May be an elevated somatic cell count (SCC)
   —Difficult to detect
   —Is the most common form

The organisms which cause mastitis can be classified as either environmental or contagious. Examples are:

Contagious	Environmental
Staphylococcus aureus	*Streptococcus uberis*
Streptococcus agalactiae	*Streptococcus dysgalactiae*
Mycoplasma bovis	*Escherichia coli*
Corynebacterium bovis	*Klebsiella pneumoniae*
	Klebsiella oxytoca
	Enterobacter aerogenes

One response of the mammary gland to an infection is to increase the number of white blood cells. These cells attempt to destroy the bacteria responsible for the infection. Somatic cells are the more common term used for white blood cells in milk. Somatic cells can be counted quickly and easily to provide an index of infection. The somatic cell count (SCC) in uninfected cows is usually in the range of 50,000 to 200,000/ml. As the cell count goes above 200,000/ml, it is highly likely that an infection exists. A milk loss of about 400 pounds is associated with a doubling of the SCC. If the SCC goes from 200,000 to 400,000, a loss of 400 lbs of milk for the lactation is anticipated.

The primary goal of a mastitis control program should be to prevent rather than treat the disease. Since this is a bacterial infection, steps must be taken to prevent organisms from entering the udder via the teat canal. Two key words in this context are clean and dry. Hygienic milking procedures should be followed after the teat is cleaned and dried. A number of tested and approved teat dips can be used both before and after milking. Treatment with organism-specific antibiotics may also be warranted in some cases. When this is done, the milk must be discarded for a period of time stated on the label of the product. Increasingly, dairy producers are using treatment therapies which eliminate or minimize antibiotic use. A specific mastitis control and treatment plan needs to be developed for each farm. The herd veterinarian is one person who can assist the dairy producer in developing this program.

BOVINE VIRAL DIARRRHEA (BVD). BVD is a viral disease which frequently results in lesions in the digestive tract and diarrhea. This virus can also cause abortion in pregnant animals. Vaccination is the best control program.

BRUCELLOSIS. This bacterial disease was common in the early 1900s. Eradication programs based on blood testing, vaccination, and culling were initiated in the 1930s. The most prominent sign of brucellosis in cattle is abortion after 5 to 6 months of gestation. Heifer calves are routinely vaccinated for brucellosis.

INFECTIOUS BOVINE RHINOTRACHEITIS (IBR). IBR is another viral-based disease. This is a disease which affects the respiratory tract and may cause abortion in pregnant animals. Vaccination is the common preventative approach.

LEPTOSPIROSIS. This is a bacterial disease which can also induce abortion. A routine vaccination program is the best control measure.

LISTEROSIS. This is a bacterial disease caused by the organism, *Listeria monocytogenes*. Typically, the brain of the animal is affected. Even though this is not a common disease, it may cause abortion. The source of the bacteria is contaminated water and feed.

VIBRIOSIS. This is a venereal disease associated with either natural breeding or use of infected semen. Symptoms may include lower fertility, embryonic death, or abortion. The use of AI is one of the best prevention measures. Vaccination can also be helpful in problem situations.

BOVINE PARATUBERCULOSIS (JOHNE'S DISEASE). This disease is caused by the bacterium, *Mycobacterium paratuberculosis*. Symptoms include a normal appetite associated with weight loss and diarrhea. Infection occurs most commonly in young calves, who can pick up the organism from infected manure or bacteria contained in milk. Work is in progress to evaluate the effectiveness of vaccination programs. The best control strategy is to use management and sanitation practices which minimize exposure and transfer of the organism to young calves.

NUTRITION AND FEEDING

Water

Water is the nutrient required in the greatest quantity per day by dairy cattle. It is usually also the cheapest of the nutrients supplied to the cow.

Milk contains about 87% water. Thus, a cow producing 100 lbs of milk per day is excreting 87 lbs of water via the milk. Water also comprises 50 to 80% of the animal's body weight. Physiological functions and many biochemical processes are dependent on water. Body fluids, such as blood, contain water. Water is also required for the excretion of urine and feces from the animal.

There are two primary ways by which dairy cattle can obtain water. The largest contribution is via drinking. Feeds consumed are another source. Water content in feeds such as pasture and silages may be 40 to 85%. Water can also be obtained from the chemical reactions involved in metabolizing feeds within the body. This potential source is not considered when calculating total water intake because it is so small.

If dairy cattle do not obtain adequate water by drinking and from the feed, milk production will decrease. Additional symptoms of low water intake include firm, dry manure, decreased urine output, and elevated packed cell concentration in blood. Drinking behavior may also be altered and cows may drink urine from other cows or lick puddles. These alterations in drinking behavior may also be related to mineral balances in some situations. Thus, they are not specific indicators of low water intakes.

The quantity of water required daily varies primarily due to level of milk production and feed intake. Other factors such as temperature, humidity, protein intake, and mineral intake (especially salt) influence water intake.

One guideline used to estimate needed water intake is 4.5 to 5 lbs of water for each pound of milk produced. An equation can also be used to estimate the quantity of water needed per day. One equation (Murphy, 1992) is:

$$\text{Water (gallons/day)} = 4.2 + (0.19 \times 16 \text{ DM}) + 0.108 \times \text{lbs milk}) + \\ (0.374 \times \text{ounces of Na}) + (0.06 \times \text{minimum daily temperature in F degrees})$$

This equation estimates total daily water intake. Figure 13-6 contains expected daily total water intakes calculated using this equation. An adjustment needs to be made for water contained in the feed to estimate drinking water needs. An example of this is:

Total water needed (drinking + feed) =	233 lbs/day
Feed water (100 lbs feed, 50% water) =	50 lbs/day
Drinking water = 233 − 50	=	183 lbs/day (22 gallons).

Forages

Forages provide the base upon which efficient and profitable dairy rations are built. The ruminant animal has the unique ability to convert forages into meat and milk. A large proportion of the land on which forages are produced is not suitable for grain crop production.

Forage quality is a combination of intake, digestibility, and chemical composition. The key nutrient class which influences both intake potential and digestibility is fiber. As the fiber content of the plant increases, both intake and digestibility tend to decrease. The environment in which the plant grows has a significant effect on forage quality (Van Soest, 1996). Key factors which influence this are sunshine, water, temperature, fertilizer, and day length. Forages with the highest digestibility are produced in cool and moder-

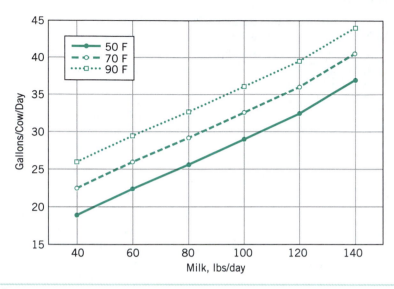

FIGURE 13-6

Predicted daily water intake.

ately dry environments. There are also differences in quality between corn silage hybrids grown in the same environment (Allen et al., 1997).

How much milk could be produced if an all-forage ration were fed to a dairy cow? Table 13-9 contains estimated milk production which could be obtained from feeding only forage. Predicted milk production on a protein basis is higher than from energy for legume and grass forages. Energy predicted milk production is higher than protein for corn silage. The cow's milk production will be controlled by the nutrient with the lowest predicted milk level.

TABLE 13-9

POTENTIAL MILK PRODUCTION FROM AN ALL-FORAGE DIET[a,b]

Forage	CP	NDF	NE_l	DMI	Milk, CP Basis	Milk, NE_l basis
	(% of DM)		Mcal/lb	(lbs)	(lbs)	(lbs)
High-quality pasture (legume)	27	38	.72	35.5	103	51
Alfalfa hay	20	42	.61	32.0	65	31
Alfalfa hay	16	48	.59	28.0	43	21.5
Grass hay	19	50	.70	27.0	50	29.0
Grass hay	10	66	.59	20.4	13.5	7
Corn silage	8	46	.72	29.3	17.1	36.3

[a]1350-lb mature cow, forage NDF intake = 1% of bodyweight.

[b]Does not include any nutrients for maintenance.

Maturity is the single most important factor which determines potential milk production from forages. Nelson and Satter (1990) used rations containing either early-cut (21% CP, 40% NDF), mid-cut (18.6% CP, 52% NDF), or late-cut (17% CP, 54.9% NDF) alfalfa silage. All rations contained 55% forage and 45% concentrate on a dry-matter basis. Average daily milk was 66.7, 63.6, and 57.6 lbs/day for the early-cut, mid-cut, and late-cut silages.

Even though forages vary in protein, energy, and fiber content, concentrate supplementation can be used to adjust for these differences. Table 13-10 contains an example of this. In this trial, ration NDF level was held constant by varying the proportion of forage and concentrate in the ration. Dry-matter intakes and milk production were similar for the five silages used in this study. However, ration costs would have varied depending upon the quantity of grain fed.

Alternative Feed Sources

The ruminant animal can utilize a wide variety of diverse feeds to produce high-quality food sources such as meat and milk. A large number of alternative feeds are routinely used by the feed industry. Many of these are the result of processing foods for human consumption. Thus, the ruminant animal becomes a recycler and decreases the need to dispose of these feed sources by landfilling, burning, or other methods.

Some of the alternative feed sources which can be utilized in dairy cattle diets include:

Feed	Source
Almond hulls	Almond processing
Apple pomace	Apple processing
Beet pulp	Sugarbeet processing
Bakery byproducts	Bakery industry
Brewer's grains	Brewing industry
Distiller's grains	Distilling industry
Fishmeal	Fish processing
Hominy	Corn dry milling
Soyhulls	Soybean processing
Soybean meal	Soybean processing
Corn gluten feed	Corn wet milling
Corn gluten meal	Corn wet milling
Wheat bran	Wheat milling
Wheat middlings	Wheat milling
Corn cannery waste	Sweet corn processing
Potato waste	Potato processing
Fats, oils	Rendering industry, food processing
Whey	Cheese industry
Blood meal	Rendering industry
Feather meal	Poultry processing

TABLE 13-10

MILK PRODUCTION RESPONSE WHEN DIFFERENT SILAGES ARE FED IN DIETS WITH SIMILAR NDF LEVELS

	Sorghum—Sudan	Orchardgrass	Alfalfa	Wheat	Corn
CP, % of DM	12.8	15.5	17.2	10.2	8.3
NDF, % of DM	54.8	48.4	45.2	54.4	41.6
Ration, NDF, %	31.0	31.1	31.4	30.3	30.5
% Forage in ration	42.2	51.5	57.2	43.6	63.6
DMI, lbs/day	48.4	51.3	51.9	49.9	48.4
Milk, lbs/day	71.3	74.1	73.9	73.7	76.1
Milk fat, %	3.6	3.8	3.6	3.4	3.5

Source: Mertens (1996).

The majority have limited use as human food. However, it is possible to combine these alternative feeds with forages to provide a balanced diet to support milk production. Using these feeds in dairy rations provides an alternative to disposal by landfilling or burning.

Nutrient Management

The relationship between animal production and the environment is an issue which is receiving more attention. The challenge for the dairy industry is to design nutrition and management systems which minimize nutrient excretion into the environment.

Table 13-11 is a sample daily balance sheet for a high-producing dairy cow. The nutrient output, expressed as % of nutrient input, ranged from 89 to 97%. The proportion of the daily nutrient intake excreted via the milk ranged between 26.8 and 36.3%. Total nutrient excretion in the urine and feces ranged between 62 and 67%. These figures provide a base of information for an individual cow.

The next step is to consider the nutrient balance on a total farm basis. This accounting process must include all nutrient sources which enter or leave the farm. These items can be represented for a dairy farm as:

Inputs	Outputs
Fertilizer	Milk
Feed	Meat
N fixation by legumes	Crops sold
Rainfall	

Klausner (1993) reported actual mass N, P, and K balances on New York dairy farms. These farms ranged in size between 45 and 1300 cows. Nitrogen which remained on the farm ranged between 64 to 76% of the total inputs. Corresponding values for P and K

TABLE 13-11

DAILY NUTRIENT BALANCE SHEET[a]

Item	Nutrient			
	Water (lb/day)	Nitrogen (g/day)	Calcium (g/day)	Phosphorus (g/day)
Inputs				
Drinking	187	—	—	—
Feed	53	780	216	108
Outputs				
Milk	87	212	60	29
Urine	56	307	1	1
Feces	91	219	132	66
Input-Output	+6	+41	+23	+12
Output, % of input	97.5	94.6	89.4	88.9

[a]1350-lb dairy cow, 100 lbs milk/day, 53 lbs dry-matter intake.

were 68 to 81% and 67 to 89%. The largest source of imported N on these farms was purchased feeds. This source accounted for 62 to 80% of the total imported N.

A number of approaches can be used to decrease the environmental impact of dairy production. Where possible, a higher proportion of the feeds could be produced on the farm. This will decrease the need for imported feed nutrients. A second approach is to use soil-testing results to develop fertilizer recommendations. This may decrease the need for imported fertilizers and will minimize overapplication. Credit should also be given for the nutrients contained in the manure which is applied to the fields. An additional consideration is to spread the manure over more acres. This will decrease the manure applied per acre and reduce excess nutrient loading.

Diet balancing also provides an opportunity area. When nutrients are supplied to dairy cows in excess of requirements, they are normally excreted via urine and feces. The goal is to design diets which optimize milk production and efficiency of nutrient use. We have used the Cornell Net Carbohydrate and Protein System Model to assess this impact. A commercial dairy herd of about 300 cows was used. Rebalancing the ration to optimize rumen function resulted in a decrease of about 10% in ration protein content. Daily milk production increased while feed cost decreased. Nitrogen excretion was reduced by 25 to 30%. This example indicates the potential to reduce nutrient excretion to the environment by altering nutritional management strategies.

Dry Cows

About 60% of the total fetal growth occurs during the dry period. This places a high demand on the cow for nutrients to support fetal growth. If inadequate nutrients are available, the cow may be forced to use body reserves to support fetal growth. Cows which mobilize body reserves and lose body condition in the dry period are at a higher risk for postcalving disorders.

A confounding factor is the depression in dry matter intake (DMI) that occurs in the last 2 to 3 weeks prior to calving. An increased ration nutrient density is needed during this time period to attain adequate quantities of nutrients per day. Table 13-7 contains nutrient requirements for dry cows. The adequacy of the nutrition program during this period has a significant impact on postcalving health and milk production (Hutchinson and Chase, 1997).

Lactating Cows

The cornerstone of diet formulation is DMI. The expected DMI of a dairy cow can be calculated with the following equation:

$$DMI \text{ (lbs)} = (BW \times .0185) + (FCM \times .305)$$

where:

BW = Bodyweight, lbs
FCM = 4% fat corrected milk, lbs

Protein is the most expensive component of the feeding program. Crude protein has traditionally been used in diet formulation programs. This system makes no differentiation between protein types and qualities. Microbial protein synthesis (MPS) is also not considered in the crude protein system.

The National Research Council (NRC) has proposed a new protein system which addresses these points. The main terms in this system are:

IP   = Intake (crude) protein
DIP = Degraded intake protein (rumen)
UIP = Undegraded intake protein

This system utilizes an evaluation of the UIP content of a feed. The UIP value depends on the rate of protein degradation in the rumen and the length of time the feed stays in the rumen. An additional protein term used in some ration formulation programs is soluble intake protein (SIP). Soluble intake protein is that portion of the DIP which is rapidly degraded in the rumen.

It is important to remember that a cow does not really have a "protein" requirement. In the rumen, the microorganisms need ammonia, peptides, and amino acids as building blocks for MPS. Amino acids are required for milk and tissue synthesis. Amino acid sources include microbial protein, amino acids in the UIP fraction, and rumen-protected amino acids. Microbial protein can provide up to 75 to 80% of the total amino acids required by the cow. Hoover (1996) reviewed the factors which influence MPS. A dairy cow producing 100 lbs of milk per day has a total essential amino acid requirement in the small intestine of about 2 lbs/day (Schwab, 1996; Chase, 1996).

Total carbohydrates comprise 70 to 80% of the total DMI consumed by the cow. A dairy cow consuming 50 lbs of dry matter will have a total carbohydrate intake of 35 to 40 lbs. The terms used to describe carbohydrate fractions in feeds include:

ADF (acid detergent fiber) = cellullose + lignin
NDF (neutral detergent fiber) = ADF + hemicellulose
NSC (nonstructural carbohydrates) =
100 − (CP, % + NDF, % + Fat, % + Ash, %)

Forage and total intake can be estimated by using NDF. Total NDF intake is suggested to be 1.2 ± .1% of bodyweight. About 75% (0.9% of BW) of this total should be from forages with adequate particle size to maintain chewing, rumination and rumen function. One way to evaluate this is that 15 to 20% of the forage particles should be >1.5" long. This should be adequate to provide for 550 to 600 minutes of chewing and rumination time per day.

Microbial protein synthesis is highly dependent upon NSC as an energy source for the rumen microorganisms. The NSC level is suggested to be 35 to 40% of the total ration DM. The NSC portion of the feed can vary greatly in composition (Chase, 1993). It can be primarily starch in some feeds while other feeds contain more sugars. These variations in composition affect the rate of breakdown and utilization of the NSC component in the animal. Feed processing, such as roasting or steam-flaking, can also alter the use of feed carbohydrates. Theurer (1996) indicated that cows fed steam-flaked sorghum grain produced more milk and had greater total tract starch digestibility than cows fed dry-rolled sorghum grain. Microbial protein production was also higher in cows fed the steam-flaked sorghum.

Table 13-8 contains guidelines that can be used in formulating rations. These guidelines incorporate the protein and carbohydrate concepts described above.

Nutrition and Immune System Function

The immune system has a role in protecting animals against foreign substances or infectious organisms. Parasites, bacteria, or viruses can all stimulate the immune response. The immune response in the animal consists of a number of actions. In some cases, a specific antibody will be produced. Immunoglobulins are one example of extracellular antibodies. Specific cell types such as lymphocytes, macrophages, and neutrophils can also be part of the immune system response.

One factor which triggers the immune system is stress. Stress can be thought of as the response of the body to any alteration in metabolism or environment. Examples of stress-inducing situations include calving, weaning, exposure to disease, weather conditions, crowding, social interactions, metabolic disorders, and nutrient imbalances. Stress alters nutrient utilization and may increase nutrient requirements.

Once the immune response is activated, rapid metabolic changes occur. The body must quickly produce large quantities of antibodies and millions of neutrophils and lymphocytes. Nutrients, including energy, protein, vitamins, and minerals, are required for these materials to be synthesized. If a deficiency exists in the nutrients available, the ability of the immune system to respond will be depressed.

There has been renewed research examining the relationship between nutrition and immunity in the last 5 to 10 years. The majority of these research trials have been concentrated on minerals and vitamins. Copper, zinc, selenium, and vitamin E have received most of the research effort. The role of chromium in stressed animals has also received attention. Key findings from these studies include:

Copper—A copper deficiency appears to decrease the phagocytic ability of the neutrophils. Low copper status has also been linked with decreased reproductive performance and an impaired ability of the animal to resist disease challenges.

Zinc—Poor resistance to disease and stress has also been linked with low zinc levels. Zinc also plays a primary role in wound healing. An improved zinc status has also been reported to decrease mastitis and improve hoof health.

Selenium and Vitamin E—Supplementation of selenium and vitamin E in dairy cattle has been linked with reductions in both retained placentas and mastitis. Work is continuing to better define the required supplementation levels.

Chromium—At present, chromium is not recognized as a required mineral for ruminants. It is considered an essential trace mineral for laboratory animals and humans. Initial research with chromium supplementation in beef and dairy cattle has indicated a lowering of serum cortisol levels.

Where does this information fit into nutritional management of the dairy cow? The primary time appears to be the transition period around calving. Feed intake is normally depressed and rumen function may be slowed. The cow will be subjected to varying degrees of stress. All of these factors increase the probability of a depressed immune system. This could at least partially be linked with lower nutrient intake due to depressed dry-matter intake at this time. It would appear logical to increase ration vitamin and mineral levels during this critical time. However, research data upon which to base these adjustments are lacking.

REPRODUCTIVE MANAGEMENT

Reproductive management is an integral component of herd management. Traditionally, the goal has been to maintain a 12- to 13-month calving interval. This is critical because dairy herds commonly replace 30 to 35% of the cows each year. Thus, heifer calves must be available to replace the culled cows. This should also increase genetic progress in the herd since the heifers should have a higher genetic index than the cows.

A number of measures can be used to evaluate the success of the reproductive management program. These include:

Calving interval	12–13 months
Days open	90–110 days
Days to first service	70–75 days
Services per conception	<2
Percent of heats detected	>65
Abortions	<4%
Retained placenta	<10%
Metritis	<10%

How can the calving interval be controlled? Before this can be answered, the factors which influence calving interval must be considered. Gestation length is fixed at about 280 days for Holstein cows. If a calving interval of 12 months (365 days) is desired, cows must be pregnant by 85 days after calving. Thus, the only way to really alter the calving interval is by the structure and efficiency of the breeding program.

After the cow calves, it normally takes 30 to 50 days before the first heat is observed. One factor which influences this is energy balance. Cows in negative energy balance postcalving tend to be delayed in the initiation of ovulation. Once this starts, the estrous cycle is repeated every 18 to 21 days.

The estrous cycle can be divided into four phases:

1. Proestrus

    —Progesterone is declining

    —The corpus luteum (CL) is regressing

    —Estrogen is increasing

    —Lasts 3 to 4 days

2. Estrus

    —Standing heat

    —High estrogen levels

    —Low progesterone levels

    —Lasts 12 to 18 hours

3. Metestrus

    —Ovulation occurs

    —Progesterone levels begin to increase

    —CL develops under the influence of luteinizing hormone

    —Estrogen levels are low

    —Lasts 3 to 4 days

4. Diestrus

—CL is functional

—High progesterone levels

—Low estrogen levels

—Lasts 10 to 14 days

The cow exhibits estrus with both primary and secondary signs. The primary sign is a cow standing to be mounted. Secondary signs include nervous behavior, increased activity, rubbed hair in the tailhead area, swollen vulva, and mucous discharge.

The dairy manager needs to observe cows for heat and record this information. Cows are not normally bred at the first observed heat postcalving. It is common to have a 50- to 60-day voluntary waiting period postcalving before cows will be bred.

The challenge in many herds is the development and implementation of an effective heat detection program. Cows are normally in standing heat (estrus) for 15 to 18 hours. It is easy to miss these heats even with a good heat detection program.

An alternative which is being used more frequently is estrus synchronization or programmed breeding. The goal is to make estrus a more predictable event. There are a variety of programs used which assist in attaining this goal. Cows are injected with prostaglandin or progesterone to alter CL function. Prostaglandin injection stimulates regression of the CL and estrus will usually occur within 2 to 5 days after the injection. Progesterone works by delaying follicular maturation. Once the progesterone injections stop, follicular development is completed and estrus should occur. Stevenson (1997) reviewed a number of approaches used in designing programmed breeding programs. These programs used combinations of palpation and hormonal treatments.

DAIRY REPLACEMENTS

Dairy replacements represent the future of the dairy herd. These animals should have the highest level of genetics on the farm. Goals for a replacement program include:

1. Mortality = <2% of live births
2. Age at first breeding = 12 to 14 months of age
3. Weight at first breeding = 60% of mature weight
4. Age at first calving = 22 to 24 months
5. Bodyweight after first calving = 80 to 85% of mature weight

How many heifers are needed? This depends on the age at first calving and the culling rate in the herd. Table 13-12 provides an estimate of the number of heifers needed to maintain a constant herd size.

The cost of raising a dairy heifer to 23 to 25 months of age has been estimated to be

TABLE 13-12

NUMBER OF REPLACEMENT HEIFERS REQUIRED IN A 100-COW DAIRY HERD[a,b]

Culling Rate, %	Age at First Calving, Months					
	22	24	26	28	30	32
20	40	44	48	51	55	59
24	48	53	57	62	66	70
28	56	62	67	72	77	82
32	65	70	76	82	88	94
36	73	79	86	92	99	106

[a]Includes a 10% allowance for mortality and culling.
Source: Adapted from Menzi (1988).

between $1100 and $1300. Feed costs account for 50 to 60% of this total cost. Average age at first calving in the recent USDA:APHIS survey was 25.8 months.

Feeding the Dairy Calf

The dairy calf at birth has basically no immunity from disease. First milking colostrum is a concentrated source of immunoglobulins. These immunoglobulins are absorbed across the intestinal wall into the blood to provide immunity. It is important to feed large quantities of high-quality colostrum as quickly as possible to the calf. This is because the ability of the intestine to absorb immunoglobulins decreases rapidly after the first 12 to 24 hours of life. Calves should be fed 2 to 4 quarts of high-quality colostrum the first feeding. Colostrum feeding is usually continued for 2 to 4 days. One index of colostrum quality is the content of immunoglobulin G (I_gG). An I_gG content >50 g/l is usually considered adequate when colostrum is fed at the levels listed above.

One measure of the immunity status of a calf is the serum level of immunoglubulin G (I_gG). It has been suggested that a serum I_gG value of 1,000 mg/dl in a calf at 1 day of age is a realistic goal (Quigley, 1996). Mortality rates for calves with serum I_gG levels of $<1,000$ mg/dl were higher than for calves with I_gG levels 1,000 mg/dl in a recent survey (USDA:APHIS 1993).

After this time, calves are shifted to either a whole milk or milk replacer liquid feeding program. Daily feeding rates are about 8 to 10% of birth weight per day. The choice of whole milk or milk replacer will depend on economics. A milk replacer should contain 20 to 22% protein, 10 to 20% fat, and a maximum of 0.5% crude fiber. Milk replacers which contain milk protein sources or specially processed soy products are acceptable.

At about 4 days of age, a calf starter grain is offered to the calves. This feed needs to be both highly digestible and palatable. Starters should contain 20 to 22% crude protein, 80% TDN, and at least 3% fat. Calf starter intake is a common method of determining when to wean calves from liquid feeds. A starter intake of 1.5 to 2 lbs/day for a 3- to 4-

day period is used as an index to wean calves. Age at weaning will usually be in the range of 5 to 8 weeks of age.

Rumen development begins during the calf starter feeding period. The growth of the rumen papillae is dependent upon the presence of volatile fatty acids, primarily butyrate. Butyrate is produced when the calf starter is digested in the rumen.

Feeding the Dairy Heifer

After weaning, calves should be fed high levels of both energy and protein to stimulate body growth and development. Table 13-13 contains nutrient composition goals for replacement heifers.

Rations should be designed to attain a targeted daily weight gain. Assume that the calf birth weight is 90 lbs. Desired breeding weight is 800 lbs. An average daily gain (ADG) of 1.7 lbs is needed if the heifers are to be bred at 14 months of age. However, if breeding age is changed to 12 months, ADG must be 1.95 lbs/day. It is important to remember that feed efficiency is highest and the feed cost/unit of gain is lowest for heifers in this part of the growth curve.

TABLE 13-13

SUGGESTED DIET SPECIFICATIONS FOR DAIRY REPLACEMENT HEIFERS

	Age, Months			
	3–6	7–12	13–18	19–22
	Average Weight, Lb (Large-Breed Heifers)			
Item	300	600	900	1200
Estimated DMI, lb/day	7–9	12–16	17–21	24–28
DMI, % of BW	2.9	2.7	2.5	2.2
	Nutrient Specifications, % of DM			
Crude protein	16	16	14	12
TDN	68–74	64–70	60–63	60–63
ADF (minimum)	19	22	22	22
NDF (minimum)	23	25	25	25
Ca	0.50–0.60	0.40–0.50	0.40–0.50	0.40–0.50
P	0.35–0.40	0.32–0.35	0.28–0.32	0.28–0.30
Trace mineral salt	0.30	0.30	0.30	0.30
NE_m, Mcal/lb DM	0.78	0.66	0.65	0.62
Ne_q, Mcal/lb DM	0.50	0.44	0.40	0.40
Vitamin A, IU/lb DM	1000	1000	1000	1000
Vitamin D, IU/lb DM	140	140	140	140
Vitamin E, IU/lb DM	11	11	11	11

Source: Adapted from Hoffman (1996), NRC (1989).

Bovine Somatotropin (bST)

Bovine somatotropin was approved for use in dairy cattle by the Food and Drug Administration (FDA) in February 1994. Prior to approval over 1,500 studies using more than 30,000 cows were conducted. The FDA evaluated both animal performance and human food safety data before granting approval. Somatotropin is a protein hormone produced in the cow by the anterior pituitary gland. Commercially available bST is produced by bacteria transfected with the bovine gene. The product is administered via an injection every 14 days.

Exogenous bST has been shown to increase milk production from 5 to 20% in full lactation research trials. Increased milk production occurs immediately. An increase in dry-matter intake is observed in a few weeks. Nutrient digestibility and the partial efficiency of energy use for milk synthesis are not changed when bST is used. Milk composition is also not altered. The primary mechanism of action of bST is to shift nutrient partitioning so that a larger portion of the nutrients is directed toward synthesis of milk.

In early 1996, 15 to 20% of the cows in the United States were estimated to be receiving bST. There is a trend for a higher rate of use as herds get larger.

ECONOMICS

The efficiency and profitability of a dairy farm are influenced by many factors. One parameter is the biological relationship between milk production and nutrient utilization. Figure 13-7 contains the relationship between level of milk production and nutrient

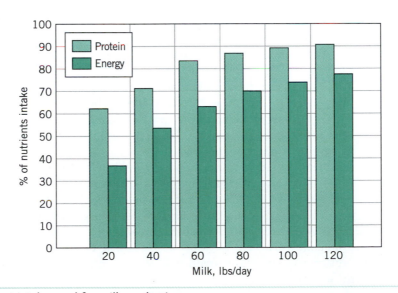

FIGURE 13-7

Percentage of total nutrient intake used for milk production.

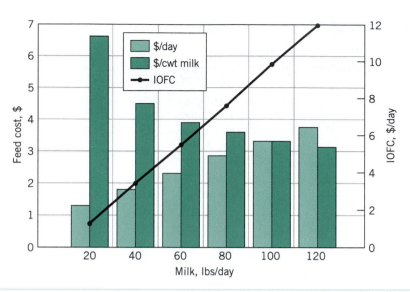

FIGURE 13-8

Relationship of milk production, feed cost, and income over feed cost.

use. As the level of milk production increases, a greater portion of the protein and energy intake is utilized for milk synthesis. This enhances the efficiency of feed utilization. The relationship between milk production, feed cost, and income over feed cost (IOFC) is in Figure 13-8. Even though daily feed cost increases with higher levels of milk production, feed cost per 100 lbs of milk decreases and IOFC increases. The data in Table 13-14 from herds on DHIA test indicate a similar trend between milk production, feed cost, and IOFC.

The economic status of a dairy farm can be assessed using a number of approaches. One approach is to use detailed farm business records. An example of this is the New York Dairy Farm Business Summary (Knoblauch and Putnam, 1998). The 1997 summary included data from 253 dairy farms. These farms averaged 190 cows/farm with 20,651 pounds of milk sold per cow. Net farm income (NFI) minus appreciation averaged $36,928 ($194 per cow). NFI is a measure of return to the farm family for labor, management, and equity capital.

Net farm income for the top 10% of the herds was $203,721 ($452 per cow). A subset of 146 farms participated in this program from 1994 through 1997. Net farm income per cow was $420, 362, 402, and 235 for 1994, 1995, 1996, and 1997.

Table 13-15 contains selected business management factors for all farms and the top 10% of the herds. This comparison provides an index of factors related to higher levels of profitability. The top 10% of the herds had more cows, more milk per cow, higher NFI/cow, and more cows/worker. However, these herds also had a lower total cost of producing milk.

TABLE 13-14

MANAGEMENT PARAMETERS BY MILK PRODUCTION LEVEL FOR HOLSTEINS ON DHIA

	Quartile			
	1	2	3	4
Milk, lbs/cow	13,740	16,648	18,601	21,267
Milk fat, lbs	493	595	666	760
Milk protein, lbs	443	537	597	679
Milk fat, %	3.58	3.57	3.58	3.57
Milk protein, %	3.22	3.23	3.21	3.19
% days in milk	83	86	87	89
Days dry	72	66	67	63
Calving interval, days	414	413	418	421
% cows by proven sire	30	44	60	75
Somatic cells	329,000	290,000	256,000	315,000
Milk, $	1,685	2,008	2,243	2,562
Feed cost, $	811	905	1,006	1,070
IOFC, $	874	1,103	1,237	1,492

Source: Heart of America DHIA (1995). Unpublished data.

TABLE 13-15

FARM BUSINESS MANAGEMENT FACTORS

Item	All Farms	Top 10%
Number of cows	190	451
Milk sold/cow, lbs	20,651	22,325
NFI total, $	47,139	208,513
NFI/cow, $	248	462
Hired labor, $	77,617	234,736
Hired labor/cow $	409	520
Cows/worker	38	48
Tillable acres/cow	2.43	1.86
Forage acres/cow	2.02	1.64
Forage dry matter, tons/cow	7.07	6.89
Crop expense/acre, $	64.95	68.94
Machinery expense/acre, $	176.46	202.79
Milk receipts/cow, $	2,823	3,042
Purchased feed/cow, $	958	1,019
Total cost of producing milk, $/100 lbs	14.71	12.84
Milk receipts, $/100 lbs	13.65	13.62

Source: Knoblauch and Putnam (1998).

SUMMARY

The dairy industry in the United States continues to increase milk production per cow due to both genetic and environmental factors. Farm numbers continue to decline while cows per herd are increasing. Even though total dairy product consumption has increased, there has been a shift in the types of products consumed.

GLOSSARY

ADF Acid detergent fiber. This consists of cellulose and lignin.

BFP Basic formula price. Calculated monthly by the National Agricultural Statistics System to provide a benchmark milk price.

Brucellosis A bacterial disease which can cause abortion.

BVD Bovine viral diarrhea. A viral disease which may cuase lesions of the digestive tract and diarrhea.

Calving interval The time between two calvings in a cow.

Colostrum The first milk produced after a cow calves. This has a high concentration of nutrients and antibodies.

CL Corpus luteum. A structure of the ovary associated with progesterone production.

Days to first service The number of days from calving until the cow is bred for the first time.

Days open The number of days between calving and conception.

DHIA Dairy herd improvement association.

DIP Degraded intake protein. The portion of the total intake protein that is degraded in the rumen.

DMI Dry matter intake.

FCM Fat corrected milk.

Heritability The portion of the variation in a specific trait that is due to genetic differences.

IBR Infectious bovine rhinotracheitis. A viral disease of the respiratory tract.

IOFC Income over feed cost.

IP Intake protein. The total protein consumed by the cow.

MFP Milk, fat, and protein dollars. This term combines PTAs for milk, fat, and protein plus a pricing formula for each component.

MPS Microbial protein synthesis.

NDF Neutral detergent fiber. This carbohydrate fraction consists of cellulose, hemicellulose, and lignin.

NE Net energy lactation.

NFI Net farm income. This represents the total return to the farm operator for labor, management, and equity capital.

NRC National Research Council.

NSC Nonstructural carbohydrates. This is the total feed dry matter minus the sum of protein, NDF, fat, and ash.

PD Predicted difference. The estimated difference in daughter performance between two bulls.

PTA Predicted transmitting ability. An estimate of the ability of the sire to transmit production traits to his daughters.

Reliability This term is an index of the accuracy of PTA values. It is expressed as a percent ranging from 1 to 99. Reliability increases as more daughters are included in the sire's proof.

SCC Somatic cell count.

S/C Services/conception. The number of breedings required to obtain conception.

SIP Soluble intake protein. The portion of the AIP that is rapidly degraded in the rumen.

TDN Total digestible nutrients. A measure of energy content of a feed. It represents the sum of digestible protein, fiber, nitrogen-free extract, and fat.

UIP Undegraded intake protein. The portion of the total protein that is not degraded in the rumen.

REFERENCES

Allen, M. S., Oba, M., and Choi, B. R. 1997. Nutritionist's perspective on corn hybrids for silage. *Proc. Silage: Field to Feedbunk North American Conf,* Hershey, PA, p. 25.

Ax, R. 1993. Utilization of genetic markers to breed cattle. *Proc. Cornell Nutr. Conf.,* Rochester, NY, p. 99.

Chase, L. E. 1993. Starch digestion in the dairy cow—What are the limits? *Proc. Cornell Nutr. Conf.* Rochester, NY, p. 90.

Chase, L. E. 1996. Practical application of amino acid concepts for dairy cattle. *Proc. Cornell Nutr. Conf.,* Rochester, NY, p. 208.

Dyk, P., and Emery, R. 1996. Reducing the incidence of peripartum health problems. *Proc. Tri-State Nutr. Conf.,* Fort Wayne, IN, p. 41.

Ferris, T. 1996. Managing genetics through expansion and beyond. *Proc. Midwest Dairy Mgmt. Conf.,* Minneapolis, MN, p. 114.

Freeman, A. E. 1992. Integrating genetic evaluations into a breeding plan. In H. H. Van Horn and C. J. Wilcox (eds.), *Large Dairy Herd Management.* Champaign, IL: American Dairy Science Association, p. 78.

Grohn, Y. T., Eicker, S. W., and Hertl, J. A. 1995. The association between previous 305 day milk yield and disease in New York dairy cows. *J. Dairy Sci.,* 78: 1693.

Hoffman, P. C. 1996. Optimum growth rates for Holstein replacement heifers. *Proc. Calves, Heifers and Dairy Profitability National Conf.,* Harrisburg, PA, p. 25.

Hoover, W. H. 1996. Contributions of microbial protein to amino acid supply. *Proc. Cornell Nutr. Conf.,* Rochester, NY, p. 199.

Hutchinson, L., and Chase, L. 1997. Managing the transition cow. *Proc. Mid-Atlantic Dairy Management Conf.,* Hershey, PA, p. 44.

Jordan, E. R., and Fourdraine. 1993. Characterization of the management practices of the top milk producing herds in the country. *J. Dairy Sci.* 76: 3247–3256.

Klausner, S. D. 1993. Mass nutrient balance on dairy farms. *Proc.* Cornell Nutrition Conf., Rochester, NY, p. 126.

Knoblauch, W. A., and Putnam, L. D. 1998. Business summary New York State. *Res. Bull. 98-06.* Dept. of Agricultural, Resource and Managerial Economics. Cornell University, Ithaca, NY.

Menzi, U., Jr. 1988. Planning heifer housing facilities. *Animal Sci. Mimeo* 102. Dept. of Animal Science, Cornell University, pp. 102–112.

Mertens, D. 1996. Using fiber and carbohydrate analyses to formulate dairy rations. *Proc. Dairy Forage Research Center Conference,* US Dairy Forage Research Center, Madison, WI., p. 81.

Morrill, J. L. 1996. Rations for dairy heifers. *Proc. Tri-State Dairy Nutr. Conf.,* Fort Wayne, IN, p. 203.

Murphy, M. R. 1992. Water metabolism of dairy cattle. *J. Dairy Sci.,* 75: 326.

NRC. 1985. Ruminant nitrogen usage. National Academy of Science, Washington, DC.

NRC. 1989. Nutrient requirements of dairy cattle. 6th rev. ed. National Academy of Science, Washington, DC.

Nelson, W. F., and Satter, L. D. 1990. Effect of stage of

maturity and method of preservation of alfalfa on production of lactating dairy cows. *J. Dairy Sci.*, 73: 1800.

Norman, H. D., and Powell, R. L. 1992. Genetic change attained and possible. In H. H. Van Horn and C. J. Wilcox (eds.), *Large Dairy Herd Management.* Champaign, IL. American Dairy Science Association, p. 59.

Quigley, J. D. III. 1996. Management of the neonatal calf. *Proc. Tri-State Dairy Nutr. Conf.,* Fort Wayne, IN, p. 189.

Rotz, C. A., and Harrigan, T. M. 1997. Economics of silage-based cropping systems. *Proc. Silage: Field to Feedbunk North American Conf.,* Hershey, PA, p. 3.

Schwab, C. G. 1996. Amino acid nutrition of dairy cows: Current status. *Proc. Cornell Nutr. Conf.,* Rochester, NY, p. 184.

Stevenson, J. 1997. Systematic breeding programs. *Proc. Mid-Atlantic Dairy Management Conf.,* Hershey, PA, p. 104.

Stevenson, J. S., and Smith, J. F. 1996. Cost-effective reproductive management. *Proc. Midwest Dairy Mgmt. Conf.,* Minneapolis, MN, p. 97

Theurer, C. B. 1996. Steam-flaking improves starch utilization and milk production parameters. *Proc. Cornell Nutr. Conf.,* Rochester, NY, p. 121.

USDA-APHIS. 1993. Transfer of material immunity to calves. National Animal Health Monitoring System. USDA-APHIS, Fort Collins, CO.

USDA-ERS. 1997. Livestock, dairy, and poultry situation and outlook. Economic Research Service, Washington, DC.

USDA-NASS. 1997. Milk production, disposition and income. National Statistics Service, Washington, DC.

USDA-NCDHIP. 1997. USDA summary of 1997 herd averages. Nutritional Cooperative Dairy Herd Improvement Handbook, Washington, DC.

Vanderboom, R. J., Tappan, R., McCauley, T. C., and Ax, R. L. 1994. Designing tomorrow's genes. In E. R. Jordan (ed.), *Proc. National Reproduction Symposium,* Pittsburgh, PA, p. 33.

Van Soest, P. J. 1996. Environment and forage quality. *Proc. Cornell Nutr. Conf.,* Rochester, NY, p. 1.

Van Vleck, L. D. 1992. Animal model for bull and cow evaluation. In H. H. Van Horn and C. J. Wilcox (eds.), *Large Dairy Herd Management.* Champaign, IL: American Dairy Science Assoc., p. 8.

CHAPTER FOURTEEN
BEEF CATTLE

A. D. HERRING
TEXAS TECH UNIVERSITY
LUBBOCK, TX

HISTORICAL ASPECTS

CATTLE STATISTICS

PRODUCTION SYSTEMS

BREEDING AND GENETIC CONSIDERATIONS

REPRODUCTIVE MANAGEMENT

NUTRITIONAL MANAGEMENT

HERD HEALTH CONCERNS

GENERAL MANAGEMENT CONSIDERATIONS AND ISSUES

SUMMARY

Cattle are not native to North America; however, they have been in this geographic area for almost 500 years. The first imported cattle were the Spanish ancestors of the Texas Longhorn. Many other types have been imported with varying levels of acceptance during this time span. Through the years, cattle breeders have changed body size and production traits to suit various uses here in the United States and across the globe, and continue to do so. Many technologies have been developed to improve performance. These developments include hormonal treatment to enhance reproductive management, anabolic growth implants to increase lean muscle mass and decrease fat, feed processing treatments to boost nutrient utilization, and various chemical and mechanical processes to enhance the eating qualities of beef. High-quality beef is the ultimate product of the industry. New technologies must be considered in all segments of the beef cattle industry in order to meet the desires of consumers. The purpose of this chapter is to familiarize the student with the background information relative to beef cattle production in the United States.

HISTORICAL ASPECTS

All of our present-day breeds of cattle have descended from one ancestral type, the Aurochs, which were the prehistoric type of cattle of the Middle East; however, today it has been estimated that 1000 breeds of cattle exist (Porter, 1991). Across these 1000 breeds is tremendous variation in body size, milk production, muscle shape, environmental adaptation, and beef-eating quality. Within the United States there are over 60 breeds, and numerous breed crosses, many of which have been developed into new breeds. Spanish explorers brought cattle to North America in the early 1500s that would give rise to the Texas Longhorns. Settlers from central Europe and Britain also brought cattle to the New World in the seventeenth and eighteenth centuries for draft purposes, to produce milk and meat, and for hides to use as shelter and clothing. These cattle were typical of those found in the different localities from which these pioneers emigrated.

The concept of recording pedigrees as done by breed associations originated about 1822 when *Coates Herdbook* in England was established to record Shorthorn cattle ancestry; Shorthorn was therefore the first pure "breed" of cattle officially recognized as such, although distinct types of cattle have existed for centuries. Shorthorn in 1783, Hereford in 1817, and Angus in 1873 were the first pure beef breeds to officially be imported to the United States. Bulls of these breeds were bred to local cattle in various regions to "improve" the cattle for beef conformation and size. "New" breeds continue to be imported, including Tuli from Zimbabwe, Boran from Kenya, and Parthenais from France. The acceptance of a new breed depends on the production characteristics of the cattle, current market conditions, perceived needs, and managerial abilities of the breeders.

CATTLE STATISTICS

Beef cattle are found in all 50 of the United States. In many states, beef cattle are the number-one agricultural cash crop. The total number of beef cattle in the United States has varied considerably during our nation's short history. Texas leads the nation in number of beef cows and feedlot cattle (Tables 14-1 and 14-2). According to the 1860 U.S. Census, there were 30 million people in the United States and 26 million head of cattle within the state of Texas. The number of cattle in the United States increased from under 30 million in 1867 to a peak of about 131 million in 1975, and as of January 1, 1998, was estimated at 99.5 million (USDA, 1998a). This total included 33.7 million mature

TABLE 14-1

TOP TEN STATES IN BEEF COW NUMBERS AS OF JANUARY 1, 1998

Region	Number of Beef Cows[1]	Number of Operations[1]	Average Herd Size[2]	Operations with <50 Cows[1]	Operations with 100+ Cows[1]
Texas	5.520 million	133,000	41.5	104,000	11,500
Missouri	1.990 million	60,000	33.2	48,000	3,700
Oklahoma	1.965 million	54,000	36.4	42,000	4,000
Nebraska	1.930 million	22,000	87.7	12,200	5,200
South Dakota	1.559 million	17,000	91.7	7,200	5,300
Montana	1.542 million	11,800	130.7	4,800	4,850
Kansas	1.461 million	29,000	50.4	19,000	4,500
Kentucky	1.140 million	44,000	25.9	38,000	1,600
Tennessee	1.085 million	50,000	21.7	45,000	1,400
Florida	1.010 million	20,000	50.5	16,400	2,000
Total of top 10	19.202 million	440,800	43.6	336,400	44,050
Total for United States	33.683 million	882,600	38.2	703,300	74,480

[1]Data from National Agricultural Statistics Service, *USDA Cattle Report,* January 30, 1998.
[2]Calculated by dividing beef cow numbers by number of operations.

beef cows, 9.2 million mature dairy cows, and 56.6 million young animals and mature bulls. The total number of operations with beef cows in 1997 was 882,600 (average herd size of 38) according to USDA (1998a). These operations were classified in relation to number of cows maintained: 703,300 operations had 1 to 49 cows, 104,820 operations had between 50 and 99 cows, 68,845 operations had 100 to 499 cows, and 5,635 operations had 500 or more cows (USDA, 1998a). Producers with small herds do not rely on

TABLE 14-2

TOP TEN STATES IN CATTLE FEEDING AS OF JANUARY 1, 1997

Region	Number of Cattle on Feed[1]	Number of Total Cattle and Calves[2]
Texas	2.630 million	14.100 million
Kansas	2.220 million	6.550 million
Nebraska	2.220 million	6.550 million
Colorado	1.130 million	3.150 million
Iowa	1.000 million	3.900 million
Oklahoma	0.400 million	5.400 million
California	0.375 million	4.550 million
South Dakota	0.320 million	3.800 million
Minnesota	0.300 million	2.750 million
Idaho	0.270 million	1.750 million
Total of top 10	10.865 million	52.500 million
Total for U.S.	13.216 million	101.209 million

[1] Data from National Agricultural Statistics Service, *USDA Cattle on Feed Report,* January 24, 1997.

[2] Data from National Agricultural Statistics Service, *USDA Cattle Report,* January 31, 1997.

beef cows for their primary source of income; consequently, many of these producers are not motivated to manage their animals as efficiently as possible.

PRODUCTION SYSTEMS

The beef cattle industry is divided into five basic segments: (1) calf production (cow-calf producers), (2) cattle growing and finishing (stocker calf and feedlot operations), (3) conversion of animal to wholesale product (beef packers), (4) sale of retail cuts (restaurants and supermarkets), and (5) consumption of beef (the consumer). Each of the first four segments is dependent upon the others for survival. Here we describe calf production, growing and finishing cattle, and conversion of animals to products.

Calf Production

Cow-calf producers control the genetic makeup of the beef cattle in the United States. Therefore, they are generally referred to as either seedstock or commercial producers. Seedstock producers (purebred breeders, representing more than 60 registered breeds) sell

FIGURE 14-1
Cow-calf pairs in Palouse area of Washington.

cattle for breeding purposes. Purebred breeders need to be concerned about all aspects of the beef industry. They may sell breeding animals to other purebred breeders, but more commonly they sell breeding stock to commercial cow-calf producers who want to have proven and reliable genetic sources. Purebred breeders as well as commercial cow-calf producers are generally concerned with increasing reproductive efficiency, growth and size traits, milk production, animal health and disease prevention, and proper nutritional management.

Seedstock producers commonly sell breeding animals that are over 12 months of age, but they may sell animals of any age. The primary goal for many of these producers is to sell young bulls to commercial cow-calf producers, but most also sell some breeding females each year. Only the most desirable animals should be sold for breeding purposes. Therefore, many purebred calves are sold as stocker or feeder calves and enter the food chain along with purebred cows or bulls no longer useful for breeding. Almost all beef cattle from both purebred and commercial herds ultimately are used for food.

About 95% of the cow-calf producers in the United States are commercial producers. As a result, the vast majority of beef cows in the United States are commercial cows. Commercial cow-calf producers are usually one step closer to the consumers than seedstock producers because the majority of their animals go directly into the production of beef. Cow-calf pairs on pasture just before weaning are shown in Figure 14-1. Their calves are typically sold as stocker calves for a forage-based growing period (Figure 14-2) or as

FIGURE 14-2
Yearling steers about to come off wheat pasture.

FIGURE 14-3

Feed lot for receiving stocker calves.

feeder calves going into a feed yard (Figure 14-3). Like their seedstock counterparts, commercial cow-calf producers must be concerned with reproductive performance in their cow herd. Both nutritional management and proper health programs are vital to ensure optimal reproductive performance. Most of these producers sell their calves on a weight basis either shortly after weaning or later as yearlings. Traits that are important to commercial cow-calf producers in addition to reproduction include calf growth ability, cow size and milk production, adaptability to extensive management conditions, animal health, and cow longevity.

Cattle Growing and Finishing

Producers who specialize in stocker and feeder calf and finished beef cattle production are primarily interested in traits related to growth ability, conversion of feed to weight gain, cost of weight gain, degree of muscularity, degree of fatness, and animal health. Stocker calves are those recently weaned and managed on a forage-based diet. Many of these calves graze small grain pastures, such as wheat or oats, or grass pastures for a growing period of two to four months, before going into a feed yard. Stocker calves typically weigh about 400 to 700 lbs when they enter the stocker phase. Calves that go through a stocker phase are approximately one year old when they enter a commercial feed yard weighing 600 to 900 lbs. However, not all commercial calves go through a stocker program. Many cow-calf producers put calves into a feed yard shortly after weaning at about 6 months of age at a weight of about 400 to 700 pounds (referred to as calf-feds) and feed them a high-energy growing-finishing diet. These calves usually are fed 160 to 220 days consuming a high-energy, grain-based diet. Calves about to enter a feed yard are generally referred to as feeder calves. Calves that have gone through a stocker program usually require a feeding period of 100 to 160 days to a slaughter weight of 1000 to 1300 pounds.

Once in the feed yard, calves are gradually adapted to a high-energy, grain-based diet through three or four rations, each with less roughage and more grain. When cattle are fed a high-energy diet for several weeks, they deposit sufficient intramuscular fat (marbling) that increases eating quality. Cattle can be finished on forage or pastures also, but it takes longer for them to develop adequate market weight. The fat of grain-fed cattle is white, whereas the fat of grass-fattened cattle tends to be yellowish. This color does not affect the nutritional aspects, but consumers tend to prefer beef with white fat. Cattle finished on a grain-based diet may be processed at a younger age at an acceptable slaughter weight, while yielding a more desirable product.

Conversion of Animals to Products

Cattle that are ready to be processed into beef are referred to as "finished" or "fat" cattle. These terms have both historical and practical meaning. Cattle were traditionally fed until they had about 0.5 inches (or more) of fat cover over the ribs to ensure that their carcasses would be graded Choice at the packing plant. Beef carcasses are cut between the twelfth and thirteenth ribs to expose the longissimus (rib-eye) muscle. The amount of marbling within the muscle dictates the U.S. quality grade, and the suface area of this muscle cross section is the rib-eye area. A higher-quality grade (Choice or Prime) carcass is worth more due to its perceived higher eating quality. With recent emphasis on lower fat consumption, leaner beef is being produced to meet consumer demands. Cattle now are fed to have approximately 0.3 to 0.4 inches of fat cover. Beef packers are concerned about traits such as carcass weight, marbling, muscularity, external fatness, and age of animals. They are also concerned about factors such as hide trim losses due to brands and parasites, bruises, and injection site lesions, which reduce carcass value. These problems can occur at the cow-calf, stocker, or feed yard level.

CARCASS INSPECTION AND GRADING.
All beef carcasses in the United States are inspected for wholesomeness. Additionally, commercially sold carcasses are assigned USDA yield grades and quality grades. Yield grade is based on carcass weight, muscularity (rib-eye area), external fat cover, and internal fat. Yield grade estimates percentage of the carcass formed into retail cuts. Quality grade is based on muscular and skeletal maturity of the animal and amount of marbling. Finished cattle may be sold to beef packers alive based on their body weight, time on feed, and visual evaluation of muscularity and fatness. However, increasingly more cattle are being sold on a formula basis for their actual quality grade and yield grade at the packing plant.

OWNERSHIP STRATEGIES. Cow-calf producers may retain ownership of their animals through the stocker or finishing stage or even through the wholesale carcass stage. The further through the production chain producers retain ownership, the more information they obtain about their cattle. They can then more effectively evaluate how their cattle fit into current market demands, and at what points in the production chain they can most profitably market their animals.

BREEDING AND GENETIC CONSIDERATIONS

All breeds of cattle have certain unique and desirable attributes. In many instances, it is more important to be concerned about the performance of the animals than about their breed identity. Table 14-3 summarizes breeds that have been imported into the United States. Photographs of some of the breeds common in the United States are in Figure 14-4a–h.

It is useful to group breeds into biological types that have certain traits in common. We can broadly group cattle as British, Continental European, zebu, dairy, or some combination of these. Among the British and Continental European groups, there are some breeds with much higher milking potential (known as dual purpose) because their ancestors were used to produce milk for human consumption in addition to beef and/or for draft purposes. In general, British beef breeds are considered to be moderate in skeletal size, moderate in milk production, moderate in muscularity, to produce well-marbled and tender beef, and to be very fertile. Continental European breeds are larger in skeletal size, and tend to be leaner and more muscular than the British breeds. All of these breeds are classified as *Bos taurus* breeds. Brahman cattle are an example of *Bos indicus*, or zebu, cattle. These are the shoulder-humped breeds of the world. As a group, zebu breeds tend to be well adapted to tropical environments, to have high tolerance levels of parasites, and to be long-lived. *Bos indicus* tend to reach puberty later than British and European breeds and produce beef that is less tender on average than most *Bos taurus* breeds. Some dairy breeds are lighter-muscled than the beef breeds. It is important to remember that genetically superior and inferior animals for specific traits can be found among all cattle types. Table 14-4 summarizes breeds of cattle evaluated at USDA-MARC (Clay Center, NE) for four production criteria.

Crossbreeding Systems

Approximately 95% of the commercial beef cows in the United States are crossbreds, and the vast majority of cattle that enter our food chain are crossbreds. Crossbreeding offers several advantages to comercial cow-calf producers, including heterosis (hybrid vigor), combination of desirable characteristics from the parental types, and the utilization of specialized sire types and specialized dam types. Heterosis is the increased performance of crossbred animals compared to the parental breed average. The single biggest advantage crossbreeding offers to commercial cow-calf producers is utilization of the crossbred cow

TABLE 14-3

BREEDS OF BEEF CATTLE IMPORTED INTO UNITED STATES

Breed	Origin	Biological Grouping
Africander	South Africa	Sanga
Angus	Scotland	British—beef
Ankole-Watusi	Zaire, Uganda	Sanga
Ayrshire	Scotland	Dairy
Beef Friesian	Ireland	Continental European—dual purpose
Belgian Blue	Belgium	Continental European—beef
Belted Galloway	Scotland	British—dual purpose
Blonde d' Aquitaine	France	Continental European—beef
Bonsmara	South Africa	Sanga-British composite
Boran	Ethiopia, Kenya	Zebu
Braunvieh	Switzerland	Continental European—dual purpose
British White	England	British—beef
Brown Swiss	Switzerland	Dairy
Charolais	France	Continental European—beef
Chianina	Italy	Continental European—beef
Corriente	Mexico	Criollo
Devon	England	British—beef
Dexter	Ireland	British—dual purpose
Dutch Belted	Netherlands	Dairy
Galloway	Scotland	British—beef
Gelbvieh	Germany	Continental European—dual purpose
Guernsey	English Channel	Dairy
Hereford	England	British—beef
Highland	Scotland	British—beef
Holstein (Friesian)	Netherlands	Dairy
Jersey	English Channel	Dairy
Limousin	France	Continental European—beef
Maine-Anjou	France	Continental European—dual purpose
Marchigiana	Italy	Continental European—beef
Mashona	Zimbabwe	Sanga
Milking Shorthorn	England	Dairy
Murray Grey	Australia	British—beef composite
Nellore	India	Zebu
Normande	France	Continental European—dual purpose
Parthenais	France	Continental European—beef
Piedmontese	Italy	Continental European—beef
Pinzgauer	Austria	Continental European—dual purpose
Red Poll	England	British—dual purpose
Romagnola	Italy	Continental European—beef
Romosinuano	Columbia	Criollo
Salers	France	Continental European—dual purpose
Senepol	Virgin Islands	Tropically adapted *Bos taurus*
Shorthorn	England	British—beef
Simmental	Switzerland	Continental European—dual purpose
South Devon	England	British—dual purpose
Tarentaise	France	Continental European—dual purpose
Tuli	Zimbabwe	Sanga
Wagyu	Japan	*Bos taurus*—beef
WhitePark	England	British—beef

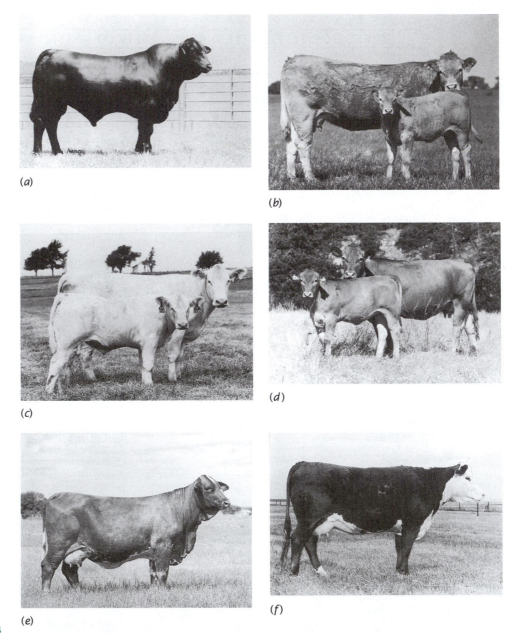

FIGURE 14-4

Breeds of beef cattle common in the United States.
A. Brangus (Courtesy International Brangus Breeders Association, San Antonio, TX)
B. Limousin (Courtesy North American Limousin Foundation, Englewood, CO)
C. Charolais (Courtesy International Charolais Association, Kansas City, MO)
D. Gelbvieh (Courtesy American Gelbvieh Association, Westminster, CO)
E. Beefmaster (Courtesy Beefmaster Breeders United, San Antonio, TX)
F. Hereford (Courtesy American Hereford Association, Kansas City, MO)

(g)

(h)

FIGURE 14-4 (continued)

G. Angus (Courtesy American Angus Association, St. Joseph, MO)
H. Brahman (Courtesy American Brahman Breeders Association, Houston, TX)

because many maternal traits such as pregnancy rate, calving interval, and milk production show large amounts of heterosis. Additionally, research has proven two to three times as much heterosis occurs when crossbreeding *Bos taurus* with *Bos indicus* breeds than when crossbreeding two *Bos taurus* or two *Bos indicus* breeds.

Crossbreeding systems have traditionally been classified as terminal or rotational. One example of a terminal system is a three-breed terminal cross. A bull of one breed (e.g., Charolais) is bred to cows that are F_1 crosses between two other breeds (e.g., Angus-Hereford). Calves produced here are 50% Charolais, 25% Angus, and 25% Hereford. These calves are usually marketed as stocker or feeder calves. Consequently, another herd must be used to produce replacement F_1 females. One example of a rotational system is a two-breed rotation, or criss-cross. Here two breeds of sires are used where females sired by one breed are bred to bulls of the other breed. If Simmental and Hereford were the two sire breeds used, females sired by Hereford bulls would be bred to Simmental sires and vice versa. After several generations in this system, calves sired by Simmental bulls will be about 67% Simmental and 33% Hereford, whereas calves sired by Hereford bulls will be 67% Hereford and 33% Simmental. Here, replacement females are automatically produced; however, two separate breeding pastures are needed and two different types of calves are produced. With a three-breed terminal cross, one type of cow is used (one breeding pasture) and one type of calf is produced.

Composite Breeds

In the early part of the twentieth century, several cattle producers noticed that crosses between Brahman and British breeds produced calves with improved growth and survivabil-

TABLE 14-4

SIRE BREEDS EVALUATED AT USDA-ARS MARC GROUPED INTO BIOLOGICAL TYPES FOR FOUR PRODUCTION CRITERIA[a]

Breed	Growth Rate & Mature Size	Lean-to-Fat Ratio	Age at Puberty	Milk Production
Jersey	X	X	X	XXXXX
Texas Longhorn	X	XXX	XXX	XX
Hereford-Angus	XXX	XX	XXX	XX
Red Poll	XX	XX	XX	XXX
Devon	XX	XX	XXX	XX
Shorthorn	XXX	XX	XXX	XXX
Galloway	XX	XXX	XXX	XX
South Devon	XXX	XXX	XX	XXX
Tarentaise	XXX	XXX	XX	XXX
Pinzgauer	XXX	XXX	XX	XXX
Brangus	XXX	XX	XXXX	XX
Santa Gertrudis	XXX	XX	XXXX	XX
Sahiwal	XX	XXX	XXXXX	XXX
Brahman	XXXX	XXX	XXXXX	XXX
Nellore	XXXX	XXX	XXXXX	XXX
Braunvieh	XXXX	XXXX	XX	XXXX
Gelbvieh	XXXX	XXXX	XX	XXXX
Holstein	XXXX	XXXX	XX	XXXXX
Simmental	XXXXX	XXXX	XXX	XXXX
Maine Anjou	XXXXX	XXXX	XXX	XXX
Salers	XXXXX	XXXX	XXX	XXX
Piedmontese	XXX	XXXXXX	XX	XX
Limousin	XXX	XXXXX	XXXX	X
Charolais	XXXXX	XXXXX	XXXX	X
Chianina	XXXXX	XXXXX	XXXX	X

[a]Increasing number of X's indicate relatively higher values.

Source: Presented by L. V. Cundiff at the *Beef Improvement Federation 25th Anniversary Conference,* Asheville, NC, 1993.

ity, especially in the southern United States. As a result, some new American breeds were established, including Santa Gertrudis, Beefmaster, and Brangus. These early composite breeds combined desirable characteristics from their parental types to produce animals that were intermediate between parental breeds for most traits. Recently, several other composite cattle types have been developed. Three composites were developed at the USDA Meat Animal Research Center (MARC) in Clay Center, NE, where the focus of research was to study heterosis rentention and provide a means for cow-calf producers with small herds to take advantage of an organized crossbreeding program. Several composite breeds have been developed in the United States and are listed in Table 14-5.

TABLE 14-5

BREEDS OF BEEF CATTLE DEVELOPED IN THE UNITED STATES

Breed	Origin	Breed Composition
American	New Mexico	1/2 Brahman, 1/4 Charolais, 1/8 bison, 1/16 Hereford, 1/16 Shorthorn
Amerifax		5/8 Angus, 3/8 Beef Friesian
Barzona	Arizona	1/4 Africander, 1/4 Hereford, 1/4 Angus, 1/4 Santa Gertrudis, (5/32 Shorthorn, 3/32 Brahman)
Beefalo	varied	3/8 bison, 5/8 bovine (not breed specific)
Beef Machine	Texas	
Beefmaster	Texas, Colorado	1/2 Brahman, 1/4 Hereford, 1/4 Shorthorn
Braford	Florida	5/8 Hereford, 3/8 Brahman
Brahman	Texas, Louisiana	Developed from 4 Asian zebu breeds (Nellore, Gir, Guzerat, and Indu-Brazil)
Brahmousin	varied	5/8 Limousin, 3/8 Brahman
Brangus	Louisiana, Texas, Oklahoma	5/8 Angus, 3/8 Brahman
Charbray	varied	5/8 Charolais, 3/8 Brahman
Char-Swiss	Nebraska	3/4 Charolais, 1/4 Brown Swiss
Chiangus	varied	1/8 to 3/4 Chianina, 1/4 to 7/8 Angus
Gelbray	varied	1/4 to 3/4 Gelbvieh, 0 to1/2 Red Angus, 1/8 to 3/8 Brahman
Hotlander	Texas	1/4 Angus or Red Angus, 1/4 Senepol, 1/2 Simbrah (5/16 Simmental, 3/16 Brahman)
Noble Line	Oklahoma	1/3 Gelbvieh, 1/3 Angus or Red Angus, 1/3 Brahman
Red Angus	varied	Developed from black Angus cattle
Red Brangus	Texas	Most are about 1/2 Red Angus, 1/2 Brahman, but percentages vary
RX3	Montana, North Dakota	1/2 Red Angus, 1/4 Hereford, 1/4 red and white Holstein
Salorn	varied	5/8 Salers, 3/8 Texas Longhorn
Santa Cruz	Texas	1/4 Red Angus, 1/4 Gelbvieh, 1/2 Santa Gertrudis (5/16 Shorthorn, 3/16 Brahman)
Santa Gertrudis	Texas	5/8 Shorthorn, 3/8 Brahman
Simbrah	varied	5/8 Simmental, 3/8 Brahman
Texas Longhorn	Texas, Mexico	Spanish Criollo cattle

Performance Records and Genetic Evaluation of Animals

Evaluation of performance traits is very important in selection of breeding animals. Animal evaluation methods that adjust for environmental effects help show genetic differences. Established procedures of evaluation include: use of a single location for measuring performance traits in developing bulls from different herds, adjusting weaning weights of calves to a constant age basis, and adjusting birth weights and weaning weights of calves

TABLE 14-6

STANDARD AGE-OF-DAM ADJUSTMENT FACTORS FOR BIRTH WEIGHT AND WEANING WEIGHT

Age of Dam in Years	Birth Weight (lb)		Weaning Weight (lb)	
	Males	Females	Males	Females
2	+ 8	+ 8	+ 60	+ 54
3	+ 5	+ 5	+ 40	+ 36
4	+ 2	+ 2	+ 20	+ 18
5 through 10	+ 0	+ 0	+ 0	+ 0
11 and older	+ 3	+ 3	+ 20	+ 18

Source: Beef Improvement Federation (1996).

for different ages of their dams. Table 14-6 provides adjustment factors developed by the Beef Improvement Federation (1996) for age-of-dam effects on birth and weaning weight. Proper contemporary group designation is vital in obtaining accurate performance data for genetic improvement. Most breed associations have herd improvement programs whereby seedstock producers record and submit performance records such as birth, weaning, and yearling weights, scrotal circumference, and hip height. The use of these records helps individual producers to improve the genetic merit of their herds. Many breed associations utilize performance data to calculate EPDs (expected progeny differences) on these animals.

EXPECTED PROGENY DIFFERENCES. EPDs provide the most useful single indication of an animal's genetic potential because not only is the performance of the individual included, but also the performance of relatives (parents, siblings, and progeny). Once an animal has produced several offspring, the progeny performance gives a much more accurate estimate of its genetic value than does its own performance. EPDs are used to estimate the difference in performance between progeny groups for animals within a breed. EPDs of animals within a breed can be fairly compared across time periods and geographic regions. Researchers are developing methods to compare EPDs across breeds and developing EPDs for crossbred animals. Three bulls of a given breed along with their EPDs are illustrated in Table 14-7. When these bulls are randomly bred to a similar set of cows, Bull A is expected to sire calves that average 3 lb lower birth weight than those sired by Bull B and 4 lb more than those sired by Bull C. These expected differences can be similarly determined for average weaning weight and average yearling weight of calves sired by these bulls. Additionally, daughters of bull A should wean calves that average 4 lb more than daughters of Bull B and wean calves that weigh 8 lb less than daughters of Bull C due to level of milk production.

An important aspect to consider in evaluating EPDs of animals is the associated accuracy value, which gives an indication of how closely the EPD lies to its true genetic value. For animals with low accuracies (close to 0.0), their true genetic value may be

TABLE 14-7

EXPECTED PROGENY DIFFERENCES AND ACCURACY VALUES FOR THREE BULLS OF SAME BREED

Bull	Birth Weight		Weaning Weight		Yearling Weight		Milk	
	EPD	ACC	EPD	ACC	EPD	ACC	EPD	ACC
Bull A	+ 3	.60	+ 18	.57	+ 30	.52	+ 10	.35
Bull B	+ 6	.45	+ 30	.43	+ 47	.40	+ 6	.20
Bull C	− 1	.90	+ 16	.86	+ 28	.80	+ 18	.60

higher or lower than the EPD; however, in animals with high accuracy values (close to 1.0), the EPD and the true genetic value are very similar. The more offspring performance records an animal has, the higher its accuracy value will be. Most breed associations publish sire summaries with EPDs on bulls of their breed.

REPRODUCTIVE MANAGEMENT

Reproduction is the single most important trait to consider for calf production. However, it is very important to realize that reproductive efficiency is interrelated with genetics, nutrition, and animal health, and it is inappropriate to discuss one adequately without including the others. Proper nutritional management and health programs must be in order for reproductive efficiency to occur. Reproductive performance is a direct concern only of the calf production segment of the beef industry, but it has indirect consequences for the growing-finishing and meat packer segments on the pounds of retail beef sold.

Researchers at USDA Meat Animal Research Center (MARC, Clay Center, NE) have been studying the genetics of twinning in beef cattle since 1981. Through selection, they have increased twinning rate in this herd from 5% in the mid 1980s to 33% in 1996 (Gregory et al., 1997). These researchers have suggested that with adequate feed resources and intensive management, twinning in beef cattle is a viable way to increase reproductive efficiency. It is suggested that a twinning rate of 40% or more must be obtained to offset the increased economic inputs and to compensate for the fact that about 96% of heifers born as twins to bulls are infertile (freemartins).

Age at Puberty and Subsequent Production

Age at puberty determines the age at which heifers can first be bred. A high body weight and a high plane of nutrition (energy intake exceeding maintenance requirement) reduce age at puberty. Average age at puberty varies among different breeds. Two traits are related to age at puberty: mature body size and level of milk production. In general, breeds of similar mature size that have higher milk-producing potential are younger at puberty than breeds with lower milk production. Additionally, breeds of similar milk-producing ability that have larger mature size tend to be older at puberty than breeds of smaller mature size. Also, *Bos indicus* breeds tend to be older at puberty than most *Bos taurus* breeds.

AGE AT FIRST CALVING. Age at puberty and gestation length must be considered in determining when a heifer will give birth to her first calf. It is advantageous for heifers to calve first at approximately 23 to 24 months of age when considering overall lifetime productivity. Average gestation length in *Bos taurus* beef cows is approximately 283 days whereas that of *Bos indicus* is approximately 290 days. Gestation length varies among and within breeds, as well as across years due to different environmental conditions. Usually, in first-calf heifers gestation length is seven to ten days shorter than in mature cows. Knowing that a heifer should calve at 23 to 24 months of age and that gestation length is about 275 days (about nine and one-half months), the age at breeding must be when the heifer is about 14 months old. It is important that heifers reach puberty well before the age to be bred because the conception rate of heifers bred at first estrus tends to be low. The average estrous cycle in cattle is 21 days. Therefore, heifers should be allowed to go through one or two estrous cycles before the breeding season begins. This means they need to reach puberty by 12 to 13 months of age to increase their chance of calving around 24 months of age.

Breeding heifers to calve for the first time at 2 years of age is much more productive than breeding them to calve at three years of age. The average productive life of a beef cow is not extremely long (about five years), and cows that calve first at three do not have as many chances to wean calves as those that begin a year sooner. It has been well documented that cows that first calve at two years of age do not experience much greater calving difficulty (dystocia) than those that first calve near three years of age at their first parturition (act of giving birth).

CONTROL OF DYSTOCIA. The most common reason for cows to have dystocia is giving birth to a large calf. However, calving problems can arise for other reasons which cannot be avoided even by good management, as in the case of calves delivered in the wrong presentation (backwards, leg or head turned back). (See Chapter 4.) However, the incidence of dystocia can be reduced by several management strategies. Body size of pregnant heifers at calving is important. The first parturition (whether at 2 or 3 years of age) in cattle has the highest incidence of dystocia. As a result, pregnant heifers must be managed carefully during the first gestation period so that they grow at the proper rate to obtain adequate body weight at calving. Underfeeding of pregnant heifers reduces birth weight of calves, but also reduces maternal growth. Some of the instruments used in beef cattle reproductive management are shown in Figure 14-5a–f.

Sire Selection. Bulls that are known to produce calves with large birth weight should not be bred to heifers. Birth weight of the calf is the single most influential factor causing calving difficulty in heifers in most cases. The ratio of the calf size to the size of the pelvic opening of the heifer determines the chance of dystocia. There are large differences in average birth weight across breeds of cattle. Bulls that sire low-birth-weight calves can be

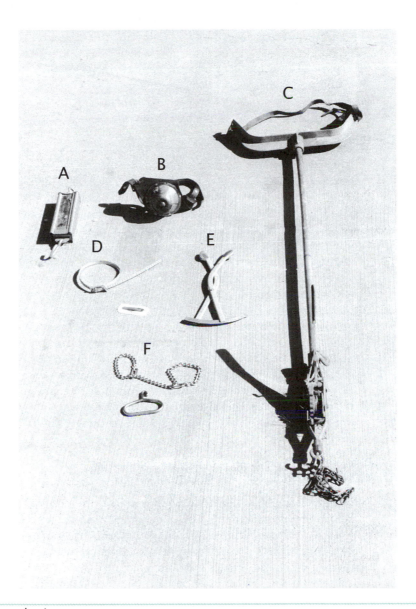

FIGURE 14-5

Instruments useful in reproductive management.
A. Scales
B. Chin bull marker
C. Calf puller
D. Scrotal circumference tape
E. Rice pelvimeter
F. OB chain

found in all breeds. Breed of sire is also important because crossbred calves will usually have some heterosis for birth weight. When *Bos indicus* bulls are bred to *Bos taurus* cows, very large calves can be produced, especially among bull calves. In most instances, it is recommended that *Bos taurus* heifers not be bred to *Bos indicus* bulls to produce their first calf.

Bull Fertility

When one cow fails to conceive, one potential calf is lost, but when a subfertile bull is with a cow herd, 20 or 30 potential calves may be lost. Fertility of bulls can be checked rather easily by a veterinarian before the breeding season begins. This is usually done through a breeding soundness examination where the sex organs of the bulls are visually and physically checked and a semen sample is obtained to ensure that adequate numbers of live and motile sperm cells exist. Usually this will cost around $25 to $35 per bull. If a subfertile bull is identified before the breeding season, nothing is lost, but if he is not identified until after the breeding season, it is too late to adjust breeding plans.

Scrotal circumference is a trait easily measured on a restrained bull. Bulls tend to reach puberty when they have attained approximately a 26-cm scrotal circumference; fertility of bulls increases as scrotal circumference increases up to 38 to 40 cm (Coulter, 1994). Scrotal circumference is positively associated with sperm-producing capacity. As a result, bulls should have a minimum scrotal circumference of 32 to 34 cm when turned in with cows for breeding. Scrotal circumference has also been shown to be negatively associated with age at puberty in the bulls and in their relatives. This means that if daughters of bulls with larger scrotal circumferences are kept for breeding, these daughters should have earlier age of puberty than those from sires with smaller scrotal circumferences.

Reproductive Traits to Monitor

Many traits are important for cow-calf producers to monitor, but those relating to reproductive success are crucial. These include pregnancy rate (percent of cows exposed to breeding that become pregnant), calf crop born (percent of cows exposed to breeding that calve), and calf crop weaned (percent of cows exposed to breeding that have a calf at weaning time). These traits indicate overall herd performance from one year to the next and provide insight as to other management areas that need attention.

CONTROLLED CALVING SEASON.
Having a controlled breeding season is very important because this will ensure a controlled calving season. Efficient cow-calf producers try to have a 60- to 75-day breeding season which then results in a 75- to 90-day calving season. Advantages to having a controlled calving season include: a short, defined period to observe intensively for dystocia; a more uniform calf crop; and better utilization of labor and management. If year-long calving occurs, it is not possible to optimally manage the cows or the calves since there are so many different ages of calves and cows in different stages of pregnancy and lactation. Adjusted 205-day weaning weight is a commonly used

performance trait. But calves more than 45 days younger or 45 days older than 205 days at weaning are beyond the age for useful adjustment. Therefore, 90-day range in age is the limit for a useful contemporary group.

Both the length of the breeding season and the time of the year are important considerations in order for calving to occur around the time when the most abundant (and cheapest) feed resources become available; otherwise, expenses for supplementation may be too great. Spring calving in areas where the predominant grasses are warm-season species is advisable because as the calving season begins, spring growth of pastures will coincide. Fall calving in areas where there are predominantly cool-season grasses offers the same advantage.

CALVING INTERVAL. It is important to monitor calving date for each cow in the herd and to calculate a calving interval for each cow. Calving interval refers to the number of days between calvings. Cows should have a 365-day (or less) calving interval. If they have a calving interval greater than 365 days, they will calve later and later every year. Eventually, cows with greater than 365-day calving intervals will calve so late that they will not have time to get bred back in the controlled breeding season. Traditionally, heifers will take longer to start the estrous cycle (referred to as post-partum interval) after calving than older cows. Consequently, breeding heifers for their first calves should begin 2 to 4 weeks before (and end 2 to 4 weeks before) the normal breeding season of the mature cows. This gives the first-calf heifers more time to rebreed after their first calf and ensures that their second calving season will correspond with that of the older cows.

NUTRITIONAL MANAGEMENT

Cattle, like other ruminant species, can take advantage of high-roughage diets. Land that is utilized for most cow herds is not suitable for growing crops. The cheapest way to provide nutrients to cows is to let them harvest these forages themselves. It is important to be familiar with the growing seasons and the nutritional characteristics of these forages in order to optimize animal performance. If nutritional management is not adequate, other areas such as reproduction may be harmed. Visual evaluation of cows for body fat (body condition) is a good way to determine the general nutritional status of the cow herd. This entails estimation of fat thickness over the ribs and back, around the tail head, and in the brisket. Stocker calf producers and feed yard managers rely on proper nutritional management because their profitability depends upon animal rate and efficiency of weight gain and price of feed resources.

Cow Herd Considerations

In some instances, the energy level in the diets of cows may be inadequate. Cows, like people, lose body weight when their caloric intake is less than their caloric expenditure. The amount of energy and protein needed in the diet of cattle varies with age and stage of production. Gestating (pregnant) cows require more energy and protein for maintenance of body weight than similar-size cows that are not pregnant. Lactating cows (producing milk) require more energy and protein than similar-size cows that are not nursing calves. Additionally, cows with higher milk production require more energy and protein during lactation than similar-size cows with lower milk production. If cattle are in proper nutritional status, feeding excessive energy and protein is a waste of money.

Mineral status of the soil in pastures where cattle graze is important to know because this directly affects the mineral concentrations in the forages that grow there. Mineral mixes containing iodized salt (NaCl), Ca, P, Mg, and, in areas in which soil is deficient in one or more trace elements, particularly Cu, Se, Co, and Zn should be provided to the cow herd year-round. Soil samples should be analyzed to determine soil pH, N, P, K, and other mineral elements likely to be deficient in the area, based on information available from county and state farm service agencies and commercial soil-testing laboratories. The species of forage and its stage of maturity and other measures of quality also affect its fat-soluble vitamin content. Since cattle are ruminants, their rumen microflora synthesize the water-soluble vitamins in sufficient amounts to meet requirements under most conditions.

BODY CONDITION EVALUATION. Body condition scoring of cattle is useful for producers to monitor and control nutritional energy status of their cow herds. The most common body condition scoring system is that of classifying animals on a 1 to 9 scale where a score of 1 represents an animal that has greatly depleted fat and muscle mass, and a score of 9 represents a very obese animal (Herd and Sprott, 1994). Cows classified as body condition score (BCS) of 6 have about .3 inches of fat cover over the last two ribs, and those classified as BCS of 5 have about .2 inches of fat cover. It is important to monitor BCS at certain points in the calf production cycle: at beginning of the breeding season, at calving, and at weaning. It is recommended that cows be in BCS of 6 at start of breeding season, and not allowed to fall below BCS of 5 at any time to ensure optimal reproductive performance and to prevent large fluctuations in body fat reserves; however, cows typically lose some body condition between calving and weaning due to the increased energy and protein demands of lactation.

ENERGY AND PROTEIN. The energy in feed can be expressed as net energy (NE). Net energy requirement may be divided into components used for maintenance, growth, pregnancy or lactation. An animal's NE requirement for maintenance is the amount consumed that meets the energy requirement to maintain constant body weight and composition in the nonpregnant, nonlactating animal, whereas the NE requirement for gain is the amount of feed energy above maintenance to allow maximum deposition of protein and fat (Ritchie, 1997). The NE requirements for pregnancy and lactation refer to the increased energy demands for these productive functions. An animal's total NE requirement is the sum of NE for maintenance and the respective productive functions (growth, pregnancy, lactation).

Cows may be fed a variety of different types of feeds, but the least expensive, most useful source is usually forage that the cattle harvest themselves by grazing. On average,

TABLE 14-8

NUTRIENT REQUIREMENTS FOR TWO BEEF FEMALES

Description	NE (Mcal/day)	MP (g/day)	Ca (g/day)	P (g/day)	ADG (g/day)
Pregnant heifer, 15 mo old at breeding, 80-lb calf expected, 1300-lb predicted mature weight					
1 month since conception	9.05	450	21	13	1.0
5 months since conception	10.55	507	22	14	1.3
9 months since conception	18.03	733	34	21	2.5
Lactating cow, 1300 lb, 5 yr old at calving, above average milk yield, calf weaned when 7 months old					
2 months since calving	20.16	965	42	28	0.0
5 months since calving	14.90	733	31	22	0.1
8 months since calving	9.79	479	18	14	0.4
11 months since calving	15.01	592	29	19	1.1

Source: National Research Council (1996).

mature cows eat between 2 and 3% of their body weight in forage, on a dry-matter basis. This means that a cow weighing 1,100 pounds will eat about 22 to 33 pounds of forage dry matter daily. In certain cases, such as wintering cows on dormant grass pastures, the cows may not get enough nutrients in the grass because forages of this type generally are deficient in digestible energy and protein. In these cases, the diet should be supplemented with a higher protein ingredient such as cottonseed meal or soybean meal, or alfalfa hay, or with grains such as corn, barley, or sorghum.

The nutrient requirements of beef cattle at various stages of production (National Research Council, 1996) are summarized in Tables 14-8 and 14-9. Crude protein (CP) is

TABLE 14-9

NUTRIENT REQUIREMENTS FOR TWO GROWING BEEF MALES

Description	NE (Mcal/day)	MP (g/day)	Ca (g/day)	P (g/day)	ADG (g/day)
Bull calf, 1960 lb mature weight					
660 lb current weight	12.12	716	42	20	3.3
1320 lb current weight	20.38	702	36	21	3.3
Feedlot steer, 1175 lb weight to grade Choice					
660 lb current weight	11.29	716	42	20	3.3
990 lb current weight	15.31	723	39	21	3.3

Source: National Research Council (1996).

based upon the nitrogen content of the feed (nitrogen% $\times$ 6.25) and has been histori-cally used to formulate rations and estimate protein content of feeds. Recently, the con-cept of metabolizable protein (MP) has been recommended for use (NRC, 1996). Protein supplementation helps to increase forage intake and improve the utilization of low-quality forages. Protein supplementation twice a week is generally as effective as daily supplementation. Protein supplememts are more expensive than energy, so it is important to feed sufficient energy to avoid the breakdown of protein for use as energy.

Cows can make efficient use of many crop residues such as corn or grain sorghum stalks, wheat straw, and corn cobs. Such feeds will usually provide adequate energy for the animal, but protein will need to be supplemented. It has been estimated that 2.2 acres of corn stalks can provide 100 days of grazing for each mature cow (Perry, 1995). In some cases, sorghum or corn stalks can be obtained in baled form, but they should be pur-chased at much lower prices (40 to 50%) compared to typical hay crops much higher in nutritional value.

WATER. Environmental temperature, stage of production, and type of diet all have major impacts on water requirements for cattle. If cattle do not receive the adequate amount of clean water, their performance will suffer (NRC, 1996). Distance between water sources is also an important consideration in pasture management because cattle usually will not travel more than one mile away from water sources. Having all stock ponds and water troughs within two miles of each other will help to completely utilize grazing resources.

Stocker Calf Considerations

Many cattle producers grow calves on forage-based diets between weaning and the time they enter a feedlot. These animals are known as stocker calves. The objective of a stocker program is to take advantage of a relatively cheap feed source for three to five months and convert it into calf weight gain. Calves coming from a stocker program need shorter time in the feed yard for finishing. They are older when they enter the feed-lot and are less prone to respiratory diseases than calves recently weaned. Most of these calves enter feedlots when they are about one year old (yearlings). Calves entering feed yards as yearlings tend to have more marbling when finished than those entering feed yards directly after weaning.

Approximately 70% of the commercial beef herds in the United States calve in the spring months; consequently, most beef calves are weaned in the fall months. Stocker programs allow for more times of distribution when calves are placed into feedlots. Many cow-calf producers have become involved in stocker programs to diversify their ranching or farming operations, or to retain ownership of their animals farther into the food chain.

Many feed resources can be effectively used in stocker programs, including hays, small grain pastures, grass pastures, crop residues (corn or sorghum stalks), and silage. Generally, the goal for weight gain in stocker calves is 1.5 to 2.0 lb ADG during this pe-riod. This prevents the animals from becoming fat. Calves with excessive fat cover receive price discounts when sold to feedlots because they tend to have lower ADG during the finishing phase than thinner animals. Typically, calves should have the same body condition at the end of the stocker phase as the beginning. Many replacement heifers are also developed on these same feeds as calves destined for the feed yard. Generally, replacement heifers should gain 1.0 to 1.5 lb per day between weaning and breeding times. Sample stocker rations are presented in Table 14-10.

Stocker calves destined for a feedlot are normally implanted with a steroid hormone growth promotant. These anabolic agents are proven to be cost effective during the stocker and finishing phases because implanted cattle have higher ADG and greater feed efficiency than those not implanted. Additionally, some implants have been approved for use in replacement heifers; however, bull calves potentially used for breeding should not be implanted. Implants of specific composition are used for different age groups and for heifers and steers. Examples of commercially available implants are presented in Table 14-11.

Ionophores are feed additives that can be useful to increase profitability in stocker programs. Ionophores such as monensin and lasalocid have antibiotic properties that alter rumen bacteria to change volatile fatty acid production and increase average daily gain (ADG) and feed efficiency.

TABLE 14-10

SAMPLE RATIONS FOR STOCKER PROGRAMS[a]

	Ingredient	Percentage		Ingredient	Percentage
Example A	sudan hay	55.7	*Example D*	grass hay	54.7
	wheat	20.0		wheat	20.0
	corn	18.0		grain sorghum	19.0
	soybean meal	5.0		soybean meal	5.5
	dicalcium phosphate	.5		dicalcium phosphate	.5
	limestone	.5		limestone	.5
	salt	.3		salt	.3
Example B	grass hay	52.2	*Example E*	sudan hay	57.2
	grain sorghum	40.0		corn	35.0
	soybean meal	7.0		soybean meal	7.0
	dicalcium phosphate	.5		dicalcium phosphate	.5
	limestone	.5		limestone	.5
	salt	.3		salt	.3
Example C	alfalfa hay	67.7	*Example F*	alfalfa hay	59.2
	corn	31.5		grain sorgum	40.0
	dicalcium phosphate	.5		dicalcium phosphate	.5
	salt	.3		salt	.3

[a]Recommended that hays be ground and grains be rolled or ground.
Source: Adapted from Lusby and Gill (1982).

TABLE 14-11

ANABOLIC IMPLANTS APPROVED FOR USE IN U.S. SLAUGHTER CATTLE

Product	Type of Cattle	Dose & Compound	Response Time (d)
Calf-oid	calves	10mg estradiol benzoate 100 mg progesterone	80–120
Compudose	steers	24 mg estradiol	200
Finaplix-S	steers	140 mg trenbolone acetate	70–90
Finaplix-H	heifers	200 mg trenbolone acetate	70–90
Heifer-oid	heifers	20 mg estradiol benzoate 200 mg testos. propionate	80–120
Implus-C	calves	10 mg estradiol benzoate 100 mg progesterone	80–120
Implus-S	steers	20 mg estradiol benzoate 200 mg progesterone	80–120
Implus-H	heifers	20 mg estradiol benzoate 200 mg testos. propionate	80–120
Ralgo	all ages	36 mg zeranol	70–90
Revalor-G	stocker steers	8 mg estradiol 40 mg trenbolone acetate	70–90
Revalor-S	steers	24 mg estradiol 120 mg trenbolone acetate	80–120
Revalor-H	heifers	14 mg estradiol 140 mg trenbolone acetate	80–120
Magnum	steers	72 mg zeranol	70–100
Steer-oid	steers	20 mg estradiol benzoate 200 mg progesterone	80–120
Synovex-C	calves	10 mg estradiol benzoate 100 mg progesterone	80–120
Synovex-S	steers	20 mg estradiol benzoate 200 mg progesterone	80–120
Synovex-H	heifers	20 mg estradiol benzoate 200 mg testos. propionate	80–120
Synovex +	steers	28 mg estradiol benzoate 200 mg trenbolone acetate	80–120

Source: Unpublished data, R. L. Preston, Texas Tech University.

Feedlot Cattle Considerations

Feedlot operators have two crucial aspects that determine profitability: nutritional management and animal health. Cattle are very versatile in their ability to utilize many different feed resources. Commercial feed yards have finishing diets that are 85 to 90% energy concentrate and only 10 to 15% roughage. One of the most trying times for a feedlot operator is receiving new cattle. Newly arrived cattle are more prone to sickness than at any other time, especially if they have come to the feed yard immediately after weaning. Calves that have been backgrounded or come from a stocker program have better developed immune systems and have overcome weaning stresses.

TABLE 14-12
SAMPLE CORN-BASED FEEDLOT DIETS FOR FINISHING CATTLE

Ingredient	Diet			
	Receiving	Intermediate	Intermediate	Finishing
Ingredient percentage (dry-matter basis)				
rolled corn	50	65	75.6	84.25
ground alfalfa	34	14.3	5	
corn silage	15	15	13	10
soybean meal		4	4	3
urea	.15	.25	.45	.60
limestone		.6	1.1	1.3
salt	.4	.4	.4	.4
dicalcium phoshate	.3	.3	.3	.3
vitamin-mineral premix	.15	.15	.15	.15

Source: Adapted from Neumann and Lusby (1986).

The first objective for newly received cattle is to encourage feed consumption, starting with a "receiving" ration high in roughage (hay) and low in grain. Animals that are slow to start eating may be administered a probiotoc medication to stimulate appetite and reestablish bacterial populations in the digestive tract. Over a period of two to three weeks the cattle are fed three or four different rations, with progressively higher grain and lower roughage percentages, culminating in the finishing ration, which is fed throughout the rest of the feedlot period. The finishing ration contains 85 to 90% grain and other high-energy feedstuffs and protein supplements and 10 to 15% roughage to help prevent digestive problems such as bloat and acidosis.

The two most commonly used grains for cattle feeding in the United States are corn and grain sorghum. Barley, wheat, oats, and other high-energy grains and grain byproducts may also be used, depending on price and regional availability. Typical roughage sources include corn silage, grain sorghum silage, alfalfa hay, and cottonseed hulls. Protein sources include soybean meal, cottonseed meal, and distillery and brewery grain byproducts. Urea is often used as a nonprotein N source to reduce the cost of protein supplementation. Tables 14-12 and 14-13 illustrate some different feedlot rations.

HORMONE IMPLANTS. Implants (slow-release pellets inserted under the skin) containing protein anabolic steroids are commonly used in feedlot cattle to increase feed efficiency and ADG. Implanted cattle may require a longer feeding period (two weeks) to attain an acceptable amount of marbling. However, the benefits of implants far outweigh this small disadvantage. Depending upon the implant used, its effect lasts 70 to 120 days. The U.S. Food and Drug Administration (FDA) closely regulates the use of implants and approves their use based on tests of efficacy and safety. Many foods contain steroid hormones in amounts comparable to or higher than the amounts present in implants. Fur-

TABLE 14-13

SAMPLE SORGHUM GRAIN–BASED DIETS FOR FINISHING CATTLE

Receiving (Initial) Diet		Intermediate Diet		Finishing Diet	
Ingredient	(%)	Ingredient	(%)	Ingredient	(%)
steam-flaked milo	42.10	steam-flaked milo	57.90	steam-flaked milo	80.00
cottonseed hulls	41.00	cottonseed hulls	27.10	cottonseed hulls	7.30
blood meal	2.67	blood meal	1.87	cane molasses	4.30
corn gluten meal	2.64	corn gluten meal	1.85	fat	2.30
cottonseed meal	2.61	cottonseed meal	2.29	corn gluten meal	1.90
fat	2.40	fat	2.10	calcium carbonate	1.04
cane molasses	3.30	cane molasses	3.30	salt	.12
calcium carbonate	.81	calcium carbonate	.90	trace mineral premix	.23
dicalcium phosphate	.31	dicalcium phosphate	.17	vitamin A premix	.30
salt	.15	salt	.15	vitamin E premix	.16
trace mineral premix	.22	trace mineral premix	.23	monensin	.91
vitamin A premix	.37	vitamin A premix	.36	tylosin premix	.55
vitamin E premix	.09	vitamin E premix	.11	urea	.50
monensin	.35	monensin	.51	potassium chloride	.39
AS700 premix	.81	AS700 premix	.80		
urea	.17	urea	.26		
		potassium chloride	.10		

thermore, the hormones present in implants are released slowly in small amounts that do not result in tissue concentrations higher than physiological levels. Therefore, there is no basis for concern by consumers about the safety of beef from implanted cattle.

FEED ADDITIVES.   Feed additives such as ionophores are often used in feedlot rations to increase feed efficiency, control infectious diseases, and help prevent bloat. Melengesterol acetate (MGA) may be fed to feedlot heifers to suppress estrus. Antibiotics are also sometimes fed to feedlot cattle because the low-roughage diet does not stimulate the rumen wall as with higher-roughage diets, increasing the occurrence of disorders such as acidosis, rumenitis, and liver abscesses. The liver, an economically important carcass byproduct for beef packers, may develop abscesses associated with the acidosis-rumenitis-liver abscess complex in feedlot cattle.

HERD HEALTH CONCERNS

A proper health program can be developed through the use of veterinarians and beef cattle extension agents. However, it is important for producers to have a general understanding of potential disease problems and an observant eye to identify problems. Prevention of disease is a key management consideration in order to ensure the possible profit in cow-calf, stocker, and feedlot programs. Many contagious diseases of economic importance to the cattle industry can be prevented by use of vaccines administered at the proper ages and dosages. Herd health vaccination programs should be developed in consultation with a veterinarian. A reference source such as the Merck Veterinary Manual (1998) is a useful resource for general and specific information on diseases and their treatment and prevention.

Infectious Diseases

REPRODUCTIVE DISEASES. Many infectious diseases affect reproduction in beef cattle. Some of the most common ones and management strategies for their control are shown in Table 14-14. For cow-calf producers it is critical to develop a prevention program to avoid these diseases because they can potentially devastate an entire future calf crop.

CALFHOOD DISEASES. Most bacterial and viral diseases of calves can be controlled by appropriate vaccination programs. Calves should be vaccinated against a class of bacterial diseases known as clostridial diseases (blackleg, tetanus, botulism, malignant edema, enterotoxemia, Black disease, and red water disease) first at 2 to 4 months of age. The calves should receive a booster at weaning. This type of vaccination schedule usually provides lifetime immunity because clostridial diseases typically only infect young, growing calves. The clostridial diseases can infect unimmunized, young calves very rapidly, and in many cases, by the time manifestation of the disease can be seen, it is too late for treatment.

When calves are 6 to 8 months old, they should be vaccinated for pathogens involved in the bovine respiratory disease complex. These include four types of viruses (IBR, PI-3, BVD, and BRSV) and one type of bacteria (*Pasteurella* spp.). Calves usually have passive immunity from colostrum for these diseases until 6 months of age. A booster needs to be given 30 days after the initial vaccinations to provide complete immunity. It is recommended that calves not be shipped to a feed yard until 45 days after weaning (referred to as a backgrounding period).

Vaccination and backgrounding give the calves time to develop adequate immunity against problem diseases and recover from stress of weaning. Proper vaccination administration along with backgrounding have been shown to be vital in reducing the incidence of bovine respiratory disease in stocker and feeder calves.

Nutritional and Metabolic Diseases

Many diseases of cattle can be referred to as nutritional or metabolic in nature. These may be due to a pathogen ingested from feed, water, or soil, or due to certain chemical properties of the feed or water. Some of the more common of these illnesses are discussed here.

Bloat is common and is due to the accumulation of gases (mainly methane and carbon dioxide) in the rumen. Gas production is a normal end-product of rumen fermentation; however, with certain feeds, a frothy mixture may form in the rumen, preventing gas from being expelled through the mouth. An animal with a swollen left side due to a dis-

TABLE 14-14

REPRODUCTIVE DISEASES IN COW-CALF HERDS

Disease	Pathogen Type	Symptoms	Treatment	Prevention
brucellosis	bacteria	abortions, depressed fertility, retained placenta	slaughter of infected animals	vaccination of all replacement heifers before 12 mo of age
trichomoniasis	protozoa	early fetal death, abortions, depressed fertility	3 mo of rest from breeding in cows, slaughter of bulls, antibiotics	annual vaccination 30 to 60 d before breeding
leptospirosis	bacteria	abortions in third trimester	slaughter of infected cows, antibiotics in bulls	annual vaccination 30 to 60 d before breeding
vibriosis	bacteria	general infertility, irregular heat cycles, early fetal death	slaughter of infected animals	annual vaccination 30 to 60 d before breeding
infectious bovine rhinotracheitis (IBR)	virus	abortions last half of gestation, depressed fertility	slaughter of infected animals	vaccinate all calves at 6 to 8 mo, annual vaccinations 30 to 60 d before breeding
bovine viral diarrhea	virus	abortions early to mid-gestation, depressed fertility		vaccinate all calves at 6 to 8 mo, annual vaccinations 30 to 60 d before breeding

Source: Information adapted from Merck & Co. (1995), *The Merck Veterinary Manual*, 8th ed.

tended rumen is bloated. Many times giving the animals mineral oil breaks up the gas bubbles, but in emergency situations, a tube may need to be placed into the rumen, or the rumen wall may need to be punctured to relieve pressure affecting the circulatory system.

Grass tetany (also called magnesium tetany or wheat pasture poisoning) is a nutritional disease that may occur in cattle grazing lush, small grain pastures low in magnesium and high in potassium. Giving animals access to a mineral mix with adequate magnesium is the best prevention. Affected animals have muscle tremors and can die in a short time after symptoms develop.

Animals grazing plants with high nitrate levels may develop nitrate toxicity. In the body, nitrates are converted into nitrites which interfere with oxygen transport by converting hemoglobin into methemoglobin, which does not carry oxygen.

Prussic acid (hydrocyanic acid) poisoning can be a problem for certain sorghum forages. Young plants of this group produce a cyanide-containing compound (prussic acid) during regrowth after undergoing stressed conditions such as drought or freezing. It is advisable to avoid grazing these affected plants that are less than 10 to 12 inches tall.

Acidosis may become a problem in cattle fed grain-based diets. When the pH of the rumen contents gets too acidic, the pH of the blood may be reduced to a dangerous level. Cattle have to be adapted to a high-grain diet from a forage-based diet over a period of two to three weeks to avoid acidosis.

Parasite Control

Many parasites of cattle can cause reduced productivity, but in some instances parasite infestations may become severe enough to endanger the life of the animal. Parasites can be broadly grouped into internal and external classes. Internal parasites include cattle grubs (larvae of heel flies), stomach worms, and liver flukes. Various types of medications can be used to control internal parasites, including liquid pour-ons applied on the back, orally administered pastes and drenches, and injectable medications. Common external parasites include lice, ticks, horn flies, and face flies. Medications used to control external parasites include liquid pour-ons, sprays, powders or dusts, and applicators against which cattle can rub or brush. Control of parasites in cattle requires knowledge of the general aspects of the life cycles for these organisms and applying medications at the appropriate stages.

It is extremely important that cattle producers monitor their animals regularly and observe their general appearance and condition so as to identify problems in the beginning stages.

GENERAL MANAGEMENT CONSIDERATIONS AND ISSUES

The production of beef cattle deals with management practices that have been utilized for many years. These practices include castration, dehorning, and branding. There is much interest in promoting the concept of total quality management in production of beef calves and their efficient management from birth through slaughter. Total quality management has caused producers to reevaluate traditional practices to enhance the overall value of animals and promote the image of the beef industry as a whole. Several of these practices are discussed below.

Identification Methods

Animal identification is at the heart of a successful record-keeping program. Ideally, all animals in the breeding herd are identified by some unique manner, and each calf is identified as to its dam and sire. Parentage identification may be labor intensive, but in studies evaluating practicality of animal identification, the labor and time involved has been offset by increased genetic gains. It is important to identify both the superior and inferior animals in a breeding program so they can be dealt with accordingly. Instruments used in permanent individual identification of beef cattle are illustrated in Figure 14-6a–d.

Branding has great historical significance in the United States. In the days before pas-

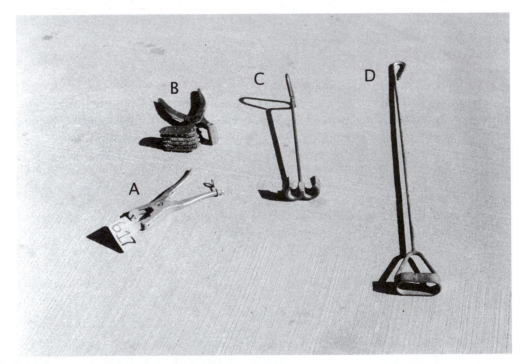

FIGURE 14-6

Instruments for cattle identification.
A. ear tag
B. tattoo
C. freeze branding iron
D. fire branding iron

tures were fenced, cattle brands were the only means of providing proof of ownership of most animals. Hide brands may be applied by use of heat with a hot iron brand or by extremely low temperature with a freeze brand. Fire brands produce a permanent scar on the skin that prevents hair from growing back, whereas freeze branding kills the pigment-producing cells in the area, causing the hair to grow back white. Cattle producers are urged to place brands on the hip or shoulder, because brands placed in these areas minimize reduction in value from hide damage.

Cattle can also be ear-tattooed as a permanent method of identification. The animal has to be restrained for the tattoo to be read. The instrument has a series of pins in the shapes of numbers and is pressed against the nonpigmented skin of the inner ear. Ink is rubbed into the pin puncture holes and remains in the skin. Many breed associations require their animals to be tattooed as a backup measure of identification. Ear notches are also sometimes used to permanently mark an animal, and some systems of notching cattle ears have been developed that are similar to those used in pigs. Both metal and plastic tags provide temporary identification. Larger plastic tags are popular because they are easier to read from a distance and do not require restraint of animals. Other methods of temporary identification include numbered neck chains or collars and paint brands. All animals in a cow-calf breeding program need to be permanently identified for proper herd record-keeping. Breed associations require their cattle to be permanently identified by brand or tattoo in order to be entered into their herdbook.

Castration Methods

Cattle producers castrate bull calves for several reasons, including control of behavior in male slaughter cattle, prevention of males from passing on undesirable genetics, and production of more palatable beef from male cattle. Carcasses of bulls are not quality graded. Research results dealing with feeding young bulls have generally shown that intact males gain weight faster in the feed yard, have leaner carcasses, and produce beef that can be tougher and more flavor intense compared to steers.

Male calves with no potential of becoming herd sires should be castrated. Early castration provides less stress to the animals and is less labor intensive. Castration tools include the burdizzo, elastrator, emasculator, and the old standard, the knife. These instruments are shown in Figure 14-7a-d.

Dehorning Methods

The most effective long-term approach to dehorn calves is to use bulls that are homozygous polled. Polled is genetically dominant to horned, and bulls that are homozygous polled will produce polled calves regardless of genotypes of cows to which they are bred. In calves with horns, dehorning is necessary for several management reasons, including the prevention of animal bruising, ease in handling, reduction in space needed for pens and feed troughs, and avoidance of price discounts by packers. Dehorning, like castration, should be performed as early as possible in the life of the calf, because it is less stressful to the animal, and less labor intensive than at a later age. If calves cannot be dehorned

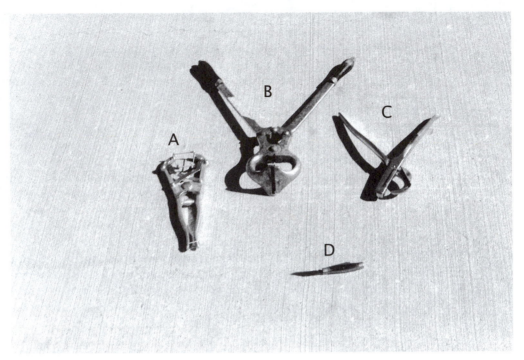

FIGURE 14-7

Instruments used for castration.
A. elastrator
B. burdizzo
C. emasculator
D. knife

and castrated around time of birth, these procedures should be done when they are branded and receive their first round of clostridial vaccination at 2 to 4 months of age. Instruments to dehorn calves include the Barnes or tube dehorner, spoon dehorner, or an electric hot iron. Calves no more than 7 days old may be dehorned by chemical means with a dehorning paste or liquid, or a caustic stick, which stops the tissue of the horn bud from growing. Dehorning older calves and cattle may require a surgical saw. Examples of these instruments are shown in Figure 14-8a–d.

Handling Facilities

Cattle-handling facilities should be designed for overall working efficiency and complement animals' behavioral characteristics so as to reduce handling stress. Corral and working facilities should be constructed where there is adequate drainage, easy access for trucks, convenient utility access, and room for expansion if needed (Huhnke and Harp, 1994). Curved crowding chutes have been built in many feed yards (Figure 14-9) because

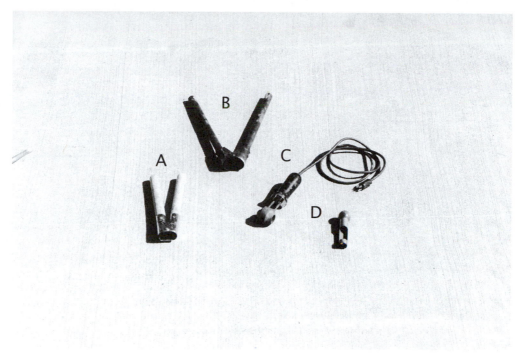

FIGURE 14-8

Dehorning instruments.
A. and B. Barnes dehorner
C. hot dehorner
D. spoon dehorner

cattle tend to naturally move in a circular manner, and it prevents the animals from seeing exactly where they are headed (Grandin, 1994).

Cow-calf producers that usually work animals alone need to have a type of chute that can be operated by a single person. Many different brands and styles of manual and hydraulic chutes are available, all of which have certain advantages and disadvantages. The value of investing in a good squeeze chute and efficient working facilities will be recognized at its first use.

Modern technology includes the growing use of embryo transfer in beef cattle production. (See Chapter 4 for a further discussion of embryo transfer in animals.) An aerial view of the physical layout of an embryo transfer facility for beef cattle in Ashland, Kansas is shown in Figure 14-10. (Note the laboratory building and adjacent cattle-holding paddocks and the three radials with pie-shaped pens.)

Marketing Avenues

Methods to sell recently weaned calves for both seedstock and commercial cow-calf producers include auction barns, private or direct contract, and electronic auctions. Each of-

FIGURE 14-9
Manually operated squeeze chute.

fers advantages and disadvantages. Many seedstock producers market their animals through private contract and special auctions. More and more commercial calves are being sold directly to feed yards and through electronic means (video and Internet), with less emphasis on traditional sale barn auctions, although this is still the major way culled cows and bulls are dispersed from breeding herds. Commercial calves are valued based upon their weight, sex class, frame size, and muscle thickness. Generally, larger animals are worth less per hundred pounds than lighter animals, but their total value is greater.

Most fed (finished) cattle are sold directly to the beef packing companies, either on a live weight and grade basis, or on actual quality and yield grades of each individual carcass (this is value-based marketing). Animals of known dairy breeding generally are worth less per hundred pounds on a live basis than nondairy breed types. The U.S. beef industry has started to move toward value-based marketing with increasing numbers of fed cattle sold on a carcass formula basis. Most beef packers discount the carcass price for extremely heavy (greater than 950 lb) and extremely lightweight (under 600 lb) carcasses because they produce retail cuts that differ drastically from the average size specifications needed for boxed beef. Packers prefer carcasses in the 600-to-950-lb range. Some very succesful programs such as the Certified Angus Beef™ program have been developed that pay premiums for carcasses that meet special specifications to ensure eating quality and consistency.

FIGURE 14-10

Aerial view of the physical layout of an embryo transfer facility for beef cattle in Ashland, Kansas. (Courtesy of Gardiner Angus Ranch, Ashland, KS.)

SUMMARY

The beef cattle industry is extremely diverse in production environments and cattle types, and has a tremendous impact on the U.S. agricultural economy. Sale of beef cattle is the number-one agricultural cash crop for several states. Total cash receipts for U.S. meat animals (cattle, hogs, sheep) for 1995 was $44.6 billion, of which cattle and calves accounted for $34.0 billion (USDA, 1996). Consumer demands of less external fat in retail beef have changed many management and breeding strategies in the beef industry since the late 1980s. In 1997, there were 882,600 cow-calf operations in the United States that had 33.7 million beef cows (USDA, 1998a, b). Continually increasing consumer acceptance of lean beef and improving the production efficiency by total quality management within all segments of the beef cattle industry through genetics, reproduction, nutrition, and health management will continue to be the primary concerns among cattle producers in the twenty-first century.

GLOSSARY[1]

Accuracy Correspondence between an animal's EPD and its actual genetic value.

Adjusted 205-day weaning weight Weaning weight adjusted to 205 days of age and mature age of dam equivalence.

Artificial insemination (AI) The placement of semen from the male into the female reproductive tract by a human.

Average daily gain (ADG) Measurement of body weight change for a defined period divided by the number of days. A steer that gained 520 lb over 160 days had ADG of 3.25 lb per day.

Birth weight The weight of a calf taken 24 to 48 hours after its birth.

Body condition score (BCS) A score on a 1 to 9 scale that reflects amount of body fat, where 1 = extremely thin and 9 = extremely obese.

Bos indicus These are the Zebu, or shoulder-humped breeds of the world. Brahman is most common example in United States.

Bos taurus These are nonhumped cattle and include the British and Contintental European breeds.

Breed Animals which have a common origin, common characteristics, and are distinguished from other groups of animals within their species.

Breeding Soundness Exam Inspection of bulls that involves reproductive organ physical examination, scrotal circumference measurement, and semen evaluation.

British breeds Breeds developed in Great Britain for meat or meat and milk.

Bull Uncastrated male of cattle species. Those under one year of age are referred to as bull calves.

Calf Animal of cattle species under one year of age, no reference to sex of animal.

Carcass quality grade An estimate of palatability based on marbling and physiological maturity, with consideration of color, texture, and firmness of rib-eye muscle.

Castration Removal of testicles from male animal.

Central test Location where animals from several herds are brought together to evaluate differences in performance traits.

Colostrum Milk produced immediately after birth that is high in energy and contains antibodies.

Compensatory gain Weight gain in cattle that have been nutritionally deprived. Older, underweight calves will gain weight very efficiently for a brief period when fed a high-energy diet.

Composite Group or breed developed from crossbred base.

Conformation Shape and arrangement of body parts of animals.

Contemporary group Group of animals of same breed and sex and of similar age that are managed together.

Continental European breeds Breeds developed in Europe for meat or meat and milk.

Crossbreeding Mating of animals of different breeds.

Cow Female of cattle species that has reproduced and is close to or at maturity.

Criollo breeds Cattle such as Texas Longhorn, Corriente, and Romosinuano that trace back to Spanish and/or Portugese origin.

Culling Removal of less productive or less desirable animals from breeding herd.

Dairy breeds Breeds such as Holstein, Jersey, and Brown Swiss used primarily for milk production.

Dam The female parent.

Dystocia (calving difficulty) Abnormal or difficult labor causing difficulty in delivery of the calf and/or placenta.

Environment All external, nongenetic conditions (including management) that influence animal performance. Animals in a contemporary group are subjected to the same environmental influences.

---

[1]Several definitions adapted from Beef Improvement Federation (1996).

Expected Progeny Difference (EPD) An estimate of the genetic merit of an animal as a parent which is used to predict progeny performance. Differences between EPDs of two animals in a breed predict the expected difference between respective progeny groups.

F_1 Animals produced by mating a sire of one breed to a dam of another breed.

Fat thickness Depth of fat cover; generally refers to fat cover over the next-to-last (12th) rib.

Feed conversion (feed efficiency) Units of feed consumed per unit of weight gained.

Feed yard or feedlot Location where cattle are fed high-energy, grain-based diets.

Feeder calves Calves with enough age and physical development to be placed in a feedlot and fed a high-energy, grain-based diet.

Frame score Score based on subjective evaluation of height or actual measurement of hip height and is related to mature skeletal size.

Freemartin Infertile female born twin to a bull calf. Over 95% of heifers born twin to bulls are freemartins.

Genotype Actual genetic makeup as to the genes in the animal.

Genotype x environment interaction Differences in performance of different breeds of cattle across environments. The best-performing animals in one environment may not be the best in a different environment.

Gestation Time from conception until birth.

Heifer Female of cattle species that has not reproduced and is under three years of age.

Heterosis (hybrid vigor) Increased performance of crossbred animals compared to the average of the parental breeds.

Kidney, pelvic, and heart fat (KPH) Internal carcass fat associated with the heart, kidneys, and pelvic cavity expressed as a percentage of carcass weight.

Lactation Period following parturition during which milk is produced.

Longissimus dorsi Muscle of support that extends down the back. Cross section of this muscle on carcasses at the 12th rib is known as rib-eye area.

Marbling Specks of fat distributed within muscle (intramuscular fat) evaluated in the longissimus dorsi at the 12th rib in beef carcasses.

Metabolism The transformation by which energy is made available for cellular body uses.

Palatability Degree to which meat is acceptable in taste, moisture, and flavor.

Parturition Act of giving birth.

Performance data Record of the individual animals for reproduction, growth, or carcass traits.

Performance testing Systematic collection of production information (performance data) for use in decision making to improve production efficiency and profitability.

Polled Naturally having no horns.

Postpartum Time after parturition.

Postweaning gain Weight gained after weaning often expressed as ADG.

Preweaning gain Weight gained between birth and weaning used to calculate adjusted 205-day weaning weight.

Progeny Offspring produced from parents.

Puberty Time when reproductive organs become functional, secondary sex characteristics develop, and reproduction is possible.

Purebred Animal of known ancestry within a recognized breed that is eligble for registration in the official herd book of that breed.

Ratio Expression of animal's performance for a particular trait relative to its contemporary group average. Usually calculated as (individual record ÷ group average) × 100.

Rib-eye area (REA) Surface area of longissimus muscle cross section at 12th rib measured in square inches.

Sanga breeds Neck-humped cattle such as Africander, Tuli, and Ankole that are native to Africa.

Scrotal circumference Measure of testicle size obtained by placing a measuring tape around the scrotum.

Seedstock producers Cow-calf producers that produce breeding stock for purebred and commercial producers.

Selection Act of allowing certain animals to reproduce and allowing certain animals to reproduce more than others.

Sire   The male parent.

Sire Summary   Published EPDs on sires from national cattle evaluation programs.

Steer   Male of cattle species that has been castrated at an early age.

Stocker calves   Calves placed on a forage-based diet for a growing phase after weaning.

Straightbreeding   The mating of two animals of the same breed.

USDA Quality Grade   A grade (Prime, Choice, Select, Standard) assigned by a federal beef grader to predict palatability.

USDA Yield Grade   A grade on a scale from 1 to 5 assigned by a federal grader to estimate proportion of carcass weight formed into boneless, closely trimmed retail cuts. A grade of 1 refers to a carcass with high muscle-to-fat ratio, and a grade of 5 refers to a carcass with very low muscle-to-fat ratio.

Zebu breeds   See *Bos indicus*.

REFERENCES

Beef Improvement Federation. 1996. *Guidelines for Uniform Beef Improvement Programs,* 7th ed. Reno: Writing & Business Support.

Coulter, G. H. 1994. Heterosis and breed effects on reproduction. In M. J. Fields and R. S. Sand (eds.), *Factors Affecting Calf Crop.* Boca Raton, FL: CRC Press.

Grandin, T. 1994. Livestock psychology and handling-facility design. In *Texas Beef Cattle Management Handbook.* Texas Agricultural Extension Service, College Station.

Gregory, K. E., Bennett, G. L., Van Vleck, L. D., Echternkamp, S. E., and Cundiff, L. V. 1997. Genetic and environmental parameters for ovulation rate, and weight traits in a cattle population selected for twinning. *J Anim, Sci.* 75: 1213–1222.

Herd, D. B., and Sprott, L. R. 1994. Body condition, nutrition and reproduction of beef cows. In *Texas Beef Cattle Management Handbook.* TAES, Texas A&M University System, College Station.

Huhnke, R. L., and Harp, S. 1994. Corral and working facilities for beef cattle. In *Texas Beef Cattle Management Handbook.* Texas Agricultural Extension Service, College Station.

Lusby, K., and Gill, D. 1982. Formulating Complete Rations. OSU Extension Facts No. 3013, Stillwater, Oklahoma.

Merck & Co., Inc. 1998. *The Merck Veterinary Manual,* 9th ed. Rahway, New Jersey.

National Research Council. 1996. *Nutrient Require-*

ments of Beef Cattle, 7th rev. ed. Washington D.C.: National Academy Press.

Neumann, A. L., and Lusby, K. S. 1986. *Beef Cattle,* 8th ed. New York: Wiley.

Perry, T. W. 1995. Forages and environmental effect on brood cows. In T. W. Perry and M. J. Cecava (eds.), *Beef Cattle Feeding and Nutrition.* San Diego: Academic Press.

Porter, V. 1991. *Cattle: A Handbook to the Breeds of the World.* New York: Facts on File.

Ritchie, H. D. 1997. A review of applied beef cattle nutrition. Michigan State University Extension Publication. Internet access at http://www.msue.msu.edu/msue/.

Taylor, R. E., and Field, T. J. 1999. *Beef Production and Management Decisions,* 3rd ed. Upper Saddle River, NJ: Prentice Hall.

USDA. 1996. Meat Animals: Production, Disposition and Income, 1995 Summary (April 11, revised April 23). National Agricultural Statistics Service, United States Department of Agriculture. Internet access at http://usda.mannlib.cornell.edu/.

USDA. 1998a. Cattle Report, January 31. National Agricultural Statistics Service, United States Department of Agriculture. Internet access at http://usda.mannlib.cornell.edu/.

USDA. 1998b. Cattle on Feed Report, September 18. National Agricultural Statistics Service, United States Department of Agriculture. Internet access at http://usda.mannlib.cornell.edu/.

CHAPTER FIFTEEN
POULTRY AND EGG PRODUCTION

R. A. ERNST

UNIVERSITY OF CALIFORNIA, DAVIS, CA

Chickens originated from wild jungle fowl that were first domesticated in Asia about 8,000 years ago. Selection probably began shortly after domestication and many breeds and varieties were developed with widely varying phenotypes.

The commercial production of poultry and eggs in America began in earnest in the early 1800s and gradually evolved into modern systems during the succeeding 200 years. While the Egyptians and Eurasians have practiced artificial incubation for more than

2,000 years, the development of artificial incubation in America started about 1870. The Industrial Revolution brought new and more efficient incubators which facilitated development of large commercial hatcheries. The availability of large groups of uniform chicks from these hatcheries permitted the development of specialized poultry farms. Advances in feed milling, transportation, mechanized feeding, watering, and egg collection were other key factors which led to modern production systems.

The modern poultry and egg industry is faced with the challenge of efficient production of large volumes of safe poultry meat and eggs without creating nuisance problems such as odors, flies, or pollution of air or water. The industry must also address welfare concerns in regard to bird care and housing. Recent concerns regarding the safety of poultry meat and eggs has led to the development of farm-level quality assurance programs. These programs are expected to become commonplace during the next decade.

INTEGRATED PRODUCTION SYSTEMS

Shortly after World War II the concept of integrated poultry meat production began to evolve. Integration allowed coordination of growing capacity with the hatchery, feed mill, and processing plant capacity, raising efficiency to new levels. This new production system started with broilers but the model was quickly adopted by the turkey and egg industries. Integration often started with a feed mill or poultry processor as the coordinating company. Farmer cooperatives played a similar role in many regions with producers joining together to produce feed, and process and market poultry or eggs. The key to the success of this system was efficient product flow. The hatchery knew how many eggs to set on appropriate dates to provide the needed chicks to growers for uniform flow of chickens to the processing plant. With growers, hatcheries, and processors all operating independently, effective coordination of product flow had not previously been accomplished.

To make a vertically integrated production system work, a new company needed growing facilities. Development of company-owned facilities would have required extensive capital and large numbers of trained employees for bird care. Most companies solved this problem by contracting production with local farmers who were interested in growing poultry for added farm income. These farms typically were in a good position to obtain credit for construction of new poultry houses and needed an additional farm enterprise to improve farm income. Contract production has been so successful that today nearly all of the broilers in the United States are produced under some type of contract system. The system is used less frequently in turkey production; however, if a contract is not used, production is coordinated by some other arrangement between the processor and growers. Contract production has fewer advantages for egg production, and the economic success of on-farm processing has resulted in development of large, independent, vertically integrated production, processing, and marketing companies.

REPRODUCTION

Female Reproductive System and Egg Formation

The reproductive organs in the hen consist of the ovary and oviduct. While the chick embryo contains two ovaries and oviducts, only the left system normally develops (see Figure 15-1). The chicken ovary contains large numbers of ova or potential egg yolks. These

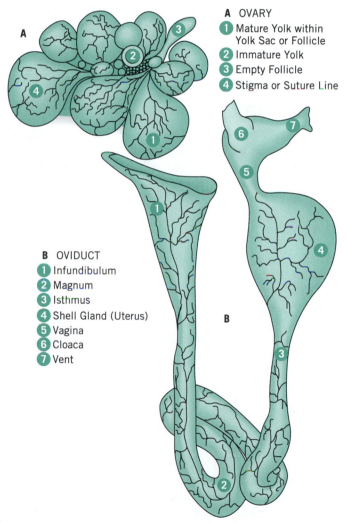

A OVARY
1. Mature Yolk within Yolk Sac or Follicle
2. Immature Yolk
3. Empty Follicle
4. Stigma or Suture Line

B OVIDUCT
1. Infundibulum
2. Magnum
3. Isthmus
4. Shell Gland (Uterus)
5. Vagina
6. Cloaca
7. Vent

FIGURE 15-1

Ovary and oviduct of a laying hen.

begin to mature in the pullet in response to secretion of follicle-stimulating hormone by the pituitary gland. As ovarian follicles develop they secrete estrogen, which stimulates the development of the oviduct; androgen, which influences development of the comb and secondary sex chacteristics; and progesterone, which influences albumen formation and ovulation. The oviduct consists of five parts: (1) infundibulum, (2) magnum, (3) isthmus, (4) shell gland (uterus), and (5) vagina. When a yolk is ovulated it falls into the body cavity and is engulfed by the infundibulum. As the yolk moves through the magnum the thick albumen is secreted. The isthmus adds the two shell membranes to the developing egg. When the egg first enters the shell gland, fluid is added, which plumps the egg and causes formation of the three remaining albumen layers. Next, shell formation begins, followed by addition of the pigment (colored eggs) and the waxy cuticle layer. This entire process requires about 24 hours divided as follows: infundibulum, 15 minutes; magnum, 3 hours; isthmus, 1.25 hours; and shell gland, 19 to 20 hours.

Male Reproduction

The testes of the cock are located in the body cavity adjacent to the kidneys. Each testis is connected by a convoluted duct (ductus deferens) to the cloaca where it terminates in a papilla. The cock also has a small phallus which functions during mating to channel the semen to the everted vaginal tissue of the hen.

Mating and Fertilization

Natural mating begins with the approach of the cock and hen. If the hen is receptive she will squat before the cock and evert her cloaca to expose the opening of the vagina. The male will then mount the hen and deposit semen on the exposed vaginal tissue of the hen. Spermatozoa travel upward in the oviduct where they may enter sperm glands located at the junction of the shell gland and vagina or in the infundibulum. Fertilization takes place in the infundibulum a few minutes after ovulation. A hen may remain fertile for three weeks or longer following one mating.

Artificial Insemination

Semen can be easily collected from male poultry by abdominal massage followed by application of pressure on the sides of the everted cloaca. The semen is often collected in an eye cup (chickens) or with an aspiration tube (turkeys). The semen can be extended with 1% saline or commercial dilutents, but needs to be used within one hour for best results. Longer fresh or frozen storage is possible but requires specialized techniques. The hen is inseminated by everting the oviduct to expose the opening of the vagina. About .05 ml semen is deposited into the vagina using a 1-ml syringe or a plastic insemination tube.

BREEDING

Traditional breeds of chickens or varieties of turkeys are not currently used for commercial production. Modern breeders have taken stock from these breeds and developed superior meat or egg production stocks. The male chicks from egg production stocks are not useful for meat production. The comparative growth rate of traditional and modern meat stocks, and white- and brown-shell egg lines are illustrated in Figure 15-2.

Modern poultry breeding is an exact science involving pedigree mating of commercial grandparent lines. Numerous qualitative and quantitative traits are measured on these lines. With the use of computers, massive amounts of data are stored and complex criteria used in making selection decisions. The male and female line parent chicks are sold to hatcheries and large integrated poultry production companies. These chicks are usually two- or three-way crosses.

About 25 major breeding companies exist worldwide with about half of these producing the majority of commercial birds. Integrated poultry meat producers usually purchase male and female line parent stock and use this to produce their hatching eggs. Commercial egg producers require fewer chicks and usually purchase these from large commercial hatcheries.

Meat Chickens

Modern chicken meat strains evolved primarily from the White Plymouth Rock and White Cornish breeds. While other breeds had useful meat qualities, processors demanded white plumage so that pin feathers were eliminated. Most breeding companies now offer stocks with white or yellow skin to satisfy regional customer demands. Some markets, particularly where birds are sold to consumers live, prefer chickens with colored plumage and red and black meat strains are now available.

FIGURE 15-2

Growth rate of four types of chickens.

Breeding objectives for meat poultry are improved growth rate, feed conversion, body conformation, breast meat yield, and disease resistance. Less emphasis would be placed on traits like egg production, fertility, hatchability, leg strength, and reproductive fitness.

Egg Production Stocks

In certain commercial egg markets brown- or white-shelled eggs are preferred. The Single Comb White Leghorn breed is the progenitor of most strains which produce white-shelled eggs. This breed is characterized by small body size, high egg production, good feed efficiency, heat resistance, and disease resistance. Commercial strains developed from this breed comprise the bulk of white egg production stocks in current world use.

Commercial strains which produce brown eggs have been developed from Australorp, Plymouth Rock, Rhode Island Red, and New Hampshire Red breeds, which were originally developed as dual-purpose breeds for meat and egg production. Intensive selection has been applied to these stocks to develop smaller body size (see Figure 15-2), which results in better conversion of feed to eggs. Egg production has been improved until they now lay as well as competing strains developed from the Leghorn breed. The breeds used to develop brown-shelled laying strains were noted for calm behavior and have retained this desirable trait.

Typical breeding objectives for egg production stocks are number of eggs produced, egg size, conversion of feed to eggs, interior egg quality, egg-shell quality, shell color, and disease resistance.

Turkeys

Several turkey varieties were developed by early breeders starting in Europe following importation of wild turkeys from America. Domestic turkeys from Europe were imported back into North America as the continent was settled. Some of the varieties developed were Bronze, White Holland, Black, Slate, Narragansett, Bourbon Red, and Beltsville Small White. Most commercial turkey stocks were derived from the Bronze variety. When white plumage was desired, these were crossed with the White Holland variety to get the recessive white gene.

There are now three international companies which produce most of the commercial stock. A major difference in turkey breeding programs, in contrast to chicken breeding programs, is the use of artificial insemination to produce the commercial hatching eggs. Artificial insemination, originally developed by USDA researchers, was first applied in a commercial breeding program by the late George Nicholas (Nicholas Turkey Breeding Farms, Inc., Sonoma, California). This was a bold step because use of the technique in a breeding program resulted in rapid gains in growth but loss of the toms' ability to mate naturally. It meant that all commercial hens from their breeding program would also need to be artificially inseminated to obtain good reproduction. This change resulted in rapid genetic progress and Nicholas turkeys soon gained a major market share. Other breeders quickly followed the Nicholas lead and today all commercial turkeys are reproduced by artificial insemination. Nicholas was also a leader in converting all of his stocks to white feather color, which was soon preferred and later required by processors.

INCUBATION

American poultry producers first started incubating in gravity-ventilated cabinets heated by an oil flame or hot water. Humidity was provided in these units by placing water pans in the bottom. When electricity became available, incubator design was quickly improved by switching to clean electric heaters. Early improvements were development of mechanical systems to turn the eggs and fans providing more uniform temperature and ventilation. Fan ventilation made it possible to construct large machines which could incubate thousands of eggs. Modern incubators are constructed with insulated cabinet walls to improve energy efficiency and temperature uniformity, and smooth interior surfaces for easy cleaning and sanitation. Systems for control of temperature and humidity have improved as new technology developed. Solid-state control systems linked to computers are now often used.

The time required for incubation of the eggs of domestic species varies (see Table 15-1). Standard incubating conditions are shown in Table 15-2. The exact optimum temperature and humidity vary with species, genetic stock, egg size, type of incubator, and age of eggs. Small alterations in these two conditions may result in improvements in hatch and chick quality. For high hatching success, eggs must be set with the large end up or in a horizontal position, never small end up. Other positions result in excessive numbers of malpositions, which do not hatch well. For successful hatching, eggs must be turned every two to four hours (often done hourly) during the first two-thirds of incubation. They should not be turned during the last three days of incubation. Turning prevents adhesion of the embryo to the embryonic membranes during early development but causes an increase in malpositioned embryos if continued during the final two days.

Chick Processing

Hatcheries often vaccinate chicks and may perform other services such as beak trimming, toe trimming, and antibiotic injection. Chicks should always be handled carefully

TABLE 15-1
INCUBATION TIMES FOR DOMESTIC POULTRY

Species	Days
Chicken	21
Turkey	28
Most Geese	30
Most Ducks	28
Muscovy Ducks	35

TABLE 15-2

RECOMMENDED INCUBATION CONDITIONS FOR DOMESTIC POULTRY

	Dry Bulb Temperature (°F)	Wet Bulb Temperature (°F)
Setting Conditions	99.5–99.7	85.0–87.0
Hatching Conditions	98.0–99.0	88.0–92.0

when the hatch is removed from the hatching trays and during processing, counting, and boxing. Chicks should be placed in new or sanitized boxes and held in temperature-controlled rooms until delivery.

BROODING AND REARING

Artificial brooding of young poultry is so successful that natural brooding is no longer used commercially. Most poultry are brooded in houses with earthen or concrete floors covered with three to six inches of a good litter material. Good litter materials must be absorbent, low in cost, readily available, free of contaminants, with relatively small particle size so they don't mat down. Soft-wood shavings, rice hulls, chopped straw, peanut hulls, and processed newsprint are often used.

During the first few days of life poultry are very susceptible to disease agents and stressful conditions. It is critical that they are moved from the hatchery to the brooding area without experiencing excessive dehydration or other stressful conditions. Brooding pens or cages should be cleaned and disinfected before the birds are introduced. The facility should be prepared in advance and temperature adjusted to the desired level on the day before the birds arrive.

Temperature

Day-old chickens require a brooding temperature of approximately 88 °F. This requirement declines about 5 °F per week as chicks grow and develop feathers. Young turkeys and game birds need a temperature about 5 °F higher than chickens. Waterfowl have a lower temperature requirement. Regardless of the species the best guide to proper brooding temperature is the behavior of the young birds. When they are comfortable, they will be active during daylight hours and spread out in the area provided. At night they will form a uniform ring around the heat source. Cold birds will huddle together and often issue a mournful chirping call. Young poultry should always be checked in the evening to assure that none have settled in a group away from the heat source. The room temperature often decreases at night and birds away from the heat source will press together for warmth, smothering those in the center.

Two types of brooding systems are in common use. These are sometimes called "warm-room" and "cool-room" systems.

WARM-ROOM BROODING. Warm-room brooding is accomplished by heating the entire house or pen to the required temperature (85–90 °F for day-old chickens). This system requires very careful temperature control so that birds are kept within their comfort zone as they grow and develop feathers. Overheating will delay feather development and may stress chicks. This system is used extensively for cage brooding egg-type pullet chicks.

COOL-ROOM BROODING. With this system a concentrated heat source such as a radiant gas brooder stove is used. The young poultry are provided sufficient space so that they can move away from the stove to find their comfort zone. The stove is adjusted to provide a starting temperature of 90–95 °F on the edge of the stove at bird level. This system works well for litter brooding; it promotes fast feathering of birds and makes it easier to properly adjust the heater settings. A low fence (or chick guard) 12 to 18 inches high is usually placed around the stove to confine the young poultry close to the heat and prevent drafts (Figure 15-3).

FIGURE 15-3
Brooding ring for young poults.
(Photo courtesy of Suzanne Paisley, University of California.)

Feed and Water

Young poultry hatch with enough residual yolk to supply their nutritional needs for about 36 hours. Dehydration is a frequent cause of early mortality. Research has demonstrated that providing water before feed can help to reduce this early mortality. Feeders and waterers of appropriate size should be place at frequent intervals close to the heat source and positioned so that they will not block the chicks' travel back to the heat. Troughs are often oriented like spokes of a wheel. Young poultry should be started with feed in shallow trays or on egg flats until they learn to eat from larger feeders. Feed on the trays is decreased after two or three days and the trays are gradually removed. To reduce labor, birds can be quickly trained to eat from mechanical feeders and drink from water delivery systems. Watering systems have traditionally provided water in small troughs or cups, but nipple drinkers are gaining in popularity since they reduce bacterial contamination of water.

FEEDING AND NUTRITION

Nutrient requirements of commercial type poultry are estimated from available experimental data, updated and published in the United States by the National Research Council (see Table 15-3). In general, poultry have the highest dietary requirement for protein (amino acids) when they are day-old and this declines as they mature. Pullets or hens in production require higher dietary protein levels than cocks of the same age. Hens also require a high calcium level (3 to 4%) for egg-shell formation. Maintaining the optimum Ca:P ratio in growing diets is critical for bone development. Laying or breeding diets should never be fed to growing poultry, as the high calcium content inhibits phosphorus absorption and may cause rickets.

Feed Formulation

Poultry diets are commonly formulated by computer programs which match ingredient composition with diet specifications to achieve the lowest-cost feed. Diets are composed of grains, protein supplements, byproduct feedstuffs, minerals, and vitamin supplements. Fats may be added to increase energy and reduce dustiness. The most frequently used grains are corn, grain sorghum, wheat, oats, and barley. Soybean meal, meat meal, fish meal, safflower meal, feather meal, and canola meal are typical protein supplements. Byproduct ingredients (e.g., corn gluten meal, wheat bran, rice bran, bakery byproduct meal, or brewer's grains) are also used in poultry diets when warranted by availability and price. The energy value of soybean meal and some varieties of barley can be enhanced by addition of enzyme preparations to diets.

Ingredient quality is important and ingredients must be free from mold toxins (e.g., aflatoxin), harmful bacteria, and chemical contaminants for successful use in poultry feeds. Most high-protein seeds contain antinutritional factors which must be destroyed by heat treatment before they are useful for poultry feeding. Antioxidants and mold inhibitors are often added to poultry feeds to protect critical nutrients from oxidative destruction and growth of molds which can produce mycotoxins. Quality control at the feed mill is extremely important to assure that the feeds produced will result in optimum flock performance and production of poultry and eggs free from residues.

Feed Processing

Feeds can be pelleted and pelleting can be preceded by treatment with steam or other preconditioning. Advantages cited for these processes are improved nutrient utilization, reduced separation during transportation or when conveyed by mechanical feeding systems, and reduction of bacterial contaminants in feeds. Pelleting also allows additional fat to be added to produce higher-energy diets. Typical pelleting produces particles that are too large for young poultry. Pellets are commonly crushed to produce a crumbled feed for young birds. Pelleted feeds are widely utilized for growing poultry but are less popular for laying hens.

HOUSING

The purpose of a poultry house is to confine the birds, provide them a desirable environment, protect them from predation, and facilitate bird care and management. Poultry houses can be constructed from a variety of locally available building materials. Smooth interior surfaces are preferred for effective sanitation. House width is usually limited to 40 feet to facilitate more uniform ventilation. Houses can be of any length but are usually 600 feet or less due to the limitations of the equipment which will be used to deliver feed and raise and lower equipment and curtains. Most houses are constructed with a gable roof. In areas with significant periods above 90 °F or below 40 °F insulation is recommended in the roof and sidewalls. The amount of insulation to use depends upon the severity of the weather expected. Table 15-4 gives some general guidelines for insulating poultry houses.

Naturally Ventilated Houses

In mild climates poultry houses with open sides covered with poultry netting are often used. The side openings are usually equipped with a curtain which can be raised or lowered to control ventilation. When temperatures over 100 °F are expected, the house should also be equipped with insulation, a fogging system, and/or horizontal or vertical fans to move air over the birds during high-temperature periods.

TABLE 15-3
NUTRIENT REQUIREMENTS OF POULTRY AS A PERCENTAGE OF DIET*

Type of Poultry and Age	Typical Dietary Energy (kcal MEₙ/kg diet)**	Crude Protein (%)***	Methionine (%)	Lysine (%)	Calcium (%)	Nonphytate Phosphorus (%)	Linoleic Acid (%)
CHICKENS:							
White-egg-laying strains:							
0–6 weeks	2850	18.0	.30	.85	.90	.40	1.0
6–12 weeks	2850	16.0	.25	.60	.80	.35	1.0
12–18 weeks	2900	15.0	.20	.45	.80	.30	1.0
18 weeks to 1st egg	2900	17.0	.22	.52	2.00	.32	1.0
Laying Hen (100g/day intake)	2900	15.0	.30	.69	3.25	.25	1.0
Brown-egg-laying strains:							
0–6 weeks	2800	17.0	.28	.80	.90	.40	1.0
6–12 weeks	2800	15.0	.23	.56	.80	.35	1.0
12–18 weeks	2850	14.0	.19	.42	.80	.30	1.0
18 weeks to 1st egg	2850	16.0	.21	.49	1.80	.35	1.0
Laying Hen (110g/day intake)	2900	16.5	.33	.76	3.60	.28	1.1
Broilers:							
0–3 weeks	3200	23.0	.50	1.10	1.00	.45	1.0
3–6 weeks	3200	20.0	.38	1.00	.90	.35	1.0
6–8 weeks	3200	18.0	.32	0.85	.80	.30	1.0

	Energy (kcal ME_n/kg)					
TURKEYS:						
Males — Females						
0–4 weeks — 0–4 weeks	2800	28.0	.55	1.60	1.20	.60	1.0
4–8 weeks — 4–8 weeks	2900	26.0	.45	1.50	1.00	.50	1.0
8–12 weeks — 8–11 weeks	3000	22.0	.40	1.30	.85	.42	.8
12–16 weeks — 11–14 weeks	3100	19.0	.35	1.00	.75	.38	.8
16–20 weeks — 14–17 weeks	3200	16.5	.25	.80	.65	.32	.8
20–24 weeks — 17–20 weeks	3300	14.0	.25	.65	.55	.28	.8
Breeders, Holding	2900	12.0	.20	.50	.50	.25	.8
Breeders, Laying Hens	2900	14.0	.20	.60	2.25	.35	1.1
GEESE:						
0–4 weeks	2900	20.0	—	1.00	.65	.30	—
over 4 weeks	3000	15.0	—	.85	.60	.30	—
Breeding	2900	15.0	—	.60	2.25	.30	—
DUCKS:						
0–2 weeks	2900	22.0	.40	.90	.65	.40	—
2–7 weeks	3000	16.0	.30	.65	.60	.30	—
Breeding	2900	15.0	.27	.60	2.75	—	—

*90% dry matter basis; no safety factor included.

**Typical energy concentrations for diets based mainly on corn and soybean meal; kcal ME_n/kg = kilocalories metabolizable energy per kilogram diet.

***Poultry do not have a requirement for crude protein per se but rather for minimum levels of essential amino acids and enough nitrogen for synthesis of nonessential amino acids.

TABLE 15-4

RECOMMENDED INSULATION FOR POULTRY HOUSES FOR DIFFERENT CLIMATIC CONDITIONS*

Expected High Temperature	Expected Low Temperature	Suggested Resistance Value**	
(°F)	(°F)	Roof	Walls
<90	−20	20	12
<90	−10	17	10
<90	0	14	8
<90	>10	11	6
<90	>20	8	4
<90	>30	5	2
<90	>40	2	0
>90	>40	5	2
>100	>40	8	4
>110	>40	11	6

*These recommendations are based on the experience of the author.

**The Resistance value or R value is a measure of the resistance of the wall to heat transfer.

Mechanically Ventilated Houses

Mechanical ventilation allows more complete control of the environment within the house. For this reason it is often used in climates with extremely high or low temperatures. Successful ventilation systems may utilize either positive (fans pump air in) or negative pressure (fans pump air out). Ventilation systems should be designed to provide uniform conditions throughout the house. With the most advanced systems temperature can be maintained within a two-degree Fahrenheit range. In hot climates incoming air is often cooled with evaporative pad coolers or fogging systems.

Ventilation Designs

Historically one of the most common poultry house designs was called a slot and fan system (Figure 15-4). This design utilizes exhaust fans (in any location) with a uniform slot air inlet along both side walls. This can be used with or without evaporative cooling pads. If desired, the cooling pads can be replaced with high-pressure misters located in an inlet chamber to reduce the maintenance required with pad coolers. Many naturally ventilated houses with side curtains have been converted to this ventilation system by simply adding exhaust fans and using the curtain openings as slot inlets. The house can then be used with either natural ventilation or mechanical ventilation as weather and economics dictate.

A tunnel ventilation design has become popular in recent years, which uses exhaust fans in one end of the house and inlets (often cooling pads) in the other (Figure 15-5).

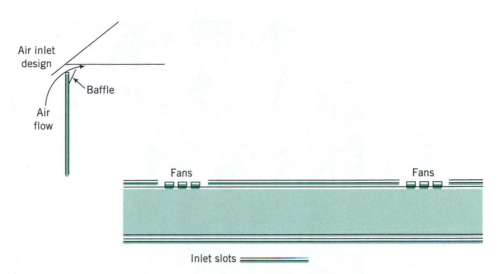

FIGURE 15-4
Slot and fan poultry house design.

Advantages are the economical grouping of fans and cooling pads and increased bird comfort during hot weather from the high air velocity achieved with this system. A disadvantage is the gradation in temperature along the length of the building. The system does not work as well in cold weather. Houses are usually constructed so that the pads can be closed and side inlets opened during cold weather, converting the house to a slot and fan design. This system is most popular with birds reared on litter floors but can also be found in many cage laying houses.

A design which is gaining in popularity uses the attic as a plenum or inlet duct to distribute air uniformly. A flat ceiling is constructed with slot inlets to bring air uniformly into the house. The attic must be insulated with this design to prevent an increase in incoming air temperature. An air inlet is provided in the form of an opening at the ridge. The design can be used with fans pumping air into the attic (positive ventilation) or with exhaust fans in the walls. With inlet slots which can be accurately controlled this design can provide extremely uniform temperatures in a house of any width. It is often used for

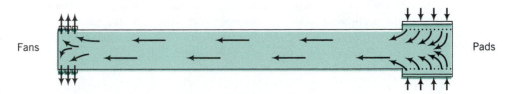

FIGURE 15-5
Diagram of tunnel ventilation system for a poultry house.

FIGURE 15-6
Turbo house design with a multiple-deck cage system and manure storage area below cages. Air enters the house through the slots in the ceiling. (Photo courtesy of Chore-Time Equipment Company, Milford, IN.)

laying hens in multideck cages with a manure storage pit. This is called a Turbo House[1] design in the industry (Figure 15-6).

EQUIPMENT

In floor houses used for broilers or turkeys, the feeders, water system, and brooder stoves are suspended from the rafters by cables connected to a winch at the end of the house. This allows simple adjustment of the equipment height; it can be adjusted daily if needed and pulled up out of the way for bird removal, manure removal, and house cleaning. Ventilation curtains utilize a similar system, allowing easy adjustment. Curtains can also be attached to a motorized winching system with thermostatic controls; the curtains are automatically adjusted by the control system to maintain a preset temperature in the house. With more advanced control systems ammonia sensors can be added to the system so that a preset maximum ammonia level is maintained.

[1]Trademark of Chore-Time Equipment Company, Millford, IN.

LIGHTING POULTRY

Light has been shown to affect the behavior and reproduction of poultry. It is well demonstrated that low light intensity reduces cannibalism and as a result poultry raised in light-controlled housing can be raised successfully with less severe beak trimming. Day length (photoperiod) influences feeding behavior, and long day length (e.g., 23L:1D)[2] is often used to stimulate feed consumption and rapid growth of meat poultry. Intermittent programs can be used to achieve the same end and reduce electrical costs. A typical program would be 1L:2D repeated eight times per day in light-controlled housing or used during the night period in open housing.

Recent research has shown that lameness of growing broilers can be reduced by modifying the lighting program. A program of 8L:16D given from 4 to 14 days of age followed by long days or gradually increasing photoperiods has reduced broiler lameness with little or no reduction in growth to 7 weeks of age.

Light penetrates into the brain of poultry where it stimulates cells in the hypothalamus to produce gonadotrophin-releasing hormone. The latter stimulates the pituitary gland to produce follicle-stimulating hormone and luteinizing hormone, which initiate and maintain reproductive function. The minimum light intensity to stimulate this response is about one-half foot candle (5 lux) under practical conditions.

Poultry have a diurnal photosensitive period which occurs 11 to 16 hours after dawn (see Figure 15-7). Continuous light is not required to stimulate reproduction but a significant duration of light must be provided within this photosensitive period to stimulate good egg production. When poultry are exposed to more than one light period during a 24-hour cycle, the end of the longest dark period is perceived as dawn.

Controlled lighting programs are used to sustain good semen or egg production. Replacement pullets are grown under short days or decreasing day length to prevent the onset of egg production before females reach the desired body size. At the correct age or weight for the genetic stock, the day length is increased to provide a photostimulatory photoperiod (13 or more hours of light per day). To achieve good fertility males must be exposed to photostimulatory day length at least a week prior to the females because their response to light is slower. Day length should never be decreased when egg production is desired. Typical lighting programs for table-egg layers are 16L:8D or .5L:5.5D:8L:10D.

Lighting Breeding Turkeys

Turkeys must experience short photoperiods before they will lay well. For in-season flocks receiving natural light, this requirement is satisfied by winter photoperiods. After light stimulation and egg production they will again become refractory to light stimulation. This refractory condition can be reversed by exposing them to short photoperiods for 10 weeks and then providing a photostimulatory photoperiod (e.g., 14L:10D) to initiate egg production.

---

[2] 23L:1D is defined as 23 hours of light followed by 1 hour of darkness.

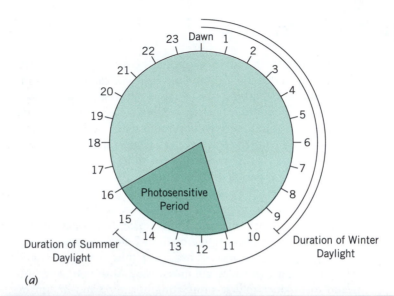

(a)

(b)

FIGURE 15-7

(a) Hours of light after dawn illustrate the duration of the longest and shortest day at latitude 38 degrees north. Short days of winter become nonstimulatory as they do not provide light during the photosensitive period. (b) Turkey growing barn.

PRODUCTION SYSTEMS

Hatching Egg Production

The parent stocks used to produce commercial chicks for meat or egg production require special care and management. They are usually kept on litter floors or pens with part litter and part raised slatted or wire floors. The litter areas are necessary for effective mating. Female feeders and waterers are located over the wire or slat area so that the bulk of the manure accumulates there. This reduction of droppings in the litter section assists in keeping the floor in good condition without constant removal of caked droppings. Nests are located so that they are easily accessed by the hens directly from the raised floor area. Nest units should always have landing perches to assist hens entering nests.

MEAT-TYPE BREEDERS. Meat-type breeder chickens must have feed restricted to control body weight or they rapidly become overweight, resulting in a decline in mating, fertility, and egg production. Feed restriction is usually started by three weeks of age and continues throughout life. Cocks and hens are raised separately for more effective weight control. At sexual maturity they are housed together but specially designed feeders are used. Male feeders are located high enough so that females cannot reach the feed. Female feeders are covered by special grids with openings which are too small to allow the cocks to dine. This system allows the manager to control the body weight of both sexes. A sample of each sex should be weighed at frequent intervals to monitor the effects of the feed restriction program. Body weight should follow breeder's guidelines closely and the flock should maintain high uniformity. A ratio of 10 to 15 cocks per hundred hens is adequate for good fertility.

EGG-TYPE BREEDERS. Egg-type breeders do not require feed restriction. Some egg-type strains may mate successfully on wire floors or in cages, but others require that at least a third of the floor area is covered with litter.

Hatching-Egg Care. Only clean, sound-shelled eggs of normal size and shell quality should be kept for hatching. If eggs are held before setting they should be stored at 55 °F to 70 °F and 75% relative humidity. Lower temperatures are used as the length of intended storage increases. Chicken and turkey eggs begin to loose hatchability after about three days of storage and the rate of this decline increases with age. Eggs are usually set within ten days of lay. Hatch of eggs stored longer than 10 days can be improved by turning eggs daily and by packaging them in plastic bags to reduce moisture loss and albumin quality decline. Hatching time is increased with egg storage time (about 10 hours after 14 days of storage).

The following are suggestions for hatching-egg production:

- Collect eggs frequently (at least four times a day).
- Keep nests filled with clean nesting material.
- To keep floor eggs to a minimum, provide one nest for every four hens. Be sure nests are in place before egg production starts.
- Exclude hens from nests at night to reduce broodiness and keep nests clean.
- Use semitrap gates on turkey nests. These prevent two hens from entering the same nest.
- Maintain dry litter in floor pens at all times.
- Collect eggs on clean, sanitized, plastic flats.
- Separate cracked, stained, and dirty eggs as you collect them and do not set them.
- Wash or fumigate clean eggs as soon as possible after collection. This kills microbes on the outside of the shell.
- Cool eggs overnight in flats before placing them in cases.
- Always wash hands thoroughly with a disinfectant soap before handling eggs.
- Never allow eggs to sweat; they may sweat when moved from storage into a warmer room.

Chicken Meat Production

Most meat chickens are produced under a contract between the processor and the grower. Typically the farmer provides the houses, equipment, labor, litter, and brooding fuel and receives the manure and a contract payment. The integrator provides the chicks, feed, medication, health care, and supervisory service. Contract payments are usually about five cents per pound of live weight marketed but vary with house type and bonuses paid for good performance (e.g., feed conversion). Assuming that all capital is borrowed at 9% interest, a 15-year loan payback, average chick placement schedules, and average fixed and variable costs, a grower needs about 80,000 square feet of housing (e.g., four houses 40 feet by 500 feet) to realize an after-tax income of $25,000 per year. After the loan is paid this would increase, but after fifteen years of use the buildings will probably need renovation.

The husbandry used to raise broilers, Cornish game hens, roasters, and other sizes of meat chickens is very similar. Broilers are started on litter floors, often grown to seven weeks of age and allowed floor space of from 100 to 144 square inches per bird depending on the season and the extent of environmental control available in the house. Growing chickens at market weight produce large amounts of heat and moisture, which must be removed from the house. House density is often reduced during periods when high ambient temperatures are expected. If the house is equipped with a good evaporative cooling system, higher densities can be raised successfully without danger of heat stress mortality.

During cold weather periods the fuel required for chick brooding increases dramatically. To minimize this cost many growers start chicks in the first one-third of the house, which is fitted with extra insulation. As the flock grows, birds are given access to additional floor space. To realize the maximum fuel savings the brooding area must be ventilated with the minimum air exchange required to maintain good air quality. Horizontal or vertical fans (paddle fans) are often used to circulate air and maintain uniform air quality throughout the brooding area. A makeup heater may be placed in one wall and used to supply all of the incoming fresh air using a positive ventilation system with air exhausted through curtain outlets on both side walls.

If litter is allowed to cake over in high-use areas, the flock is likely to experience health problems and lameness. Litter cake should be removed frequently. If plastic dome or trough waterers are used, they should be cleaned daily. Nipple drinking systems are preferred because they do not require cleaning and water is always clean and free of harmful bacteria. Feeding equipment should be adjusted so that the lip of the trough is at the birds' back height. Most commercial strains of broiler chicks do not require beak trimming.

Turkey Production

Turkey growing is very similar to growing of broiler chickens; however, a two-stage system is used. Day-old poults are started in a brooder house and then transferred to larger growing houses at about six weeks of age. Toms and hens are grown separately due to their disparity in size and growth rate. This allows more precise feeding (see Table 15-3) and avoids aggression between sexes. Hens are usually marketed at younger ages than toms. The processing plant must also adjust equipment to match the size of the birds processed and mixed sexes would cause problems at this stage.

The growing houses for turkeys must be equipped with larger feeders than those used for starting poults or chickens because the turkeys will be marketed at 10 to 40 pounds in weight (Figure 15-7b). Turkey poults are often beak trimmed at the hatchery and may have the inside toes trimmed to reduce carcass downgrading. Litter in turkey growing houses is often tilled to help keep the litter from packing down.

Raising Replacement Pullets

Pullets may be grown on litter floors like broilers or in flat wire-floor cages specially designed for starting and growing birds. In litter-floor systems Leghorn pullets are usually provided about one square foot of floor space. Brooding and management is much the same as for broilers. When pullets are cage reared, they may be started and grown in one house or transferred from a brooding-cage system to a grow-cage system at about six weeks of age. Leghorn chicks in starting cages should be provided 24 square inches of space and in growing cages 45 square inches. Cage brooding is usually done with a warm-room brooding system.

Pullets are usually beak trimmed to control cannibalism. Trimming can be done at 7 to 10 days by a precision method or at 6 to 12 weeks with a conventional cut. In either case a hot blade trimmer is used to prevent beak regrowth. The precision method requires a trimmer with a cam-operated blade so that cauterization time is precisely two seconds.

A guide plate with a 11/64-inch hole is used. Both beaks are inserted through the hole and cut at the same time. Detailed instructions should be obtained before attempting this method. With conventional trimming each beak is cut and cauterized separately. The upper beak should be cut 3/16 inch in front of the nostrils while the lower beak is left slightly longer. If the hens will be confined in light-controlled houses, the early precision method is often adequate to control cannibalism, while conventional beak trimming is more often used for pullets to be housed in open-type houses. After trimming feeders should be kept at least half full until the beaks are healed.

Pullets are usually vaccinated several times during the growing phase (see Health Maintenance, below). All operations done during the growing period should be carefully scheduled to avoid multiple stresses at any time. The growth and uniformity of egg-type pullets should be monitored by weighing of a sample of birds weekly. Underweight flocks can be fed higher protein levels.

Table-Egg Production

CAGE SYSTEMS. Most commercial table-egg hens are kept in laying cages with sloping wire floors so that eggs roll out the front of the cage into an egg tray. Cages reduce labor, result in cleaner eggs, and keep the hens away from their droppings, which assists in disease prevention. Cage systems of many designs are in use. Early cage systems were developed in Southern California and used one level of cages with droppings falling to the floor. The cages were positioned at a convenient height for egg collection and feeding. With this system feeding is often done with a motorized or electric feed cart which conveys the feed into the trough as the cart is driven down the aisle. Several machines have been developed to remove the manure from these houses. Some growers allow the manure to accumulate under the cages for several months to a year before cleanout. If it dries sufficiently to stop fly emergence this system can provide adequate fly control. If the manure does not dry, fly production can be enormous and must be controlled with chemicals, which are costly. Flies usually become resistant to the chemicals after a few seasons and control may fail completely. An alternative manure management system is frequent cleanout (seven days or less). The manure must then be processed or stored in such a way that fly breeding and water pollution are prevented.

With the development of mechanical feeding, watering, egg collection, and cleaning it became possible to stack cages (Figure 15-8). Systems up to ten levels high are in use. Systems more than four high require special equipment to access the birds in the upper levels for mortality removal, bird handling, and system maintenance. Cages can be of any size but depths of 12 to 18 inches are most popular. Leghorn hens should be housed to provide from 60 to 72 square inches of cage floor space per bird. Manure in a stacked cage system is often removed with belts or scrapers; however, some cage configurations allow manure to be deflected or scraped into a storage area under the cages. Manure in storage pits presents the same fly control challenges as described above.

FLOOR SYSTEMS. Management of table-egg hens on litter floors is similar to management of Leghorn breeders except that cocks are not required. Houses with part litter and part raised wire or slat floors are sometimes used. Hens can also be housed in pens

FIGURE 15-8

Five-tier layer cage system. (Photo courtesy of Chore-Time Equipment Company, Milford IN.)

with only wire or slat floors. Built-up litter is commonly used and it must be maintained in a loose, dry condition for good bird health. Coccidiosis resistance needs to be developed during the pullet growing phase because preventive drugs are not approved for laying hens.

To produce clean eggs with this system, nests must be kept bedded with clean litter or clean plastic nest pads. Nest systems with mechanical egg collection are available but it is more difficult to train birds to lay in nests with pads and the number of floor eggs can be a management problem.

FLOCK RECYCLING. Commercial laying hens can be economically recycled for a second and third laying period by inducing a cessation of lay accompanied by a feather molt. Successful recycling requires that the entire flock be reduced to zero egg production. The flock can then be held out of production for a period of one to five weeks. Egg production is usually stopped by feed withdrawal for 7 to 14 days followed by feeding of a diet low in protein, calcium, and sodium (such as cracked grain) for periods up to 18 days. Stimulatory lighting is discontinued during this time and is resumed when the flock is returned to the complete laying ration. Water should be provided at all times. If an increase in mortality occurs during the fast, the flock should be fed at least a limited amount of the recycling diet immediately. Sample body weights should be taken during recycling to determine the impact of the fast and recycling diet on the smaller hens. Some recycling programs specify a certain weight loss but this is not necessary. There are hundreds of variations used in recycling programs such as feeding limited amounts of feed for varying times. In general, if the hens are rested for a longer time there is a greater improvement in egg quality after the rest. Shorter rests would be recommended if egg prices are high and longer rests when egg prices are low. Second-cycle flocks lay large eggs immediately after the rest but typically reach a peak rate of lay about 10% lower than the pullet cycle.

Ducks and Geese

Ducks and geese can be successfully raised in confinement on litter floors and do not require swimming water for growth, health, or reproduction. Young ducklings are sometimes started on slatted or raised wire floors because of the wetness of the droppings. Commercial houses often provide an indoor litter area and an outside run. The Pekin and Muscovy breeds are frequently raised for meat production. Indian Runner and Khaki Campbell breeds are used for high egg production.

Geese are excellent grazers and can be grown on pasture with limited supplemental feeding, although many geese are raised in confinement without pasture. Emden or Toulouse breeds of geese are often raised for meat production. The White Chinese breed has often been used for weeding commercial crops.

HEALTH MAINTENANCE

The production of commercial poultry in large flocks requires effective disease prevention and control. This involves appropriate vaccination, medication, biosecurity, and sanitation programs.

Vaccination

Vaccination is an effective method of preventing a variety of poultry diseases from causing economic damage to flocks. Vaccination programs should be developed after careful study and consultation between the owners or manager and a well-trained avian veterinarian. Typical factors to consider are: (1) disease history of the farm, (2) previous success in excluding disease agents, (3) number of age groups on the farm, (4) separation from other poultry in the area around the farm, (5) farm security, (6) infectious diseases known to have caused problems in the surrounding area, and (7) the economic impact of an outbreak of the disease on this farm.

Medication

Medication is typically used to control bacteria, mycoplasma, coccidia, and internal parasites. Coccidiosis seems to be ubiquitous and control drugs are typically fed to meat birds until seven days before slaughter. They are also used during the growing period for table-egg pullets and breeding poultry. By 18 weeks of age, poultry usually develop enough immunity to coccidia so that medication is no longer necessary.

Antimicrobials can be used to control bacterial diseases (e.g., *E. coli* or Salmonella); however, with careful management most problems should be prevented. When a grower must resort to medication, it is usually an indication of management failure and economic damage to the flock has already occurred. A careful review of the housing, ventilation, litter management, chick quality, and brooder temperature (if appropriate) should be made before the next flock is housed. With the exception of preventive drugs, antimicrobials should not be needed to routinely produce healthy poultry or eggs.

Biosecurity

Some disease agents such as coccidia, *E. coli,* and Marek's virus cannot be readily excluded from commercial farms. However, many disease problems can be successfully controlled by excluding the agents. The following steps are recommended to maintain a good biosecurity program.

- Use all-in, all-out management whenever possible with only one age of poultry per farm.
- Exclude all unnecessary visitors.
- Require necessary visitors to wear clean protective clothing, footwear, and head coverings if they enter poultry houses.
- Remove mortality daily and dispose of them in a sanitary manner.
- If rendering truck pickup is used, place the mortality pickup station at the edge of the property as far from the poultry as possible.
- Keep delivery personnel out of poultry houses.
- Control property access with fences and gates.
- Disinfect the wheels of delivery vehicles which must enter the farm.
- If outside employees are used, require them to change clothing and footwear when they enter the farm.
- Clean and sanitize any equipment brought to the farm.
- Put concrete pads at the entrance to houses with a disinfectant pan or spray and use it every time!
- Require chick or poult delivery trucks to be cleaned and disinfected between deliveries.
- Require any live haul trucks to be cleaned and disinfected before entering the farm. An exception might be if the entire farm is to be depopulated within three days.
- Establish a good rodent control program and exclude wild birds from houses.
- Remove shrubs, trees, and trash from the area adjacent to poultry houses and keep vegetation mowed short.

Cleaning and Disinfection

Poultry dust can cause respiratory disease in flocks and should be avoided. Except for ventilation fans and other dust-sensitive equipment, cleaning should not be attempted while poultry are in the house. Manure can be safely removed from houses if excessive dust is not raised. When houses are depopulated, they should be carefully cleaned and disinfected before repopulation. If litter is to be reused, the upper portions of the house can still be cleaned. Management should be aware of the risk of reusing litter. If the previous flock has experienced a disease problem, the litter should be completely removed.

Cleaning and disinfection cannot guarantee a sterile facility but the numbers of disease agents can be greatly reduced. The following steps are recommended to clean and disinfect a poultry house:

- Remove all litter and droppings from the floors, building surfaces, and equipment.
- Clean, disinfect, and flush water lines in the house.
- Wash the building and equipment with a high-pressure washer using a cleaning compound.
- After washing let the building dry and then apply a disinfectant.
- Open the house and allow it to dry and remain empty for at least 36 hours.

Summary of Health Maintenance

Disease prevention using these techniques is infinitely more cost effective than attempting to treat a disease after it occurs. The keys to a healthy flock are: (1) starting with clean chicks and a clean house, (2) ventilating to provide good air quality without temperature extremes, (3) feeding a balanced diet adequate in all nutrients, (4) preventing introduction of disease agents, and (5) vaccinating for diseases known to occur in the area.

SUMMARY

Poultry and egg production have tremendous potential to produce large quantities of high-protein food. Coordinated production and processing, genetically improved stock, efficient reproduction, scientific nutrition, use of labor-saving equipment, and effective disease control have made it possible to produce meat and eggs with minimum use of high-quality feed. With modern technology poultry can be successfully grown in any location or climate in the world. Successful poultry producers are those individuals who follow known principles of good husbandry and practice these continuously.

GLOSSARY

All-in, all-out management All poultry on a farm are removed and replaced after each cycle.
Biosecurity A management system to minimize the pathogen exposure of flocks.

Broiler A young meat chicken of either sex (usually under 13 weeks of age) that has tender meat and flexible breastbone cartilage.
Chick guard A fence made of corrugated paper

or wire used to confine young poultry close to the heat source.

Coccidia Protozoans which cause damage to the intestine of poultry.

Cock A sexually mature male chicken.

Cornish game hen A young female meat chicken less than 2 pounds dressed weight produced from Cornish cross stock.

Depopulation Removal of all birds from the premises.

Egg-type Chickens that have been genetically selected to produce eggs for human consumption.

Layer or laying hen A sexually mature female chicken.

Marek's disease A transmissible disease caused by a herpesvirus which results in various types of lymphoid tumors.

Meat-type Chicken stocks selected for meat production.

Poult A young turkey of either sex.

Pullet A sexually immature female chicken.

Recycling Induction of a pause in egg production usually accompanied by a feather molt. The flock returns to lay with a dramatic improvement in egg quality and productivity.

Replacement pullets A pullet flock grown to replace the laying flock.

Roaster A meat chicken grown to a weight of 6 to 8 pounds for roasting.

Table eggs Eggs for human consumption as opposed to hatching eggs.

Tom A male turkey.

REFERENCES

Bell, D. D. 1989. *General Molting Recommendations.* Poultry Fact Sheet No. 5. Department of Avian Sciences, University of California, Davis, CA 95616.

Calnek, B. W., Barnes, H. J., Beard, C. W., Reid, W. M., and Yoder, H. W. Jr. (ed.). 1991. *Diseases of Poultry* (9th ed). Ames, IA: Iowa State University Press.

Classen, H. L., and Riddell, C. 1989. Photoperiodic effects on performance and leg abnormalities in broiler chickens. *Poultry Sci.,* 68: 873.

Crawford, R. D. 1990. *Poultry Breeding and Genetics.* New York: Elsevier.

Cunningham, D. L. 1996. *Poultry Production Systems in Georgia: Costs and Returns Analysis.* Cooperative Extension Service, College of Agricultural and Environmental Sciences, University of Georgia, Athens, GA.

Daghir, N. D. 1995. *Poultry Production in Hot Climates.* Wallingford, UK: CAB International.

Ernst, R. A. 1990. *Lighting Programs for Replacement Pullets.* Poultry Fact Sheet No. 13. Department of Avian Sciences, University of California, Davis, CA 95616.

Ernst, R. A. 1991. *Lighting Programs for Table Egg Layers.* Poultry Fact Sheet No. 14. Department of Avian Sciences, University of California, Davis, CA 95616.

Ernst, R. A. 1996. *Hatching Egg Production, Storage and Sanitation.* Poultry Fact Sheet No. 22. Department of Avian Sciences, University of California, Davis, CA 95616.

Esmay, M. L. 1978. *Principles of Animal Environment.* Westport, CN: AVI.

Leeson, S., and Summers, J. D. 1991. *Commercial Poultry Nutrition.* Guelph, Ontario, Canada: University Books.

National Research Council. 1994. *Nutrient Requirements of Poultry* (9th rev. ed.). Washington, D.C.: National Academy Press.

North, M. O., and Bell, D. D. 1990. *Commercial Chicken Production Manual* (4th ed.). New York: Chapman & Hall.

Scott, M. L., and Dean, W. F. 1991. *Nutrition and Management of Ducks.* Ithaca, NY: M. L. Scott of Ithaca.

CHAPTER SIXTEEN
HORSES AND THE HORSE INDUSTRY

DON R. TOPLIFF
WEST TEXAS A & M UNIVERSITY, CANYON, TX

Few activities rival the thrill of equine competitions, whether it be a down-to-the-wire stretch drive between Thoroughbreds, an American Quarter Horse out-maneuvering a cow in a cutting competition, an Arabian endurance horse completing a 100-mile ride with seemingly little effort, a European Warmblood completing a grueling cross-country eventing course, or a team of Belgians pulling twice their weight in an overload pull. The horse's ability to perform athletic feats is truly amazing. At the same time, the bond that develops between this noblest of all animals and their human caretakers is unequaled with other domestic livestock species.

Horses apparently evolved on the North American continent and spread throughout the rest of the world. Their closest relatives in the animal kingdom are the tapir and rhinoceros. Ironically, the ancestors of the modern-day horse disappeared from the continent for unknown reasons about 10,000 years ago and did not reappear on the continent until reintroduced by the Spanish conquistadors in the sixteenth century. No one knows exactly when or where horses were first domesticated, but most evidence seems to indicate that it occurred somewhere between 4500 and 2500 B.C. in China and Mesopotamia. From that time until the recent past, the horse has played a critical role in the development of society as a means of transportation and a beast of burden. But perhaps the horse's greatest influence on the destiny of humankind was as an instrument of war. From the earliest records of horses and chariots, to the horses used during the Crusades, to the Civil War, and Teddy Roosevelt's charge up San Juan Hill, the horse has had a great influence on the outcome of the battle.

Today, horses in the United States are used largely for recreational purposes, although in some areas of the world and even in isolated parts of this country horses are still the primary means of transportation and power. The industry in the United States has undergone significant change over the past twenty years and will likely continue to undergo change in a changing society and world. But as the great Will Rogers once said, "There is something about the outside of a horse that is good for the inside of the man." That profound statement is the essence of why people have always been and will likely continue to be involved with these noble creatures.

HISTORY OF THE HORSE AND THE HORSE INDUSTRY IN THE UNITED STATES

The horse industry in the United States is a very popular and thriving industry that encompasses a wide variety of horse types, activities, and people from virtually every walk of life. The industry today has evolved over time from one of necessity to one of recreation; history has had a great influence on today's industry.

Archeological records indicate that horses or horse-like creatures disappeared from the North American continent about 10,000 years ago. They were reintroduced to the continent by the Spanish explorer and conqueror Hernan Cortes at Vera Cruz, Mexico in 1519. It is reported that those horses came from breeding farms in Cuba. Even though large numbers of horses were used in expeditions north of the Rio Grande, repopulation of what is now the United States did not begin until Juan de Onate established a breeding herd at the Spanish mission in what is now Santa Fe, New Mexico in about 1598.

At about the same time, horses appeared in the southeastern part of the United States in the area that is now Georgia, along with a series of Franciscan missions that were established by the Spanish. Horses also came to the east coast with the English, Dutch, and French colonists who brought horses with them to the New World. The colonists would eventually import more horses, but most of them came from breeding farms in the West Indies and not continental Europe. Therefore, most of the horses brought to the continent had a strong Spanish influence, more refined in appearance as opposed to draft-like.

Throughout the eighteenth and nineteenth centuries, horses played a key role in the settlement of the West, the changing of Indian culture, the Civil War, and the homesteading of the central plains. In short, the West was won because of the horse. However, at the close of the nineteenth century, developments occurred that would soon change the face of the horse industry. The adaptation of the steam engine for farm work, closely followed by the invention of the internal combustion engine, doomed the horse to near obsolescence as a source of power on the U.S. farm. It would be another 20 years before the decline of horse numbers would begin, but it was nonetheless inevitable.

Organized racing in this country dates back to about 1665 on Long Island, where records exist of a track being built. Other sporting events involving the horse grew out of contests that centered around the daily life of a cowboy on the range. Another sport that has evolved from the pride of owning the best is the horse show. That aspect of the industry encompasses myriad events from Western Pleasure to Show Jumping to Cutting Horse competitions to Eventing to Conformation competition and provides the U.S. economy with significant economic activity.

The use of the horse has certainly changed since its reintroduction to the continent, but one thing is certain. Horses bring great joy to their owners and enhance the quality of life of everyone associated with them. They are even now being used for therapeutic purposes in patients with physical and mental disabilities to improve their coordination and mental health. Will Rogers was right; there *is* something about the outside of the horse that is good for the inside of the person.

Horse Numbers

The United States Department of Agriculture (USDA) counted horses on farms and ranches from 1862 to 1960. Horse numbers reached a peak of 21 million head in 1920 and then began to decline. Most of those horses in 1920 were of the draft or heavy type and the decline in numbers from 1920 to 1960 was due primarily to the mechanization of agriculture and the displacement of the horse by the internal combustion engine, which is more efficient. Interestingly, engines today are still rated by "horsepower."

By 1960, there were an estimated three million horses on farms and ranches and it is likely that most of those were light horse breeds. At that point USDA made a decision to stop counting horses as they concluded that horses were no longer an important component of agriculture. Since then a complete counting of the horses in the United States has not been done. The American Horse Council attempted to take a horse census in 1985 by surveying a sample of horse owners. The results of that survey were seriously challenged and another survey was designed and conducted and the results released in 1996. The latest survey indicates there are 6.9 million head, most of which do not reside on farms and ranches. The draft horse breeds have made a comeback in the last ten years and are growing in numbers; however, the majority of horses today are of the light horse breeds. The top-ten states in terms of horse numbers are listed in Table16-1.

The American Horse Council in 1996 estimated the value of goods and services produced by the horse industry at $25.3 billion, making it roughly the same size as the apparel manufacturing and motion picture industries. Further, the horse industry contributes

TABLE 16-1
THE TOP-TEN STATES IN HORSE NUMBERS

Texas	678,000
California	642,000
Florida	299,000
Oklahoma	278,000
Illinois	219,000
Colorado	194,000
Ohio	192,000
Kentucky	150,000
New York	146,000
Idaho	120,000

Source: American Horse Council (1996). The Economic Impact of the Horse Industry in the United States, Vol. 2: Eleven Focus States.

338,500 full-time equivalent jobs directly to the economy and pays about $1.9 billion in taxes annually. Table 16-2 shows the annual GDP from horses by state.

Breeds of Horses

Breeds of horse vary greatly in mature size. Breeds are divided generally according to size into draft horses, light horses, and ponies. The top-ten breeds in terms of numbers are shown in Table 16-3. A list of the breed associations and their addresses can be found in Table 16-4.

LIGHT HORSES. The modern light horse breeds can all trace their roots back to the oriental "hot bloods" of Asia. The best known of those is the Arabian (Figure 16-1a).

TABLE 16-2
GROSS DOMESTIC PRODUCT OF HORSES BY STATE*

California	11.4
Texas	7.1
Florida	6.5
New York	4.8
Illinois	3.8
Kentucky	3.4
Oklahoma	3.3
Ohio	2.8
Colorado	2.6
Maryland	1.5

*In billions of dollars.

Source: American Horse Council (1996). The Economic Impact of the Horse Industry in the United States, Vol. 2: Eleven Focus States.

TABLE 16-3

THE TOP-TEN BREEDS OF HORSES BY NEW REGISTRATIONS IN 1996

Quarter Horse	108,604
Paints	45,419
Thoroughbred	32,185
Standardbred	11,598
Tennessee Walker	10,918
Appaloosa	10,069
Arabian	9,404
Miniature	9,112
Anglo & Half Arabs	3,983
Morgan	3,088

Pedigree information on Arabian horses has been kept for at least 2,500 years. They are known as a very refined and intelligent-looking breed with great endurance. Today, Arabians are largely a show horse breed although significant numbers of purebreds and Arabian crosses compete in endurance riding competitions.

The American Quarter Horse (Figure 16-1b) was developed in Virginia in the 1700s as a short-distance race horse that had tremendous power. The lineage of many horses in the breed trace to the Thoroughbred named Janus. A similar horse was developed in the Southwest and used on ranches to work cattle. As east met west and these lines were crossed, the American Quarter Horse of today was born. The American Quarter Horse Association was formed in 1940 to collect, record, and preserve the pedigrees of American Quarter Horses. It is the largest equine breed registry in the world. American Quarter Horses are used for show, race, and rodeo, in addition to still doing the ranch work for which they became famous.

Thoroughbreds (Figure 16-1c) trace their ancestry to three oriental hot blood horses, the Darley Arabian, the Godolfin Barb, and Byerly Turk. Pedigrees on these "thoroughly bred" horses were first kept in England and today are kept by the Jockey Club located in New York City. Thoroughbreds are bred to race at intermediate distances from 6 furlongs (3/4 of a mile) to a mile and a half. The Kentucky Derby, Preakness Stakes, and Belmont Stakes are the most famous races for Thoroughbreds and constitute what is known as the "Triple Crown." Thoroughbreds are also popular in the hunter-jumper industry because of their size, speed, and athletic ability.

Another American breed developed on the east coast during colonial times is the Morgan horse (Figure 16-1d). These horses are all descended from the stallion, Justin Morgan, who was named after his owner. Morgans have been selected and bred as a multipurpose breed suited to both riding and pulling a wheeled vehicle. They have a natural way of going and today are primarily a show horse. The American Morgan Horse Association is the registry for the breed.

The Standardbred (Figure16-1e) is a breed of racing horse that pulls a two-wheeled sulky while trotting or pacing. The trotters perform a two-beat diagonal gait, that is, the opposite hind and fore legs move together, whereas the pacers exhibit a two-beat lateral

TABLE 16-4

EQUINE BREED ASSOCIATIONS IN THE UNITED STATES

Appaloosa
Appaloosa Horse Club, Inc.
P.O. Box 8403
Moscow ID 83843

Arabian
Arabian Horse Registry of America
1200 Zuni Street
Westminster CO 80234

International Arabian Horse Association
P.O Box 33696
Denver CO 80237

Belgian
Belgian Draft Horse Corporation of America
P.O. Box 335
Wabash IN 46992

Buckskin
American Buckskin Registry Association
P.O. Box 3850
Redding CA 96049

International Buckskin Association
P.O Box 268
Shelby IN 46377

Clydesdale
Clydesdale Breeders of the USA
17378 Kelly Rd.
Pecatonia IL 61063

Hanoverian
The American Hanoverian Society
14615 N.E. 190th Street, Suite 108
Woodinville WA 98072

Miniature
American Miniature Horse Association
5601 South IH 35 W
Alvarado TX 76009

Morgan
American Morgan Horse Association
P.O. Box 960
Shelburne VT 05482

Mustang
Bureau of Land Management
U.S. Department of Interior
18th and C. Streets N.W.
Washington D.C. 20240-0001

Paint
American Paint Horse Association
P.O Box 961023
Ft. Worth TX 76161

Palomino
Palomino Horse Breeders of America
15253 E. Skelly Drive
Tulsa OK 74116

Paso Fino
Paso Fino Horse Association
101 North Collin St.
Plant City FL 33566

Percheron
Percheron Horse Association of America
P.O. Box 141
Fredericktown OH 43019

Pinto
National Pinto Horse Registry
P.O. Box 486
Oxford NY 13830

Pinto Horse Association of America, Inc.
1900 Samuels Ave.
Ft. Worth TX 76102

POA
Ponies of America Club, Inc.
5240 Elmwood Ave
Indianapolis, IN 46203

Quarter Horse
American Quarter Horse Association
P.O Box 200
Amarillo TX 79105

Saddlebred
The American Saddlebred Horse
4093 Iron Works Pike
Lexington, KY 40511

Standardbred
United States Trotting Association
750 Michigan Ave
Columbus OH 43215

Tennessee Walker
Tennessee Walking Horse Breeders and Exhibitors
Association
P.O Box 286
Lewisburg TN 37091

Thoroughbred
The Jockey Club
821 Corporate Drive
Lexington KY 40503

FIGURE 16-1

Breeds of horses.

A. Arabian (Courtesy Arabian Horse Trust. Polly Knoll, photographer.)
B. American Quarter Horse (Courtesy K.C. Montgomery.)
C. Thoroughbred (Courtesy Kentucky Horse Park.)
D. Morgan (Courtesy American Morgan Horse Association. Brooke Deardorff, photographer.)
E. Standardbred (Courtesy Don R. Topliff. West Texas A & M University.)
F. Tobiano Paint (Courtesy K.C. Montgomery.)

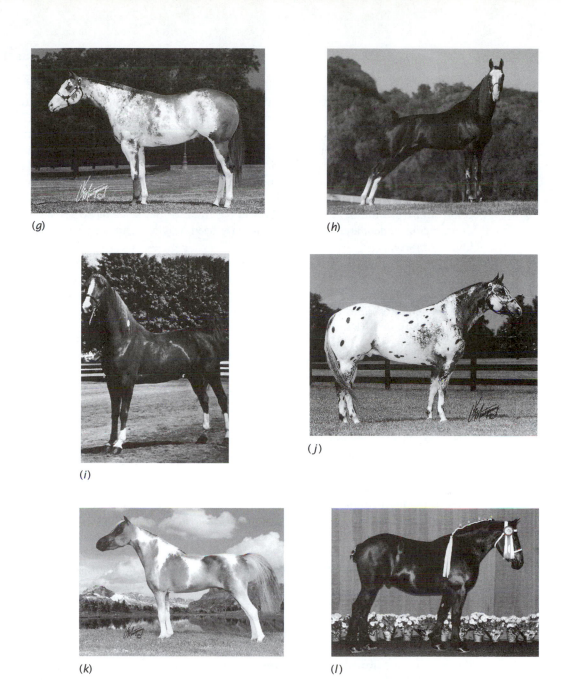

(g)

(h)

(i)

(j)

(k)

(l)

FIGURE 16-1 *(continued)*

Breeds of horses.

G. Overo Paint (Courtesy K.C. Montgomery.)
H. Tennesee Walking Horse (Courtesy Tennessee Walking Horse Breeders' and Exhibitors' Association. ©Stuart Vesty, photographer.)
I. American Saddlebred (Courtesy Don R. Topliff. West Texas A & M University.)
J. Appaloosa (Courtesy K.C. Montgomery.)
K. Miniature (Courtesy K.C. Montgomery.)
L. Clydesdale (Courtesy K.C. Montgomery.)

gait, where the fore and rear legs on the same side move in unison. The breed is named for the practice of registering only horses that could trot or pace under a "standard" time.

Paint horses are a color breed of stock-type horse that exhibit one of two coat color patterns. The tobiano color pattern (Figure 16-1f) has a dark background with white spots that look as though they were formed by pouring white paint from the top down. The white must cross the topline. The overo color pattern (Figure 16-1g) looks as though it was formed by splashing the white on from the sides and bottom. The background color can be palomino, gray, sorrel, brown, bay, dun, or black. Paint horses are used for show, racing, rodeo, and ranch work and have been heavily influenced by the American Quarter Horse.

The Pinto is also a breed of horses that exhibit the tobiano or overo coat color pattern. The difference is that the Pinto Horse Association has divisions for all types of horses including miniatures, saddle horse types, hunter horse types, and stock horse types. Therefore, Pinto horses can look like Arabians, Saddlebreds, Thoroughbreds, or Quarter Horses with spots.

The Tennessee Walking Horse (Figure16-1h) was developed on the plantations of the Southeast as a horse to provide a comfortable ride over long distances. The "running walk" distinguishes these horses from other breeds. This gate has four distinct beats as does a normal walk, but the horse overstrides (places the hind foot in front of the track left by the front foot) by up to twelve inches and there is a nodding motion of the head in time with the front feet. High knee action and animation are also desired in the horses that show. The foundation sire is listed as Allan, who was of Thoroughbred descent.

The American Saddlebred (Figure 16-1i) was developed out of the necessity for riding horses that could cover ground and were easy on the rider. Today the American Saddlebred are mainly a breed of three- or five-gaited show horses. The stallion, Denmark, is listed as the foundation sire and traces back to the three foundation Thoroughbred sires.

The Appaloosa (Figure 16-1j) is a color breed of horses developed by the Nez Perce Indians in the Palouse river valley of Idaho and Washington. Their name is derived from the description of "A Palouse Horse." The first written accounts of these horses with white spots on their rumps are found in the journal of Lewis and Clark from their travels in the Northwest Territories in 1806. Through the years as the white men took their land and the Nez Perce were forced to move to reservations and stripped of their horses, the breed nearly died. A few stallions and mares did remain in the Northwest and in 1938 a group of horsemen formed the Appaloosa Horse Club, which began recording and preserving the heritage of the spotted horse. Today the spotted horse is used for show, race, rodeo, and ranch work much as the other stock horse breeds.

The Palomino is a breed ideally the color of a newly minted gold coin. Palominos were known to exist in Europe in the 1500s and came to the New World with the Spanish as did other breeds. Prized as parade horses, the palomino coat color exists in many breeds. The Palomino Horse Breeders of America was formed in 1941 in California by a group of horsemen who wanted to record the pedigrees and preserve the history of the golden horse. Palominos can be of stock type, saddle type, or pleasure type and may be registered in other breeds as well and are known as double registered.

The Buckskin is a color breed also with a golden body color and black legs, mane, tail, and ears. As with Palominos, the Buckskin color pattern can be found in other breeds and double registry is possible. This registry also accepts horses that are dun (a reddish-gold color) or grulla (a mouse-gray color with black points). The exact genetics of these colors is not well understood, but most geneticists believe that these horses result from a dilution of the base coat color.

The Miniature horse (Figure 16-1k) is a breed of horse, not pony. Measuring no more than 34 inches tall they appear almost doll-like. The Miniature breed has gained significantly in number and popularity in the last few years. Miniatures can be any color and most of the coat color patterns are represented. In addition to use as pets, they are shown in a number of classes including driving.

DRAFT HORSES.   Draft horses are regaining popularity and their numbers are on the rise. There are five major draft horse breeds in the United States and all of them originated in Europe. Draft horses are descended from the heavy horses used to carry knights in the middle ages and are generally 16 to 18 hands[1] tall (height is measured at the withers—top of shoulder) and weigh from 1600 to 2400 pounds. The most famous of those are the Clydesdales, which were first bred in the Clydesdale area of Scotland. The eight-horse hitch pulling the red beer wagon made these the most-recognized horses in America. Clydesdales (Figure 16-1L) are sorrel to chestnut in color with distinctive white markings on the face and long white silky hair, called feathering, on the legs. They are also noted for their flashy action while on the move. Percherons, noted as the breed of blacks and grays, came from the La Perche region of France. Unlike the Clydesdale, the Percheron does not have feathering on the lower legs. Percherons are known for being light on their feet and are generally a heavier-appearing breed. Shires are the largest of the draft breeds and have white markings on their head and feathering on their lower legs, which may also be white. Their body color is usually black, although other colors do occur. This breed was developed in the "shire" areas of England. The Suffolk, developed in the Suffolk area of England, is a sorrel or chestnut breed that does not have feathering on the lower legs. Because of their rounded and punched-up appearance, they are often called Suffolk Punches. The most numerous of the draft breeds in the United States is the Belgian. Belgians are predominantly sorrel with light-colored (flaxen) mane and tail and may have very sparse feathering on the fetlock. Belgians lack the animation and high knee action of some of the other breeds but are popular because of their even temperament and ease of management.

PONIES.   Ponies are technically any horse under 14 hands tall at the withers. There are horses registered in major breeds that are under 14 hands, but are not considered to be ponies. There are a number of breeds of ponies in the United States and the majority of them are considered to be children's horses, primarily because of their size. The smallest and possibly the most numerous of the pony breeds is the Shetland. Developed in the Shetland Islands north of Scotland in the North Sea, the Shetland is a hardy breed noted

---

[1]One hand = 4 inches.

for its shaggy winter coat. The modern breed has been refined with the infusion of Arabian blood over the years. The Welsh pony is an intermediate-sized pony between the Shetland and full-sized horses. They are truly the child's pony as they are big enough for older children to ride and are noted for a good disposition for younger children. The Hackney, on the other hand, is used almost exclusively by adults for driving purposes. Elegant and animated in their movement, their fiery temperament is too much for children to handle. The Connemara pony is famed for its jumping ability and used as a youth hunter and jumper. It is generally gray in color and generally more refined in appearance than the other pony breeds. The original ancestors of the modern breed were developed in the Connomera region of Ireland. In the 1950s an Appaloosa mare was crossed with a Shetland pony and the resulting cross became the foundation of the Pony of America breed. Colored like an Appaloosa, they are the size of a Welsh and are very popular as a child's show horse. They are very versatile, and compete in both judged and timed events.

OTHER BREEDS. In recent years, a significant number of European warmbloods have been imported into the United States. These horses have been developed by crossing draft horses (coldbloods) with Thoroughbreds (hotbloods) or other light horses to form a warmblood. There are a number of warmblood breeds that generally are named for the area in which they were developed. The prominent are the Traekaner, Holsteiner, and Dutch Warmbloods. These horses are used mainly in dressage and jumping competition.

Events and Activities

Horse events and activities can be loosely broken into two categories, English and Western. The distinction is based on the equipment and attire used in a particular event. English equipment was developed in Europe while Western equipment evolved from the saddles and bridles used by the Spaniards in the Southwest and the cowboys of the Old West. English saddles are much lighter and are designed for close contact with the horse and a minimum of restriction on the rider. The Western saddle is much heavier and has a saddle horn mounted on the front of the saddle to which is tied a rope for roping cattle. The saddle horn is also handy for the rider to grasp if the mount becomes unruly and attempts to throw the rider. English events were largely brought to this country from Europe while Western events originated on this continent. Western events are much younger and are becoming very popular the world over.

RODEOS AND RODEO EVENTS. Rodeo has grown immensely popular over the years. Today, it is a multimillion-dollar sport. Both the bucking horses in the rough stock events of bareback riding and saddle bronc riding and the horses used in the timed events of calf roping, team roping, steer wrestling, and barrel racing are considered working athletes. The exact number of horses used in rodeos is not known, but a typical rodeo could involve more than 200 head of horses. The bucking horses owned by the rodeo company are generally a heterogeneous mixture of breeds, although many of the great bucking horses have been draft horse crosses. The horses used by contestants in the timed events are predominantly of the stock horse type (Figure 16-2). Most of the horses used in these

FIGURE 16-2

A calf-roping horse. (Courtesy K.C. Montgomery.)

events are American Quarter Horses, although significant numbers of Paints, Appaloosas, Palominos, and Buckskins also compete. There are rodeos for all levels of competition from youth to amateur to professional.

REINING. Reining is a competition in which horses run a prescribed pattern and are judged on their ability to stop, spin, and gallop circles under complete rider control. Sliding stops (Figure 16-3) of 30 to 40 feet are the reining horse's trademark. The National Reining Horse Association (NRHA) is the governing body that sets the rules and conditions for the event, which has grown in popularity. Reining competitions occur throughout much of the world, and the export of reining horses to Europe and Japan is a thriving business. The NRHA Futurity is the ultimate competition and is restricted to 3-year-old horses of any breed.

CUTTING. Cutting is a sport that dates back to the beginnings of rodeo. It grew out of the necessity of range cowboys to separate or "cut" one cow from the rest of the herd and hold that animal out of the herd for a period of time to be doctored or penned with a different group. It has evolved into a competition in which a horse is allowed 2 1/2 minutes

FIGURE 16-3

A reining horse. (Courtesy K.C. Montgomery.)

to demonstrate its ability to quietly enter a herd of cattle and drive out and separate a single animal and hold that animal out of the herd while other riders, called "turnback help," drive the animal back toward the herd. The horse is judged on its ability to hold the cow in positions by countering each move without help from the rider. The National Cutting Horse Association (NCHA) is the body that standardized the rules and conditions under which the event is conducted. Like reining, cutting can be found around the world. The premier event, the NCHA Futurity, is restricted to 3-year-old horses.

RACING. Racing is called the "Sport of Kings," owing that title to the fact that in Europe in the sixteenth and seventeenth centuries, only the nobility could afford horses to race. Today, horse racing is a worldwide, multibillion-dollar sport that encompasses people from all walks of life. Purses for race horses in the United States topped $890 million dollars in 1994. Most of the purse money comes from taxes on wagers called pari-mutuel. In most states 18% of the money wagered on a race is deducted from the betting pool before winning bets are paid off. About one-third of that percentage is then used as purse money for the winning horses. For example, if the handle (amount of money bet) at a track for one day was $1 million, then $60,000 would be available for purse money. The other 2/3 of the mutual tax is divided between the track operators and the state in which the track is located. Thoroughbreds, Standardbreds, and Quarter Horses comprise the majority of race horses although Paints, Appaloosas, and Arabians may also race at certain tracks. The racehorse industry often is under economic pressure because of casino-type gaming establishments and the number of states with lotteries. Still, the Kentucky Derby, Breeders Cup, and All American Quarter Horse Futurity are high-profile events that attract huge crowds and large sums of money are wagered. It is not uncommon for several racehorses to win over a million dollars each year.

HUNTERS AND JUMPERS. Across many parts of the southeastern United States the sport of fox hunting is a favorite pastime of many horse enthusiasts. These hunts are highly organized and full of tradition. It is much less about catching a fox than taking a favorite mount in English tack out to the field to gallop behind the hounds, jumping the fences and obstacles found on the land. Thoroughbreds and Warmbloods are the predominant breeds used in this activity because of their height and jumping ability.

Hunters are a class of show horses that evolved from the field hunters. They perform in competition judged on suitability for the hunt field and style of jumping. Although there are hunter divisions in many breed associations, the American Horse Shows Association is the main sanctioning body for hunters and jumpers. The premier event is the National Horse Show held annually in Madison Square Garden.

Some horses are shown strictly on their ability to jump. Show jumping is a high-profile, high-money event in which horses jump a course of up to 15 jumps that can be as much as six feet high and equally wide. The object is to jump the course without knocking down or refusing any of the fences. Show jumping is an international and Olympic sport that attracts media attention around the world. Thoroughbreds and Warmbloods predominate in the sport because of their size and speed, although other breeds are occasionally represented.

Dressage is a discipline in which precision and control of the horse is judged in the performance of a prescribed pattern. Horses begin at what is termed the "training" level and, after years of schooling, demonstrate complex maneuvers. Dressage too is an Olympic sport, represented in this country by the United States Dressage Federation. As in show jumping and hunters, Thoroughbreds and Warmbloods predominate in this sport.

Eventing is a sport which combines the precision of dressage and the athleticism of show jumping with a third phase of competition known as cross country. Each of these competitions are held on successive days, hence the title "three-day eventing." The cross-country phase is done on a course that tests the courage and endurance of both horse and rider with some very large and imposing obstacles (Figure 16-4). Training for these events is demanding and only the best-fit horses and riders compete successfully.

TRAIL RIDING. Not all horse activities are competitive. One of the most popular non-competitive activities is trail riding. There are trail riding organizations in many states that conduct organized rides throughout the year. These are activities whose purpose is to provide a relaxed form of entertainment.

FIGURE 16-4

A horse jumping a cross-country obstacle in a 3-day event. (Courtesy Don R. Topliff. West Texas A & M University.)

HORSE CARE AND HEALTH PROGRAMS

To manage horses effectively and ensure their health and well being, one must be able to recognize and understand what is "normal" before one can detect and treat the abnormal. There are both physiological and behavioral norms that can be assessed to determine the status of the horse. Some physiological measurements used to make these assessments are briefly described.

Body Temperature

The normal core body temperature of the horse ranges from 100 to 101 °F and averages 100.5 °F. Body temperature is a valuable measure of the horse's health but must be correlated with other factors before a decision can be made about its significance and what action, if any, should be taken. It is rare for a horse's core temperature to be significantly below 99 °F, but temperatures up to 105 °F are common. The significance of a temperature reading that is higher than normal depends on the circumstances. For example, if a horse is standing in the sun on a hot, humid day, a temperature of 102 °F would be acceptable. Conversely, a temperature of 102 °F on a cool day when the horse had not been exercising would be cause for concern. Horses that have been exercised intensely on a hot day could have a core temperature of 105 °F and recover back to normal without medical intervention. In general, when the temperature reaches 104 °F and exercise is not the cause, medical attention is advisable. A body temperature of 106 °F or higher may be fatal if steps are not taken immediately to lower it.

Heart Rate

Perhaps the most sensitive measure of a horse's overall status is heart rate. The normal resting heart rate for an adult horse is 36 to 48 beats per minute (bpm). Resting heart rate can be affected by level of fitness as in humans, but the effect is not as profound. An extremely fit horse might have a resting heart rate between 25 and 30 bpm and the most unfit horse a resting heart rate of 50 to 55 bpm. In general, a resting heart rate above 70 bpm in the absence of any other factor is cause for concern. Resting heart rate can be easily taken by placing the middle finger under the horse's jaw to find the submandibular artery, which lies just beneath the skin. Once the pulse is detected, count the number of pulses for 15 seconds and multiply by four to obtain the heart rate.

Respiration Rate

The normal resting respiration rate for an adult horse is about 18 breaths per minute. Respiration rate, however, is most closely associated with internal temperature and is one of the major mechanisms that horses use to rid themselves of excess heat. A horse that has accumulated excess heat for any reason, be it from exercise, an inflammatory disease process, or standing in the sun on a hot humid day, will have an increased respiration rate. The oxygen debt and increased concentration of carbon dioxide in the blood as a result of strenuous exercise will also cause respiration rate to rise. Respiration rates near 150 breaths per minute are common in horses that have been strenuously exercised on a hot day. As a single indicator, respiration rate is a poor measure of the status of the horse. However, when taken together with other measurements, it is useful in deciding if the horse needs medical attention.

State of Hydration

Skin turgor is an indication of the state of hydration. To measure skin turgor, pull up a flap of skin on the neck or shoulder. When the flap is released, it should immediately snap back flat. If the skin remains in a peak, it is an indication that the horse is dehydrated. Check to make sure that the horse has unlimited access to clean, fresh water. In severe cases of dehydration a veterinarian may need to administer fluids intravenously.

Packed cell volume (PCV) is also a measure of the state of hydration. Normal packed cell volume is in the 36 to 39% range. Values above 42% indicate dehydration. Extreme excitement may cause the PCV to rise irrespective of the horse's state of hydration.

The horse normally forms a relatively firm fecal ball that retains its shape upon hitting the ground, but can be broken by light pressure from the foot. If fecal balls are very hard, it is an indication of dehydration. Extremely soft feces that resemble those of the cow may indicate a bacterial upset in the hindgut of the horse; this can be caused by sudden changes in diet composition or by the ingestion of lush forage or pasture by an unadapted horse. Watery feces and diarrhea are of particular concern because dehydration and death can ensue if left untreated.

Behavior Patterns

The behavior patterns of a horse can indicate normality or abnormality. Behavior patterns vary much more widely among horses than do other physiological measurements, and the indications are less quantitative and, in some cases, purely subjective. Nonetheless, these behavior signs are important in successful horse management. Obvious and serious signs include a droopy demeanor about the head and ears or failure to come to eat at feeding time. Biting at the flank and/or lying down are also important cues that the horse needs medical attention.

Capillary Refill Time and Blood Pressure

Other physical indications of the horse's status include capillary refill time and blood pressure. Capillary refill time is measured by pressing the thumb firmly against the horse's gums above the upper incisors for a few seconds and then releasing. Initially the gums will be white from the lack of blood and then return to a nice pink color as the capillaries refill with blood. This should take about one second to occur. Capillary refill times exceeding three seconds indicate a lack of blood flow to the extremities and low blood pressure. The ears may also feel cold and clammy.

Colic

Colic is a generic term that means abdominal pain usually due to involvement of a portion of the gastrointestinal tract. It is a symptom rather than a specific disease. There are many causes of colic including overeating, internal parasite infestation, rapid diet change, lack of water, reproductive events in mares, and general stress. Even changes in the weather can bring on episodes of colic in some horses. Signs of colic can include elevated heart rate, distension of the abdomen, slowed capillary refill time, cold and clammy-feeling extremities, biting of the flanks, lying down, and rolling. The correct treatment of a particular colic depends on the portion of the digestive tract involved. Therefore, it is advisable to seek veterinary care as soon as it is detected. Severe colic may indicate pending rupture or necrosis of a section of the gut and is one of the leading causes of death among horses. Fortunately, colic is a problem that can be significantly reduced by proper health care and feeding management.

Founder

Founder is the lay term for the disease, laminitis. It is caused by many of the same circumstances as colic and disrupts or blocks the blood flow in the hoof, resulting in oxygen shortage to the hoof and death of the tissues that connect the outer covering of the hoof to the underlying bone, the third phalanx or coffin bone. In severe cases, the coffin bone may penetrate the sole of the horse's foot. The horse must then be humanely destroyed. Fortunately, colic and founder can be significantly reduced by proper health care and feeding management.

Every horse needs a health maintenance program that includes a base vaccination program and internal parasite control. Different regions of the country require slightly different approaches to health care and the owner should consult with a local veterinarian to address specific concerns for a given area.

Vaccinations

The base immunization program should be developed in consultation with a veterinarian. Vaccinations for eastern and western equine encephalomyelitis (EEE and WEE), commonly referred to as "sleeping sickness," tetanus, and equine influenza are the most common. Horses located east of the Missouri river may also be vaccinated for Potomac Horse Fever and horses located in states that border Mexico may be vaccinated for Venezuelan equine encephalomyelitis (VEE). In addition, breeding farms routinely vaccinate for Rhinopneumonitis (Equine Herpes I), which causes abortion in mares in the last trimester of gestation. In some cases it is advisable to immunize against strangles, caused by the bacterium, *Streptococcus equi,* which causes swelling and rupture of the lymph nodes under the jaw. Most immunizations begin when the foal reaches 60 to 90 days of age with a series of two vaccinations, four to six weeks apart. Yearly boosters are sufficient to maintain a reasonable level of immunity for VEE, WEE, tetanus, strangles, and Potomac horse fever and, in most cases, Equine influenza. Additional boosters may be needed for protection against EEE and rhinopneumonitis, particularly in pregnant mares.

Internal Parasite Control

Control of internal parasites is accomplished by treatment with anthelmintic agents (dewormers). A number of internal parasites can cause significant health risks and even death. Most internal parasites are ingested by the horse when grazing, nosing around on the bare ground, or licking egg cases attached to hair shafts on the front legs. Others are carried by an intermediate host. The common internal parasites, their effects, and routes of infestation are shown in Table 16-5. Owners should consult with their local veterinarians to develop a control program. Some factors that increase the risk of high internal parasite loads are high concentration of horses, areas of high rainfall, poor sanitation practices, and confining horses in dry lots. At the minimum, horses need to be dewormed twice per year, once in the spring and once in the fall, and at the maximum every 60 days. A list of the commonly used anthelmintics is given in Table 16-6.

Hoof Care

Horses that are kept in stalls, dry lots, or pastures that are not abrasive need hoof care on a routine basis. When hooves become excessively long they tend to break off and may cause lameness in the horse. To avoid this, a farrier can trim the excess hoof wall every 6

TABLE 16-5

COMMON INTERNAL PARASITES, THEIR LIFE CYCLES AND ROUTES OF INFESTATION

Strongyles
(*S. Vulgaris, S. Edentatus,* and Small Strongyles)
Life Cycle: Eggs are in the feces—1st- and 2nd-stage larvae in feces or soil and larvae become infective after one week—3rd-stage larvae present in water droplets on vegetation, stable walls, and such—Larvae are ingested via contaminated feed or water—4th-stage larvae move throughout the body and especially the anterior mesenteric artery where they cause inflammation—Six months later larvae become adults and are attached to the mucous membranes of the cecum and colon—Eggs are then deposited in feces
Route of Infestation: Ingestion of fecal-contaminated food or water

Ascarids
Life Cycle: One-celled eggs are in feces—1–2 weeks later 2nd-stage larvae become infective—Larvae are ingested via contaminated feed or water—Migrating larvae travel through the liver, then lungs, and are coughed up, then swallowed—Three months later the adult matures in the small intestine—Eggs are then deposited in feces
Route of Infestation: Ingestion of fecal-contaminated food or water

Stomach Bots
Life Cycle: Pupae present in soil—Adult flies deposit eggs containing 1st-stage larvae on forearm and chin—Eggs hatch and enter mouth via licking—1st-stage larvae migrates through the mouth—2nd-stage larvae—3rd-stage larvae attach to mucosa of stomach and intestines—Bot larvae detach and pass out with feces (entire cycle takes one year)
Route of Infestation: Licking of eggs or 1st-stage pupae "crawl" from chin to mouth edges

Pinworm
Life Cycle: Eggs attached to skin around anus—In 4–5 days attachment dries up and eggs fall from skin—Infective eggs are ingested off of feed or stable walls—4th-stage larvae are attached to large intestine—Five months later larvae mature into adult—Adult migrates to anus and attaches eggs to skin
Route of Infestation: Ingestion via contaminated feed or water

---

to 8 weeks. Unless the horse is being ridden on rocky terrain or has other special needs, shoeing is not normally necessary.

Tooth Care

Horses should have their teeth examined yearly and dental care provided as needed. The primary concern with a horse's teeth are the development of "points" on the molars or jaw teeth. The upper arcade of teeth is set outside of the lower arcade, which allows the horse to "grind" its food. In the wild, horses apparently ingest enough sand and dirt to keep the teeth ground down. Domestic horses, however, may develop razor-sharp points on the outside of the upper teeth and the inside of the lower teeth. These points tend to cut and irritate the cheeks and tongue, making eating uncomfortable.

Affected horses tend to slobber their food and can often be observed turning their

TABLE 16-6

COMMONLY USED ANTHELMINTICS AND THEIR PERCENT EFFECTIVENESS ON VARIOUS INTERNAL PARASITES

| Active Anthelmintic* | Bots | Ascarids | Strongyles | | | Pinworms |
			S. Vulgaris	S. Edentatus	Small	
Ivermectin[a]	95–100	90–100	95–100	95–100	95–100	95–100
Fenbendazole[b]	0	90–100	90–100	90–100	90–100	90–100
Cambendazole[c]	0	95–100	95–100	95–100	95–100	95–100
Mebendazole[d]	0	95–100	95–100	65–95	80–95	95–100
Oxibendazole[e]	0	90–100	95–100	95–100	95–100	95–100
Dichlorvos[f]	80–100	95–100	95–100	70–80	85–95	90–100
Pyrantel[g]	0	90–100	95–100	65–75	90–100	60–70

*Corresponding Trade Names:
[a]Eqvalan
[b]Panacur
[c]Camvet
[d]Telmin
[e]Anthelcide-EQ
[f]Equigard
[g]Strongid-T or P

head sideways to chew in an effort to get the cheek tissue away from the teeth. Neglect of dental care can lead to weight loss and increased feed cost. To correct the problem an instrument called a "tooth float" is used to file down the sharp points. "Floating" a horse's teeth is very difficult and dangerous work.

NUTRITION

Horses are classified as nonruminant herbivores. They have characteristics of both ruminants and nonruminants. Because they are an animal of flight, their digestive system is designed to consume small meals on a frequent basis (Figure 16-5). Their stomach is relatively small and the rate of passage of food through the stomach and small intestine is quite rapid (4 hours). Digestion typical of other nonruminants occurs here and allows horses to take advantage of high-quality nutrients such as those found in the springtime grass. The fibrous portion of the diet that requires bacterial enzymes to digest is processed in the cecum and large intestine, termed the "hind gut." Here the resident microbial population breaks down the fibrous material by fermentation and releases short-chain fatty acids which are absorbed. The bacteria also synthesize vitamins and amino acids which are excreted in the feces. In times of shortage or low-quality foodstuffs such as dead winter grass, the horse ingests these nutrients by coprophagy. Horses, rabbits, and several species of rodents practice coprophagy, which allows them to survive in the wild. Domestic horses that are properly cared for generally do not manifest this behavior. If they do, it is usually related to boredom.

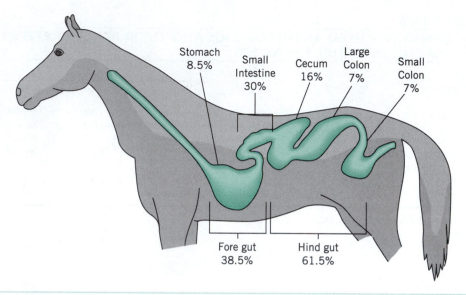

FIGURE 16-5

Schematic diagram of the horse's digestive tract.

Guidelines on the nutrient requirements of the horse are established by the National Research Council (NRC). These requirements are related to the size, age, and productive state of the horse as well as the environment.

Energy

Energy is the single biggest nutrient need for horses. Energy required for maintenance is a function of body weight. Energy is also required to heat and cool the horse, so environment plays a crucial role in the horse's energy needs. The amount of body fat and hair also play a crucial role. Body fat and hair insulate horses, preventing heat loss, an advantage at cold temperatures but a disadvantage at hot temperatures. Mares can produce up to 3% of their body weight daily in milk, essentially doubling the energy requirement. A summary of nutrients and factors that affect their requirement is shown in Table 16-7. It is difficult to predict an individual horse's energy needs on a short-term basis. However, over the long-term, estimating body fat using a scale developed by researchers at Texas A&M University (Table 16-8) is a useful way to adjust feed intake.

Protein

An adult horse requires about 8.5% crude protein in the diet. Most feeds are significantly higher than that in protein. Providing adequate feed to meet the energy requirement also meets the protein requirement of the adult horse. For the growing horse and lactating

TABLE 16-7
NUTRIENTS AND FACTORS THAT AFFECT THEIR REQUIREMENTS

Nutrient	Factor	Effect
Energy	Heat	Increase by as much as 20%
	Cold	Increase by up to 100%
	Growth	Depends on age & growth rate
	Milk production	Increase up to 100%
	Work	Increase from 10–100%
Protein	Heat	No increase
	Cold	No Increase
	Growth	Depends on age & growth rate
	Milk production	Increase by 70–100%
	Work	Increase by 10% or less
Vitamins	Heat	No effect
	Cold	No effect
	Growth	Depends on age & growth rate
	Milk production	Increase*
	Work	Slight increase
Minerals	Heat	No effect
	Cold	No effect
	Growth	Increase in proportion to growth
	Milk production	Increase by up to 100%
	Work	Increase in proportion to losses in sweat
Water	Heat	Increase
	Cold	Decease
	Growth	Increase in proportion to size
	Milk production	Increase in proportion to production
	Work	Increase in proportion to sweat and respiratory losses

*Metabolic requirements for most vitamins are increased during lactation in proportion to the amount of milk produced, but most of the water-soluble vitamins are supplied by microbial synthesis in the rumen of cows, sheep, and other ruminant animals.

mare, additional protein needs can be met by feeding alfalfa hay, which contains up to 18% crude protein, or by adding a small amount of a protein supplement such as soybean meal to the grain. The exercising adult horse does not require protein supplementation to a normal diet.

Vitamins

Most vitamins are contained in sufficient amounts in the diet to meet the requirement. The one vitamin commonly added to commercial rations is Vitamin A. Deficiencies of the other vitamins are rare and the addition of vitamin supplements is usually not warranted. Advertisements for various supplements may tempt owners to spend money unnecessarily for little or no benefit.

TABLE 16-8

DESCRIPTION OF THE BODY CONDITION SCORING SYSTEM

1 Poor—Animal extremely thin. Backbone, ribs, tailhead, hooks and pins, withers, and shoulders project prominently. No fat tissues can be felt.

2 Very Thin—Animal thin. Limited fat over bottom of spinous processes. Withers, shoulders, and neck structures are faintly visible.

3 Thin—Fat has built up about halfway on spinous processes, with the transverse processes unable to be felt. Small fat cover over ribs yet they are still visible. Hook bones are visible but pins cannot be discerned.

4 Moderately Thin—Slight outline of ribs visible. Prominence of tailhead depends on conformation. Hook bones are not visible.

5 Moderate—Back is level. Ribs cannot be seen, but can still be felt. Area around tailhead becomes soft. Shoulders and neck blend smoothly with body.

6 Moderate to Fleshy—Slight crease down back. Fat over ribs feels soft. Fat deposits begin to form around withers, behind shoulders, and along the neck.

7 Fleshy—Definite crease down back. Individual ribs can be felt, but fat deposits are forming between ribs.

8 Fat—Prominent crease down back. Ribs difficult to feel. Neck begins to thicken. Fat deposits form along inner hip and gaskin.

9 Extremely Fat—Very obvious crease down back. Bulging fat around tailhead, withers, neck. Flanks are filled in flush.

Minerals

The two minerals of greatest concern are calcium and phosphorus, which need to be included in the diet in the proper amount and ratio. Commercially prepared rations from reputable companies contain the proper amounts and ratios of these and other minerals. Excessive minerals can be toxic to horses, so caution should be used when providing mineral supplements.

Water

One of the most often neglected nutrients is water. A horse that goes without water for as little as 24 hours during hot weather is at risk. Clean, fresh water should be provided at all times with the exception of just after exercise, when the horse should be allowed to cool down before unlimited access is given. Allowing the horse to consume a half-gallon of water every 15 minutes during cool-down will speed up the process. At all other times water intake should not be restricted.

Feeds and Feeding Management

Horses can consume a variety of feedstuffs, contrary to popular myth. When horses suffer from a feed-related illness, generally the cause is not *what* the horse was fed, but rather *how* it was fed. Some feedstuffs are much more easily managed because of a low nutrient density. Those feeds have a larger "margin for error" and therefore are safer for the average horse owner to use. Oats and grass hay such as timothy or bermuda grass are examples of relatively safe feeds. They also tend to be expensive and in horses requiring large amounts of nutrients in a small amount of intake, safety may need to be sacrificed for performance.

Horses can be safely fed a variety of grains, including corn, barley, wheat, milo, rice; silages, including corn and sorghum silage; hays, including alfalfa, bermuda grass, orchard grass, and native prairie hay; protein supplements, including corn gluten feed, brewer's yeast, whey, casein, soybean meal, cottonseed meal, linseed meal, cottonseed hulls, soybean hulls, rice hulls, rice bran, wheat bran; and mineral supplements, including Ca and P (ground limestone, dicalcium phosphate, monosodium phosphate), and common salt (Na Cl) containing trace minerals. Table 16-9 contains a list of the common feed ingredients and the nutritional attributes of each.

For most horse owners, the safest alternative is to feed a commercially prepared feed from a reputable company according to the directions on the bag. Processing of feed ingredients is usually done to improve the availability of the nutrients and a variety of processing methods are commonly used for horse feeds. Processing of most feed ingredients improves availability by only 5 to 10% and does add appreciably to the cost of the feed. Often the cost outweighs the benefits. Pelleting allows the use of feed ingredients that tend to separate or sift out. It also eliminates the sorting of feed ingredients by the horse. Extrusion is another method of including nontraditional feed ingredients and at the same time improving the safety of the feed by decreasing the weight per unit of volume. Table 16-10 summarizes the most common processing methods used in feed manufacturing, the feedstuffs they are commonly used on, the relative cost of each, and the effects of their use.

The horse is a continuous feeder by nature that is designed to live primarily on forage. When the horse is placed in a 12 × 12 stall and fed once a day a ration that does not

TABLE 16-9

COMMONLY USED FEEDS AND THEIR PROPERTIES*

Feed	Energy Mcal/lb.	Protein %	Fiber %	Fat %	Calcium %	Phosphorus %
Oats	1.45	13	12	5	.09	.38
Corn	1.76	10	3	4	.05	.36
Wheat	1.75	14	3	4	.08	.38
Milo	1.60	12	3	3	.04	.36
Barley	1.67	13	6	2	.05	.38
Brome hay	.97	14	32	2	.29	.28
Timothy hay	.90	10	34	2	.48	.23
Alfalfa hay	1.00	18	28	2	1.4	.21
Prairie hay	.74	6	34	2	.35	.14
Soybean meal	1.60	50	7	2	.40	.71
Soybean oil	4.00	0	0	100	0	0

*Dry matter basis.

TABLE 16-10

PROCESSING METHODS USED FOR HORSE FEEDS

1. Whole grain
Definition: Entire kernel of grain is present with no mechanical or chemical processing used.
Advantages: Low cost because of no processing charge.
Disadvantages: Lower digestibility resulting in lower gain and more fecal waste.

2. Rolled
Definition: The process of compacting grain between two smooth or corrugated rolls. Product is either cracked in the case of hard grain like corn, or crimped for oats and barley.
Advantages: Better digestibility.
Disadvantages: More fine particles and dust, have to pay processing charge.

3. Steam flaked
Definition: Grain is passed through a hot steam tower to raise the moisture content to 18–20%, then the grain is rolled to produce a flat flake.
Advantages: Higher digestibilities and gains. Less fine particles and dust.
Disadvantage: Higher cost and increases storage loss due to spoilage.

4. Pelleting
Definition: Grinding of feed ingredients then forcing with steam and pressure through a mold to form a compact product.
Advantages: Can incorporate an entire ration into pellet, resulting in less waste due to animal sorting out feedstuffs. Easier handling and less dust.
Disadvantages: Higher cost. Animals may rapidly eat pellets that are not compressed to a hard consistency, resulting in colic.

5. Extruding
Definition: Similar to pelleting except the grain is brought to a boil and then forced through a mold where air is injected into the feed, resulting in a bulkier product. Most dry pet foods are extruded.
Advantages: Same as pellets, but animals tend to eat slower due to the bulkier product.
Disadvantages: High cost. Not widely available for equine diets.

6. Wafers or cubes
Definition: Roughage is dried and ground, then packed into a wafer or cube about 2 in. tall. Usually used for alfalfa or other hay products.
Advantage: Easily handled, and more consistent product.
Disadvantages: High cost. Problems with choking have been observed.

contain adequate forage, the consequences can be deadly. Here are 10 feeding management rules that, if strictly followed, will minimize the chances of feed-related illness:

1. *Always feed at least 1% of the horse's body weight daily in long-stem roughage.* Either hay or pasture is satisfactory.

2. *Feed by weight, not by volume.* A 3-pound coffee can only weighs 3 pounds when filled with coffee. It weighs 4 pounds filled with oats and 5 1/2 pounds filled with corn. A bale of hay may vary greatly in weight, depending on the type of hay and how tightly the hay-baler packed it.

3. *Never feed more than 8 pounds of grain at one feeding.* If more is required, increase the number of feedings and space them equally.

4. *Never force horses to compete for food.* When group feeding horses, provide at least one feeder for each horse. Also, spread the feeders out such that the dominant horse cannot control access to several feeders. Pour feed into all feeders as quickly as possible.

5. *Provide unlimited access to clean fresh water at all times.* Clean waterers daily. Poor water intake is a major cause of colic in horses. In the winter, heating the water to 45–50 °F will increase water intake. If automatic waterers are used, they should be checked frequently to insure proper operation. Waterers with electric heating elements should be checked frequently for electrical leakage. (Horses are extremely sensitive to electricity and even a small current will deter them drinking.)

6. *Feed only grains and hays free from dust and mold.* Grains should have high test weights and hays should be leafy, immature, and free of weeds. Green color may be indicative of vitamin A content but does not indicate high energy or protein content.

7. *Maintain a regular internal parasite control program.* Large infections of the parasite, *Strongylus vulgaris,* can cause blockage of blood flow to the digestive tract, resulting in colic and/or death.

8. *Concentrates need to be at least 10% crude fiber.* Concentrates less than 10% crude fiber require careful feeding management.

9. *Encourage the horse to eat slowly.* Feed the complete ration at each feeding. Do not feed the hay at one feeding and the grain at the next. If the horse eats very quickly, place some physical barrier such as large rocks in the feed pan to slow eating. Feeding hay first may slow grain consumption by giving the horse a sense of fullness before the grain is fed. Contrary to popular myth, this procedure does not slow the passage of grain through the digestive tract and increase digestion.

10. *Feeding schedule should be consistent.* Provide equally spaced meals, or if feeding schedule is daily, feed at the same time of day, including weekends. If ration changes are to be made, including turning the horse out on lush pastures, make the changes gradually over at least one week. Mix the new ration in with the old gradually or in the case of pasture, turn out for an increasing amount of time each day. Be observant. Horses tend to be very predictable physiologically and in their behavior patterns. Even slight changes in either are cause for investigation.

HOUSING AND CONTAINMENT

Horse owners also have a responsibility to provide safe housing for their horses. It does not have to be expensive but it does need to be clean and safe. Because horses have a high sense of curiosity, if their surroundings are not safe, serious injury can occur. Fences should be constructed of a material sturdy enough to keep the horse in and at the same time minimize the chance of injury should they run into it. Board fences or fences constructed of polyvinyl chloride (PVC) are the safest. Pipe fences are sturdy and will not scrape or cut a horse, but a high-speed collision with a pipe fence usually ends in serious injury. Cable fences with a pipe top rail are popular in some parts of the country and are very sturdy also. They have the same disadvantages as pipe fences and some types of cable are extremely abrasive and can cause serious injury to the horse. Wire fences are the least desirable as horses tend to become entangled in them. Because they are inexpensive, they are attractive to many owners. If wire fences are used, they need to be of the smooth type. Barbed wire is extremely dangerous to horses and is not recommended.

Barns should be constructed of wood, concrete, or heavy-gauge metal. Careful attention should be given so that no contact with exposed sharp metal edges is possible. If concrete is used in alleyways it should have a rough finish so that horses will not slip when it becomes wet. For mature normal-size horses, stalls should be at least 12 feet by 12 feet and should be bedded with a moisture-absorbent material such as wheat straw, oat straw, pine wood shavings (or other type of wood product), rice hulls, shredded newspaper, or grass hay. Shavings or sawdust from walnut trees should not be used as they may cause the horse to develop laminitis.

Loafing sheds enclosed on three sides to provide shelter from the elements in a paddock or pasture are recommended if they are properly constructed and placed. They should be placed on high ground or elevated so they stay dry and, like stalls, should be constructed so that no sharp edges are exposed. Horses are prone to fight when loafing shed space is restricted. It is not advisable to feed groups of horses in these loafing sheds because the dominant horse can control access to the feed and overeat, causing colic and/or founder.

RAISING HORSES

Horse breeders are a very important part of the total industry. The owner of the mare at time of breeding is considered the "breeder" of a particular foal. Mare owners often have significant money invested in both mares and facilities. Broodmares capable of producing foals that will sell for top dollar bring high prices. Breeders provide the "raw material" for the industry. They generally fall into one of three categories: (1) market breeders, (2) breeders who retain ownership of foals for competitive purposes, and (3) recreational breeders.

1. Market breeders are in the business to raise foals specifically to sell at a profit. These breeders must pay special attention to market trends and fads and are very conscious of pedigrees. They are in the business of raising what will sell.

2. Breeders who retain ownership are somewhat less concerned with pedigree. They raise horses with the idea of competing with what they raise and often their ob-

jective is to promote the specific line of horses that they own. They may sell the animals after the competition or may put those horses that competed successfully back into their breeding program.

3. The recreational breeders usually do not have a specific profit motive, although some do make significant profit selling the foals they raise. Many breeders fit into more than one of the above categories.

The stallions used to breed the majority of mares in a given breed are usually owned by people heavily involved in the industry and who have a considerable influence over the direction of it. Stallions that have performed well in competition, and therefore are likely to attract large numbers of mares to breed, tend to be expensive to purchase. The farms on which they reside, called "breeding farms" or "stallion stations," are generally very attractive and expensive in layout, labor, and overhead costs. Some farms stand stallions that belong to other individuals for a part of the breeding fee or have other financial arrangements with the owners. That particular type of business arrangement is becoming more common as stallion farms look for ways to increase revenues and reduce the risks of owning several stallions.

BREEDING HORSES

It has been written that horses are less reproductively efficient than other species of domestic livestock. One figure that is often quoted is 55%. That figure apparently came from a calculation of the number of yearling Thoroughbred foals registered in a particular year as a percentage of the number of mares bred during the corresponding breeding season. Many factors are involved in that percentage which have little to do with reproductive efficiency. It is quite common on good breeding farms to achieve conception rates above 90% and foaling rates approaching 90%. With application of modern technology and management, high reproductive efficiency is possible.

All horses in the northern hemisphere have a "universal" birth date of January 1. That means a horse born on December 31 would be considered one year old on January 1, even though it was only one day old. The origin of the universal birth date is not clear but it has remained as the method of assigning age for purposes of competition. For example, the Kentucky Derby is for 3-year-old Thoroughbreds. That means that horses born anytime during that year would be eligible. Obviously, a horse born in January would have an advantage over one born in December of the same year. But for competition purposes, they are considered to be the same age. Coupled with the fact that most of the big money events are for young horses, breeders are encouraged to breed mares to foal as close to January 1 as possible. Herein lies the problem because mares normally begin to cycle and breed in late March, April, and May. In fact, some breeds of ponies normally reach the height of the breeding season in June and July. Therefore, the first challenge faced by breeders is that the managed breeding season does not coincide with the natural breeding season.

The second challenge is nutritional. When a mare foals, the stress of foaling and producing milk creates a nutrition demand essentially double that of maintenance. A certain amount of body fat is required before a mare will cycle and conceive. If the mare was in marginal condition to begin with she will be less likely to breed or rebreed successfully and may experience lactational anestrus (she may fail to cycle until the foal is weaned). Feeding to increase her body fat to the proper level increases the risk of colic and other nutritional diseases, so the best approach is to have the mare in sufficiently good condition prior to the breeding season. Most research indicates that foaling mares should be kept at a body condition score (Table 16-8) of 6.5 to 7.5 and open mares at a body condition score of 5.5 to 6.5. Mares in good body conditions (as indicated by the condition scores in Table 16-8) are no more likely to experience dystocia (difficult foaling) than mares in thinner condition.

The Estrous Cycle

Mares are seasonally polyestrus. As the days get longer in the spring, the increasing photoperiod stimulates the onset of cyclicity and the breeding season. Because photoperiod is the main driving force for the onset of the breeding season, it can be artificially advanced with supplemental light. By exposing mares to 16 hours of daylight and 8 hours of dark beginning about December 1, mares will be cycling and ready to breed early in February. Given a gestation length of just over 11 months, foals will then be born close to the first of January, which is the solution to the first challenge mentioned previously.

Nutrition and temperature also play a role in the onset of the breeding season but the main factor is light. The increasing day length is perceived by the optic nerve and transmitted to a small structure in the brain called the pineal gland. This gland produces melatonin, which inhibits cyclicity by inhibiting the production of gonadotropin-releasing hormone (GnRH) from the hypothalamus, located at the base of the brain. Increasing day length suppresses the production of melatonin, which in turn allows the hypothalamus to produce GnRH. This hormone then stimulates the anterior pituitary, also located at the base of the brain, to produce luteinizing hormone (LH) and follicle-stimulating hormone (FSH), which stimulate the onset of the ovulatory season. This mechanism is shown graphically in Figure 16-6. As the days get shorter in the fall the process is reversed and the mares enter anestrus.

As day length increases, the mare begins a transition from the anovulatory period into the ovulatory period. This transition sometimes lasts 30 days or more and the mare may show moderate interest in the stallion but does not ovulate. Once through transition, the mare completes an estrous cycle every 21 to 23 days. The endocrine relationships and stages in the estrous cycle were described in Chapter 4. The mare will ovulate about 24 hours prior to the end of estrus and if sperm are present, fertilization and conception will occur.

Breeding Methods

The three most common methods of breeding mares are (1) pasture breeding, (2) hand mating, and (3) artificial insemination.

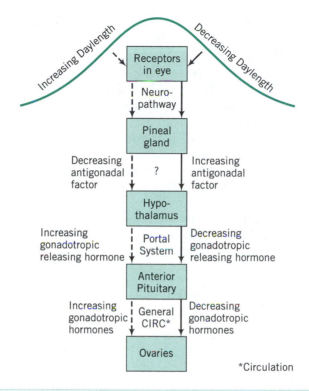

FIGURE 16-6

Schematic diagram of photoperiod mechanism triggering the onset of the breeding season.

1. *Pasture breeding.* This is the simplest and least labor-intensive method. The mares and stallion are simply turned out together in a pasture and mother nature handles the rest. Even though the conception rates resulting from pasture breeding can be very good, this method is dangerous to both mares and stallions. Young, inexperienced stallions can be severely injured by mares and young mares can be injured by a seasoned stallion, although this occurrence is much less frequent. One of the keys to a successful pasture breeding program is to have a pasture large enough for the stallion and his mare band. The acreage required will depend on the number of mares running with the stallion at a given time. A mature stallion can handle a band of about 30 mares under this type of management.

2. *Hand mating.* Hand mating requires knowledge of the mare's estrous cycle and some additional facilities and labor. It is most commonly practiced in the Thoroughbred industry because the breed association does not allow the use of artificial insemination as the primary means of breeding a mare. Once the mare is determined to be in estrus (heat) and ready to breed, she is brought to the breeding shed. The mare is often restrained with a set of breeding hobbles so that she cannot kick and injure the stallion. The stallion is then led to the mare and allowed to mount and breed the mare. High conception rates are also possible with hand

mating and the number of mares can be increased to 60 mares per stallion with little problem.

3. *Artificial insemination (AI).* AI is widely used by the horse industry. The stallion is brought to the breeding shed and mounts a phantom mare (sometimes called a breeding dummy). The stallion then services a device called an artificial vagina (AV) and his semen is collected in a bottle at the end of the AV. An amount of the semen that has been determined to contain sufficient numbers of spermatozoa is then transferred into mares that are in estrus and ready to breed. This method minimizes the risk to both stallion and mare and allows for the greatest number of mares to be bred to a single stallion. As many as 800 mares have been bred to a single stallion in a breeding season with good results, although a more reasonable number is 200 mares. AI is also effective in controlling sexually transmitted diseases. The Thoroughbred industry has experienced outbreaks of sexually transmitted diseases that have virtually brought that industry to a standstill at various times because of their reluctance to accept AI as the primary means of breeding mares.

Pregnancy and Parturition

The fertilized ovum will descend into the uterus about 5 to 6 days after ovulation and will float about the uterus until day 14. Beginning about day 10 the embryo and embryonic vesicle can be detected with an ultrasound scanner. At day 14 the uterus develops significant tone and "traps" the vesicle in place, although the embryo does not begin to attach to the uterus until about 45 days into gestation. By day 25, ultrasound can detect a heart beat in the embryo. Figure 16-7 shows various stages of embryonic development from

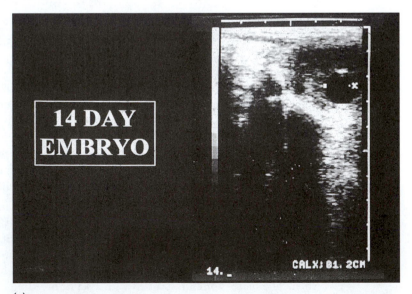

(a)

FIGURE 16-7

Ultrasonic images showing embryonic development from day 14 to day 48 of gestation. (Courtesy Don R. Topliff. West Texas A & M University.)

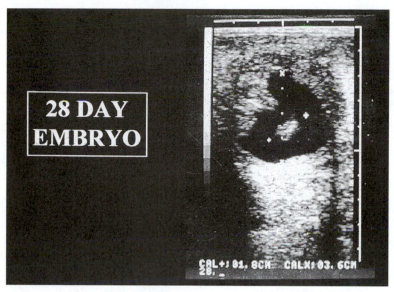

(b)

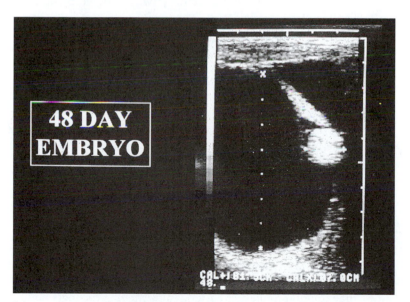

(c)

FIGURE 16-7 *(continued)*

day 14 to day 48 of gestation. From day 45 until day 145 the process of placentation or attachment of the fetus to the uterus continues. After the process is complete the foal continues to grow until it reaches term at about 340 days. Gestation lengths in mares do vary considerably and range from 325 to 365 days. The length of gestation is affected by nutrition, photoperiod, breed, and latitude.

Once the mare nears full term, she will likely begin to exhibit signs that indicate she is near foaling. Foaling can be done outside in a grassy paddock, weather permitting, or in a foaling stall that is sufficiently large to allow plenty of room for the mare. Foaling stalls should be at least 14 feet by 14 feet at a minimum. Stalls that are 16 feet by 16 feet or 12 feet by 24 feet are preferable. The stall should be bedded deeply enough to provide ample cushion for the mare when she lies down. Straw or grass hay are the most common bedding materials used in foaling stalls. Shavings tend to be dusty and can suffocate a foal should its nose be pushed down into the bedding during foaling.

About two weeks prior to foaling the muscles over the mare's croup (top of the hip) begin to relax and feel almost jelly-like. About one week prior the mare's udder and teats will fill out and look ready to produce milk. Approximately 48 hours before foaling a wax-like substance will accumulate on the end of the teats and the mare may actually begin to drip milk. Immediately before foaling the mare will begin to exhibit signs of colic or abdominal pain which usually indicates that the preliminary uterine contractions have begun. The mare may actually sweat and will be up and down and looking at her flank in obvious pain.

The next event is the presentation of the fetal membranes containing amniotic and allantoic fluids ("water bag"). Shortly after the "water bag" breaks, the mare commences hard labor. The foal is usually born 30 to 45 minutes later. If this stage of parturition lasts longer than one hour, qualified help should be summoned immediately. Dystocia is uncommon in mares, but when it occurs, it can result in death of the foal or mare or both.

In normal birth, the front feet of the foal appear first with the nose resting on the front legs, which point downward. If not, the foal is either backward or upside down, either of which requires immediate medical attention. See Chapter 4 (Figure 4-11) for a diagram of abnormal presentation of the newborn in cattle.

Care of the Newborn Foal

Immediately after the foal has been delivered, check to see that the placenta is not covering the nostrils and that the foal is breathing on its own. Shortly thereafter the placenta will separate from the foal, leaving an umbilical stump that should be treated with an iodine solution to prevent bacteria from entering the foal's body. If everything appears normal it is best to leave the mare and foal alone for a short time so that they can bond and the foal can nurse. The foal's first steps are important in the development of neuromuscular coordination, so it is best to allow the foal to stand on its own. The first steps will be very clumsy, but the foal will learn to stand and walk without help under most circumstances. The foal should stand and nurse within about two hours. If the foal does not nurse within two hours, experienced assistance will likely be necessary.

On many farms, a blood sample is drawn from the foal at about 12 hours after birth to determine the extent to which the foal has absorbed antibodies from the mare's first milk (colostrum). Colostral antibodies are detected by an IgG test that determines the level of passive immunity the foal received from the mare's milk. If the level of protection is low, the foal may need additional antibodies, which can be obtained either from feeding the foal additional colostrum from a pooled supply taken from other mares (a colostrum "bank") or a transfusion of plasma from geldings that have been hyperimmunized. When the foal is 24 to 48 hours old it is best to move it outside. There are far more pathogens in the barn, no matter how clean, than in the fresh outdoors. Young, healthy foals can withstand nasty weather more successfully than they can withstand nasty bacteria in a barn. If they are to be kept in a barn, the temperature should not be maintained above 50 °F and the barn must be well ventilated.

Rearing the Foal

Rearing a foal for competitive purposes can be a challenge. In some competitions, maximum growth at an early age is paramount to success. Even in the sale ring, size is important. If the foal is to obtain maximum growth rates, careful management must be used. By the time the foal is 60 days old, the nutrient needs for maximum growth are already greater than the nutrients supplied by the mare's milk. Therefore, supplemental feed (termed creep feed) must be supplied. The creep feed must be of the highest quality, and special attention must be given to feeding management. An example of an acceptable creep feed is shown in Table 16-11. Fresh creep feed should be available continuously to

TABLE 16-11
CREEP FEED FORMULATION

Feed	% (DM Basis)
Oats	44.5
Corn	18.0
Soybean Meal	15.0
Skim Milk (dried)	10.0
Dehydrated Alfalfa	5.0
Molasses	5.0
Limestone	0.4
Dical	1.1
TM Salt	0.5
Vitamin Premix	0.5
Nutrient analysis	
Crude Protein	18.1
Calcium	0.71
Phosphorus	0.52
DE	1.37 Mcal/lb

encourage the foal to eat small amounts frequently so as to avoid overeating after filling an empty feeder. Foals nurse the mare as many as 70 times per day, which indicates the necessity of continuous access. Also the feed should be placed such that the mare cannot gain access to it.

During this period of life, deworming and vaccination programs are also important. Most vaccination programs start at about 60 to 90 days of age. Young foals that become sick may grow poorly and therefore be less competitive. Internal parasites can slow growth by as much as 20%, so an effective control program is necessary. Foals are also particularly susceptible to roundworms (parascaris equorum), so deworming with a product that is effective against this internal parasite is important. Foals can be dewormed beginning as early as ten days of age and should be dewormed every 60 days thereafter or placed on a recommended program of oral anthelmintics.

Rapid growth rate is important in many segments of the horse industry. However, rapid growth has also been linked to some developmental orthopedic diseases (DOD) such as physitis and osteochondrosis. The mechanisms involved in these diseases are not well understood. They appear to be multifactorial problems that involve genetics, diet, exercise, housing, and management. The most prudent course of action appears to be to feed a properly balanced diet in amounts to maintain moderate body condition (condition score of 4.5 to 5.5, Table 16-8) and house the foal outside as much as possible while limiting forced exercise. Even under the best management, developmental problems can occur and it appears unlikely that a cure for all of these problems will be found in the near future. Further, in segments of the industry in which a premium is placed on large size at an early age, a conservative nutrition program that limits foal growth in an attempt to avoid DOD results only in a noncompetitive foal.

The foal is commonly weaned at four to six months of age. By that time the mare's milk production has begun to decline and the foal's nutrient needs are much greater than the mare can supply. Also, the stress of lactation may reduce the mare's body condition score and make her difficult to rebreed. The stress of weaning on the foal is lessened by consuming creep feed. Weaning can be accomplished by abrupt and complete separation in which the mare and foal are quickly separated with the foal placed in a stall and the mare removed to a location where the foal cannot see, smell, or hear its mother. It is less stressful to wean foals in pairs by a technique called partial separation. In this method, two foals are placed in a stall together and their mothers are placed in stalls on either side of them where the foals can see, hear, and smell their mothers, but the physical barrier of the stall prevents the foal from nursing. In about five days, the foals will not even know whether or not mother is present. If the foal has not been broken to lead, this is also a good time to do so.

From weaning until horses begin their training as long yearlings or as early 2-year-olds, the main concerns are to keep them healthy and growing at a consistent rate. To do so, owners should feed them a properly balanced ration, maintain a consistent vaccination and deworming program, and take proper care of their feet.

Once horses begin training, their need for energy will increase in proportion to the amount of exercise they are performing. Additional protein, vitamins, and minerals are not necessary as any additional needs for those nutrients will be met from the increased feed intake necessary to meet the energy requirement. Again, feeding the horse at a rate of at least 1% of body weight per day of good-quality forage and then using a commercially prepared concentrate in amounts necessary to maintain the desired body condition is all that is necessary for the vast majority of horses.

TRAINING HORSES

Training horses for any event can be considered in two parts, psychological training and physiological training. The first is the training of the horse to do what is required on cue and the second is the training to be able to accomplish the task. Psychological training is based on the classic principles of learning and physiological training is based on the principles of exercise physiology.

Horses do not score well on many of the classical measures of intelligence. They do, however, have the capacity to learn quickly if properly taught. Horses can be trained by applying the basic learning principle represented by the formula SRSr. The first S stands for stimulus. The horse is given a stimulus (S), called a cue, which is a signal to perform some act. The horse then responds in some way (R) and the response is then reinforced positively or negatively based on the correctness of the response. This reinforcement stimulus is the Sr in the formula. Positive reinforcement encourages the horse to remember the correct response and negative reinforcement encourages the horse to make an alternative response. By repeating the process over and over, the horse eventually learns and remembers the correct response to that cue. For learning to occur, the following criteria must be met. First the initiating stimulus or cue must be the same each time and it should suggest to the horse the desired response. For example, assume the trainer is teaching a foal to lead and wants the horse to turn to the left. The cue should point the horse in that direction, perhaps by pulling the lead rope to the left. The trainer must recognize an approximation of the correct response. In this example, if the foal has never been led before, just moving the head to the left and giving slightly to the pressure is an approximation of the correct response. The foal cannot be expected to know the entire correct response the first time. Second, the reinforcement stimulus must be contingent. That is, it must be able to be linked to the response. Therefore the reinforcement must be immediate to have the desired effect. If the trainer waits until tomorrow to let the horse know whether or not the response was correct, learning will not occur and the horse will become agitated and nervous because it does not understand what is expected. Horses have great ability to learn but virtually no ability to reason. Also, they learn to learn so that each succeeding task becomes easier for them to learn. That is why beginning training at an early age can be important in achieving top performance in competition. The level to which a horse can be trained is amazing, but it takes time, consistency, and above all, patience.

Exercise and Fitness

The science of exercise physiology or the study of how the horse's body responds to exercise is a relatively new area. During the process of psychological training, some physiological training occurs at the same time. Yet for the horse to be truly fit and ready for competition, additional work may be required. Two principles are central to understanding fitness in horses. The first is metabolic specificity of exercise. This principle states that most of the exercise in training must be similar to that expected in competition (i.e., a horse that swims laps in a pool will not be specifically fit to run a 1 1/2-mile race). Swimming may make the cardiovascular system fit but does nothing for the skeletal system. Horses trained in this manner would appear fit but would not likely perform up to expectations. The second principle is that of progressive loading. This concept states that for training or fitness to occur the system being trained must be overloaded to the point of fatigue (i.e., if the horse's systems are not challenged no additional fitness is gained). However, the system must not be taxed to the point of failure or the horse may be injured. Most catastrophic injuries occur because the system was taken beyond fatigue and into the failure zone.

Fitness can further be divided into two categories, aerobic and anaerobic. Aerobic work occurs at heart rates below 150 beats per minute and anaerobic work begins when the heart rate goes over 150. During aerobic work, energy is metabolized using oxygen and the end products of metabolism are carbon dioxide and water, both of which can be eliminated from the body relatively easily. During anaerobic work, the amount or pace of the work performed has outstripped the body's ability to provide the energy necessary from aerobic sources, so the body metabolizes energy sources without oxygen. Such metabolism leads to the formation of a byproduct called lactic acid. The body cannot get rid of lactic acid easily as oxygen is required to metabolize this strong acid to carbon dioxide and water. Anaerobic metabolism is also inefficient from the standpoint of the amount of energy derived and therefore exercise cannot continue indefinitely. The horse becomes fatigued and eventually some system will fail if work is continued.

Aerobic systems can be conditioned in about four to six weeks by working the horse at a heart rate of 150 for 20 minutes per day, five days per week. Anaerobic fitness may take an additional 45 to 60 days for a total of approximately about 90 days to build a base level of fitness. For very strenuous events such as racing, additional time will be required to get the horse completely fit.

Fitness can be estimated and monitored by assessing heart rates at various points throughout exercise. Heart rate monitors are relatively inexpensive and can actually be used to predict an oncoming injury.

BUYING AND/OR SELLING A HORSE

Hundreds of thousands of horses change owners every year. The exact number of sales in a given year is difficult to estimate because most horses are sold by private treaty in which the two parties come together and agree on a price and seal the deal with a handshake. Others are sold by private treaty negotiated through a third party and a contract may or may not be executed, and still others are sold through auctions.

Private Treaty

Private treaty sales can be an advantage to both the buyer and seller. The sale takes place in a much more private setting and generally under calmer conditions than an auction. Both parties can freely negotiate the price and if an agreement is not reached the seller has the option to find another buyer. The buyer, on the other hand, can generally discover what is the "bottom dollar" on a given horse. The disadvantage to both buyer and seller comes in getting them together in the first place. The seller has to either advertise or have an established reputation that draws buyers. Alternatively, the seller can hire an agent to broker the horse. Agents have a list of clients that buy horses from them and they make their living putting the buyer and seller together to make a deal. Generally the agent earns a commission on the sale of the horse and may also charge for any other costs associated with the deal. Some agents have farms to which the seller's horse may be brought and prepared for sale, of course for an additional fee.

Auction Sales

Auction sales are also a very important part of the industry. They are an open market that helps to establish the going price for the various types of horses. Some auctions are held in a local livestock sale facility, others in multipurpose facilities that have been adapted to horse sales, others in facilities designed and used solely for horse sales, and occasionally a sale is held in the ballroom of an upscale hotel. Obviously the quality of the offering determines the caliber of facility in which it is held and the expectation of prices to be obtained. Many auctions are for any kind of horse any seller wishes to bring and they do bring every size and description of horse imaginable. Others are just for one breed and all the horses entered in the sale must be registered with that breed association. Still others are limited to horses of a certain breed, age, and purpose, such as the Heritage Place Racing Quarter Horse Yearling Sale.

Nevertheless, all auctions have similarities. First the horses must be consigned or entered in the sale. The cost to enter the sale also varies from as little as $15 to as much as $2,000. The sale company conducting the auction does the advertising, which may be as little as a flyer posted at the local feed store or, in the case of the prestigious sales such as the Keenland Summer Thoroughbred sale, full-page four-color ads in national equine publications. The sale company's job is to get the buyers to the sale. Once sale day arrives the entries are numbered with marking paint or a tail tag so that potential buyers can inspect them prior to the sale. The entries then enter the sale ring in predetermined order and the bidding begins. The auctioneer begins the bidding at the "upset" price or minimum bid. Some sales have a preset upset bid and others simply let the auctioneer find the first bid by asking a lower and lower price until someone bids. Bidding is done by hand signals. You might just end up owning a horse. The bidding then continues until the auctioneer has determined that no further bids are forthcoming. At that point the auctioneer's gavel "falls" (actually he bangs it on the table) and the horse is considered sold unless the price is less than what the seller wanted. There are two ways in which the seller may retain ownership in the horse. First the seller can set a reserve price on the horse prior to the auction. This price is known only to the auctioneer and the sale company and if the bidding does not exceed this price the last bid is that of the owner. In the sale results that horse will be listed as RNA, which stands for reserve not attained. The second method used in some sales is for the owner to simply say at the end of bidding that the horse is being "passed out" or PO'd. This simply means that the horse is not for sale at that price and the owner invokes the right to retain ownership. States govern how auctions can be conducted and the method by which the sellers protect their interest is usually set forth by law.

Whatever the method of obtaining a horse, many people's lifelong dream is to own a horse. The pride and satisfaction of owning a horse cannot be measured in dollars and cents and, though most horses today are a luxury and not a necessity, they enhance the quality of life for their owners and for others who have a chance to observe their performance.

SUMMARY

The U.S. horse industry is a diverse and exciting industry that relies heavily on recreational dollars for its existence. Its roots trace back to the Spanish Conquistadors and the European settlers along the east coast who reintroduced the horse to the North American continent. The horse served a vital role in the development of this country until the mechanization of agriculture rendered it nearly obsolete as a source of power and transportation. Today horses are used in a variety of sporting events that have both English and Western heritages. Owning a horse carries with it a privilege and a responsibility and requires knowledge of the horse's physiological and psychological norms to formulate a management strategy that keeps the horse healthy and happy. Health care, nutrition, and housing programs should be scientifically based and applied on a consistent basis. Raising horses also requires extensive scientific knowledge of horse physiology and technical expertise in breeding management, foaling and foal care, and proper rearing procedures. Training horses, as with basic management, involves both psychological and physiological modification to be successful and, as with the other aspects of the industry, involves a scientific approach. If raising a horse is not possible, one can be purchased either by private treaty or at public auction. The auctioneer's call and the excitement of the crowd are a thrill to be experienced. Whatever the method by which ownership comes about, owning a horse is the experience of a lifetime.

GLOSSARY

Aerobic work   Physical exercise or work that uses energy developed from aerobic metabolism, usually with a heart rate less than 150 beats per minute.

Allowance race   A horse race where all horses are handicapped with weights to make the race more equal.

Anaerobic work   Physical exercise or work that

develops energy from anaerobic metabolism, usually with a heart rate more than 150 beats per minute.

Anthelmintics   A type of drug used that is selectively toxic to certain internal and external parasitic organisms.

Artificial insemination   The injection of semen into the vagina or uterus by means of a syringe or other similar utensil.

Artificial vagina   A sleeve used during semen collection of the stallion used for AI that surrounds the penis and captures semen during ejaculation.

Auction sale   A sale of horses where the horse is sold to the highest bidder.

Body condition score   A system of numerical rating of horses based on the amount of fat or finish of the horse; ratings range from 1 (very thin) to 9 (very obese).

Breed   A distinctive kind of horse that has distinct lineage and/or characteristics.

Claiming race   A horse race in which any horse entered can be purchased by anyone who has made a bid before the race.

Colic   Applies to various conditions of the digestive tract of which pain is the chief symptom.

Colostrum   The first milk given by a mare that is rich in antibodies and establishes passive immunity in the foals.

Concentrate   A type of food for livestock with concentrated nutrients such as a sweet feed or pellets.

Derby   An equine event or race for 3-year-old horses.

Developmental orthopedic disease   A generic term used for a collection of equine growth disorders that affects the bones and joints.

Dry mare   A mare of reproductive activity that is not producing milk.

English   A style of riding that uses a flat-seated saddle with no horn; has roots in Europe.

Estrous   The time between the periods of estrus (standing heat).

Estrus   Period of time when the female is receptive to the male and will stand for mating.

Farrier   A person who shoes horses.

Foal   A newborn or young horse of either sex.

Forage   Vegetative food for livestock such as pasture or hay.

Founder   A noninfectious inflammation and circulatory restriction of the sensitive laminae of the equine hoof.

Furlong   A measure of length used in horse races that measures 1/8 mile or 220 yards.

Futurity   An equine event or race for 2-year-olds, where the horses are entered at a specified time in advance.

Gelding   A male horse that has been castrated.

Gestation length   The period of pregnancy, usually lasting 340 days on average for the horse or approximately 11 months.

Maiden   A horse that has not yet won a race.

Maiden mare   A female horse that has never been bred.

Mare   A mature female horse.

Market breeder   A person who breeds and produces stock based upon what is popular in the market at that time.

Packed cell volume   The proportion of a blood sample that is packed red blood cells.

Pari-mutuel   A form of betting on race horses, in which those holding winning tickets divide the total bet in proportion to the wagers.

Parturition   Process of giving birth.

Passive immunity   Immunity to diseases that a horse gets without actually suffering through the disease, typically from the mare's colostrum.

Placentation   Union of the endometrium (mucosal lining of the uterus) and the extraembryonic membranes forming the placenta.

Private treaty sale   An agreement between the buyer and the seller on a negotiated price that does not have to be made public.

Rodeo   A contest of cowboy events such as roping and bronc riding with roots in nineteenth-century America.

Skin turgor   The elasticity of the skin and its ability to return to normal position after a small fold is pulled away from the body; used as a sign of dehydration.

SRSr The teaching method used in training a horse; stands for Stimulus, Response, and Stimulus Reinforcement.

Stakes race A horse race that has added money and is for only the best horses.

Stallion An intact male horse mainly used for breeding purposes.

Ultrasound A method of checking reproductive status using a device that utilizes ultrasonic waves converted into a video picture.

Vaccination To inoculate a healthy body with a weakened or killed form of a virus to establish immunity against the virus.

Weaning Removing or preventing a foal from nursing on the mare.

Weanling A young horse that has just been weaned off the mare.

Western A style of riding using a heavy saddle with horn and extra leather for protection; has roots in nineteenth-century America.

Wet mare A female horse that has delivered a foal and is producing milk.

Yearling A male or female horse that is one year of age as determined by the universal birthdate of January 1 of each year.

REFERENCES

American Horse Council. 1996. *The Economic Impact of the Horse Industry in the United States,* Vol. 2: Eleven Focus States.

American Horse Council. 1999. *Horse Industry Directory.* Washington, DC.

Butler, D. 1995. *Principles of Horse Shoeing.* LaPorte, CO: Butler Publishing Co.

Evans, J. W., Borton, A., Hintz, H. F., and Van Vleck, L. D. 1990. *The Horse* (2nd ed.). San Fransisco, CA: W. H. Freeman Co.

Gifflin, J. M., and Gore, T. 1988. *Horse Owner's Veteri-nary Handbook.* New York: Howell Book House.

Lewis, L. D. 1995. *Equine Clinical Nutrition, Feeding and Care.* Media, PA: Williams and Wilkins.

National Research Council. 1989. *Nutrient Requirements of Horses* (5th ed.). Washington DC: National Academy Press.

Stashak, T. S. 1995. *Horse Owner's Guide to Lameness.* Media, PA: Williams and Wilkins.

Swinker, A. M. and Heird, J. C. 1994. *Horse Industry: Trends, Opportunities, and Issues.* Encyclopedia of Agricultural Science. San Diego: Academic Press.

CHAPTER SEVENTEEN
SWINE

Swine contribute to society in two important ways: (1) as a source of food and other products of value in societies throughout the world and (2) as an increasingly used animal model in biomedical research. In this chapter we emphasize the former, although the similarity of pigs and humans in many aspects of nutrition and physiology makes the pig an attractive animal model for human medicine, a subject that is briefly discussed at the end of the chapter.

Swine production varies from small "backyard" efforts, in which household kitchen wastes and locally grown feedstuffs are fed to pigs to provide pork for home use, to large, highly specialized pork production systems geared for large commercial production. Pork production, regardless of the size of the enterprise, represents a major human food resource and requires inputs related to capital, labor, feed resources, physical facilities, disease control, waste management, and product quality assurance. The integration of all inputs and outputs into pork production systems on the farm and at the regional, national, and international levels is an ongoing interdisciplinary effort in which human ingenuity and resourcefulness is a key factor. In this chapter we describe the scope and trends of swine production, the biological characteristics of the pig, and the husbandry, management, and marketing technologies that continue in an ongoing process to meet the ever-growing world demand for pork. With the steady growth of swine production has come increased effort to address issues of environmental quality, feed resources, animal well-being, and other challenges. Some of these issues, although common to all of animal agriculture, are briefly discussed with particular pertinence to swine production.

DESCRIPTION AND CHARACTERISTICS OF SWINE PRODUCTION

Past

The domestic pig (*Sus scrofa* or *Sus domesticus*) is the result of many thousands of years of natural selection before domestication and of selective breeding since domestication (believed to have occurred first in what is now the Mideast about 9,000 years ago). Recorded domestication appears in Biblical accounts as early as 2000 B.C. Despite ancient cultural and religious taboos forbidding the consumption of pork, the domestication of swine as a source of human food persisted, and the continued increase in numbers of swine throughout the world provides evidence of the contribution of the pig to human nutrition through the ages.

The pig is believed to have been introduced into North America by Columbus in 1493 on his voyage to the West Indies; not until 1539 was it brought to the United States by Hernando DeSoto. The pig has always been an important part of animal agriculture in the United States; the growth of the swine industry paralleled the growth of the human population for many years. Annual per-capita consumption of pork in the United States has remained stable at about 60 lb (27 kg) per person for many decades. Traditionally the pig has been a scavenger, and in early domestication it was raised as a means of utilizing human food wastes.

Present

In many parts of the world, the pig still performs this function as a backyard inhabitant. Even in the developed countries, some swine produced for commercial pork are fed kitchen wastes. By far the greatest proportion of commercial swine production is based on the availability of large quantities of cereal grains, corn (maize), and other high-energy feeds and byproducts at low cost. In the United States, the largest numbers of swine are produced in the "corn belt," located in the North-Central region where soil and climate conditions are ideal for the production of large amounts of high-yielding corn and soybeans, the two crops on which a large segment of the swine industry is based. For example, Iowa, in the heart of the corn belt, produces about 20 million pigs per year, nearly 25% of the total U.S. production. During the past decade, several areas outside the corn belt have had dramatic increases in swine production. Most notable is North Carolina, where swine numbers are now second only to Iowa. The large swine industry in North Carolina is based on shipment of grain and other feed resources from the Midwest and the development of slaughter plants and pork-processing facilities near the sites of production to meet the demand for pork by the large population in the Eastern United States. Similar trends are underway in the arid and sparsely populated regions of Texas, Oklahoma, and Colorado and other western states. The growth of swine production in these areas is largely supported by extensive production systems based on low animal density, which averts some of the environmental concerns associated with intensive production systems in confinement in the Midwest. Environmental issues related to air, water, and soil pollution have discouraged expansion of swine production in the Midwest with urbanization and encroachment of housing developments and shopping malls in traditional swine farming areas.

Swine are produced in virtually all parts of the United States as a means of utilizing local feedstuffs and human resources, and in this way they contribute to the local economies. The six states of Iowa, North Carolina, Minnesota, Illinois, Indiana, and Nebraska produce more than two-thirds of the total of 96 million swine marketed annually in the United States. Other states ranking in the top 10 in swine production are Missouri, Ohio, South Dakota, and Kansas. More than 80% of the swine marketed in the United States are produced on farms raising more than 1000 head annually (Table 17-1). This trend accompanies the steady reduction in the number of farms reporting swine (Table 17-2).

Swine production has evolved to a primary enterprise on many farms as a means of converting processed feedstuffs and breeding stock resources into marketable pork prod-

TABLE 17-1
PRODUCER AND PRODUCTION PROFILE (1997)

Size	Pigs Marketed	Percent of Producers	Percent of Pigs Produced
(Head Marketed Per Year)	*(Million Head)*		
1,000 & less	4.8	61.5	5.4
1,001–2,000	10.9	19.1	12.1
2,001–3000	8.7	8.2	9.7
3,001–5000	8.9	5.6	9.9
5,001–10,000	8.9	3.2	9.9
10,001–50,000	14.5	2.2	16.2
50,001 Plus	33.1	0.2	36.8
Total	**89.8**	**100**	**100**

Source: 1998 Pork Industry Structure Study (University of Missouri, NPPC, *Pork 98*, PIC, DeKalb Swine, Land O'Lakes & Iowa State University), preliminary results.

TABLE 17-2

NUMBER OF U.S. PIG OPERATIONS

Year	Operations	Year	Operations
1968	967,580	1983	462,110
1969	873,840	1984	429,580
1970	871,200	1985	391,000
1971	869,000	1986	348,000
1972	778,200	1987	331,620
1973	735,700	1988	326,600
1974	733,100	1989	306,210
1975	661,700	1990	275,440
1976	658,300	1991	253,890
1977	647,000	1992	248,700
1978	635,300	1993	225,210
1979	653,600	1994	207,980
1980	670,350	1995	181,750
1981	580,060	1996	156,250
1982	482,190	1997	138,690

Source: USDA, *Hogs and Pigs*, December of each year.

ucts. The concept of a "systems approach" analogous to the production of goods in other industries has become important in commercial pork production. Modern production often occurs in environmentally controlled facilities with automated feed delivery and manure disposal. This technology requires highly skilled personnel and careful record keeping and cost accounting. The major controllable inputs are the breeding system, the feedstuffs, and the formulated diets. The output from the production system determines the income to offset costs, and hopefully a margin of profit. Income is determined by: number of animals sold; weight of each animal; and value (price received) per unit weight. Briefly stated, the profitability of the enterprise is determined by the efficiency of the production system in integrating the inputs and outputs to maximize efficiency and by overcoming the adverse effects of extraneous factors such as harsh climate and threat of disease. Environmentally controlled facilities and effective disease control programs have evolved in response to the need to minimize the impact of these factors on animal productivity. Continuing changes in economic and marketing conditions and advances in technology that affect the structure of the swine industry are underway. For example, North Carolina has become a major swine production center during recent years as a result of these changing forces. A trend is also underway toward development of large swine production systems in the arid areas of the southern plains states such as the panhandles of Texas and Oklahoma and in Utah and other western states. The changing structure is related to many factors, including transportation and marketing of crops, feed, and livestock and their products, and growing concerns about air pollution from odors and water pollution from animal wastes (manure and urine).

SWINE NUMBERS. Pork continues to occupy an important position as a food source in all parts of the world and in affluent societies as well as in developing countries with

TABLE 17-3

TOP 15 PORK-PRODUCING COUNTRIES 1997

Country	Weight	Inventory	Slaughter
	(1,000 Metric tons, carcass wt.)	(1,000 Head)	(1,000 Head)
1. China	42,500	457,130	560,000
2. United States	7,835	56,141	91,961
3. Germany	3,570	24,283	38,500
4. Spain	2,320	18,631	28,980
5. France	2,186	14,968	25,470
6. Denmark	1,625	11,081	21,120
7. Poland	1,600	17,697	21,400
8. Brazil	1,540	31,369	20,865
9. Russia	1,500	19,500	29,149
10. Italy	1,417	8,100	12,000
11. Netherlands	1,366	14,253	15,200
12. Japan	1,273	9,809	16,960
13. Canada	1,255	12,301	15,300
14. Belgium-Luxembourg	1,036	7,108	11,258
15. Taiwan	1,012	10,698	11,701
Total European Union	16,175	115,700	187,589
Total World	80,874	792,303	1,032,715

Source: USDA Foreign Agriculture Service.

slower economic growth. World swine production is increasing to meet the needs of the growing human population. Total meat consumption continues to increase and currently stands at more than 170 million tons per year (32 kg/capita). Pork accounts for about 40% of total meat consumption and remains first among all meat sources in total consumption, followed in descending order by beef, poultry, lamb, and goat meat.

The world swine population has steadily increased for many decades, and now exceeds 800 million (this is a census figure, not total production for the year, which is considerably higher). China is the world's leading pork consumer and producer. It reported an inventory of about 442 million swine in 1996, compared with 58,000 in the United States, the world's second-largest producer (Table 17-3). Exports of pork from the United States have steadily increased for many years. In 1996, pork exports were 305,881 metric tons. Differences among regions of the world in swine reproductive rates and animal weights at slaughter result in discrepancies among a country's census figures and its annual pork production. For example, Asia has about 50% of the world's total swine but produces about 40% of the world's pork. North America has about 12% of the world's swine but produces about 14% of the world's pork.

On the consumption side, the total demand for pork in the United States has increased in proportion to population growth in recent years; nearly 8 million metric tons of pork are produced annually to meet the recent per-capita demand for approximately

60 to 65 lb per year. Pork consumption in other parts of the world continues to increase, particularly in developing countries where per-capita incomes are improving and stimulating greater consumption of animal products. Annual per-capita consumption of pork is highest in Denmark (145 lb in 1996) followed by several European and Asian countries that are ahead of the United States (63.3 lb in 1996). Hungary, Spain, Germany, Hong Kong, Taiwan, and Poland all consumed pork at greater than 80 lb per capita in 1996. France, Sweden, China, and Canada consumed more than 70 lb per capita in 1996, and several others, namely Singapore, United Kingdom, Korea, Australia, Japan, and the Russian Federation, each exceeded 30 lb per capita.

Future

No one can predict with certainty the future of swine production or, for that matter, that of any segment of animal agriculture, or of agriculture itself. Nonetheless, we may infer from current trends some aspects of the future of swine. Technology development and transfer as well as trends in human population and grain production will affect the future of pork production.

USE OF COMPUTERS AND THE INTERNET IN PORK PRODUCTION DECISION MAKING. The accumulated knowledge acquired over many years of observations and research on the genetics, reproduction, and growth of swine has provided a database to allow the collection and processing of the knowledge in the form of a set of computer programs to simulate the numerous alternative courses of action in swine production and to predict the likely outcome. The future pork producer (indeed, a few innovative producers already are doing so) will use these computer-simulated models, together with management information systems, to aid in decision making. Such computerized systems, termed integrated decision support systems (IDSS), are already in use in several countries and probably will be increasingly used in the future in guiding pork production.

CONSUMER DEMAND FOR PORK. Projections of human population growth indicate that total world population will, except by the most conservative scenario, approach 9 billion by 2030. Swine production is closely tied to grain consumption, which is by far the largest single component of global agriculture. Global consumption of all grains has grown at an annual rate of about 1.5% for the last 20 years. It has been predicted that this rate will continue to 2030, resulting in a doubling of total consumption of grains (human food and animal feed) during that time. More than 90% of total growth in grain production is projected to occur in the developing countries, mostly in Asia.

The coarse grains (corn, sorghum, and millet), which are used mostly for animal feeding, are projected to increase more rapidly than the principal food grains (wheat and rice). The reason is the known relationship between rising income and demand for meat and other animal products. Increased land area devoted to coarse grain and food grain production and increased yields will be required to meet these projected needs. Ultimately, the long-term future of swine production will probably be determined not only by the degree to which pork is preferred in the diet relative to alternative foods, but by constraints imposed by economic, ecological, and other forces external to biological characteristics of the pig.

ANIMAL PERFORMANCE. For the foreseeable future, animal performance traits such as lean tissue growth, efficiency of feed utilization, and reproductive efficiency, will continue to improve. This seems predictable, based on rapidly developing technology, such as recombinant DNA (gene-splicing) techniques for production of nutrients, vaccines, and metabolic modulators; advanced methods of genetic manipulation, including population genetics and transgenic techniques; development of nutrient repartitioning agents that improve growth, reproduction, and lactation; and refinements in design and management of pork production systems.

ISSUES FACING THE PORK INDUSTRY

Animal Well-Being

The well-being and proper care of animals has always been a concern of swine producers. Heightened concern by society in general in recent years has stimulated animal producers to more carefully examine the impact of production practices on their animals. Practices that have received the most attention in animal agriculture are those related to space and restricted movement. In swine production, the restraint of sows in gestation stalls and farrowing crates has been brought into question. Farrowing crates first came into use as an effective means of protecting piglets from injury and death caused by crushing or overlaying by the mother. This and most other husbandry practices were developed to reduce costs of production and improve the comfort and productivity of the animal. As new knowledge is gained about animal behavior and the nature and causes of stress in swine, pork producers will continue in their efforts to provide environments and husbandry practices that achieve animal well-being during all phases of the life cycle. Dedication to this end is built into the future of swine production. The well-being of farm animals is an important issue for agriculture and for society in general. See Chapters 10 and 11 for more detailed discussions of the topic.

Environment and Ecology

Swine production, like all of animal agriculture, must be approached so as to promote environmental stability and ecological balance. Intensive swine production has potentially negative effects on the environment. Odors from swine produced in confinement formerly went relatively unnoticed, but encroachment of agricultural areas by activities such as residential housing developments and shopping malls has created concerns about air pollution. Pollution of water supplies by swine waste runoff in large, intensive production facilities also is an increasing concern. Broad awareness of these problems has awakened efforts to devise systems of swine production that eliminate the negative impact of swine production on the environment. Environmental quality concerns will continue to have an impact on the location and size of new swine production facilities, including an acceleration of the trend for large swine production units to migrate to areas of the United States where human population density is low. The needs and goals of swine production will continue to stress adaptation to fit on a local and global basis within the broad context of agriculture, forestry, rangeland, and animal ecological systems. The interrelationships among swine production, production of other animals and crops, and the human population in competing for available resources will be more and more atuned in the future to preserving environmental quality and ecological balance. The subject of environmental quality is important to every citizen. See Chapter 11 for a more detailed discussion of this issue.

Waste Management

Swine manure has been used for centuries to fertilize soils for increased crop production and improved soil structure. However, as the human population has grown, and residential and business establishments have been built in close proximity to intensive swine production enterprises, increased concern has arisen about offensive odors. These objectionable odors from swine facilities have resulted in many lawsuits against swine producers and the passage of ordinances and restrictions on construction of new or expanded swine facilities.

Soil and water pollution from manure constituents produced in intensive swine production facilities are also of increasing concern. The main nutrients in manure are nitrogen, phosphorus, and potassium, the same three that are provided in commercial fertilizers. Excess nitrogen and phosphorus accumulation in soils may result in runoff into streams and lakes, with detrimental effects on the environment.

Oversupplementation of swine diets with nutrients to maximize growth and ensure nutritional adequacy is accompanied by high levels of excretion of these nutrients (notably nitrogen and phosphorus, but also sodium, copper, and zinc) in urine and feces. Manure from swine operations is spread on cropland to provide fertilizer. Application of excess amounts of nitrogen and phosphorus affects overall water quality. Excess nitrogen leads to high nitrate content of ground water and surface water, contaminating water wells and the environment. Excess phosphorus leads to high buildup of soil phosphorus, which may ultimately create excessive phosphorus in lakes and streams, which, in turn, stimulates growth of algae and aquatic plants whose decomposition products reduce water quality, termed eutrophication.

Efforts are underway by swine nutritionists to improve the efficiency of utilization of ingested nitrogen and phosphorus by the pig, resulting in less excretion of these two nutrients, thereby reducing their accumulation in soils on which the manure is spread. The future of pork production, and all of animal agriculture, will be governed to a large degree by the success with which solutions to waste management are developed.

Antimicrobial Agents in Swine Feeds

Naturally occurring antimicrobial agents (antibiotics) and chemotherapeutics (chemically synthesized) have been used for many years at low (subtherapeutic) levels in swine diets to improve growth, efficiency of feed utilization, and reproductive performance. The magnitude of improvement in these production traits over animals not fed antimicrobial agents has remained constant during a period of more than 40 years of routine use in billions of swine in commercial pork production. Yet, concern persists over the possibility of increased threat to human health by the development of strains of disease-producing bacteria resistant to the disease organism controlled by a specific antimicrobial. The use of subtherapeutic levels of antibiotics in swine feed has been banned in Europe and there is sentiment by some for similar restrictions in the United States. A total of more than 15 different antimicrobial agents are currently approved for use in swine feeds in the United States. Some of these require their withdrawal from the feed before slaughter to avoid residues of the antibiotic in the meat. The transfer of antibiotic resistance has been shown in the test tube, but the extent to which it occurs in the animal is not well understood. To date there is no direct evidence to establish the existence of a health hazard in humans caused by the use of subtherapeutic levels of antimicrobial agents in swine feeds. Nevertheless, continued vigilence is needed concerning the possible adverse effects on human health resulting from the use of subtherapeutic levels of antibiotics in swine feeds. If the use of antimicrobials in swine feed were to be disapproved there would be a serious increase in the cost of pork production through markedly reduced levels of efficiency of growth and reproduction.

Shift from Family Farms to Corporate Pork Production

The structure of pork production in the United States is rapidly changing, driven by economic forces related to new technology, changes in the infrastructure of the swine slaughter and pork processing industry, and environmental concerns and regulations associated with waste management and environmental quality in large intensive swine production facilities. These and other forces have changed pork production from an industry dominated by family-based, small-scale, independent enterprises to one comprised of larger firms tightly aligned across the production, processing, and marketing chain. This trend toward intregration, whereby the producer may produce swine under contract with feed supplier, meat packer (slaughterer and processor), or both feed supplier and meat packer, is radically changing the way in which pork reaches the consumer.

Purdue University agricultural economists have predicted several major changes ahead for the pork industry, summarized here (McMahon, 1998):

- *Site-specific microproduction management*—Medication may be administered to an individual pig rather than to a group; diets may be tailored to specific groups of pigs based on genetics, sex, age, and consumer market.
- *Supply chains for pork*—Pork will be produced, processed, and sold increasingly through supply chains, like what has occurred in the poultry industry. However, unlike the poultry industry, the producer may maintain ownership of the animals and will be aligned with a pork chain which will link major pork producers with a processor and retailer.

■ *Environmental control*—Regulation of building sites and construction and waste management will continue to escalate. Larger farms will be the most able to adapt cost effectively to new technology to protect the environment. Technological breakthroughs in solution of environmental problems will be needed to stabilize the Midwest as the major swine production area of the United States. If solutions are not developed, the present trend will continue for growth of pork production in the Great Plains of the United States, Canada, and Mexico.

■ *Traceback*—The ability to trace ownership of individual pigs or herds is critical to an effective food safety and disease containment system. The development of animal identification procedures to facilitate traceback is underway in the United States and the procedure is already in place in some countries.

■ *Production/processing centers*—Due to high capital costs, new processing centers will not be built unless sufficient hogs are available, and production facilities will not be built unless sufficient processing is available in the area. This interdependence of the two segments of the industry indicates that new processing facilities will be built only where there is assurance from one or more large producers that volume of supply will match the processing capacity.

■ *Product attributes, diversity*—Many new pork products will be developed to build the customer base. Attention to pork quality and to pork products to be eaten at all meals as a snack food will be critical to increasing market share of animal products.

■ *Global ownership*—Global pork firms (perhaps 5 to 10) will be major players in world pork production and processing in the future. U.S. pork companies have built facilities in Canada and Mexico, and look for opportunities in Asia, Eastern Europe, and South America.

PORK AS HUMAN FOOD

Pork, along with other animal products, provides protein of higher nutritive value than that present in most plant proteins and also provides other nutrients not present in adequate amounts in plants. Pork provides nearly one-half of the meat from domestic animals in the world and about 40% of the meat (excluding poultry) in the United States. The longstanding acceptance of pork is the result of its high nutritive value as well as the variety of processing and cooking methods available for its inclusion in the diet of many cultures. It is axiomatic that the consumer ultimately determines the amount and kind of pork produced. In this section we briefly describe the nutrient composition of pork and other properties that affect its acceptability to humans. Additional information is provided in Appendix Table I.

Nutrient Composition

Pork is an excellent source of high-quality protein, water-soluble vitamins (B vitamins), and trace mineral elements. Pork from modern, muscular swine, unlike that from pigs of earlier generations, is lean (similar to broiler meat) and contains about the same amount of cholesterol as poultry meat, beef, and lamb. The protein, fat, water, mineral element, vitamin, and energy contents of pork from the fresh whole carcass and from the fresh ham and loin and the cooked (roasted) loin are summarized in Appendix Table IA. Cooking reduces the water content of pork so that percentages of protein, fat, and minerals (ash) are increased and calorie concentration is increased.

Not only is pork high in total protein, but it is well balanced in essential amino acids. Pork, along with most animal products, contains a better balance of amino acids than most plant products provide. Most plant proteins are deficient in lysine, tryptophan, threonine, or the sulfur-containing amino acids (methionine and cystine) or a combination of two or more of them.

The water-soluble vitamin content of pork is high compared to most foods. Pork is especially high in thiamin (B1). A 100-gram serving of pork loin provides 70% of the daily thiamin requirement for adult humans. Vitamin B12 is a component of animal and microbial products only, so unless a meat, dairy, or poultry product is eaten, a vitamin B12 deficiency may result. Pork is comparable to milk, beef, and lamb as a source of riboflavin (B2) and niacin and is considerably higher than almost all plant products in these two vitamins. Moreover, the niacin of cereal grains and maize is almost completely biologically unavailable for use by the body because it is chemically bound in an indigestible form.

Pork is also an excellent source of some of the mineral elements and a poor source of others. It is a good source of phosphorus, but almost devoid of calcium. It is high in potassium but low in sodium. It is a good source of iron, zinc, manganese, and magnesium. In addition, all of the mineral elements in pork are present in highly bioavailable form.

The fat content of pork has dramatically decreased as a result of producers' efforts to select lean breeding stock. In fact, the lard yield of pork carcasses has declined from about 14% of carcass weight 30 years ago to less than 4% today. The composition of the fat in pork varies directly in response to the dietary fat composition. In general it is more unsaturated (softer) than beef or lamb fat and becomes progressively less saturated when pigs are fed diets high in polyunsaturated fatty acids. Digestibility of pork fat is high and similar to that of plant fats.

Properties Affecting Pork Acceptability

Pork quality is determined by palatability factors, including tenderness, juiciness, color, aroma, and flavor. Pork is less variable in these criteria, in general, than are beef and lamb because differences in age, breed, and environment have relatively small effects on pork quality. Carcass measurements and evaluation of pork quality are discussed in more detail in Chapter 22. A genetically controlled syndrome termed pork stress syndrome (PSS) causes the production of pale, soft, exudative (PSE) pork in affected pigs. The incidence of PSE pork is determined by stress susceptibility. The condition results from lactic acid accumulation in the muscles postmortem and seems to be associated with strains of extremely heavily muscled pigs. Efforts are underway by producers and researchers to identify stress-susceptible animals and avoid propagation of the trait.

Meat from mature boars has an objectionable odor and flavor when cooked, due to the presence of specific fat-soluble androgen derivatives. The "boar odor" is detected in taste panel studies in most boars weighing more than 90 kg and occasionally in sows, gilts, and barrows. Boars grow faster, require less feed per unit weight gain, and produce leaner carcasses than barrows. Therefore, it would be to the advantage of the producer and consumer alike if a way of eliminating or reducing the boar odor problem without castration could be developed.

For many years, a major deterrent to pork consumption was the threat of infection with the parasite, *Trichinella spiralis,* from eating raw pork. The incidence of infection (trichinosis) in the United States is now less than 50 reported cases per year, but the incidence remains high in many parts of the world. Heating pork to an internal temperature of 77° C or freezing for 20 days at −15° C destroys the parasite. Exposure of pork carcasses to high-energy radiation, expected to be approved for use in the United States, destroys the parasite without affecting the nutritive value or palatability of the pork. The drug thiabendazole is an effective treatment in infected animals and humans.

LIFE CYCLE

The time sequence of important events in the life cycle of pigs under most production systems is listed in Table 17-4. The generation interval in swine is about one year. The early sexual maturity, prolificacy, and short gestation period of swine compared with other food animals, and the associated high degree to which such traits as growth and body composition are passed to the next generation (high heritability), make possible relatively rapid changes in economically important production traits.

Females and males reach puberty at about 6 months of age and can be mated by 8 months of age (some breeds of Chinese pigs and some miniature pigs reach puberty at 3 to 4 months of age and can be mated by 5 months) to produce a litter at about 1 year of age (gestation is 114 days). Average number of pigs born per litter is 9 to 12 and an average of 8 to 10 pigs is weaned at 2 to 5 weeks of age. After weaning, pigs are usually full-fed a nutritionally complete diet throughout the growing-finishing period of about 4 to 5 months at which time they are marketed for pork or retained as breeding animals (5 to 6 months of age). Lactating sows do not normally ovulate during the suckling period, but within a few days after their pigs are weaned, they ovulate and are receptive to the male. Mating at this first postweaning estrus usually results in pregnancy, and a second litter is born 3.8 months later. Therefore, it is common for one sow to produce 2 to 2.5 litters of 8 to 10 market-weight pigs yearly, weighing an average of 240 lb (110 kg) per pig at 5 to 6 months of age (a total weight of approximately 10 times the body weight of the mother!).

Growth

By 11 days after conception, embryos begin to show signs of attachment to the lining (endometrium) of the uterus. Attachment of the embryo in the uterine wall to form the

TABLE 17-4

TIMETABLE OF IMPORTANT EVENTS IN THE LIFE CYCLE OF SWINE

Period	Duration
Prenatal period, days	114 = 4
Suckling period, wks.	3–8[a]
Growing-finishing period (to 105-kg body wt.), days	100–160
Age at 105 kg. days	135–205[b]
Age at puberty	150–200[c]
Optimum age at first service, months	7–8[d]
Reproductive longevity, years	4–8
Longevity, years	12–15[e]

[a]Pigs can be weaned to cow milk or synthetic diets at birth but it is more common in commercial production to wean at three weeks or older.

[b]Boars and male castrates grow slightly faster than females, so can be expected to reach 105 kg body wt. several days earlier.

[c]Chinese breeds may reach puberty at less than 100 days.

[d]Since puberty is reached before growth stops, better reproductive performance is obtained (large litters in females and more sperm produced in males) if reproductive service is not initiated before 7 months of age.

[e]Most female and male breeding stock are slaughtered when their reproductive efficiency begins to decline, so that the longevity figure is based on a very small sample of the total swine population.

placenta does not occur until day 18. By day 20, the crown–rump length of the fetus is about 10 mm. From this stage onward, the rate of fetal growth is enormous. At birth (about 94 days later), the length is about 30 cm and the weight ranges from about 800 to 1800 g or greater. The newborn pig contains about 82% water, 12% protein, 5% minerals (ash), and less than 1% fat.

Body weight during a 4-week suckling period doubles the first week, and is 6 to 10 times the birthweight by 4 weeks. Males grow faster than females and females grow faster than male castrates at all stages of the growing-finishing period. Males also deposit much more body protein during postweaning growth than females, and females deposit more protein than male castrates. These differences are depicted in Figure 17-1.

Animals in the United States are marketed weighing 220 to 260 lb or more at 5 to 6 months of age. Market weight varies considerably among countries and regions due to differing consumer preferences and economic factors. Animals retained for breeding are normally placed on limited feed intake to avoid excessive fatness. By breeding age of 8 months, females weigh about 240 to 280 lb and males weigh 280 to 300 lb or more. Body weight and skeletal size continue to increase until 3 years of age or beyond, despite restricted feeding after market weight is attained. Mature females often weigh more than 400 lb and males 700 lb or more, depending on genetics and on how liberally they are fed after maturity.

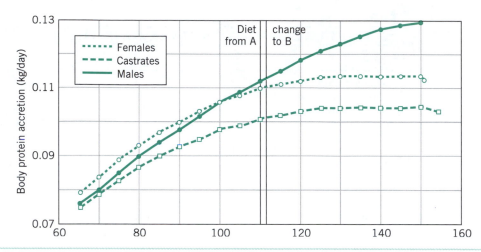

FIGURE 17-1

Changes in daily body protein accretion in female, male, and male castrate pigs as generated from computer simulation. Note the greater lean tissue growth rate of intact males than of castrates and the intermediate position of females.

Source: Pomar et al., *Journal of Animal Science* 69: 1468–1488, 1991. With permission.

Reproduction

A high reproductive rate is a prerequisite for a successful swine enterprise. The anatomy and physiology of the female and male reproductive tract of mammals are described in Chapter 4. The uterine horns of the sow are long and tortuous to accommodate numerous developing fetuses. In the mature sow they may be 1 meter or more long when extended. The ovaries are lobular, owing to follicles at varying stages of development. There may be 10 to 25 individual mature follicles on each ovary. Onset of puberty (first estrus) is influenced by social environment (close proximity to boars during the growing-finishing period hastens it), and degree of spacial confinement. Relocation or exposure to a boar consistently advances puberty. The number of ova released per estrus gradually increases over the first several estrous cycles. There are wide variations even among normal animals in the ovulation rate (number of ova released at each estrus). The number of ova available for release over a lifetime is determined prenatally by 100 days after conception.

The estrous cycle length (onset of one estrus to onset of the next) averages about 21 days (range is about 18 to 24 days). During proestrus (1 to 3 days), females are alert to the approach of the boar, will mount other females, and may accept mounting by other females, but will not tolerate mounting by a boar. During estrus, the swollen vulva and vaginal discharge first observed during late proestrus are accompanied by restlessness (fence-walking, agitation), mounting of other animals, and acceptance of the boar. The female in estrus will mate during a 2- to 3-day period, and because ovulation lasts for several hours, mating on two successive days of estrus often results in an increase in litter size, owing to improved synchrony of contact between newly released ova and spermatozoa. Because the estrous cycle is under endocrine control, it can be altered by exogenous hormones. This technology is used in commercial swine production, particularly in conjunction with artificial insemination for genetic improvement and for tighter control of breeding schedules in individual enterprises.

Males produce viable sperm by about 4 months of age (younger in some Asian and miniature breeds), but generally are not used for breeding until 2 to 4 months later when they have attained larger size and more mature sexual activity. The testes migrate out of the body cavity to the scrotum at about 100 days after conception. Failure of one or both testes to leave the body cavity results in cryptorchidism (one or both testes not descended) in postnatal life. The condition is heritable and occurs with high frequency in swine.

Male pigs are castrated to prevent the development of boar odor in the meat after puberty is reached. The recommended age of castration is during the first week after birth or near the time of weaning at 3 or 4 weeks; the procedure is quick and the incision heals within a few days. Castration can be delayed, but older animals are more difficult to restrain and may be more stressed by the surgery.

In the intact male, stored sperm leave the epididymus via the vas deferens. The seminal vesicle, Cowper's (bulbourethral) gland, and prostate gland all contribute to semen volume, which may exceed 500 cc per ejaculate. Ten or more sows can be inseminated from a single ejaculate. Techniques for freezing semen for use in artificial insemination are available. Modern genetic evaluation procedures are stimulating the commercial application of this technology, which enables the more rapid genetic improvement of sow herds by more extensive use of superior sires.

HIGH PRENATAL MORTALITY. Prenatal deaths occur in 30 to 40% of developing fetuses in swine. More than half of these losses occur during the first 25 days after conception and most of the remainder occur before midgestation. Mummified fetuses represent deaths that have occurred after 40 days of gestation and are differentiated from stillborn pigs by partial resorption. The causes of these large prenatal losses are not fully understood, but two distinct but interrelated major components of the problem are limited uterine capacity and high ovulation rate.

Lactation

Lactation in swine, as in other mammals, provides the means by which the newborn animal acquires essential nutrients and immunological protection. The immune protection of colostrum (mammary secretion during the first days of lactation) is more critical in swine than in many other mammals because, in the pig, placental transfer of immune antibodies is almost nil, leaving colostrum as the principal source of protection of the newborn piglet against pathogenic agents. The normal duration of lactation in sows is 6 to 8 weeks, but nutritional needs of the rapidly growing pig exceed those provided by the milk after about 3 to 4 weeks, because the peak of lactation is reached at about 4 weeks. Therefore, the pigs are usually weaned at 2 to 4 weeks of age. The sow enters postweaning estrus within a few days and can be mated to produce another litter. Milk production efficiency in swine is very high and nutrient yield per unit body weight in highly productive sows is greater than in dairy cattle (sow milk contains nearly 20% dry matter compared with 12% in cattle).

Newborn pigs begin suckling immediately and do so at approximately hourly intervals over the 24-hour day throughout the lactation period (see Chapter 5 for the sow lactation curve). At the peak of lactation, milk yields of 5 to 10 kg daily with an energy concentration of 1.2 kcal per kg are expected. The amount is partly dependent on the number of nursing pigs. Systems of early weaning are available in which the pig is weaned at 1 day of age (after ingesting colostrum) to a liquid diet followed by transition to a dry diet by 4 days of age. Growth approaching or exceeding that obtained in piglets kept with the sow can be achieved. Such early weaning programs allow the possibility of rebreeding the sow earlier than usual to maximize the total number of pigs produced in a calendar year. The economic feasibility of such a program will be affected by many factors, including relative labor costs, relative prices of sow feed versus milk replacer formula, differences in the efficiency with which nutrients are partitioned for milk production, maternal nutrient stores, and piglet growth, and the long-term effects of early weaning on the reproduction of the sow.

BREEDS

The wide genetic diversity of swine is evidenced by the large number of breeds in different regions of the world. There are more than 150 recognized breeds and at least twice as many genetic groups of swine with traits unlike those of other groups. This vast number of gene combinations provides the basis for animal breeders to utilize the variability in economically important heritable traits to improve biologic efficiency and animal vigor and to develop populations of swine to meet human needs most effectively. Representative breeds and types of pigs are illustrated in Figure 17-2. A more complete presentation of photographs and drawings representing breeds around the world has been prepared by Porter (1993).

In the United States, the numbers of animals registered annually as purebreds by the various breed associations are similar for the Yorkshire, Duroc, and Hampshire breeds (approximately 150,000 to 170,000 for each breed), followed by Chester White, Landrace, Poland China, Spotted, and Berkshire. Several large corporate breeding stock suppliers compete with the purebred breeders to provide seedstock for use by commercial pork producers in their individual crossbreeding programs. Breeding stock available from corporate suppliers are produced from selected matings of animals representing two or more U.S. or European breeds to produce crossbred pigs. Each corporation sells different lines of crossbred (often referred to as "hybrids") breeding stock under their own trade name. Some sources of these specialized lines are Pig Improvement Company, Inc.; McLean County Hog Service, Inc. (Klean Lean); Land O'Lakes Co.; Newsham Hybrids; Danbred USA; Cotswold USA; Babcock Swine Herds, Inc; Farmers Hybrid Companies,

Inc.; and Genetipork. In total, corporate suppliers of swine breeding stock now provide more than 40% of all breeding stock in the United States.

APPLIED GENETICS

Important Heritable Traits

The major role of seedstock producers, whether purebred breeders or corporate suppliers, is to provide breeding stock for commercial producers. Commercial producers and seedstock producers have the same production goals and both seek animals that have high performance in economically important heritable traits, including prolificacy (large litter size and high pregnancy rates in mated sows), high milk production (as indicated by high weaning weights of the pigs), high growth rates of weaned pigs, efficient conversion of feed to body weight gain (low feed-to-gain ratio), and carcasses high in lean meat and low in fat.

Animals with heritable abnormalities such as cryptorchidism, scrotal or umbilical hernia, inverted nipples, structural defects (uneven toes, excessively straight legs, or short pasterns) or that are known to have produced abnormal progeny are excluded from use as breeding stock. Genetic improvements within a herd are achieved by attention to both female and male selection. In the case of sows, replacements in the herd are based on culling sows with inferior production and replacing them with superior gilts. In the case of boars, only those in the upper ranking of their performance test group should be retained for breeding. The performance of the boar is especially critical to genetic improvement within a herd, because its genetic merits will be distributed among many litters, whereas those of the dam will be passed on only to one litter.

Breeding and Selection Systems

Crossbreeding has become the standard practice in swine production because the performance of crossbred pigs has been shown to be superior to that of animals representing either of the parent breeds. This phenomenon is termed "hybrid vigor" or heterosis. Reproductive traits such as conception rate (percentage of mated females that become pregnant) and litter size at birth and at weaning are improved 10 to 20% or more in crossbred matings; growth rate and feed per unit gain are improved 2 to 7% or more, and carcass leanness (loin muscle cross-sectional area) and muscling score are improved 1 to 2% by crossbreeding. These improved performance traits within a litter translate to an accumulated improvement of up to 40% in total litter market weight of crossbred pigs. As a result of these remarkable improvements in performance of crossbred pigs, slaughter swine in the United States are presently composed of more than 90% crossbreds.

Several types of crossbreeding programs are in use, including rotational two- or three-way breed cross systems and terminal cross systems. It is important to recognize

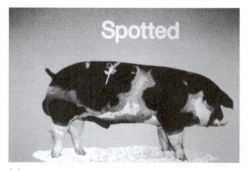

(a)

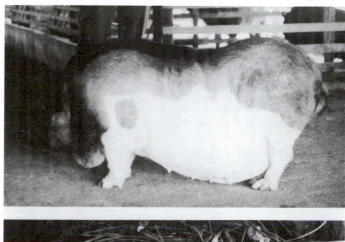

(b)

FIGURE 17-2

Breeds common in the United States: (a) Berkshire, Chester White, Duroc, Hampshire, Landrace, Poland China, Spotted, Yorkshire (Courtesy of NPPC, Des Moines, IA), and (b) other types of pigs, from Asia.

that only a well-planned cross system will produce genetic improvement. An unplanned program may not result in the desired genetic improvement if the breeding stock representing the parent breeds are not carefully selected based on their own superior performance.

Performance Records

Seedstock producers set the standards for genetic improvement for the industry by pursuing their own effective performance test programs. This requires several critical activities: (1) good records of animal identification, measurement of performance traits of all contemporary boars and gilts to be considered for breeding, followed by ranking of all of these animals; (2) consideration of the ranking of individual males and females in the measured performance traits (e.g., growth rate, feed per gain, live animal estimates of carcass leanness, reproduction, and lactation traits) and combining this information with data available on performance of sires, dams, half-sibs, and other relatives; (3) use of an index related to weighted economic values of traits of interest to be used to rank the prospective breeding animals in order of their acceptability. High-ranking boars and gilts within a test group of seedstock will be primary candidates for use as breeding stock by commercial producers.

Genetic Evaluation Programs Available to Seedstock Producers

The rate of genetic improvement in any particular trait is governed by four factors: intensity of selection, accuracy of selection, genetic variability for the trait, and generation interval. A formula is given here to show how these factors relate to each other to determine rate of improvement:

Rate of Genetic Improvement =
$$\frac{\text{(Intensity of Selection) (Accuracy of Selection) (Genetic Variability)}}{\text{Generation Interval}}$$

Progress can be relatively rapid for most heritable traits in swine because of the short generation interval (one year) and the wide genetic variability in most of the economically important traits. With knowledge of the heritability of a specific trait (see Chapter 6 for definition and calculation of heritability), the expected progress in a single trait in one generation of selection is shown in the following example:

Trait: Average daily weight gain (ADG) from 35 to 170 days of age.
Heritability (h) of ADG: 29%.
ADG of females in the population from which the gilt was selected: 750 g.
ADG of selected female: 900 g.

Expected ADG of female progeny of the selected gilt is computed as follows:

Step 1: h × (ADG of gilt minus ADG of population from which she was selected):

29% × (900 minus 750) or 0.29 × 150 (selection differential) =
43.5 g (expected genetic change)

Step 2: ADG of population from which gilt was selected plus expected genetic change:

750 + 43.5 = 793.5 g (assuming the gilt is mated to a boar of equal genetic potential)

If the gilt had been mated to a boar that had an ADG of 1000 g and was selected from a population with an ADG of 800 g, the expected ADG of the female progeny of this mating would be:

$$750 + 1/2 (43.5 + (0.29 \times 1000 - 800) = 750 + 50.75 = 801 \text{ g}$$

Contrast this expected improvement with what might occur in random selection. In random selection, the average does not change, because the probability of a choice above the average is equal to that of a choice below the average.

Expected Progeny Differences (EPDs)

Purebred swine producers and corporate seedstock producers use EPDs to identify superior boars for use as herd sires. By applying the principles described above, the amount by which the offspring of a boar is expected to differ in a specific trait (such as ADG) from the average of all animals in the population is determined (EPD). Using computer software programs such as Best Linear Unbiased Predictor (BLUP) to compare the EPD of large numbers of boars, seedstock producers can select boars objectively based on their EPD for the trait under consideration.

Selection Index

In selection for more than one trait, one can devise a selection index that allows a rank order evaluation of potential breeding stock on the basis of a combined score on several traits. The weighting of the several traits can take into consideration the degree of heritability of each trait and its relative economic importance. Traits with high heritability and high economic importance, such as backfat depth (measured in the live animal by an ultrasonic instrument), would carry more weight in determining the index score than other traits of lower heritability or lower economic value or both. Selection indices are used in boar test stations and other performance test programs to rank the animals for several performance traits using one composite score.

Artificial Insemination and Genetic Improvement

The use of artificial insemination as a tool in genetic improvement of swine, through the use of semen from genetically superior sires, has rapidly increased in recent years. The 1998 Pork Industry Structure Study, reported in *Pork-98,* September 1998, revealed that nearly half of all pigs in the United States are sired by artificial insemination. In the largest herds (those producing more than 50,000 pigs annually), more than 75% of the pigs are sired by artificial insemination.

Computerized Genetic Evaluation Programs

Several computerized genetic evaluation programs have been developed for use by seedstock producers. One of these is STAGES (Swine Testing and Genetic Evaluation System). STAGES is used to assist purebred breeders in evaluating their swine and in decisions related to their individual breeding plans. Evaluation of individual animals is based on the development of economic indices for traits of interest. Each index is derived from a calculated EPD (expected progeny difference), which measures how the offspring of that individual is expected to perform compared with that of an average animal. As such systems as STAGES are accepted and more widely used by the industry, the theory of quantitative genetics finds valuable practical application.

NUTRITION AND FEEDING

Feed represents the largest single component of total swine production costs; it may vary from 55% to as high as 85% of the total cost, depending mainly on the relative costs of feed, labor, and housing in a particular case. Therefore, the formulation of nutritionally balanced diets must be based on economical as well as nutritious feed ingredients. Swine, like humans, have a digestive system that is unable to utilize large amounts of high-fiber feeds. Therefore, they are in direct competition with humans for many available food supplies. The degree of competition in a particular region is related to cultural differences in food preferences. For example, wheat and potatoes are not usually fed to swine in the United States, because the demand for human consumption holds the price too high, but in some regions of the world these crops are commonly fed to swine. Crops such as corn (maize) and soybeans are also widely used by humans, but the supply exceeds the demand, so vast amounts of both corn and processed soybeans (the high-protein residue of the soybean remaining after removal of the oil for human use) are used in commercial swine production, owing to their availability at a price competitive with alternative feedstuffs. See Chapter 8 for a description of the nutrients required by swine and the wide array of feedstuffs commonly used for swine. In this chapter, only the nutrients likely to be deficient in swine diets are discussed.

Water is so commonplace that it is often taken for granted, but it requires mention because of its importance in promoting adequate feed consumption in growing-finishing pigs. Water deprivation for only a few hours dramatically reduces feed intake. Therefore, an adequate water supply is critical for optimum performance of all swine, but is particularly important in growing pigs and lactating sows.

Some fat (about 0.06 % of the diet by weight) is needed to promote the absorption of fat-soluble vitamins. The fatty acids, linoleic and arachidonic acid, are required because the pig cannot synthesize them from other fatty acids. Cereal grains provide adequate fat intake, but when cane sugar, cassava, or other carbohydrate energy sources containing little or no fat make up a major part of the diet, a supplemental fat source may be needed to supply essential fatty acids.

Proteins probably are not required as such, except in the newborn pig during the first 24 to 48 hours after birth. Newborn pigs receive immune proteins from colostrum and absorb them intact from the intestinal tract lumen, thereby offering immunity to many diseases until the piglet is able to produce its own antibodies. The ability of the newborn to absorb intact proteins into the blood is lost after about two days of age. Natural ingredients provide most of the essential amino acids in swine diets after weaning. The amino acids most commonly deficient (the most limiting) are lysine, tryptophan, and threonine. Therefore, pure sources of one or more of these limiting amino acids are often added to the diet of growing-finishing pigs.

The major energy source in swine diets is carbohydrate. Soluble carbohydrates such as starch found in corn and cereal grains are broken down to glucose. Starches contribute most of the carbohydrate in most swine diets, although simple carbohydrates, including glucose and sucrose, high in some crops (e.g., sugar beets, cane sugar), and lactose from whey and other milk products may provide a significant part of the energy intake in some feeding programs. The digestibility of simple sugars and most starches normally exceeds 85%. Insoluble carbohydrates such as cellulose in leaves, stems, and plant seed byproducts (e.g., wheat bran, corn cobs, alfalfa, and grasses) are not well digested in the small intestine but are fermented in the large intestine to produce short-chain volatile fatty acids that can be used for energy. Fermentation of carbohydrates in the large intestine can supply up to 25 or 30% of the maintenance energy requirement of finshing pigs and sows.

The vitamins most likely to be deficient in common swine diets are vitamin A (except when yellow corn is the grain source), vitamin D (unless pigs are exposed to sunlight), vitamin E, niacin, pantothenic acid, riboflavin, and vitamin B12, all of which are normally supplied in supplemental vitamin premixes. Biotin and vitamin K requirements are normally met by microbial synthesis in the large intestine, but reports of deficiency have occurred in swine raised on slatted floors in confinement where coprophagy (the practice of eating feces) is partially prevented. Vitamin C is not synthesized by humans and a few other animal species, but synthesis in the body of swine normally meets the metabolic need, except in young pigs during the stress of weaning.

Inorganic mineral elements required in large amounts (major elements) are routinely added to swine diets. They include calcium (Ca), phosphorus (P), sodium (Na), and chlorine (Cl). Sodium and chloride are supplied as common table salt. Elements required in small amounts (minor elements) and routinely added to swine diets as a trace element supplement are copper (Cu), iodine (I), iron (Fe), manganese (Mn), selenium (Se), and zinc (Zn).

Life-Cycle Feeding

Swine producers tailor the feeding program to the metabolic needs during each stage of the life-cycle. The composition of typical diets fed at each stage of the life cycle is shown in Table 17-5. Feeding during the various stages of the life cycle can be arbitrarily divided according to physiological function as follows:

BREEDING BOARS. A complete mixed diet is fed in limited amounts daily (5 to 6 lb) to prevent overfatness. The daily ration may be increased while in heavy use during the breeding season or in cold weather.

TABLE 17-5A
COMPOSITION OF FORTIFIED SWINE DIET*

Ingredient	Percent
Corn	74.75
Soybean meal, dehulled	23.4
Dicalcium phosphate	0.7
Ground limestone	0.9
Sodium chloride	0.25
Vitamin premix	+
Trace mineral premix	+
Antimicrobial premix	+
Total	100.00

* From National Research Council (1998). The diet satisfies the requirements of a growing pig weighing 40 kg and fed the diet ad libitum. One can completely fortify a corn-soybean meal diet by adding 0.25% table salt (sodium chloride); a vitamin premix that supplies the vitamins deficient in a corn-soybean meal diet (vitamins A, D, E, K, B_{12}, riboflavin, niacin, pantothenic acid); a trace mineral element premix that supplies those that may be deficient (copper, iron, iodine, manganese, selenium, and zinc); and an antimicrobial premix, if desired. The amounts of corn, soybean meal, dicalcium phosphate (source of Ca and P), and ground limestone (source of Ca) are adjusted upward or downward to meet the protein, Ca, and P requirements of older or younger pigs and of gestating and lactating sows and adult boars. A variety of feedstuffs may be used to meet nutrient requirements for animals of different ages, sizes, and stage of production (growth, pregnancy, lactation). Proportions of feedstuffs may be changed or other feedstuffs substituted to effect lower costs. The number of combinations compatible with adequate nutrition is almost unlimited.

TABLE 17-5B
COMPOSITION OF A SOW MILK REPLACER DIET FOR PIGS WEANED AT ONE DAY OF AGE*

Ingredient	Percent
Corn oil or soybean oil	1.0
Tallow or coconut oil	9.5
Soybean flour	10.0
Whey protein concentrate	5.0
Ca caseinate	15.5
Whey (grade 1)	50.0
Dicalcium phosphate	1.7
Propylene glycol	6.0
Artificial sweetener	0.2
Vitamin premix	0.25
Mineral premix	0.63
Antioxidant-mold inhibitor	0.10
Antibiotic premix	0.12
Total	100.00

*Slightly modified from the commercial formula produced by Merrick Foods, Inc., Union Center, WI. The diet can be fed liquid (4 parts water to 1 part dry formula mixed in a blender), or fed dry beginning at about 5 days of age after gradual transition from liquid formula to completely dry feed. Vitamins and minerals to meet the requirements of the baby pig are provided in the vitamin and mineral premixes.

TABLE 17-5C

SUITABLE STARTER (CREEP) DIETS FOR PIGS TO BE FED DURING THE SUCKLING PERIOD AND IMMEDIATELY AFTER WEANING*

Ingredient	Diet A	Diet B	Diet C
	%	%	%
Ground yellow corn	57.5	41.0	—
Ground barley	—	—	12.0
Rolled oats	—	16.0	40.0
Cane (or beet) sugar	—	10.0	12.0
Dried skim milk	12.0	—	10.0
Dried whey (or plasma protein)	3.0	—	—
Soybean meal	16.0	22.0	—
Meat meal	7.5	—	—
Fish meal	—	5.0	20.0
Dried brewers yeast	—	1.0	5.0
Lard (with antioxidant)	—	2.5	—
Sodium chloride	0.25	0.25	0.25
Dicalcium phosphate	+	+	—
Ground limestone	+	—	—
Steamed bone meal	+	1.0	—
Vitamin premix	+	+	+
Trace mineral premix	+	+	+
Antibimicrobial premix	∧	∧	∧

*Ingredients with additions indicated by + are supplemented according to calculated percentage needed to supply the requirement of the pig for each nutrient contained in the ingredient. Proportions of feedstuffs may be changed or other feedstuffs substituted to accommodate cost relationships. Corn or barley may be adjusted to total 100%.

∧Antimicrobials are optional and may vary in identity and in amount in the premix.

GESTATION. The pregnant gilt or sow is fed throughout the 114-day gestation period a limited amount of feed daily (4 to 6 lb of a complete mixed diet) to avoid overfatness.

LACTATION. The lactating gilt or sow is full-fed throughout the lactation period a high-energy, high-protein diet to maximize milk production.

SUCKLING PIGS. During the first 7 to 10 days of suckling, the piglets normally receive enough milk to meet their entire feed requirement. The litter is offered free access to a creep (starter) diet beginning at about 1 week of age. As lactation advances, the rapid growth rate and voracious appetite of the litter soon overtakes the milk supply, and the starter feed consumption represents a major portion of the total nutrient intake. The diet is highly fortified and palatable to encourage early consumption and prepare the piglet for weaning with minimum postweaning growth check.

NEWLY WEANED PIGS. During the early postweaning period from 2 to 4 or 5 weeks of age until about 8 weeks of age, a pelleted starter diet identical to or similar to the creep diet is full-fed. This is a period of high efficiency of feed utilization and rapid growth, so a palatable, highly fortified diet is used to encourage consumption.

GROWING PIGS. This period of the life cycle (30 to 100 lb) represents the time during which average daily weight gain is increasing and efficiency of feed utilization is gradually starting the steady decline that will continue into and through the finishing period. Dietary protein is reduced from the level in the starter diet to match the decline in percentage required in the diet with increasing weight. Free access to feed continues during the growing period to maximize growth rate and feed consumption. In some regions (e.g., United Kingdom, Europe) limited feeding begins during the growing period to minimize fat deposition. Limited feeding is associated with some reduction in weight gain and an extended time to market.

FINISHING PIGS. The protein requirements of the finishing pig (100 to 260 lb) continue to decline as the pig approaches puberty. Free access to feed is customary throughout the finishing period in the United States. In some production systems, as in the case of the growing pig, limited feeding is practiced during the finishing period to improve carcass leanness.

Feeding Systems

Swine production depends on feeding programs that encourage efficiency of feed resource utilization and reduce costs of production. Under some conditions, maximization of feed intake throughout the growing-finishing period is preferable, whereas in others, limited intake during part of the growing-finishing period may be desirable. Moreover, some enterprises produce their own corn or cereal grain supply to be combined with commercially prepared protein-vitamin-mineral supplement, whereas others rely entirely on commercially prepared complete diets. These types of feeding systems are described and compared.

FULL-FEEDING (AD LIBITUM) VS. LIMITED FEEDING. Most commercial swine producers in the United States follow a full-feeding program for growing-finishing pigs. This ensures maximum growth rate and shortens the feeding period, thereby tying up feeding space for less time and allowing faster throughput of animals in expensive confinement facilities. On the other hand, swine producers in some countries practice limited feeding during part or all of the growing-finishing period to reduce fatness and increase leanness in the carcass. Limited feed intake, depending on the degree of restriction, may lengthen the time to market and increase the labor requirement. Sophisticated computer-controlled automatic limited-feeding systems are in use in many places to provide finely controlled and programmed feed dispensing at prescribed intervals and in appropriate amounts over a 24-hour period. Problems of feed wastage, which can be considerable, are minimized with limited feeding, and there is potential for consistent delivery of leaner carcasses than those produced in full-feeding systems.

COMPLETE DIETS VS. FREE-CHOICE FEEDING. Most swine are fed complete diets prepared at a commercial feed mill or in on-the-farm feed-mixing facilities. This enables close quality control and offers the possibility of making frequent minor changes in the formula to accommodate price changes in available ingredients. On the other hand, many swine producers find it economically feasible to store their farm-grown corn or grain rather than sell it for cash and feed it free-choice with a complete protein-vitamin-mineral supplement that may be purchased from a commercial feed mill or prepared on the farm using raw ingredients. Swine are able to select with reasonable efficiency the appropriate mixture of corn and protein supplement to meet their nutrient needs. However, the free-choice feeding system requires vigilance in monitoring intakes of corn (or grain) and supplement and making prompt adjustments [e.g., changing the ratio of feeding space devoted to corn (or grain) and supplement; reducing the palatability of the supplement if it is being overconsumed].

Most swine feeding programs now involve the use of complete mixed diets to minimize labor, improve efficiency of feed utilization, and allow the application of processing methods such as pelleting and other strategies to improve growth and efficiency of feed utilization.

Feedstuffs

A broad array of feedstuffs is available worldwide from which to formulate diets for all stages of the swine life cycle. Feedstuffs can be broadly classified according to their major contributions of nutrients to the total diet: energy sources, protein sources, vitamin sources, and mineral sources.

Common energy sources for swine include corn, grain sorghum, barley, wheat, grain milling byproducts, grain distillery and brewery byproducts, cassava, other roots and tubers, and plant and animal fats. Common protein sources include plant protein sources, notably oilseed meals such as soybean, canola, and cottonseed meal, and grain legumes such as peas and beans. Animal protein sources include meat meal, fish meal, and whey and other milk products. Common mineral sources include salt (NaCl), calcium, and phosphorus supplements such as dicalcium phosphate, defluorinated rock phosphate, ground limestone, and oyster shells. Trace elements (copper, iron, iodine, manganese, selenium, and zinc) are present in many energy, protein, and mineral sources, but often in marginal or deficient amounts, so it is customary to add them as a trace element premix that fortifies the complete mixed diet to ensure adequate intakes. Vitamins are present in virtually all energy and protein sources but often in concentrations inadequate to meet the needs of the pig. Therefore, it is customary to add a multiple vitamin supplement to diets of swine of all ages.

Nonnutritive Feed Additives

Swine fed diets that are nutritionally adequate are often fed small amounts (less than therapeutic levels) of antibiotics approved by the Food and Drug Administration (FDA) of the United States. (For the list of nonnutritive feed additives currently approved by the FDA, see *Feed Additive Compendium,* published annually by the Miller Publishing Company, Minnetonka, MN.) The inclusion of small amounts of antibiotics in swine diets has been shown for many years to improve growth, efficiency of feed utilization, and reproduction. Antibiotic supplementation results in improvements of 10 to 20% in growth rate and efficiency of feed utilization and improved reproduction. The magnitude of improvement has remained about the same during the past 40 years of continued use. Concern has been expressed about the development of antibiotic resistance in humans as a result of feeding low levels of antibiotics to animals. To date, no causative relationship has been established between the longstanding practice (starting in the 1950s) of antibiotic use in animal diets and the development of antibiotic-resistant strains of pathogens in humans. This important issue, which deserves continued research and surveillance, is discussed in more detail in Chapter 11.

Anthelmintics are used in the feed intermittently during the life-cycle for control of internal parasites and other agents are used to control external parasites. Approved compounds for control of swine internal parasites (the most common of which is ascarids, whose life-cycle includes migration of the larva through the liver and lung, creating tissue damage and reduced performance) and external parasites (Sarcoptic mange is the most important) are described in the *Feed Additive Compendium* (published annually by the Miller Publishing Company).

Bentonite, a naturally occurring clay mineral, is often used in pelleted diets to produce improved pellet integrity and reduce crumbling. Bentonite and zeolites (naturally occurring volcanic ash crystals with the ability to adsorb ammonia, mineral elements, and other charged particles) are effective, when added to swine diets, in reducing the toxicity of certain molds and fungi that are often contaminants of corn and cereal grains.

Diet Formulation

Satisfactory diet formulation depends on the use of valid measures of nutrient content and adequacy in the feedstuffs available for use. Chemical characterization of all potential feedstuffs is needed. This characterization is accomplished by proximate analysis, which includes measurement of total nitrogen (N), multiplied by 6.25 to estimate total protein; fat-soluble compounds (ether extract); poorly digested carbohydrates (these are cellulose and lignin analyzed as crude fiber or neutral detergent fiber); ash (this is all inorganic constituents determined by weight loss on ignition of fresh sample); and well-digested carbohydrates (calculated by difference). In addition to proximate analysis, further characterization may include measurement of individual amino acids, vitamins, and mineral elements with specialized instruments. Commercial feed companies maintain quality control of their feeds in their own laboratories or by contracting with specialized analytical laboratories.

Because the nutrient requirements of swine are similar to those of humans, there is a potential for the use by swine of food resources at the expense of food for humans. Fortunately, many of the feedstuffs used for swine are available in surplus of human demand or are unsuitable or unaccepted for use by humans on other grounds. Byproducts of the milling, meat-packing, fisheries, and plant oil industries all provide important feedstuffs for swine that are not well suited for human use. Note the variety of feedstuffs used in the diets shown in Table 17-5a, b, and c.

The growth of computer technology has brought a linear programming and least-cost diet formulation to the farm. Not only commercial feed manufacturers, but individual swine producers use computers to determine optimum combinations of feedstuffs for economical diet formulation.

HEALTH

Infectious Diseases

Some of the infectious diseases are of special significance because the organisms are pathogenic to humans. Examples of such diseases (termed zoonoses) are brucellosis, leptospirosis, erysipelas, and tuberculosis. Fortunately, the likelihood of spread of these diseases to humans is extremely low, because of effective control programs in swine production and effective treatments for affected animals. The major infectious diseases of concern in swine production in the United States include pseudorabies (Aujeszky's disease); swine influenza; mycoplasma pneumonia; atrophic rhinitis; transmissible gastroenteritis (TGE); porcine parvovirus and rotavirus infections; and PRRS (porcine reproductive and respiratory syndrome). All of these diseases may be controlled by aggressive herd health programs of prevention. For each specific infectious agent (pathogen), the producer, in consultation with a veterinarian, must decide which is the best route of control. This approach has reduced the cost of herd health care by emphasizing prevention rather than treatment.

SPECIFIC PATHOGEN-FREE HERDS. Many swine producers maintain specific pathogen-free (SPF) herds whereby, in the initial stage, pigs are removed from the mother by surgery and reared apart from the mother and other infected pigs under laboratory conditions to break the cycle of infection for many pathogens. These "primary" SPF pigs are then reared in isolation from other swine and are used to produce the next generation of SPF (secondary SPF) pigs. It is necessary to continue strict isolation of the SPF herd from other herds and from human traffic through the production facility. Many pathogens can be carried into a swine facility by rodents, birds, and other animals, so complete freedom from infectious diseases is unlikely. Infectious diseases and internal and external parasites are best controlled by a combination of practices, including systematic vaccination programs, routine administration of anthelmintics (worming agents), strict sanitation, isolation from other herds, introduction of new breeding stock only from other SPF herds, quarantine of newly introduced SPF animals; and control of human traffic through the swine facilities.

Metabolic and Nutritional Diseases

Swine are affected by several metabolic diseases, including gastric ulcers; osteoporosis and osteochondrosis (both of which are bone diseases that result in lameness and bone fractures); and porcine stress syndrome (PSS), in which affected animals may suddenly die following stressful activity. The condition is associated with a high incidence of pale, soft, exudative (PSE) pork in PSS animals that survive to market age. Most metabolic diseases have some degree of heritability, so their incidence in a herd may be reduced by avoiding the selection of affected animals or relatives of them.

Common nutritional diseases include parakeratosis (skin disease), cured or prevented by dietary zinc; iron deficiency anemia, cured or prevented by supplementary iron, particularly in suckling-age pigs; hepatosis dietetica (liver necrosis) or mulberry heart disease (dystrophy of heart muscle), prevented by dietary supplementation with vitamin E and selenium. With modern diet formulation, nutritional deficiency diseases in swine can be prevented.

TYPES OF PRODUCTION

Most (more than 90%) of the swine produced in the United States are crossbreds raised for slaughter. The remainder are purebred swine or seedstock produced to provide breeding stock for use by commercial crossbred producers. Purebred and seedstock producers maintain farrow-to-finish systems whereby they can keep thorough records of breeding (including mating dates and identity of both parents) and of animal performance in order to enable them to select superior breeding stock for sale to commercial producers.

Commercial producers (largely using crossbreeding programs) may be divided into three categories with regard to type of production. These are (1) farrow-to-finish, (2) feeder pig production, and (3) finishing feeder pigs for slaughter. The essence of each type of production is as follows:

1. Farrow-to-finish systems cover the entire life cycle of the pig and require records of breeding dates and matings, whether the enterprise is a purebred or a commercial (crossbreeding) operation. Extensive facilities are required to accommodate the handling of all aspects of breeding, farrowing, and growing and finishing of weaned pigs to market weight or breeding. Labor requirements are intensive and varied and feed costs are high relative to other types of production. Because of the large capital investment and the long-term commitment of resources, this type of production is less flexible than other types. However, the farrow-to-finish swine producer has complete control over the entire production system and the entire life-cycle feeding and management of the herd. Complete farrow-to-finish enterprises have continued to dominate swine production in the United States. More than 70% of all swine enterprises in the United States are farrow-to-finish, with feeder pig producers accounting for more than one-half of the remainder.

TABLE 17-6

BENCHMARKS OF EFFICIENT SWINE PRODUCTION PERFORMANCE

Efficiency Measures	Average Values
Litters/sow/year	>2.4
Wean-to-service interval	<7 days
Pigs weaned /sow/year	>23
Farrowing rate	>85%
Parities/sow/lifetime	>3
Replacement rate	<35%
Pigs born alive/litter	>11
Average weaning age	<15 days
Days in nursery	<40
ADG in nursery	>1.0 pound
Feed conversion (nursery)	<1.65 feed-to-gain ratio
ADG in finishing	>1.65 pounds
Feed conversion (finishing)	<2.9 feed-to-gain ratio
Mortality rate:	
preweaning	<10%
nursery	<2.5%
finishing	<1.5%
breeding herd	<3.0%
Whole-herd feed conversion	<3.2 feed-to-gain ratio
Carcass yield	>75%
Average lean/carcass	>52%

Source: Production and financial standards for the pork industry. *National Hog Farmer* (March 1997), p. 18.

Selected benchmarks for efficient production performance on large, modern farrow-to-finish swine operations in the United States are listed in Table 17-6. The values are based on data from the upper quartile performance of selected farms obtaining bank financing in recent years. The average swine producer does not attain these levels of production, but the values illustrate realistic target goals toward which many swine producers may aspire.

2. Feeder pig production requires less total feed and more intensive labor than the other types of production. Feeder pig production is perhaps best suited for those who have a surplus of labor available and a limited feed supply. Feeder pig producers have the disadvantage that they must depend on operators of growing-finishing enterprises for their market and are therefore limited in choice of the time of marketing and the volume of their sales. However, because of the relatively short gestation period (114 days) and short lactation (2 to 5 weeks), short-term decisions on expansion or reduction of the size of the enterprise can be made more easily than with the farrow-to-finish enterprise.

3. Growing and finishing of purchased feeder pigs requires an abundant source of feed and extensive equipment for feeding, housing, and transporting swine to

and from the production facility. Labor requirement per animal is less than in other types of production, because animals are penned in large groups, feeding systems are generally mechanized and may be automated, and manure is usually collected under slatted floors and the anaerobically treated product is removed mechanically for spreading on the land for fertility. Those engaged in growing-finishing enterprises must depend for their supply on those producing feeder pigs.

Trends in Size of Swine Production Units

The average size of the swine enterprise is steadily increasing and the number of individual producers is declining (Tables 17-1 and 17-2). Part of this shift is related to the recent increase in the number of corporate swine producers and the tendency for vertical integration of the industry. Corporate producers often formulate their own feed and slaughter and market their own pigs. Vertical integration became commonplace in the poultry industry many years ago, but until very recently has been resisted by swine producers. Vertically integrated swine production involves the integration of the swine production unit and the feed supplier and often the meat packer by a contract among the parties to stabilize the income of the swine producer and ensure a constant and dependable feed supply and a dependable market for the pork produced. The exact details of individual contracts vary.

Although many large swine production units consist of complete confinement during all stages of the life cycle in modern automated facilities, there is also a growing trend in the other direction for large extensive outdoor breeding and farrowing facilities for feeder pig production. In England, where a ban on the use of farrowing crates forced producers to try outside breeding and farrowing units, sow productivity and piglet survival are comparable to values recorded in conventional indoor units (Table 17-7). Commercial feeder pig production in Colorado and other arid regions of the United States with

TABLE 17-7

COMPARISON OF SOW PERFORMANCE IN INDOOR AND OUTDOOR BREEDING HERDS IN ENGLAND

	Outdoor	Indoor
Number of herds	68	202
Average number of sows/herd	466	218
Litters/sow/year	2.23	2.26
Empty days	42	35
Number of pigs born/litter	11.72	11.82
Number of pigs reared/litter	9.58	9.59
Pigs reared/sow/year	21.4	21.7

Source: John Gadd, United Kingdom. Cited in *National Hog Farmer* (March 1998).

low land values and low human population density has evolved into systemized outdoor sow units, some as large as 3,000 or more sows (Figure 17-3) (McMahon, 1997). Cost for these units is less than one-half that of confinement sow units. They do not need manure handling systems and odor problems are minimal and swine disease levels are reduced. The emerging trend is for swine production in the United States to continue to move toward more extensive breeding-farrowing systems of this kind in response to environmental and animal welfare concerns about intensive swine production in large automated farrow-to-finish confinement facilities.

HUSBANDRY AND MANAGEMENT

The management of swine is perhaps as varied as the environments in which they are raised, yet there are many factors over which the successful manager has control and which must be considered if the enterprise is to be profitable. Specific management practices related to production and marketing are described here.

Sows and Boars

Sows and boars require less care and attention than growing pigs, yet they are the key to a successful swine enterprise. They are often kept in outdoor drylot or pasture lots with minimum shelter during both winter and summer in temperate and tropical environments, and they thrive well as long as shade is provided in summer and a dry, well-bedded shelter, which protects from wind and snow, is provided in winter. Outdoor houses of this kind for pregnant sows can accommodate groups of 15 to 20 if adequate pen area and feeder and water space are provided. Boars that have not been penned together should be kept individually, as they fight ferociously, often leading to injury or death, when placed together. Strong woven wire or other durable fences are required for both sows and boars.

In some commercial herds, boars are allowed to live with a group of sows during breeding season (pen breeding). In purebred enterprises, it is common to hand mate to establish ancestry and breeding date. In commercial herds it is desirable to keep more than one boar with a group of sows during breeding season or to rotate boars frequently between groups of sows to avoid problems of low conception in case of temporary infertility of one boar.

Boars and pregnant sows should be fed limited amounts once daily to avoid overfatness. Feed can be provided in individual feeding stalls or, if sufficient floor space is available to accommodate all animals in a group, the appropriate total daily ration of the group can be evenly distributed on a solid floor.

Care of the Sow at Farrowing

Near term, the udder congests and the underline becomes prominent. When parturition is imminent, the sow becomes restless and begins arranging bedding (if present) in prepa-

(a)

FIGURE 17-3

Outdoor swine production. (a) Sows during gestation. (Note lane separating groups of sows and community shelters in left background and individual A-frame huts for individual lactating sows and their litters in far right background.)

ration for farrowing. The farrowing process may take several hours. To avoid the sow inadvertently overlying or stepping on newborn pigs, a farrowing crate or farrowing pen with guardrails is customarily used (Figure 17-4). Such precautions result in saving an average of one or more pigs raised per litter.

Suckling Pigs

The baby pig begins to explore its environment within a few minutes after birth and soon finds its way to a nipple and begins to nurse. Because of its curiosity, it is important to provide a clean pen environment. An ambient temperature of about 93° F is recommended during the first few days of life, because the newborn pig has inefficient body temperature control and chilling leads to hypoglycemia (low blood glucose). A heat lamp placed above the floor near the farrowing crate or in a protected area out of reach of the sow provides a warm environment for piglets.

(b)

FIGURE 17-3 *(continued)*

(b) Sows during lactation. (Note individual A-frame huts for individual sows and their litters in foreground and community housing for pregnant sows in far background. Such outdoor pork production units are becoming common in the southern and western high plains of the United States and often consist of 10,000 or more sows.)

Several important tasks should be performed during the first day:

1. Tie off the umbilical (navel) cord and dip the severed cord into an iodine solution to prevent entrance of infectious agents.

2. Clip the "needle" teeth. Baby pigs have four pairs of sharp teeth, two on each jaw, called needle or "wolf" teeth. They are of no practical value to the piglet and they may irritate the sow's udder during nursing or injure other piglets when they fight or play among themselves. The labor cost, however, may not always justify this practice.

3. Ear-notch each pig for permanent identity. Any systematic notching system is suitable. A commonly used system is shown in Figure 17-5.

4. Cut off the tail of each pig. This practice (termed tail docking) is advisable to minimize tail biting and infections whenever pigs are to be raised in confinement.

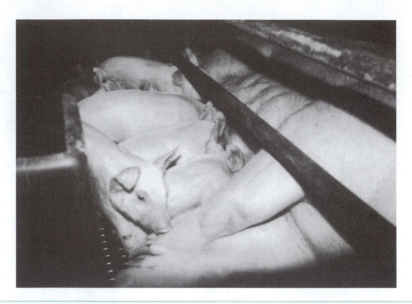

FIGURE 17-4

Sow with litter of suckling pigs.

Other tasks are as follows:

1. On about day 2 or 3, injectable iron should be administered to prevent anemia. The newborn pig is deficient in stored iron and milk provides insufficient iron to meet needs of rapid growth. If piglets are raised outdoors in dirt lots during the suckling period, iron administration is less urgent, but still recommended.

2. Castration of male pigs can be done at any age, but the recommended time is at 1 to 3 weeks of age when the restraint of the animal is easier and the stress on the animal is not great.

3. Creep (starter) feed should be introduced during the second week to encourage dry feed consumption.

4. The final task to be performed on the suckling pig is weaning. Weaning (removal of the litter from the sow) is possible as early as one day of age, but it is customary to allow piglets to remain with the sow for 2 to 5 weeks to take advantage of the high nutritional value of milk and to acquire additional immunological protection.

Orphan Pigs

Occasionally, sow death, lactation failure, or litters larger than the sow can raise occurs, resulting in "orphan pigs." Orphan pigs can be transferred to a foster sow or fed a milk re-

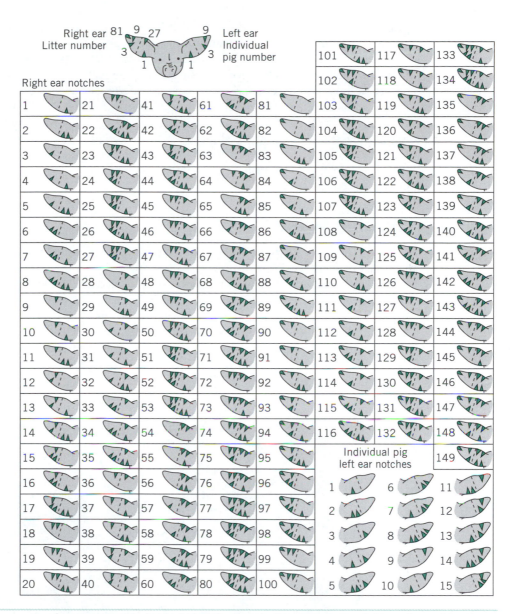

FIGURE 17-5

An ear-notching system for permanent individual identification. In this system, the right ear is used for the litter mark and all pigs from the same litter must have the same ear notches in this ear. The left ear is used for notches to show the individual pig number in the litter. The system allows identification of individual pigs in up to 181 litters. Litter number and notches for that number are shown in each square.

placer formula. In either case, it is essential that colostrum (milk produced on days one and two after parturition) be provided to unsuckled pigs to provide immune antibodies against infection. Commercially prepared milk replacer formulas are available for liquid feeding for the first few days, followed by training the piglet to eat the same formula in dry form. In large swine enterprises in which several sows farrow in a one- or two-day period, it is common practice to transfer orphan pigs to a foster dam with pigs of the same age. In many enterprises, litter size is equalized among sows that have small and large litters to provide adequate milk to all piglets. If cross-fostering is not done during the first few days, piglets will have already established their nursing position on the underline of the sow and will fight to retain it. Also, the sow may not accept foster pigs after the first few days of lactation.

Growing-Finishing Swine

The management of pigs during the postweaning period to slaughter is less demanding than that of suckling pigs. Growing-finishing swine thrive well in pasture lots or in confinement on solid or slatted floors (Figure 17-6), provided a balanced diet is fed and good sanitation and disease and parasite control are practiced. As finishing swine approach market weight their daily weight gain tends to decline, but their daily feed intake continues to increase while efficiency of feed utilization declines.

Modern commercial swine reach body weights of 220 to 260 lb without becoming excessively fat, even when full-fed. When swine have attained market weight, they resist

FIGURE 17-6

Facilities for growing-finishing pigs in confinement. (Note waste lagoon in foreground for odor control and nutrient conservation.)

movement out of the pen to which they have been accustomed. A narrow alley no more than 3 feet (1 meter) to the loading area is helpful in controlling movement to the truck. A loading dock, either portable or stationary, is a necessary part of any swine finishing operation to make loading easier on both pigs and personnel. Marketing of hogs during hot weather is hazardous because of the low ability of swine to dissipate body heat.

MARKETING

Perhaps no other single factor is more important to the overall success of a commercial swine enterprise than having a suitable and dependable marketing program. No matter how superior may be the production methods or the quality of the pig, a profit for the enterprise depends on obtaining a fair price for the product. The per-capita demand for pork in the United States has been maintained at a high and rather stable level for many years. The price paid to the producer is subject to the same supply-and-demand relationships as any other commodity in a free economy. Thus, the price fluctuates inversely to the supply. Demand for pork is inelastic. This means that, for example, although a small increase in supply will cause a decrease in price, the demand will not change greatly. Factors that affect demand for pork include consumer preferences, consumer income, and production and prices of competing products such as beef, poultry, and fish.

Hog–Corn Ratio

The hog–corn price ratio (the number of bushels of No. 2 yellow shelled corn that is equal in value to 100 lb of live hog) is an economic yardstick that helps determine whether corn will be sold for cash or be fed to livestock. For example, if the price of corn is $2.25 per bu and the price of hogs is $45 per 100 lb, the hog–corn ratio is 45/2.25 = 20. The hog-corn ratio varies widely from less than 15 to greater than 30. Changes in hog production generally follow the changes in corn production. An increased supply of corn results in an increase in hog production, which tends to drive slaughter hog prices down, and these low prices in turn affect the ratio. Thus, the price of slaughter hogs, the number of sows kept for breeding, and the hog–corn ratio tend to show a cyclical pattern. Slaughter hog and pork prices in the United States are characterized by huge fluctuations.

Trends in Structure of Marketing Slaughter Hogs

In the United States, the proportion of slaughter hogs directly procured from the producer by the meat packer has steadily increased. The terminal markets (public stockyards), at which swine were formerly assembled in large numbers at a central location often many miles from the farm where produced, have been replaced by more direct methods of sale. Direct marketing of swine from farm to meat packer is now common. A large proportion of market hogs produced in the United States are currently slaughtered in large, efficiently operated abattoirs near the farms on which they were finished for market. Thus, it has become more economical to transport wholesale and retail cuts of fresh and processed pork than to transport live animals in interstate movement, and the mode of transport is almost exclusively by truck. The close association between number of pigs produced and number of pigs slaughtered by state is a result of these factors.

Several large firms that traditionally have handled both slaughtering and processing have reduced the slaughter component of their enterprises and concentrated on processing raw pork. These firms purchase most of their raw material from new, specialized slaughter firms, whose costs are reduced by modern labor-efficient facilities. New pork processing plants tend to be built near pig slaughter plants in locations with favorable labor, transportation, and environmental attributes.

Market Grades of Slaughter Hogs and Carcasses

The U.S. Department of Agriculture (USDA) has established standards for grading the quality of feeder pigs, slaughter hogs, and hog carcasses. The standards for feeder pigs coincide with standards for slaughter hogs. The official USDA grades for slaughter hogs are discussed in Chapter 12. USDA grades of slaughter hogs (barrows and gilts) are predicated on the same two general considerations that provide the basis for the carcass grades, namely, (1) quality of lean and (2) expected combined carcass yields of the four lean cuts (ham, loin, picnic shoulder, and Boston butt). A visual image of the ideal pig as presented by the National Pork Producers Council (NPPC, 1998–99) is shown in Figure 17-7. The figure depicts the ideal pig that represents new targets of performance for the twenty-first century (standards for carcass characteristics, growth rate, reproduction, efficiency of feed utilization, and other measures of productivity. The typical market hog and its carcass characteristics are described in Figure 17-8 (National Pork Producers Council, 1998–99).

Live evaluation and grading of slaughter hogs is described in Chapter 12. Slaughter animals grading USDA No. 1 would be expected to yield more than 60% of their carcass

FIGURE 17-7

Visual image of the ideal hog. (Courtesy National Pork Producers Council, 1998–99.)

Typical Market Pig

Live weight (pounds). 250
Carcass weight (pounds) 184
Backfat, 10th rib (inches). 0.9
Loin-eye area (square inches) 5.2
Fat-Free Lean Index (pct.) 48.0
Pounds of lean meat 88.6

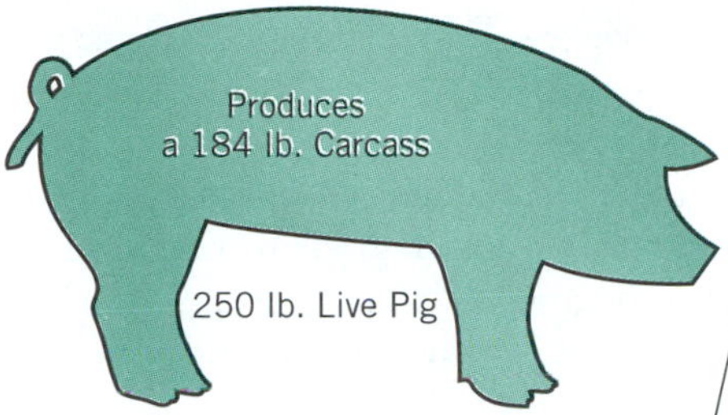

Produces
a 184 lb. Carcass

250 lb. Live Pig

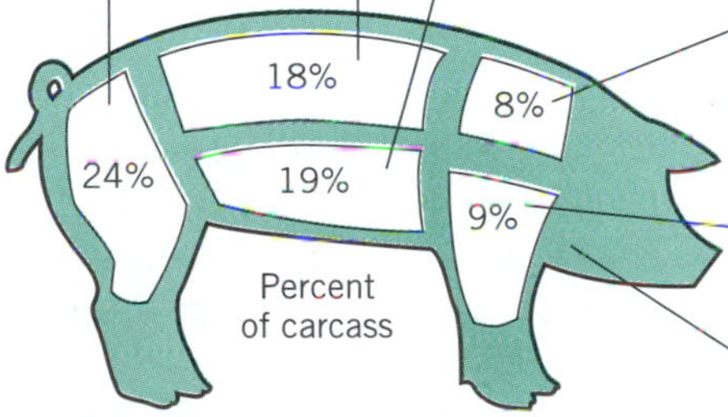

18%

8%

24%

19%

9%

Percent
of carcass

Figures are averages taken from the actual
cutting tests. Carcass data vary, depending
on cutting method and type of pig.

CARCASS BREAKDOWN			
	Retail Pork*	Other Products	Carcass Total
Ham (45.0 lbs)			
Cured ham	25.5		
Fresh ham	2.3		
Trimmings	5.8		
Skin, fat, bone		11.4	
Total	33.6	11.4	45.0
Loin (33.8 lbs)			
Backribs	3.2		
Boneless loin	10.7		
Country style ribs	7.6		
Sirloin roast	5.7		
Tenderloin	1.6		
Trimmings	1.6		
Fat & bone		3.4	
Total	30.4	3.4	33.8
Side (34.9 lbs)			
Cured bacon	19.0		
Spareribs	5.8		
Trimmings	9.1		
Fat		1.0	
Total	33.9	1.0	34.9
Boston Butt (14.7 lbs)			
Blade steaks	4.4		
Blade roast	7.8		
Trimmings	1.7		
Fat		0.8	
Total	13.9	0.8	14.7
Picnic (16.6 lbs)			
Boneless Meat	12.6		
Skin, fat, bone		4.0	
Total	12.6	4.0	16.6
Miscellaneous (39.2 lbs)			
Jowls, feet, tail, neckbones, etc	15.4		
Fat, skin, bone		22.0	
Shrink and loss		1.8	
Total	15.4	23.8	39.2
Total	139.8	44.4	184.2

*Retail cuts on semi-boneless basis. Fully
boneless would show lower retail weights.
Source:NPCC, Purdue University and Texas
A & M University, 1994

FIGURE 17-8

Carcass characteristics and the contributions of wholesale cuts to the total carcass weight of the modern
market hog.
Source: Pork Facts 1998/99, National Pork Producers Council.

weight in the four lean cuts, whereas those of lower grades would yield progressively lower percentages of the four lean cuts, approaching 50% or less for USDA No. 4 hogs. Pork quality and grading are described in more detail in Chapter 22.

Pricing

Establishment of the price of pigs is usually based on the live animal, although the trend is toward pricing based on carcass measurements. In the United States, the pricing or selling options are in three categories: live weight, live weight and grade, and carcass weight and grade (yield).

LIVE WEIGHT. Most swine in the United States are sold as a group without an attempt by the buyer to establish a specific price for each grade or weight of pig in the group. A major disadvantage is that it is difficult to accurately determine the carcass value of a group of mixed grade and weight and it provides no incentive for the producer to improve carcass quality.

LIVE WEIGHT AND GRADE. Swine from an individual producer or from a group of producers are sorted on the basis of grade and weight by visually evaluating each pig. Prices are based on the grade and weight of each pig. Some buyers rely on USDA grade standards but many have their own standards that differ from those of USDA, making it difficult for producers to compare bids between buyers.

CARCASS WEIGHT AND GRADE (YIELD). Swine carcasses are measured for weight and backfat individually on the rail as they pass from the kill floor to the chill room or after placement in the chill room. This system of pricing on carcass rather than live animal grading is common in Canada and many other countries. This method more accurately estimates actual wholesale value of the animal and allows pricing of individual carcasses, providing greater incentive for the producer to supply high-quality swine to obtain premium prices. Meat packers have more than doubled their use of carcass merit buying in the last 10 years. This form of buying is expected to motivate producers more to improve the quality of market hogs. The use of ultrasonic measurement of backfat depth and cross-sectional area of the longissimus (loineye) muscle by improved, rapid techniques as carcasses move from the kill floor to the chill room promises to provide further support for the greater use of carcass grade and yield as the preferred method of pricing swine in the United States and elsewhere (see Chapter 12).

FUTURES OR CONTRACT MARKETING. Futures or contract marketing of live swine (i.e., establishing a price for swine to be delivered in the future) may be used if the producer feels current futures market prices are higher than cash prices will be when the pigs are ready for delivery, or if he or she is unwilling to accept the risk of cash prices lower than current futures prices, even if higher cash prices at the time of delivery are predicted. This practice is called hedging. It has been estimated that 10% or more of pigs marketed in the United States are hedged on the futures market. Producers can do their own trading or negotiate with a meat packer.

EMERGING TECHNOLOGIES

Technological advances are creating rapid changes in swine production. These include:

- Applications of recombinant DNA techniques for producing pure amino acids by microorganisms for use in swine diets.
- Production of vaccines for disease control.
- Potential use of porcine growth hormone (somatotropin, PST) and other agents (a class of compounds called beta-adrenergic agonists, including cimaterol, clembuterol, and raptopamine) that increase protein deposition to increase growth and leanness in growing swine.
- Advances in swine waste management and changes in husbandry methods.
- New knowledge of animal management and behavior is providing improved animal well-being.
- Embryo transfer from the uterus of one female to that of another is possible as a means of increasing the number of progeny obtained from genetically superior swine.
- Technology is emerging to permit cloning of embryonic cells in culture for potential application in swine production. International transport of swine germ plasm in this way would offer an alternative to international transport of live animals.
- Pigs contribute significantly to human medicine by supplying nearly 40 chemical compounds and medicinals used as therapeutic agents.
- Organs and tissues from pigs are used in several ways, including:

Heart valves are used to replace defective or diseased heart valves in humans.

Skin is frequently used in the treatment of severely burned humans.

Organ transplantation from pigs to humans (xenotransplantation) offers promise for the use of pig hearts, livers, and kidneys for transplantation into humans to extend length and quality of human life.

SUMMARY

Swine production is a dynamic and important animal industry. Pork consumption worldwide is greater than that of any other meat and contributes significantly to human nutrition. In this chapter we describe the past, present, and future of swine production; life-cycle of the pig; genetics, breeds, and breeding systems; nutrition and feeding; health and disease control; types of production, including farrow-to-finish, feeder pig production, and growing and finishing swine for slaughter; husbandry and management; marketing; and trends in production systems. New technology promises the use of pig organs (heart, kidney, liver) to replace diseased organs in humans. The pig has become a valuable partner of humans as a food source and as the source of pharmaceuticals and medicinals used in human health and, in the near future, as an organ donor.

GLOSSARY

Backfat   Subcutaneous fat layer over the back of a pig; the thickness is an indicator of the overall fat content of the animal and is used in breeding stock selection and carcass grading.

Barrow   Male castrated before sexual maturity.

Boar   Male swine of any age.

Farrow   To give birth to baby pigs.

Feed efficiency   The amount of feed a pig consumes to gain one unit of body weight; can be expressed as pounds of feed per pound of gain or as pounds of gain per pound of feed.

Feeder pig   A pig weighing more than about 30 pounds and less than about 90 pounds.

Finish   To feed a pig until a market weight of 240–260 pounds is reached.

Finishing pig   Young swine generally weighing more than 120 pounds, but not yet heavy enough for slaughter.

Gestation   Pregnancy, in swine about 114 days duration.

Gilt   Female pig of any age to second pregnancy.

Growing pig   Young swine after weaning, generally weighing less than 120 pounds.

Hog   Swine of either sex, generally referring to immature gilts, barrows, or boars.

Litter   Pigs born to one mother at one farrowing.

Market hog   Young swine ready for slaughter, usually 5 to 6 months old and weighing 220–275 pounds.

Nursing pig   See Suckling pig.

Pig   In the United States, refers to young swine of either sex; in Europe, refers to all ages and either sex.

Piglet   Suckling-age pig, generally up to a few days old.

Shoat   Young weaned swine of any sex, generally weighing less than 100 pounds.

Sow   Female swine having produced one or more litters.

Stag   Male castrated after reaching sexual maturity.

Suckling pig   Young swine before weaning.

Swine   Hooved mammals of the family *Suidae*, genus *Sus*, species *scrofa* (*domesticus*).

Wean   To remove suckling pigs from their mother.

Weanling pig   Young swine after weaning.

REFERENCES

Batterham, E. S. 1995. *Manipulating Pig Production IV.* Australian Pig Science Association, Werribee, Victoria, Australia.

Consortium for Developing a Guide for the Care and Use of Agricultural Animals in Agricultural Research and Teaching. 1998. *Guide for the Care and Use of Agricultural Animals in Agricultural Research and Teaching.* Division of Agriculture, NASULGC, Washington, D.C.

Ewing, S. A., Lay, D. C., Jr., and vonBurell, E. 1998. *Farm Animal Well-Being.* Upper Saddle River, NJ: Prentice Hall.

Hennessey, D. S. P., and Cranwell, P. D. 1995. *Manipulating Pig Production V.* Australian Pig Science Association, Werribee, Victoria, Australia.

Hollis, G. R. (ed.). 1992. *Growth of the Pig.* CAB International, Wallingford, UK.

Leman, A. D., Straw, B. E., Mengeling, W. L., D'Allaire, S., and Taylor, D. J. (eds.). 1992. *Diseases of Swine* (7th ed.). Ames, IA: Iowa State University Press.

McMahon, K. 1997. Pasture farrowing '90s style. *National Hog Farmer,* June, p. 16.

McMahon, K. 1998. Brace yoururself: Big changes ahead. *National Hog Farmer,* July, p. 24.

Miller, E. R., Ullrey, D. E., and Lewis, A. L. J. (eds.). 1991. *Swine Nutrition.* Stoneham, MA: Butterworth-Heinemann.

National Pork Producers Council. 1988. Catalog of Materials and Audio-Visual Aids. De Moines, IA: NPPC.

National Pork Producers Council. 1996–97; 1997–98; 1998–99. *Pork Facts.* Des Moines, IA: NPPC.

National Research Council. 1998. *Nutrient Requirements of Swine* (10th rev. ed.). Washington, D.C.: National Academy of Science/NRC, National Academy Press.

Patten, B. M. 1948. *Embryology of the Pig* (3rd ed.). New York: McGraw-Hill.

Pond, W. G., Church, D. C., and Pond, K. R. 1995. *Basic Animal Nutrition and Feeding* (4th ed.). New York: Wiley.

Pond, W. G., and Maner, J. H. 1984. *Swine Production and Nutrition.* Westport, CT.: AVI.

Pond, W. G., Maner, J. H., and Harris, D. L., 1991. *Pork Production Systems.* New York: Van Nostrand Reinhold.

Pond, W. G., and Mersmann, H. J. 1997. *Biology of the Domestic Pig.* Ithaca, NY: Cornell University Press (in press).

Porter, V. 1993. *Pigs: A Handbook of the Breeds of the World.* Ithaca, NY: Cornell University Press.

Swenson, M. J., and Reece, W. O. (eds.). 1992. *Dukes' Physiology of Domestic Animals.* (10th rev. ed.) Ithaca, NY: Cornell University Press.

Taverner, M. R., and Dunkin, A. C. 1996. *Pig Production.* Amsterdam, The Netherlands: Elsevier.

Thornton, K. 1988. *Outdoor Pig Production.* Suffolk, UK: Farming Press Limited.

Towne, C. W., and Wentworth, E. N. 1950. *Pigs from Cave to Cornbelt.* Norman, OK: University of Oklahoma Press.

Varley, M. A. 1995. *The Neonatal Pig Development and Survival.* Wallingford, UK: CAB International.

Young, L. D. (ed.). 1990. *Genetics of Swine.* Technical Committee of the North Central Regional Research Project NC-103, USDA, U.S. Meat Animal Research Center, Clay Center, NE.

CHAPTER EIGHTEEN
SHEEP AND GOAT PRODUCTION[1]

Sheep and goats have adapted to be raised in most regions of the world including temperate, tropical, and arid lands, at sea level, and in the mountains. Many breeds and production systems are used. Worldwide, sheep and goats are extremely important in providing

---

[1]The review and improvements made in this chapter by D. E. Hogue and M. L. Thonney are deeply appreciated.

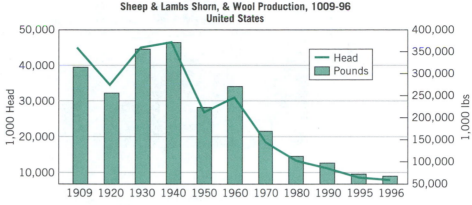

FIGURE 18-1

Sheep numbers and wool production, 1909 to 1996.
Source: USDA, National Agricultural Statistics Service.

meat, milk, wool, mohair, and other resources for humans. In many cultures they are also important in religious ceremonies.

The goat is of particular importance in that it is uniquely adapted to tolerate bitter-tasting plants and has very selective grazing and browsing habits which allow it to select the most nutritious parts of the plant. The goat can assume a bipedal stance; therefore, it is extremely useful as a biological brush controller. Goat milk, with its smaller fat globules, is more readily digested than cows' milk and is, in special cases, used as a substitute for cows' milk for children and the elderly.

In the United States the sheep population continues to decline (Figure 18-1), whereas the goat population is increasing. Although somewhat different, sheep and goat production will be covered together in this chapter. Chapter 26 describes the nature and uses of wool and mohair as animal fibers and their importance in society. The production of sheep and goats in the United States has been hampered by losses associated with predators, parasites, and changing market demand. This chapter provides an overview of the number and location of sheep and goats in the United States and worldwide, and describes the types of production systems, breeds, and breed types, and addresses sheep and goat breeding and reproduction, nutrition and feeding, management, and health.

NUMBER OF SHEEP AND GOATS

World sheep numbers exceed 1.0 billion and goat numbers exceed .6 billion. Countries with the largest numbers of sheep include Australia, China, New Zealand, Iran, and India. Countries with the largest number of goats include India, China, Pakistan, Bangladesh, and Nigeria. Approximately 94% of the world's goat population is found in

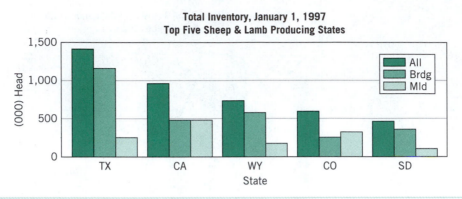

FIGURE 18-2

Total inventory of sheep in the top-five producing states, 1997.
Source: USDA, National Agricultural Statistics Service.

developing countries. The United States has approximately 9 million sheep, primarily located in Texas (1.4 million), California (0.9 million), Wyoming (0.7 million), Colorado (0.5 million), and South Dakota (0.4 million) (Figure 18-2). USDA statistics have not recorded goat numbers until recently. The estimates range from 5 million to 10 million with the states of the Southwest and Southeast having the largest number of goats. Texas has the largest number, including 2 million Angora goats used for mohair production.

BREEDS OF SHEEP AND GOATS

Sheep

Breeds of sheep located in the United States have been described in the *Sheep Industry Handbook* (Table 18-1). Wool type, size, growth, or prolificacy can separate breeds. With the loss of the federally subsidized wool price support program in the United States in 1996, less emphasis is now placed on production of sheep for wool. World market pressures have also reduced the competitiveness of fiber produced in the United States.

Sheep breeds have been classified into categories depending on their use and strengths. Some breeds (termed ewe breeds) are noted for superior performance in traits associated with ewe productivity such as high reproductive efficiency, good milking ability, or longevity (e.g., Rambouillet, Corriedale, Targhee, Finnsheep, and Border Leicester). Some breeds (termed ram breeds) are noted for excellence in growth and/or preferred carcass characteristics (e.g., Suffolk, Hampshire, Shropshire, Oxford, Southdown, and Cheviot). Others such as the Dorset are noted for their ability to breed not only in the fall, but during all seasons of the year. Still others such as the Merino and Rambouillet produce high-quality fine wool and are raised primarily for wool. There are also hair-type sheep important in the tropics and in parts of the United States (Katahdin, St. Croix,

TABLE 18-1

GENERAL CLASSIFICATIONS OF U.S. BREEDS OF SHEEP*

Breed	Country of Origin	Wool Type	Hardiness**	Mature Size***	Growth Rate**	Prolificacy	Avg. Fiber Diameter (Microns)	Ewe Grease Fleece Wt. (lb.)
Barbados Blackbelly	Barbados	Hair	M	S	L−	M	—	—
Boorooia Merino	Australia	Fine	M+	S	L	H	26-20	9-14
Border Leicester	England	Long	M−	L−	M+	M	38-30	8-12
Cheviot	Scotland	Medium	M+	S	L	M	33-27	5-8
Clun forest	England	Medium	M	M	M	M	33-28	5-9
Columbia	U.S.	Medium	M+	L	H	M−	30-23	9-14
Coopworth	New Zealand	Long	M	M	M	M+	36-30	8-12
Corriedale	New Zealand	Medium	M	M	M	M	31-24	9-14
Cotswold	England	Long	M−	L	M	L	40-33	10-14
Debouillet	U.S.	Fine	H	M	M−	M−	23-18	9-14
Delaine–Merino	Spain	Fine	H	M	M	M+	22-17	9-14
Dorset	England	Medium	M−	M	M	M+	33-27	5-8
Finnsheep	Finland	Med. to Long	L+	S	L	H	31-24	4-8
Hampshire	England	Medium	M−	L	H	M	33-25	5-8
Karakul	U.S.S.R.	Carpet	H	M	M+	L	36-24	4-8
Katahdin	U.S.	Hair	M	M	M−	M	—	—
Leicester	England	Long	M−	L	M	L	40-33	10-14
Lincoln	England	Long	M−	L	M	M−	41-34	10-14
Montadale	U.S.	Medium	M	M	M	M	30-25	5-9
Navajo	U.S.	Carpet	H	S	L	L	40-28	4-8
North Country Cheviot	Scotland	Medium	M+	M	M−	M	33-27	5-9
Oxford	England	Medium	M	L	M+	M	34-30	5-8
Panama	U.S.	Medium	M+	L−	M	M−	30-24	9-14
Perendale	New Zealand	Long	H	M	M−	M−	38-30	7-10
Polpay	U.S.	Medium	M	M	M	H−	33-25	6-10
Rambouillet	France/Germany	Fine	H	L−	M	M−	23-19	9-14
Romanov	U.S.S.R.	Medium	L+	S	H−	H	35-28	3-5
Romney	England	Long	M−	M	M−	L	39-32	8-12
St. Croix	Virgin Is.	Hair	M	S+	L	M	—	—
Scottish Blackface	Scotland	Carpet	H	M	M−	L	36-28	8-12
Shropshire	England	Medium	M−	L−	M+	M−	33-25	5-8
Southdown	England	Medium	M−	S	L	M−	29-24	5-8
Suffolk	England	Medium	L	L+	H+	M+	33-26	4-8
Targhee	U.S.	Medium	M+	L−	M+	M	25-21	9-14
Texel	The Netherlands	Medium	M	M	M+	M	33-28	4-8
Tunis	No. Africa	Medium	M	M+	M	M	33-28	4-8

*Modified from SID Handbook, 1996. The evaluation of breeds for hardiness, mature size, growth rate and prolificacy are subjective evaluations as if all breeds were performing in a common environment. **Breeds in boldface are common in United States.**
**H = High; M = Moderate; L = Low.
***L = Large; M = Medium; S = Small.

and Barbados Blackbelly) known for their disease and internal parasite resistance and heat tolerance.

The exhibition of sheep at livestock shows continues to play an important role in educational programs for youth in 4-H, FFA, and other organizations.

Goats

In the United States, there are two major goat breed associations: the American Dairy Goat Association and the American Goat Society. They both maintain registration records for purebred animals in the United States. However, most goats are not registered in breed associations. Breeds of goats (Table 18-2) can be separated into three main types: dairy breeds, meat breeds, and fiber breeds. Dairy breeds include the Nubian (considered the "Jersey" of the dairy goat), Saanen (considered the "Holstein" of the dairy goat), Toggenburg, Alpine LaMancha, and Oberhasli. Meat breeds include the "Spanish" (often a mixture of breeds) and the Boer (imported through New Zealand from South Africa). The importation of the Boer breed has increased the popularity of meat goats and improved the growth rate and carcass characteristics of the meat goat. The increase in population of ethnic groups desiring goat meat has strengthened the U.S. market for goats. The fiber breeds include the Angora (produce mohair) and the Cashmere.

PRODUCTION SYSTEMS

Successful sheep and goat enterprises include systems for producing meat, milk, and/or fiber. Purebred breeders function to provide genetic stock to the commercial producers, whose goal is to utilize sheep and/or goats to produce meat, fiber, and/or milk. Some producers own sheep and goats to utilize pastures or other land resources that would otherwise be underutilized. Combination grazing with cattle is an effective way to harvest mixed vegetation.

Purebred Producers

Purebred producers should have the goal of providing high-quality breeding stock intensively selected for desirable traits. Progressive breeders utilize the best genetic material available and have objective selection criteria. The use of superior-tested sires and the propagation of improved genetics by artificial insemination is more common in purebred than in commercial flocks. The use of performance test stations or on-farm production testing is practiced to obtain extensive recording of production information. The selection practices discussed in Chapter 6 are often used in purebred sheep and goat operations.

TABLE 18-2
BREEDS OF GOATS: ORIGINS AND CHARACTERISTICS

Breed	Origin	Characteristics	Description
Dairy Type			
Alpine	Switzerland/France	Good milk production and milk fat	Straight ears/multicolor
LaMancha	Oregon	Lower milk production, small but hardy	Small 1–2 inch ears
Nubian	England	Lower milk production, high milk fat	Large, tall, long pendulous ears
Oberhasli	Switzerland	Long-distance climbing and grazing	Red or black/straight ears
Saanen	Switzerland	Highest milk producer	White/straight ears
Toggenburg	Switzerland	High milk producer, oldest known dairy breed	Solid fawn to chocolate color/white facial stripes
Fiber Type			
Angora	Asia (United States)	Produce mohair, low fertility	Small frame size
Cashmere	Middle East	Fine hair	Varied colors and sizes
Meat Type			
Spanish	Mixed	Desirable meat characteristics	Crosses of many breeds
Boer	South Africa	Extremely meaty, fast growing	White with red/brown head, lopped ears
Pygmy	West Africa	Small, compact	Black to white dorsal stripe with dark legs

Commercial Producers

Commercial producers of lamb and goat meat utilize a variety of breeds and production schedules. Crossbreeding, as discussed in Chapter 6, is commonly utilized in systems stressing meat production. Crossbreeding results in improved growth and carcass traits through hybrid vigor (heterosis). In both purebred and commercial flocks the production system is usually designed to effectively utilize nutritional resources and to fit market demands.

Effects of Reproductive Characteristics

Variations in reproductive characteristics of sheep and goats must be considered in developing a production system (Table 18-3). Some breeds can only breed in certain seasons (termed seasonal breeders), whereas others can be bred to produce offspring during any season. Also, some breeds are noted for high prolificacy (multiple births), notably Finnsheep and Finnsheep-Dorset crosses, whereas others, notably Merino and Rambouillet, tend to have single births.

The traditional breeding season is in the fall when hours of daylight are shortening, resulting in spring production. Ovulation rate is generally highest in the middle of the fall; therefore, if multiple births are advantageous, fall breeding may be desirable. Under some production systems, such as in extensive range production, multiple births are less desirable, especially if the feed is limited. A good healthy single is more desirable than twins or triplets that are smaller and may have nutritional stresses that reduce survival rate under range conditions. During spring, high-quality vegetation (except in some climates) will be available to meet the needs of the dam and offspring. Systems that utilize confinement and provide all the nutrients to the animal are less restrictive in terms of decisions related to the timing of the lambing season.

When silage, hay, or a complete diet is fed to animals housed in confinement, the nutrition and environmental considerations are less important than the marketing opportunities. Most markets are highest at Easter or during other religious festivities. Early summer markets are also generally higher than late summer. The producer must consider all of the above factors in developing a production schedule. One-time-per-year produc-

TABLE 18-3

REPRODUCTIVE CHARACTERISTICS OF SHEEP AND GOATS

	Sheep	Goats
Puberty (m)	5–12	4–10
Gestation length (d)	146–150	150
Cycle length (d)	15–17	17
Duration of estrus (h)	20–40	20–80
Seasonal breeder	Some breeds	Some breeds
Number born	1–5	1–3

tion is the most popular, but the reproductive cycle (5 months' gestation) will support multiple breeding in flocks capable of breeding aseasonally.

Meat Production

Sheep and goats are used as a source of meat in most parts of the world. In some cases, only culled or disabled animals no longer useful for fiber or milk are used for meat, but in others, meat is the major product and fiber and/or milk are the secondary products in most flocks and herds. In this sense, sheep and goats might be considered dual-purpose animals because of the multiple uses for which they are raised.

Fiber Production

Production systems for fiber production are often heavily influenced by current market demand. Wool or mohair produced in such systems is removed from the animal once or twice per year. When fiber prices are favorable, offspring may be retained longer and grazed solely for the production of fiber. When fiber prices are depressed, the offspring may be sold for meat, adding to the returns from the system.

Milk Production

Milk and cheese from sheep and goats contribute significantly to the human diet in many cultures. Recently, the sheep and goat milk and cheese industry has taken on new life in the United States, where individual producers have developed local markets for their products and have expanded, in some cases, as large suppliers of specialized milk and cheese products. Most dairy goat and dairy sheep operations in the United States are fairly small (3 to 10 head), but some have more than 250 lactating animals and utilize milking machines and modern processing equipment.

BREEDING MANAGEMENT

The breeding season for sheep and goats is dictated by physiological and climatic limitations and production goals. Most sheep and goats are seasonal breeders. Female and male reproductive activity is highest during shortening day-lengths (fall), resulting in late winter and early spring lambing. Reproductive activity of some breeds is aseasonal, allowing out-of-season breeding. Sheep and goats raised near the equator are subjected to little seasonal difference in day length; this relatively stable light-dark cycle throughout the year favors year-round reproduction.

Flushing. Flushing is the practice of increasing the plane of nutrition of the female just before breeding. This increases the ovulation rate and improves conception, especially in females in poor condition. Treatment for parasites or rotation to a new pasture are also effective in improving ovulation rate and conception.

Mating Management

Breeding season is generally limited to two to three months, thereby limiting the lambing and kidding season to two to three months. Males are placed with the females for set lengths of time. Males are often rotated every 17 d (length of estrous cycle) and often are fitted with a marking harness that marks the females' rump as the male mounts and breeds. Date of marking is recorded to predict lambing or kidding date. Marking chalk color may be changed to record matings occurring in the subsequent cycle.

Synchronization of Estrus

Estrus synchronization is possible with hormone therapy, but has not been approved by the U.S. Food and Drug Administration for use in the United States. Methods of synchronization include the use of progesterone-impregnated sponges that are placed in the vagina, or the feeding of the synthetic steroid hormone, MGA (melengestrol acetate) for several days. Upon removal of the sponge or cessation of feeding MGA, the female will then begin to cycle and accept the male.

Artificial Insemination

Artificial insemination (AI) is used with sheep and goats but for greatest success requires laparoscopy and minor surgery. Therefore, its use has been fairly limited; however, several commercial AI companies for sheep and goats carry out successful enterprises.

Accelerated Lambing Systems

Accelerated lambing systems have been developed to increase the production of lamb and maximize use of the facilities and breeding stock. The STAR system (Figure 18-3), developed at Cornell University with the Dorset and Finnsheep breeds, has been extended to other breeds and locations. The high level of productivity achievable in the Cornell STAR system is illustrated in Figure 18-4 by the lifetime performance of an individual Dorset ewe. The system is relatively simple in that ewes are run as one flock and rams are introduced at five times during the year. After weaning at 60 days after the start of lambing, ewes are exposed to the ram again. Using this system, it is possible to have five lambings in three years. The STAR system has been adapted for use in goats.

FEEDING AND NUTRITION

Sheep and goats, like other ruminants, utilize pasture and rangelands and agroindustrial byproducts efficiently. Thus, vast areas of nontillable arid land unproductive for other purposes can be used to produce valuable meat, fiber, and milk for use by humans.

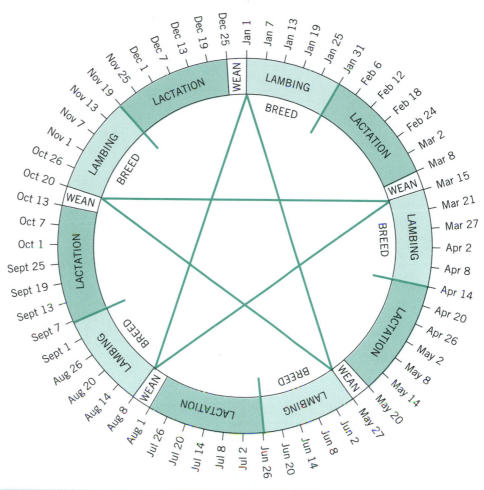

FIGURE 18-3

The STAR system for accelerated lambing. The system was developed at Cornell University by Douglas E. Hogue and Brian Magee. Ewes are kept together as one breeding flock and rams are placed with the breeding group as shown. As ewes approach lambing they are removed from the group until weaned and then reintroduced for breeding. Five lambings in three years are possible with this system.

Nutrient Requirements

The nutrient requirements of sheep and goats during various stages of the life cycle and for various productive functions (growth, pregnancy, lactation) have been described by the National Research Council (1981, 1985), and by Ensminger and Parker (1986). The major nutrients of concern in sheep and goat production are water, energy, protein, minerals, and fat-soluble vitamins.

Cornell Dorset Ewe   No. B314
Date of Birth   1/20/82

Lambing Record

Date	Birth Type	Interval (Mo)	Age of Ewe (Mo)
1/28/83	Single		12
11/2/83	Single	9.6	22
6/15/84	Twin	7.2	29
1/25/85	Twin	7.2	36
8/22/85	Twin	7.2	43
4/2/86	Triplet	7.2	51
1/25/87	Twin	9.6	60
3/27/87	Twin	7.2	67
6/5/88	Triplet	9.6	77
1/24/89	Twin	7.2	84
10/26/89	Twin	9.6	93
5/4/90	Twin	7.2	101

Ewes managed on the Cornell STAR system can lamb at 12 months of age and then at intervals of 7.2 or 9.6 or 12.0 months on a continuous basis. This ewe (B314) first lambed at 12 months with a single lamb followed by a single after 9.6 months. Since then, she has had 7 intervals of 7.2 months and 3 of 9.6 months and produced 8 sets of twins and 2 sets of triplets. As of her most recent lambing, she was 101 months old and had produced 21 lambs in 12 lambings. She reared all the lambs herself, including the triplets except for one twin from the fourth lambing that was cross-fostered.

(a)

(b)

FIGURE 18-4

(a) Lifetime record of a high-producing Dorset ewe managed on the Cornell STAR sheep management system.
(b) Dorset ewe no. B314 photographed with eighth parity twins.
(Courtesy of Jay Miller.)

WATER. Sheep and goats obtain water from their feed (lush, rapidly growing grass may contain upwards of 90% water), as well as from drinking water, snow, and dew. Water deficit reduces feed intake dramatically. Animals can survive without feed much longer than without water. Water requirement is affected by environmental and physiological factors: High environmental temperatures increase water needs by 100% or more. Pregnant and lactating animals require twice as much water as nonpregnant or nonlactating animals; growing sheep and goats have higher requirements than mature nonpregnant, nonlactating animals. Water requirements are usually expressed in terms of lb of water per lb of feed consumed. Water needed per kg of feed for growing lambs increases from about 2 lb water per lb of feed at 15° C to about 4 lb per lb at 30° C. Water needs of pregnant and lactating ewes and does also increase about twofold as temperature rises from 15 to 30 ° C (from 3 to 7 lb water per lb feed in late pregnancy and from 4 to 9 lb water per lb feed in lactation). It is clear that an adequate supply of fresh, clean water is critical to sheep and goats at all stages of the life-cycle.

ENERGY. Energy (see chapter 8, p. 148) is likely the most limiting class of nutrients in sheep and goat feeding. Major sources of energy are pasture (as in federally leased rangeland in the western United States and privately owned ranges and pastures in other areas), hay, silage, byproduct feeds, and grains. Energy deficiency results in reduced growth or weight loss, reduced reproductive performance, and reduced milk or fiber production. High-quality pasture, hay, and silage generally can be used to meet energy requirements most economically. The high-energy requirements of rapid growth, fetal development, and lactation may dictate that grain or grain byproducts (depending upon price) be supplemented to the diet for optimum performance.

PROTEIN. Sheep and goats, like other ruminant animals, rely on microorganisms residing in the rumen to synthesize essential amino acids needed for normal growth and reproduction. However, young lambs and kids whose rumens have not yet developed microbial populations capable of synthesizing sufficient amino acids and vitamins, must be fed diets high in quality protein and vitamins if they are not receiving milk.

Rumen microbes utilize nitrogen (N) of feed origin as well as nonprotein N (NPN) to synthesize amino acids and protein to meet the needs of the host animal. Because feeds high in protein often are expensive sources of N, the less-expensive nonprotein N, urea, may be used as a source of NPN. Urea is toxic if fed at high levels. It can be used at up to 1% of the diet but should not exceed 33% of the total N in the diet (Sheepman's Production Handbook, 1996). Urea should be thoroughly mixed into the diet before feeding and should not be used in diets fed to young lambs or kids or in diets high in forages.

Pastures that are in early vegetative growth or regrowth usually contain enough protein to meet protein needs of sheep and goats. Protein blocks containing natural protein and/or NPN may be provided as a supplement to sheep or goats on pasture, in addition to salt and mineral blocks.

MINERALS. The mineral requirements and toxicities of sheep are well established (National Research Council, 1985); less information is available for goats, but the mineral requirements of the two species appear to be similar. The mineral elements most likely to be deficient in common feedstuffs for sheep and goats are common salt (NaCl), Ca, P, K, S, Mg, I, Se, Co, and Zn. Of the trace (micro)mineral elements, Cu and Se have the most narrow range between the amount required and the potentially toxic level. Sheep are more sensitive than goats and other animals to high dietary Cu. In fact, feeds formulated for other species may contain levels of added Cu that are toxic to sheep. Therefore, in sheep feeding, mineral supplements and other feeds containing added Cu usually should be avoided.

VITAMINS. Sheep and goats require dietary sources of fat-soluble vitamins (A,D,E), but adequate amounts of water-soluble vitamins usually are produced by microbes in the rumen. Grazing sheep and goats generally obtain sufficient fat-soluble vitamins to meet requirements, whereas those kept in confinement and fed low-quality forages may have to be supplemented with vitamin A. Although vitamin A is absent in forages, its precursor, carotene, is abundant in growing vegetation. Vitamin D is contained in green forages and sun-cured hay and converted from a precursor by action of sunlight on skin. Confined animals not exposed to sunlight, paticularly those with heavy fleeces, may need supplementation. Vitamin E is provided in most feeds for older lambs and mature sheep and goats but is often added to diets of lambs and kids to prevent nutritional muscular dystrophy. Vitamin E and Se are both effective in preventing nutritional muscular dystrophy and liver necrosis, both fatal diseases in young lambs and kids as well as in calves and pigs, if not supplemented. Vitamin K is present in green forages and is also synthesized in the rumen, so this fat-soluble vitamin is usually not of concern in sheep and goats.

Feedstuffs for Sheep and Goats

A wide array of feedstuffs is acceptable for meeting the nutritional needs of sheep and goats. As ruminants, they consume forage, including hay, silage, and pasture, as well as byproducts of the grain milling and distillary and other agricultural and food processing industries. Common feedstuffs used for sheep and goats and feed composition tables are

TABLE 18-4
ACCEPTABLE CREEP DIETS FOR SUCKLING LAMBS AND KIDS

	Diet		
Ingredient	A	B	C
	%	%	%
Corn grain	51.5	61.0	—
Sorghum grain	—	—	65.0
Soybean meal	22.0	12.5	—
Cottonseed meal	—	—	13.0
Alfalfa hay	20.0	20.0	15.0
Cane molasses	5.0	5.0	5.0
Salt*	0.5	0.5	0.5
Calcium suppl.**	1.0	1.0	1.5
Vitamins A and D	+	+	+
Total	100.0	100.0	100.0

*Sodium chloride plus trace mineral mixture for sheep (low copper).
**Calcium carbonate supplied as ground limestone or oyster shells.
Source: Adapted from Sheepman's Production Handbook (1996).

presented in Chapter 8. Samples of acceptable rations for sheep are presented in the Sheepman's Production Handbook (1996). Some of these diets are described in Table 18-4 (creep diets for nursing lambs), Table 18-5 (diets for growing lambs), and Table 18-6 (diets for ewes in various stages of production).

GESTATIONAL CONCERNS

After breeding, the nutritional demands during early pregnancy are not much above maintenance requirements. Requirements generally can be met by grazing on pasture or range without energy or protein supplementation or with consumption of a good-quality hay. However, during the last four to six weeks of gestation the nutrient demands increase dramatically. During this time the females must be on excellent-quality pasture or fed a nutritious hay (preferably a legume such as alfalfa or clover) or fed grain as a supplement to the forage. Feeding females too much during early gestation may cause excessive body

TABLE 18-5

ACCEPTABLE DIETS FOR GROWING LAMBS AND KIDS

Ingredient	Body Weight*		
Diet A	To 30 kg	31–40kg	41 to market
	%	%	%
Cracked corn**	48.0	58.0	68.0
Chopped hay	33.0	23.0	13.0
Soybean meal	11.5	11.5	11.5
Liquid molasses	5.0	5.0	5.0
Dicalcium phosphate	1.0	1.0	1.0
Salt***	1.0	1.0	1.0
Ammonium sulfate	0.5	0.5	0.5
Total	100.0	100.0	100.0
Diet B			
Ground ear corn	60.0	30.0	—
Cracked corn**	—	30.0	60.0
Chopped alfalfa hay	27.5	27.5	27.5
Soybean meal	6.0	6.0	6.0
Liquid molasses	5.0	5.0	5.0
Salt***	1.0	1.0	1.0
Ammonium sulfate	0.5	0.5	0.5
Total	100.0	100.0	100.0

* Body weight of most goat breeds is less at each phase of the growing period. Therefore, changes in diet composition should be based on attainment of a given percentage of acceptabe market weight rather than on actual body weight.

** Grain sorghum or other grains may be substituted for some or all of the corn if a source of vitamin A is provided (grains except corn are deficient in vitamin A).

***Sodium chloride plus a trace mineral mixture for sheep (including selenium but low copper).

Source: Adapted from Sheepman's Production Handbook (1996).

TABLE 18-6

ACCEPTABLE DIETS (AS FED) FOR EWES DURING MAINTENANCE, EARLY AND LATE GESTATION, AND LACTATION (POUNDS PER HEAD PER DAY)*

Production State	Diet	Alfalfa Hay	Corn Silage	Corn	Soybean Meal	Salt/Mineral**
Maintenance	A	3.0	—	—	—	0.05
	B	—	6.0	—	0.2	0.05
Gestation (1st 15 wk)	C	3.5	—	—	—	0.05
	D	—	6.0	—	0.25	0.05
Gestation (last 4 wk) 130–150% lambing	E	3.5	—	0.75	—	0.05
	F	—	6.0	0.75	0.40	0.05
150–225% lambing	G	3.5	—	1.25	—	0.05
	H	—	7.0	1.00	0.50	0.05
Lactation (1st 6–8 wk)***	I	4.0	—	2.00	—	0.05
	J	—	9.0	1.00	0.85	0.05

*Does may be fed similar diets, but daily intake per head should be adjusted to accommodate differences in body weight.
**50% salt (sodium chloride)–50% dicalcium phosphate, including a sheep trace mineral mix containing low copper.
***Amount per head daily assumes suckling a single lamb. Ewes and does nursing more than one offspring should receive a proportionately higher daily intake to accommodate the increased milk production needed to support the extra offspring.
Source: Adapted from *Sheepman's Production Handbook* (1996).

fatness, which is unhealthy and uneconomical. Evaluation of body fatness four to six weeks before parturition is important to determine whether nutritional changes are needed.

Vaccinations and Injections

Usually a multiple vaccine containing protection against enterotoxemia, a disease caused by *Clostridium perfringens,* and against tetanus is given along with an injection for selenium and vitamin E (in areas of selenium deficiency). After vaccination, the ewe develops antibodies which are passed on to her lambs through colostrum. A veterinarian or extension agent should be consulted to obtain recommendations for a vaccination program appropriate for a particular geographic region.

Specific Diseases of Pregnancy and Lactation

Specific problems of concern during gestation include the following:

PREGNANCY TOXEMIA (KETOSIS). This *metabolic disease* (also termed twin lamb disease) is caused by insufficient energy uptake in late pregnancy. It typically occurs in older extremely fat or thin ewes or does, often carrying multiple fetuses. The high demand for glucose by the developing fetuses or the lactating mammary gland puts added stress on the ewe or doe. The reduced volume of the digestive tract in fat animals may restrict feed intake and limit energy available for use by the pregnant dam and developing fetuses. Thin animals often lack the ability to mobilize enough energy from body reserves to meet fetal or mammary gland needs for glucose. Ketosis results because of the breakdown of body fat reserves to ketone bodies. Early signs of ketosis include a general apathy and reduced activity, grinding of teeth, and frequent urination. As ketosis progresses, the urine and breath smell sweet (due to the excretion of ketones in the expired air and in the urine), and eventually the ketosis may be fatal. Treatment is usually by administration of intravenous glucose and oral glycerin or propylene glycol.

CHLAMYDIOSIS. This infectious agent produces abortions in ewes and does and is highly contagious, including transmission to humans. Extreme care should be used in handling aborted fetuses and tissues. The incubation period (the time from exposure to manifestation of the disease) is 60 to 90 days after infection. Vaccines are available to help control chlamydiosis.

TOXOPLASMOSIS. This disease is caused by a coccidial microbe that results in abortions or weak newborns. The disease is transmissible to humans. The organism is carried by cats and spread through their feces. Consumption during pregnancy of contaminated hay or grain may cause toxoplasmosis.

HYPOCALCEMIA (MILK FEVER). This is a nutritional disease caused by the inability of the lactating dam to maintain adequate blood Ca levels during the period of large demands for Ca secretion into the milk in lactation. The usual symptoms include sudden reduced appetite, muscle rigidity, and inability to stand. The condition responds dramatically to intravenous injection of calcium.

PROLAPSES. Vaginal and rectal prolapses vary from an occasional small to large (softball-size) protrusion of the inner vagina or rectum. The rapid growth of the fetus(es) and/or bulky diets can aggravate the situation in affected ewes or does. Stitching the vulva (with a knot that can be quickly released at birth) can contain large prolapses. Since the incidence of prolapses seems to be inherited, it is often a major criterion for culling. Moldy grains usually are the cause of rectal prolapse in feedlot lambs.

LAMBING AND KIDDING MANAGEMENT

Sheep and goats are adaptable to a variety of housing and management practices before and during parturition. The birth can take place on the range or pasture with little intervention or in smaller areas inside a barn. Climatic conditions and predator concerns often dictate type of management. A newborn is very susceptible to environmental stress and is easy prey for predators. Ewes with wool can be sheared a few weeks before parturition (if weather will allow or if housed in a barn) or the ewe can have the wool removed around the vulva and mammary glands (*crutching* or *tagging*) to aid in easy delivery and ease in nursing. A newborn can mistake a piece of wool near the udder as the teat and expend a lot of energy trying to get milk from a clump of wool. Shearing or crutching will help reduce this problem. Hair-type sheep and shorthaired goats require less management.

The *time of day that parturition takes place* can be modified by feeding management, if the females are being supplemented with hay and grain. To increase the probability that ewes lambed during the daylight hours, the feeding program at North Carolina State University was modified. Ewes typically had access to hay at all times but were fed their grain supplement consistently at 4:30 P.M. This combined with reduced disturbance at night changed the incidence of lambing during the day from 60% to 95%.

Signs of approaching parturition can include the following: the udder will swell in preparation for lactation (usually observed a few days before parturition); the uterus will drop so as to appear that the abdomen has shifted lower; the ewe or doe may isolate herself; suspend eating; paw at the ground attempting to build a nest; become restless, alternately standing and lying. Parturition usually occurs within two to four hours after the initiation of labor. Often there may be an hour between births when multiples are born. Once the young are born it is important that they are able to breathe and then nurse. The mother generally licks the new offspring and removes the surrounding membranes, but close observation can save a newborn. If the female is old or if it is the first delivery there is a higher chance that the attendant may need to aid in the first breath. Removing the membranes is generally sufficient, but often stimulation of breathing is required. A clean piece of straw can be used to "tickle" the inside of the nostril, causing a sneeze and the initiation of breathing.

The next concern is to assure the young have nursed to obtain the needed colostrum (first secretion from the mammary gland). At parturition, the colostrum is very thick and it is often difficult for the young to start the initial flow. Care of a newborn and mother is often referred to as strip, clip, and dip. *Strip* the teats, to make sure milk (actually colostrum) is flowing. *Clip* the umbilical cord within an inch or two of the lamb's navel and then *dip* the umbilical cord in a 7% tincture of iodine solution, making sure it is thoroughly covered. A wide-mouth jar (preferably plastic) or a spray bottle works nicely.

If the newborn is extremely weak and unable to nurse, tube feedings may be needed. It is a good idea to keep frozen *colostrum* on hand. Colostrum can be obtained from a ewe, doe, or cow and frozen for later thawing and use. Artificial colostrum mixes are also available. The colostrum should be heated to body temperature (but not in a microwave oven), placed in a syringe, and then given by tubing directly to the stomach. Weak newborns may require several tube feedings before they can get along on their own. For the first two to three days after birth, the newborn(s) and mother are often placed in smaller pens to facilitate bonding between the mother and offspring. This allows for easy checking of newborns and reduces death loss associated with starvation due to separation that can occur in larger groups.

Newborns with mothers that are not producing enough milk may need to be supplemented with milk from a bottle. A normal baby bottle and nipple can be used but the opening in the nipple needs to be enlarged to allow the lamb to obtain milk easier. Lambs and kids can be trained to use a liquid feeding system completely away from the mother. Such "lamb bars" are often used with breeds of sheep that have multiple births (such as Finnsheep).

While handling the female at lambing, it is also good practice to treat her for internal parasites with an *oral dose of a drug that interferes with the life cycle of the parasite* (termed anthelmintic). There is a natural rise in worm egg output from two weeks before to six weeks after parturition. Treatment to reduce parasite burden at this time will reduce parasite burden in the female and on the pasture or range. (Control of internal parasites in sheep and goats is discussed further under Diseases and Parasites later in this chapter).

At birth, the newborn should be identified with an *ear tag, tattoo,* and/or *ear notch.* The weight and sex of the newborn is also recorded at this time. Males that are not to be kept for reproduction can be *castrated* with use of an elastrator band or by surgical removal of the testis. Wool-type sheep should also be *docked,* either by elastrator band, surgically, or with an electrical tail docker. Docking at young ages is desirable and less stressful to the animal.

Lactation is the period of highest nutrient demand for the ewe or doe. Therefore, adequate feeding is required to achieve good milk production. A normal gestating and lactating female has changes in body weight (Figure 18-5), reflecting an increase in body weight associated with the growth of the fetus(es), a dramatic loss in weight associated with parturition, and then a continued loss during lactation. A female in heavy lactation usually does not consume enough feed to meet the high nutrient demand for milk production. Therefore, even if a high-quality diet is fed, a weight loss may be expected. She requires a high-quality feed that could be supplied by pasture (rye, wheat, oat, or fescue, or native or perennial grass), silage (corn or sorghum), or by hays supplemented with grain. Depending on size of the female and milk production, a female bearing a single offspring might need 0.5 kg of grain supplement, whereas a female with twins or triplets might need as much as 1.0 to 1.5 kg of supplement per day. Females must be fed to con-

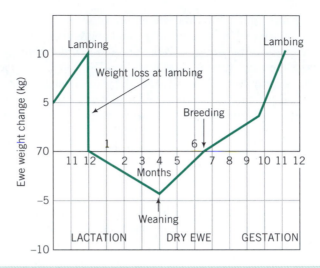

FIGURE 18-5

Expected weight changes of a 70-kg ewe with twins during a one-year production schedule.
Source: Adapted from Sheep Industry Development Program's *Sheep Industry Handbook* (1996).

dition and quantities will vary depending on quality of hay and environmental conditions. High quality of available pasture, as in spring and early summer, may provide for the female's needs without supplementation of grain. Pregnant and lactating females fed silage or moldy hay may be susceptible to *listeriosis* (circling disease), which can cause abortions and death. Care must be taken to avoid feeding moldy hay or, when feeding silage, to be sure the silage bunks (feeders) are kept clean.

Heavy-milking females can develop *mastitis (inflammation of the mammary gland)* if the supply of milk produced by the female exceeds the demand by the offspring or if the female is physically exposed to the bacteria causing mastitis. The udders should be checked and observed for signs of mastitis. A female not letting the offspring nurse may be a sign of pain to the udder and indicative of mastitis. Other signs include an udder that is large and swollen, sometimes red and hot to the touch. If the udder is cold to the touch and bluish in color then mastitis can be a significant problem that may not be treatable. With any of these symptoms treatment should begin as soon as possible with antibiotics, both systemic and applied directly to the teat by infusion. It may help to remove the milk from the udder. Mastitis can also be a problem at weaning. The female has produced milk for the offspring and then suddenly at weaning she must stop the supply of milk. To help reduce the incidence of mastitis associated with weaning it is often a good practice to reduce the feed intake a few days before weaning and to reduce the water intake.

Sore mouth is another disease of concern to the gestating or lactating female or offspring. The disease, caused by a virus, is well named because it produces a scabby covering and sores around the mouth and nose. It is very contagious and can infect the teat and udder of the dam and be transmitted to humans (the human disease is called *orf*). Children should not be allowed to have contact with infected animals.

GROWING AND FINISHING

Many lambs and kids are marketed directly off the female without additional feeding. This is especially done for *hothouse* production where smaller milk-fat animals are desired. The majority of weaned animals are grown and finished for market on a combination of grazing followed by grain feeding. The original producer of the animal may retain ownership and grow and finish the animals for market. Feeder lambs or kids are animals that have been weaned and are grown to market weight and condition. When available, good-quality range or pasture is grazed to provide slower but cost-effective growth. Feeder animals are sometimes put directly into the feedlot where more rapid gains are realized. Sheep and goats are adaptable to either method of growth. Producers with small flocks who market animals directly off their farm will often use a system of finishing called *grain on grass.* In this system, the animals remain on pasture but are supplemented grain to increase growth and to achieve desired market finish. Lambs placed in the feedlot are generally about 65 to 80 pounds (goats are smaller) and need to gain an additional 30 to 40 pounds. Gains in the feedlot are dependent on breed and previous handling but generally will average 0.75 to 1.25 or more pounds per day.

DISEASES AND PARASITES

Regardless of system, several management practices must be followed to prevent disease and parasite losses. Some of these practices are briefly described below.

Rapidly growing lambs and kids are susceptible to *overeating disease* (enterotoxemia), which can be prevented through vaccination. Usually females would be vaccinated during gestation and pass some immunity to the offspring but a booster vaccination is necessary for growing animals. Treatment for *internal parasites* is also important especially for animals that remain on pasture. As with adults, *footrot* is a very serious disease in young sheep and goats. To help prevent footrot, the feet are trimmed to remove long curled growth that can trap mud, manure, and organisms that cause the problem. Diets can also be fortified with zinc to reduce the problem. A vaccine is available for footrot but various resistant strains have developed which are not controlled by the vaccine. Footbaths that contain formaldehyde, copper, or zinc sulfate can be used to treat footrot. The animals are forced to stand in the solution that penetrates into the hoof, helping to kill the organism and toughen the foot. Nutritional concerns include *white muscle disease (muscular dystrophy), urinary calculi,* and *copper poisoning.* White muscle disease was discussed earlier but deserves attention here. It can be prevented by injection or diet fortification of selenium. Urinary calculi, often called water belly, is a nutritionally caused disease aggravated by an imbalance of calcium and phosphorus. The ratio of Ca to P in the diet should be at least 2 to 1. Crystals (stones) of mineral salts accumulate in the bladder and are unable to pass through the urinary system to be excreted. Ammonium chloride in the diet (0.25 to 0.50%) acidifies the urine and helps prevent urinary calculi. Difficult urination or straining is observed and severely affected animals die from a ruptured bladder. The presence of copper at only 25 parts per million in a feed (an amount often supplemented to cattle and pigs) can cause copper poisoning and death in sheep. Care should be taken to avoid mineral mixes formulated for cattle, horses, or swine.

Caseous lymphadenitis is a serious disease that can infect animals at young ages but is generally not seen except in older animals. It is caused by the bacterium *Corynebacterium pyogenes,* which grows in the lymphatic system and is observed as lymphatic abscesses that discharge a caseous paste. Infected animals should be culled or at least separated from the rest of the healthy animals. *Johnes disease* is transmitted by fecal contamination. Animals may not show signs of the disease until later life. Adults with Johnes disease become unthrifty and thin and show a progressively deteriorating condition. There are no tests to identify sheep that are carriers. *Ovine progressive pneumonia* is passed from adult to young primarily through the colostrum. Tests are available to determine carriers. Strict culling is often used to attempt to reduce the incidence of both of these diseases.

Moldy grains, especially corn, often contain estrogenic compounds that cause rectal prolapse in growing-finishing lambs. Care should be taken to avoid the use of grains contaminated with molds and fungi in feedlot diets for lambs.

Internal Parasites

One of the major limitations to sheep and goat production is the continual battle with internal parasites. The general cycle (Figure 18-6) involves the forage, animal, and feces. The internal parasite produces eggs that are distributed on the ground through the feces. The larva hatches from the egg, moves up the forage in water (dew), and is consumed by

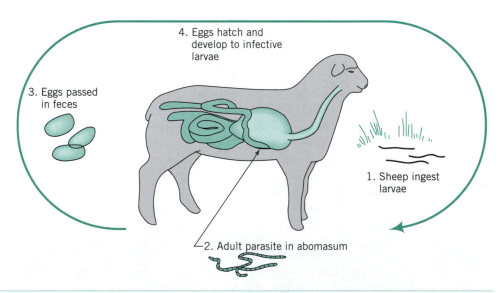

FIGURE 18-6

The general life cycle of the stomach roundworm. The cycle starts with larvae on the forage consumed by the animal. Adult worms mature in the digestive tract where eggs are deposited, then excreted in the feces and released in the grass. The eggs hatch larvae and the cycle continues.

the animal to start the cycle again. In the animal the worm often attaches to the intestinal lining and removes blood. Internal parasites greatly affect the economics of sheep production. Although expensive, anthelmintics are one tool to treat parasites.

MARKETING

Marketing can be a major limitation to profitable sheep and goat production. Producers with small flocks often develop their own market with individuals, meat markets, or restaurants. Larger cooperatives have been developed to pool production and allow marketing to occur year-round. Utilizing auction markets to sell live animals is generally ineffective. Some state sheep organizations sponsor statewide graded sales to attract buyers and truck load offerings. New lamb and kid processing plants are risky operations with low success rates. Before entering into the production of sheep and goats a marketing plan should be developed. Successful marketing of the products of the sheep and goat industry requires efforts by the producer to determine what consumers want and then to develop the production technologies and marketing strategies required to satisfy those wants. The unique nature of sheep and goat production in yielding multiple products (i.e., meat and fiber and even milk) offers opportunities for an expanded industry in the United States.

SUMMARY

Sheep and goats make a significant contribution to society worldwide by supplying meat, fiber (wool and mohair), and milk and milk products. This chapter surveys the numbers and distribution of sheep and goats in the United States and worldwide, and describes breeds, production systems, feeding and management, disease and parasite control, and marketing. Wool and mohair production and uses are described in Chapter 26.

GLOSSARY

Anthelmintic   A compound fed or otherwise adminstered to an animal to disrupt the life-cycle of one or a group of internal parasites in an effort to eliminate the parasite.

Anestrous period   The time when the female does not cycle or exhibit estrus (heat)—the nonbreeding season.

Breed   Animals with a common ancestry and characteristics, which distinguish them from other groups within the same species.

Buck   Uncastrated male of sheep (same as ram).

Caprine.   Pertaining to goats.

Castrate   To remove the testicles or ovaries.

Colostrum   First fluid secreted by the udder for a few days pre- and postpartum.

Crossbred   Animal whose parents were of different breeds.

Crossbreeding   Mating of animals of different breeds.

Cryptorchid   A testis that fails to descend is

called a *cryptorchid testis.* An animal in that condition is called a *cryptorchid.*

Culling   The process of eliminating undesirable animals.

Cwt.   An abbreviation for 100 pounds of weight.

Dam   The female parent.

Dock   To cut off the tail.

Doe   Female goat.

Dystocia   Abnormal or difficult labor, causing difficulty in delivering the fetus.

Environment   All of the conditions an animal is subjected to.

Estrous cycle (heat cycle)   Cycle of events from one heat period (or estrous period) to the next.

Estrus (heat)   The period when the female is receptive (will stand for mating) to the male.

Ewe   Female sheep, any age.

Flock   A group of sheep or goats.

Free choice   Feed available to animal at all times (same as self-fed).

Full-fed   Provided with as much feed as the animals will normally consume.

Gestation period   The period from conception to birth.

Grade (breeding animal)   Any animal (not purebred or not eligible for registration) that possesses the major characteristics of a breed (grade Angus, grade Hereford, etc.).

Heat period   The period when the female will accept the male (same as estrous period).

Kid   Immature goat (male or female).

Lactation period   The period of milk secretion.

Lamb   Immature sheep, under 1 year of age (male or female).

Libido   Male sex drive.

Mammal   Any animal that gives birth to live young, is warm-blooded, and suckles or provides milk for its young.

Mastitis   Inflammation of the mammary gland.

Maternal   Pertaining to the mother.

Ovine   Pertaining to sheep.

Parturition   The process of giving birth.

Pedigree   A record of ancestry.

Photoperiod   Length of day (or length of period artificial light is provided).

Polled   Naturally hornless.

Postpartum   Occurring after birth.

Prepartum   Occurring before birth.

Primal cuts   The most valuable cuts on a carcass (beef = loin, rib, round; swine = loin, ham, shoulder; lamb = leg, loin, rack, and shoulder).

Progeny   Offspring.

Puberty   Age at which the reproductive organs become functional and secondary sex characteristics develop.

Prolific   Tendency to produce many offspring.

Purebred   An animal of a recognized breed that is eligible for registration in the official herd book of that breed.

Ram   Uncastrated male of sheep, any age.

Registered   An animal registered (listed) in the herd book of a breed association.

Ruminant   Animals which have a four-compartment stomach (rumen or paunch, reticulum, omasum, abomasum).

Semen   A mixture of sperm and accessory sex gland fluids.

Settle   To become pregnant or conceive.

Sire   Male parent.

Unsoundness   Structural defect in an animal.

Wean   To separate nursing offspring from their dam so that they no longer receive milk.

Wether   Male sheep, castrated before secondary sex characteristics develop.

Yearling   Animals between 1 and 2 years of age.

REFERENCES

Battaglia, R. A., and Mayrose, V. B. 1981. *Handbook of Livestock Management Techniques.* New York: Macmillan.

Botkin, M. P., Field, R. A., and Johnson, C. L. 1988. *Sheep and Wool: Science, Production, and Management.* Englewood Cliffs, NJ: Prentice-Hall.

Ensminger, M. E., and Parker, R. O. 1986. *Sheep and Goat Science.* Danville, IL: Interstate Printers and Publishers.

National Research Council. 1981. *Nutrient Requirements of Goats.* Washington, D.C.: National Academy Press.

National Research Council. 1985. *Nutrient Requirements of Sheep.* Washington, D.C.: National Academy Press.

The Sheepman's Production Handbook. 1996. American Sheep Industry Assoc., 6911 S. Yosemite, Englewood, CO.

Multimedia

Cornell University Sheep Program—STAR (videotape; 22 min.). 1995. STAR Sheep Management System, video $24.95; http://www.cce.cornell.edu/publications/order.html (click to order).

Farm Flock (videotape; 10 min.). National Sheep Improvement Program, Dept. of Animal Science, Iowa State University, Ames, IA 50010.

Range flock (videotape; 10 min.). National Sheep Improvement Program, Dept. of Animal Science, Iowa State University, Ames, IA 50010.

Sheep Breed Identification (slide kit; 15 breeds of sheep). Vocational Education Productions, California Polytechnic State University, San Luis Obispo, CA 93407.

Farm Flock Production Systems; Sheep Obstetrics; Assuring Baby Lamb Survival; Castration, Docking and Identification; Raising Orphan Lambs; Marketing Practices; Feeding the Farm Flock; Applying Health Care Practices; Feed and Water Delivery Systems; Sheep Handling; and Using Equipment and Sheep Psychology (videotape series), Agricultural Products and Services, Bloomington, MN 55420.

Sheep Management Practices I & II. (videotape; 55 & 44 min.). 1989. CEV Multimedia, Lubbock, TX.

Market Lamb and Breeding Sheep Evaluation (videotape; 60 min.). 1991. CEV Multimedia, Lubbock, TX.

Selection and Care of Market Lambs (videotape; 44 min.). 1994. CEV Multimedia, Lubbock, TX.

CHAPTER NINETEEN
AQUATIC ANIMALS

R. T. LOVELL
AUBURN UNIVERSITY
AUBURN, AL

The farming of aquatic animals under partially or intensively managed conditions is one of the fastest-growing food production industries. This industry, aquaculture, supplies a significant portion of the world's consumption of several popular fish and crustacean species. Aquaculture has demonstrated extremely rapid growth during the last two decades. For example, channel catfish farming in the United States has grown from near obscurity in 1970 to an annual yield of over 223,000 tons in 1996 (USDA, 1997), and is still growing. Farming of penaeid (marine) shrimp, primarily in South and Central America and Asia, is the fastest-growing aquaculture enterprise worldwide, supplying approximately 43% of the world's consumption.

Ocean pen culture of salmon is a thriving idustry in Norway and other areas of Western Europe, where it provides 90% of the salmon consumed, a valuable export commodity. High-value marine species, such as sea breams, sea basses, turbot, and yellow tail tuna, are being cultured on a large commercial scale in Europe and Japan. Aquaculture is more than a science in its infancy; it is now recognized as a viable and profitable enterprise worldwide. It will continue to grow and supply an increasingly larger percentage of fishery products. This is assured because of a general decline in the supply of wild-caught fish from the oceans.

EVOLUTION OF AQUACULTURE

Aquaculture, or fish farming, was practiced in China as early as 2000 B.C., and a classical account of the culture of common carp was written by Fan Lei in 475 B.C. (Villaluz, 1953). The Romans built fish ponds during the first century A.D., and during the Middle Ages fish ponds for carp farming were built throughout Eastern Europe by religious men (Lovell, et al., 1978). In Southeast Asia, fish ponds were believed to have evolved naturally along with salt-making in the coastal areas; the salt beds were utilized to grow milkfish during the rainy season (Schuster, 1952). By early in the twentieth century, several forms of fish culture were fairly well established, such as milkfish farming in Southeast Asia, carp polyculture (multiple species in the same pond) in China, carp monoculture in Europe, tilapia culture in tropical Africa, culture of indigenous finfish and crustaceans in estuarine impoundments in Asian and Southeast Asian coastal areas, and hatchery rearing of salmonids in North America and Western Europe. These forms of aquaculture, with the exception of salmonid culture, were generally extensive, where the nutrient inputs into the system were restricted or limited to fertilizers and crude sources of foods, and yields were low.

Aquaculture made its greatest advancements during the latter part of the twentieth century. Technology began to develop from a scientific base. Research programs for aquaculture were established in specialized areas, such as genetics, nutrition, diseases, water management, and engineering. New species were examined for aquaculture potential by trying to "close the life-cycle," that is, to reproduce the fish and grow them to market size in a controlled environment. With the present technology and research base, yields and risks for a number of aquaculture enterprises are now predictable, which makes them attractive investment opportunities.

BENEFITS OF AQUACULTURE

The supply, price, and quality of sea-caught fish fluctuate considerably because the ocean is an unmanaged resource whose yield is difficult to predict. But when fish are cultured, like corn in a field, the supply can be controlled more effectively. High quality can be

TABLE 19-1

EFFICIENCY OF UTILIZATION OF FEED AND DIETARY PROTEIN AND METABOLIZABLE ENERGY (ME) BY FISH, CHICKEN, AND CATTLE

Animal	Feed Composition		Efficiency		
	Protein (%)	ME (kcal/g)	Weight gain per g food consumed (g)	Protein gain per g protein consumed (g)	ME required per g protein gain (kcal)
Channel catfish	32	2.7	0.75	0.36	21
Broiler chicken	18	2.8	0.48	0.33	43
Beef cattle	11	2.6	0.13	0.15	167

Source: National Research Council (1993).

maintained because the production and harvest conditions are controlled and farmed fish usually go into the processing plant alive, as do poultry, pigs, cattle, and other animals.

Resources that are unsuitable for other food production purposes may be adaptable to fish farming. In the Mississippi River floodplain (delta), where catfish farming in the United States is the most concentrated, ponds are usually sited on land too poorly drained for most crops. Crawfish have been successfully farmed in Louisiana swampland simply by enclosing such land with a levee and flooding the area. Shrimp farms are built on salt flats and other coastal lands that are unsuitable for other uses.

Fish convert practical feeds into body tissue more efficiently than do farm animals. Cultured catfish can gain approximately 0.75 g of weight per gram of practical diet, whereas chickens, the most efficient warmblooded food animal, gain about 0.48 g of weight per gram of diet (National Research Council, 1993). The reason for the superior food conversion efficiency of fish is that they are fed diets with higher percentages of protein, which is economical because of the lower dietary energy requirement of fish. Fish do not convert protein more efficiently than chickens (Table 19-1); in fact, fish and chickens are about equal in this regard. Metabolizable energy requirement per gram of protein gain is 21 kcal for channel catfish versus 43 for the broiler chicken (Table 19-1). Thus, the primary advantage of fish over land animals is the lower energy cost of protein gain rather than the superior food conversion. The nutrient content of selected species of fish and crustaceans is listed in Appendix 1.

COMPARISON OF FEEDING FISH VERSUS LIVESTOCK

As with land animals, feed is the largest variable production cost in fish farming; therefore, economical feeds and efficient feeding practices are extremely important in aquaculture. However, feeding fish in their aqueous environments takes on dimensions beyond those considered in feeding land animals. These include the nutrient contribution of natural aquatic organisms in pond cultures, the effect of feeding on water quality, and the loss of nutrients if feed is not consumed immediately. However, the concept of feeding is the same as that applied in feed in other food animals: to nourish the animal to the desired level or form of productivity as profitably as possible. Thus, application of knowledge on the nutritional requirements of fish and the husbandry of feeding various cultured species is essential to successful aquaculture.

FEEDING AND NUTRITION

Fish are fed in water. Feed that is not consumed within a reasonable time represents not only an economic loss, but can reduce water quality in the culture system. Therefore, feed allowance, feeding method, and water stability of the feed are factors that the fish culturist must consider but the livestock feeder does not. The culture environment may make valuable nutrient contributions to the fish. For example, most waters contain enough dissolved calcium to provide most of the fish's requirement. For fish that feed low on the food chain, such as shrimp and some tilapias, the pond environment can be a valuable source of protein, energy, and other nutrients.

The nutrients required by fish (finfish and crustaceans) for growth, reproduction, and other normal physiological functions are similar to those of land animals. They need protein, minerals, vitamins and growth factors, and energy sources. These nutrients may come from natural aquatic organisms or from prepared feeds.

If fish are held in an artificial confinement such as raceways where natural foods are absent, or at high densities such as intensively stocked catfish ponds where natural food is scarce, their feed must be nutritionally complete. However, where natural food is abundant and supplemental feeds are fed for additional growth, such as extensive shrimp culture, the feeds may not need to contain all of the essential nutrients.

Notable nutritional differences between fishes and farm animals are the following: (1) energy requirements are lower for fish than for warmblooded animals, thus giving fish a higher dietary protein-to-energy ratio; (2) fish require some lipids that warmblooded animals do not, such as omega-3 (n-3) series fatty acids for some species and sterols for crustaceans; (3) the ability of fish to absorb soluble minerals from the water minimizes the dietary need for some minerals; and (4) fish have limited ability to synthesize ascorbic acid and must depend upon dietary sources.

Nutritional requirements of fish do not vary greatly among species. There are exceptions, such as differences in essential fatty acids, requirement for sterols, and ability to assimilate carbohydrates, but these often can be identified with warmwater or coldwater, finfish or crustacean, and marine or freshwater species. The quantitative nutrient requirements that have been derived for several species have served adequately as a basis for estimating the nutrient needs of others. As more information becomes available on nutrient requirements of various species, the recommended nutrient allowances of diets for spe-

TABLE 19-2

NUTRIENT REQUIREMENTS FOR FIVE COMMERCIALLY CULTURED FISH

	Common Carp	Tilapia	Channel Catfish	Rainbow Trout	Pacific Salmon
Energy Base[a] (kcal/DE/kg diet)	3200	3000	3000	3600	3600
Protein, crude (digestible), %	35(30.5)	32(28)	32(28)	38(34)	38(34)
Amino Acids					
Arginine, %	1.31	1.18	1.2	1.5	2.04
Histidine, %	0.64	0.48	0.42	0.7	0.61
Isoleucine, %	0.76	0.87	0.73	0.9	0.75
Leucine, %	1	0.95	0.98	1.4	1.33
Lysine, %	1.74	1.43	1.43	1.8	1.7
Methionine+cystine, %	0.94	0.9	0.64	1	1.36
Phenylalanine+tyrosine, %	1.98	1.55	1.4	1.8	1.73
Threonine, %	1.19	1.05	0.56	0.8	0.75
Tryptophan, %	0.24	0.28	0.14	0.2	0.17
Valine, %	1.1	0.78	0.84	1.2	1.09
Fatty Acids					
n-3 fatty acids, %	1	—	0.5–1	1	1–2
n-6 fatty acids, %	1	0.5–1	—	1	—
Minerals					
Calcium, %	NT	R[b]	R	IE	NT
Chlorine, %	NT	NT	R	0.9E	NT
Magnesium, %	0.05	0.06	0.04	0.05	NT
Phosphorus, %	0.6	0.5	0.45	0.6	0.6
Potassium, %	NT	NT	R	0.7	0.8
Sodium, %	NT	NT	R	0.6E	NT
Copper, mg/kg	3	R	5	3	NT
Iodine, mg/kg	NT	NT	1.1E	1.1	0.6–1.1
Iron, mg/kg	150	NT	30	60	NT
Manganese, mg/kg	NT	2.4	13	R	NT
Zinc, mg/kg	30	20	20	30	R
Selenium, mg/kg	NT	NT	0.25	0.3	R
Fat-Soluble Vitamins					
A, IU/kg	4000	NT	1000–2000	2500	2500
D, IU/kg	NT	NT	500	2400	NT
E, IU/kg	100	50	50	50	50
K, mg/kg	NT	NT	R	R	R
Water-Soluble Vitamins					
Riboflavin, mg/kg	6	9	4	7	7
Pantothenic acid, mg/kg	30	10	15	20	20
Niacin, mg/kg	28	NT	14	10	R
Vitamin B_{12}, mg/kg	NR	NR	R	0.01E	R
Choline, mg/kg	500	NT	400	1000	800
Biotin, mg/kg	1	NT	R	0.15	R
Folate, mg/kg	NR	NT	1.5	1	2
Thiamin, mg/kg	0.5	NT	1	1	R
Vitamin B_6, mg/kg	6	NT	3	3	6
Myoinositol, mg/kg	NT	NR	300	300	440
Vitamin C, mg/kg	R	50	25–50	50	50

Note: These requirements have been determined with highly purified ingredients in which the nutrients are highly digestible; therefore the values presented represent near 100% bioavailability.

[a]Typical energy concentrations in commercial diets.

[b]R, required in diet but quantity not determined; NR, no dietary requirement demonstrated under experimental conditions; NT, not tested; E, estimated.

Source: Adopted from National Research Council (1993).

cific needs of individual species will become more refined. The NRC (1993) nutrient requirements of five species of commercially important fish are presented in Table 19-2.

AQUACULTURE AND THE ENVIRONMENT

Unassimilated nutrients from the feed enhance eutrophication of the aqueous environment. This will stimulate growth of algae and other aquatic plants. In static culture ponds, algae growth is necessary to keep the water oxygenated through photosynthesis; however, excessive algae growth can cause oxygen depletion problems in the absence of sunlight (night or cloudy days). In raceway systems, such as salmonid hatcheries, where there is a continuous outflow of water, the unassimilated nutrients do not affect the culture system but can impact outside water systems. Therefore, many states have placed restrictions on the amount of phosphorous that can be discharged daily into streams from hatcheries. In northern Europe, especially Norway, eutrophication in coastal waters caused by net pen culture of salmon has caused federal restrictions to be placed on the amount of feed that can be fed by individual salmon culture operations.

Phosphorus is the nutrient of primary concern in aquaculture because of its effect on growth of algae and other aquatic plants. Recently, much research has been done to reduce the amount of phosphorus in fish feeds and to enhance availability of phosphorus in the feeds. Eya and Lovell (1997) and Robinson et al. (1996) demonstrated that the phosphorus allowance in practical feeds for catfish fed in commercial ponds could be reduced by approximately 25% of the National Research Council (NRC, 1993) allowance which was determined with small fish in the laboratory. These workers also demonstrated that addition of fungal phytase to feeds would essentially double the bioavailability of phytate phosphorus for catfish and, therefore, negate the necessity of supplementing an all-plant ingredient feed with an inorganic phosphorus source. Eya and Lovell (1997) found great variation in bioavailability (net absorption) of phosphorus among a number of feedstuffs fed to catfish. They reported coefficients of 31–35% for plant ingredients, 60–65% for animal byproducts containing bone, and values ranging from 54% for tricalcium phosphate to 90% for monosodium phosphate. Studies with rainbow trout and with catfish have shown that phosphorus supplements can be deleted from the diets during the last one-third of the period for growing the fish to marketable size without affecting weight gain or health of the fish.

In static, earthen ponds such as catfish ponds, phosphorus discharge is not a serious problem. One reason is that many inorganic elements, including phosphorus, are precipitated out of the water and bound in the soil on the pond bottom. Gross (1996) established a phosphorus budget for catfish over a growing season and found that approximately 21% of the phosphorus in the feed was recovered in harvested fish, 74% was tied up in the bottom soil, and only 5% remained in solution in the pond water. Catfish ponds are usually not drained; the fish are selectively harvested by seining. Therefore, catfish ponds are generally not a serious source of environmental pollution.

COMMERCIAL AQUACULTURE

Desired characteristics in a cultured fish species are good market value, reproducible in captivity, rapid growth, acceptance of prepared feeds, resistance to diseases, and tolerance to variable conditions of dissolved oxygen and temperature. The major cultured species in the world generally have most of the characteristics. Table 19-3 presents recent estimates of total harvest yields for the major cultured marine and freshwater species.

Channel Catfish

The channel catfish, *Ictalurus punctatus*, is the leading farm-raised fish in the United States. It has many of the desirable characteristics for fish farming. It can be spawned in captivity and can be managed under a variety of culture conditions ranging from ponds to intensively stocked cages or raceway tanks. It grows from a 10 g fingerling to a desirable harvest size of 0.5 kg in 6–7 months. It accepts a variety of supplemental feeds and is relatively disease free when environmental stresses are minimized. It tolerates diurnal and seasonal variation in pond water conditions. It readily accepts and makes efficient weight gains from processed feeds. An important reason that the channel catfish is a marketable food fish is that the flesh is essentially all white muscle in fish less than 1 kg in size, is free of intermuscular bones, and has a mild flavor. The high quality of channel catfish flesh was not formerly known outside the southern United States, but its desirable qualities as a table fish has allowed its market to grow rapidly to keep pace with increases in farm production.

Catfish farming began in the southeastern United States. Because channel catfish was a popular food in this area, they were grown and processed for retail food markets. Initially, earthen ponds were stocked in the spring with 2500–4000 fingerlings/hectare, weighing from 10 to 40 g each, and the fish were fed pelleted concentrated feeds for 6–7 months for fall harvest at an average size of about 0.5 kg. Average yields were 1000–2000 kg/hectare. By increasing stocking densities and using more sophisticated feeds, yields increased. However, with higher stocking densities and greater inputs of nutrients, risks

TABLE 19-3

QUANTITY OF CULTURED FISH AND CRUSTACEANS HARVESTED

Species	Area	Production (metric tons)	Year
Shrimp	World	721,000	1994
Salmon	World	650,000	1995
Channel catfish	United States	220,000	1995
Rainbow trout	United States	33,000	1995
Freshwater crawfish	United States	30,000	1990

Sources: Shrimp—Rosenberry (1990); salmon—Anonymous (1996); channel catfish and rainbow trout—USDA (1997); crawfish—Huner and Romaire (1990).

concerning dissolved oxygen depletion and toxic product accumulation in the ponds increased.

Several developments have allowed production yields to increase. Mechanical aeration and understanding of the chemical and biological dynamics of fish ponds have decreased the risk of oxygen depletion in the pond and thus allowed more fish to be grown per hectare. For example, with mechanical aeration of the pond, present standing crops of 7,500 kg or more of fish per hectare can be maintained.

Another practice to increase yields of catfish in ponds is multiple harvesting. By using a harvest seine of a specific mesh size where only the larger fish are removed, the ponds are harvested two to four times a year without draining. This system makes more efficient use of pond space than does the conventional method of stocking small fish in the spring and draining the pond and harvesting all fish in the fall. By multiple harvesting, yields of 5,000–10,000 kg/hectare are obtained yearly.

REPRODUCTION. Channel catfish are sexually mature at 2 to 3 years of age at a weight of approximately 1 kg, although commercial brood fish are usually larger. The fish spawn in the spring when water temperature reaches approximately 24 °C. Some fingerling producers put male and female pairs in spawning pens and remove eggs from a spawning container after the male has fertilized them, and transfer the eggs into a hatchery. The eggs hatch within a few days into yolk sac fry. Channel catfish eggs are relatively large (2–3 mm), and thus the yolk sac provides nourishment for the fry for 5 to 7 days. After this period, the fry need an exogenous source of nutrients and begin searching for food. They will accept and assimilate prepared dry diets. After a few days, the fry are usually transferred to prepared nursery ponds where they feed on natural food organisms and supplemental feed. As the fish get larger, they become more dependent upon the supplemental feed. At the end of the first growing season (summer), the fingerlings reach a size of 20 to 40 g. The fish may be transferred from nursery to fingerling ponds at lower densities where they can grow faster. Another system for fingerling production is to hold groups of male and female fish in the same "brood" pond and allow "wild spawning." At the end of the breeding season, the brood fish are separated from the fingerlings. Fingerlings are subsequently transferred from the fingerling ponds to production ponds. If the fingerlings are to be sold to another farm, they usually are graded on basis of size.

PRODUCTION. Most production ponds are approximately 4–8 hectares in surface area and 1.5–2 meters in depth. Also, most modern ponds are levee type, where a levee impounds the water and, thus, the water surface is above natural ground level. Stocking and harvesting are done intermittently; the marketable size (>300 g) fish are removed by selective seining, which allows the undersize fish to remain in the pond. The harvested fish are replaced with an equal number of fingerlings. The ponds are not drained, and are usually harvested more than one time during the year. Catfish are harvested year-round to provide processing plants with a continuous supply of fish. This also allows more efficient use of the pond since catfish only make economical growth when water temperature is above approximately 20° C. Optimum temperature is 28–30 °C. Length of economical growing season in the southern United States is 6 to 7 months. Harvest size catfish are

0.3–1.5 kg with the optimum size being approximately 1.0 kg. The average maximum standing crop of fish (immediately before harvest) is around 7,000 kg/hectare but can be over 10,000 kg/hectare. Maximum daily feed allowances are usually over 100 kg/hectare with many farmers feeding over 150 kg/hectare/day.

FEEDS AND FEEDING. Catfish are fed floating feeds manufactured by extrusion processing. This allows the feeder to see how much the fish are feeding and avoid overfeeding. Also, the feeder can see how actively the fish are feeding to decide when to increase the feed allowance. Feeds fed in production ponds are 28–32% crude protein with a digestible energy content of 2.8–3.0 kcal/g. Fingerling feeds may contain 36% crude protein and 3.0–3.1 kcal/g. Typical ingredient composition of commercial feeds is shown in Table 19-4. Feed conversion (feed/gain) under commercial conditions is approximately 2.0. Under experimental conditions, however, it is approximately 1.5. The difference is due to the fact that in small experimental ponds, wasted feed is minimized and mortalities can be accounted for.

The fish are not fed consistently during the winter. Many farmers will feed during "warm periods," when water temperature is >12 °C, especially with fingerlings. Winter feeding schedules for channel catfish have been developed, based upon fish size and water temperature; however, research demonstrated that catfish in ponds in Alabama that were not fed during December, January, or February were the same weight in early spring as fish fed continuously over winter (Kim and Lovell, 1995).

WATER QUALITY IN PRODUCTION PONDS. Commercial ponds usually have permanent aeration equipment in place that is turned on manually or automatically when the dissolved oxygen (DO) reaches a critically low concentration, which may be 3 mg/L or less. During heavy feeding the aerators are usually run a portion of each day, namely

TABLE 19-4
EXAMPLES OF TYPICAL CATFISH FEEDS

Ingredient	Composition (% of Feed)		
	32% Protein	28% Protein	26% Protein
Soybean meal	39.0	34.0	28.5
Cottonseed meal	10.0	10.0	12.0
Whole fish meal	4.0	4.0	4.0
Meat/bone meal	4.0	—	—
Corn	20.5	32.0	41.0
Wheat middlings	20.0	17.5	12.0
Dicalcium phosphate	1.0	1.0	1.0
Vitamin mix	include	include	include
Trace mineral mix	include	include	include
Fat or oil[a]	1.5	1.5	1.5

[a]Sprayed on finished feed pellets to reduce feed dust.

during late night and early morning before sunrise when DO is lowest. The most serious water quality problems in these highly eutrophic ponds is low DO caused by respiration of algae at night or on cloudy days. Algae photosynthesize and put oxygen into the pond in the presence of sunlight, but respire and consume algae in the absence of ultraviolet light (Figure 19-1). Nitrogen metabolites such as ammonia and nitrite are also detrimental to water quality.

Catfish farming presents no threat of environmental contamination. Because the ponds are not drained, there is no pollution from discharge unless the ponds are flooded, which is a remote possibility on a properly designed farm. Most inorganic elements from feeds are bound in the pond mud. Gross (1996) found that approximately 20% of the phosphorus in feed was retained in the body of the fish, 80% was bound in the bottom mud, and less than 5% remained dissolved in the pond water. Fish digest about 85% of the nitrogen fed, retain approximately 30%, and excrete the remainder from the body primarily as ammonia. Ammonia in high concentrations is toxic to fish. However, acutely toxic levels of ammonia usually do not accrue in a pond because pond organisms convert ammonia to nitrite and subsequently to nitrate, which is inert and remains in the soil. Many commercial ponds are over 10 years old and have not been drained.

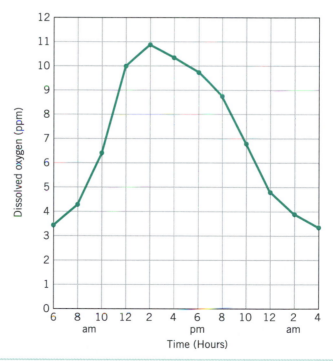

FIGURE 19-1

Typical diurnal variation in dissolved oxygen content in intensively fed catfish ponds is depicted. Oxygen concentrations of 6–7 ppm represent normal water saturation, and concentrations below 3 mg/L are stressful to the fish.

Shrimp

Farming of marine shrimp, species of the genus *Penaeus*, is the largest and fastest-growing aquaculture enterprise in the world. This is because of the high market value, availability of culture technology, and favorable growing environments in tropical coastal areas over the world. In 1992 shrimp farmers produced 43% of the shrimp placed on the world markets, whereas in 1980 shrimp farming supplied less than 10% of the world's shrimp needs (Csavas, 1994).

LEVELS OF PRODUCTION. Approximately 82% of cultured shrimp are produced in Asia. Leading shrimp-producing countries are Thailand, China, and Indonesia. Ecuador is the leading producer in the Americas, with other tropical Central and South American countries also contributing. There is no significant shrimp farming industry in the United States, mainly because of temperature and limited available coastal land. Shrimp culture systems are generally characterized as extensive, semi-intensives and intensive. Extensive farming, which is usually in impounded estuarine areas, means low production density (1–3 shrimp/m^2 and yields of around 300–400 kg/hectare) with no supplemental feeding or water circulation. Semi-intensive culture is a higher level of production and involves feeding and pumping water through ponds. Stocking rates are 5–10 shrimp/m^2 and yields are usually 1,000–5,000 kg/hectare in two crops/year. Intensive culture, with stocking rates up to 50/m^2, involves smaller rearing areas (ponds or raceways), more water exchange, aeration, and waste removal. Technology for intensive culture is more sophisticated and labor and fossil energy requirements are higher; however, yields of 10,000 kg/hectare/year are obtained.

SEED STOCK. Post-larval shrimp for stocking production ponds come from hatcheries or are harvested from estuarine waters. Prior to the mid-1980s, most post-larvae came from wild sources in Latin America; today hatcheries supply most seed shrimp worldwide. Hatchery production begins with gravid (fertilized egg-bearing) females obtained from the ocean or from production ponds. The eggs hatch and the hatchlings (nauplii) go through various stages of metamorphosis, during which time they are fed various live foods and gradually weaned onto dry feeds. When they reach the post-larval stage, they are placed in prepared nursery ponds. The post-larval shrimp feed on plankton and supplemental feed in the nursery ponds until stocked in production ponds.

PRODUCTION. Most commercial shrimp farming is semi-intensive, in ponds 5 to 25 hectares in size constructed near the coast, with a water exchange of 5 to 10% of volume per day. Salinity of the water ranges from near 0, when there is much fresh water flowing into estuaries, to 400 mg of salt/liter, which is near full-strength sea water. Aeration is generally not used, but water exchange rate can be increased if necessary. Two to three crops per year are produced, and the average harvest size per animal is 15–30 g. Ponds are harvested by draining; shrimp follow the flowing water out of the pond and are captured in nets at the drain ports. The shrimp are immediately iced, transported to a partial processing facility on the farm where the heads are removed, iced again, and transported to a further processing plant and prepared for markets.

FEEDS AND FEEDING. Shrimp in semi-intensive production ponds are fed once or twice per day, and maximum feeding rate does not usually exceed 25 kg/hectare/day. Feed must be spread uniformly over the pond or the feeding area because shrimp do not move to feed like finfishes. Shrimp are fed nonfloating, steam-pelleted or extruded pellets that are relatively small, measuring 1–3 mm in diameter. Because shrimp feed slowly, the pellets must remain intact in water for 1 hour or longer. Extruders or modified pelleting equipment, with a preconditioner to allow extra heating of the feed mixture, are necessary for processing shrimp feeds with sufficient water stability. Growth rate and feed efficiency of shrimp grown in extensive or semi-intensive cultures are highly dependent upon environmental factors, such as natural food availability, temperature, salinity, and dissolved oxygen. Table 19-5 shows ingredient composition of typical shrimp feeds for semi-intensive and intensive cultures. Crude protein content of feed for shrimp in semi-intensive production ponds is usually 25–30%. These foods are usually formulated to be nutritionally complete, with the possible exception of a sterol source, although this is not necessary during the first few weeks when the small shrimp are feeding on natural pond organisms. As the animals approach harvest size, the nutritional quality of the prepared diet becomes more critical because of the competition for natural food. In intensive culture systems where there are up to 50 animals/m^2, high-performance feeds are used. These feeds usually contain 30–40% crude protein, a high percentage of fish meal, a sterol source, fish oil

TABLE 19-5
EXAMPLES OF TYPICAL SHRIMP FEEDS

Ingredient	Composition (% of Feed)		
	38% Protein	30% Protein	25% Protein
Whole fish meal	21	12	8
Shrimp head meal	10	5	—
Squid meal	5	—	—
Soybean meal	26.45	34.45	33.25
Cereal products or byproducts[a]	27–29	39–41	49–51
Fish oil	4	4	4
Soybean lecithin	1	—	—
Cholesterol	0.2	—	—
Binder	1–3	1–3	1–3
Dicalcium phosphate	1.8	2.0	2.2
Vitamin mix	0.5	0.5	0.5
Mineral mix	0.05	0.05	0.05

[a] Cereal products or byproducts should be rich in starch and gluten and low in fiber for desirable binding properties in the pelleted feed.

(to provide n-3 polyunsaturated fatty acids), and sometimes attractants. Shrimp in intensive cultures are usually fed more often than twice daily. They are grown to sizes up to 40 g (price increases with size).

Salmonids

The salmonids include the five species of Pacific salmon (*Oncorhynchus* species), Atlantic salmon (*Salmo solar*), trout (*Oncorhynchus* and *Salmo* species), and chars (*Salvelinus* species). Salmonid aquaculture is the oldest form of fish rearing in North America and is currently second in production behind catfish and third in dollar value behind catfish and ornamental and bait fishes. Of the species of trout and salmon found in North America, the rainbow trout is by far the most extensively cultured species, both for stocking of public waters for recreational fishing and for food production. State and federal hatcheries in almost every state grow trout for release in public waters. Production of trout for food fish is approximately 50 million pounds per year. Over 75% of commercial trout production for food is located in the Hagarman Valley of Idaho. The reason for this location is the availability of enormous amounts of constant-temperature, fully oxygenated groundwater along the Snake River.

A number of government hatcheries in the Pacific Northwest produce Pacific salmon for public fisheries enhancement. About 600 million salmon fingerlings, or smolts, are released each year. Pacific salmon are spawned in freshwater hatcheries where the fingerlings eventually undergo a subtle metamorphosis that results in a transformation from the freshwater to the saltwater-tolerant form (smolts). The fish are then released into streams and rivers and voluntarily migrate to the ocean, where they remain for several years until they return to near-shore areas. It is at this point that the adult salmon enter the commercial and sport fisheries.

Commercial culture of salmon for food in the United States is currently not a large industry and is primarily concentrated on the production of pan-sized Pacific coho salmon in net pens in the edge of the ocean. Growth of salmon farming will be limited in this country, primarily because of priorities and restrictions on use of coastal waters which make marine aquaculture virtually prohibitive. However, on the Pacific coast of Canada, in Northern Europe, Chile, and southern Australia, net pen culture of Atlantic salmon is a successful industry.

FINGERLING PRODUCTION. Trout and salmon are spawned in freshwater hatcheries at temperatures of 8 to 15 °C. Eggs are expressed from the female into a container where male sperm is expelled on them for in-vitro fertilization. The eggs are incubated in hatching troughs where upwelling water keeps them agitated. The eggs hatch in 30–75 days, depending upon water temperature. About 30 days after hatch, all of the egg yolk has been absorbed and the fry begin to seek food on the surface of the water. The swim-up fry are placed in shallow tanks and fed a mash-type feed. They do not require live food. Initially, the small fry are fed almost continuously. As the fish grow, feeding frequency is reduced. Once all fry are actively feeding and growing, they are placed in raceways or tanks supplied with constantly running fresh water.

CULTURE METHODS. Salmon and trout may be raised in either freshwater or saltwater, although salmon grow more rapidly in saltwater. Pacific salmon smolts can tolerate abrupt saltwater transfer. Atlantic salmon and trout must be acclimated to saltwater by gradual exposure to increasing-strength saltwater. After saltwater transfer, the fish are fed either dry or moist diets, depending in part on the species of fish. Chinook salmon grow faster in saltwater when they are fed moist diet formulations, while coho salmon, Atlantic salmon, and rainbow trout do well on either moist or dry diets.

Most rainbow trout grown for food are cultured in freshwater raceways with constantly flowing water at 10–18 °C. In the United States the fish are grown to pan size of approximately 0.5 kg, which requires approximately 6 months in a production facility. Atlantic salmon is the primary salmon species cultured for food because it grows fast and is well adapted to net pen culture. Atlantic salmon are reared in floating net pens in the edge of the sea and marketed as 2–5 kg fish after 2–3 years in the pens. Northern Europe is the leading salmon producing area, and Norway is the leading country.

FEEDS AND FEEDING. Trout and salmon are fed dry, pelleted feeds in production systems. Most feeds are processed by extrusion. Trout accept floating feeds satisfactorily, but salmon do not feed well on the water surface. Therefore, extruded (expanded) salmon feeds are processed to sink slowly. Feeding rate can be to satiety, based on observation of the feeder, or at a fixed rate, expressed as a percentage of body weight per day. Feeding rate is affected by temperature, fish size, photoperiod, moisture and energy content of the diet, rearing density, and water quality. Reliable feeding charts have been developed for salmonids which allow near-maximum growth rate under various environmental and size conditions. The inverse relationship between feeding rate and feed efficiency for trout and salmon is well known. In most feeding situations, feeding at levels for near-maximum growth rather than for optimum feed conversion, which is at a lower level, is usually economically desirable because of the high fixed costs in production.

Salmonid feeds contain more animal protein than do feeds for warmwater fishes. This is partly through tradition, because salmonids are obligate carnivores, although some species prefer animal over plant feed ingredients. Lipid is the primary source of nonprotein energy for salmonids because they do not assimilate carbohydrates for energy uses very efficiently. Examples of commercial salmonid feeds are presented in Table 19-6. Rainbow trout are fed production feeds containing 36–38% protein and Atlantic salmon in net pen culture are fed 40–50% protein feeds.

Salmon and trout are fed by hand, automatic feeders, or demand feeders. Feeding by hand is labor-intensive, but it ensures human contact with the fish and may result in more rapid awareness of aquaculture problems as they develop. Automatic feeders are labor-saving devices, but because they deliver the feed regardless of the appetite of the fish, they must be closely monitored both by observation and by frequent food conversion determinations to ensure their effective use. Demand feeders are devices that deliver a small amount of feed in response to an action by the fish. Feeding is spread throughout the day, which generally allows for a higher rate of consumption by all fish in the culture system. As long as the delivery system is properly adjusted, little feed wastage occurs.

TABLE 19-6

EXAMPLES OF TYPICAL PRODUCTION FEEDS FOR RAINBOW TROUT AND ATLANTIC SALMON

Component	Composition (% of Feed)	
	Rainbow Trout	Atlantic Salmon
Ingredients:		
Fish meal	30.0	50.0
Wheat flour or middlings	26.5	13.5
Soybean meal	16.0	9.0
Blood meal (spray dried)	—	9.0
Corn gluten meal	8.0	—
Dried whey	5.0	5.0
Fish oil	10.0	13.0
Vitamin mix	0.5	0.5
Nutrients:		
Crude protein, %	38.0	50.0
Digestible energy, kcal/kg	4.0	4.2

SUMMARY

Several aquaculture industries are well established today. They make a significant contribution to world consumption of fishery products and are attractive investment opportunities. The most notable success stories are channel catfish, marine shrimp, and Atlantic salmon. Other species are rapidly gaining a share of the market. The primary reason for this success is the research and technology base that has been provided. The life cycle of the important commercial species has been "closed." Basic information on diseases, nutrition, and breeding have been provided, details on aquatic engineering, chemistry, and ecology are available, and husbandry strategies have been developed. This research and technology base, along with the decline in supply and stability of ocean sources of fishery products, have made aquaculture an attractive area for capital investment.

GLOSSARY

Aeration The process of increasing dissolved oxygen concentration in the water by mechanical means.

Aquaculture Culture of aquatic animals for productive or commercial purposes in a controlled environment.

Coldwater fishes Fishes with an optimum growth temperature of 12–18 °C, such as trout and salmon.

Eutrophication Enrichment of inorganic nutrients in a body of water.

Finfish True fishes, as distinguished from crustaceans or mollusks.

Food chain Organisms in a natural aquatic environment that range from simple, unicellular plants (algae and bacteria) to fish or crustaceans, which are sources of food for the various animals in the aquatic ecosystem.

Multiple harvesting   Harvesting a fish pond several times during the year without draining the pond, with a seine with specific-size mesh to allow small fish to escape. The harvested fish are replaced with an equal number of young fish.

Pen culture   The process of culturing fish in net pens or cages suspended in the sea, lakes, rivers, or other large bodies of water.

Photoperiod   Number of daylight hours during the 24-hour day.

Pond culture   The process whereby young fish are stocked and fed to marketable size in earthen ponds that are constructed especially for the culture and harvest of a particular fish species.

Salmonids   Trout and salmon.

Spawning pen   Pens in shallow water in which a pair (male and female) of fish are placed during breeding season. The fish are released after eggs are laid and fertilized.

Spawning wild   A large number of male and female fish of breeding size are placed in an open pond and allowed to pair and breed naturally. The brood fish are removed from the pond after spawning and the hatchlings remain in the pond.

Warmwater fishes   Fishes with an optimum growth temperature of 25–30 °C, such as catfishes, tilapias, and carps.

Water quality   Characteristics of the water in a culture system (pond, raceway, or tank) which affect the growth and health of the fish in the system; these include temperature, dissolved oxygen, ammonia, and pH, among others.

REFERENCES

Anonymous. 1996. Salmon production. *Fish Farm. Int.,* 18(1): 21.

Csavas, I. 1994. Success of shrimp farming. *World Aquaculture,* 25: 34–56.

Eya, J. C., and Lovell, R. T. 1997. Available phosphorus requirements of food-size channel catfish (*Ictalurus punctatus*) fed practical diets in ponds. *Aquaculture* 154:283–291.

Gross, A. 1996. Effect of five phosphorus levels in "all-plant" channel catfish diets on water quality variables in earthen ponds. M.S. thesis, Auburn University, AL, 55 pp.

Huner, J. V., and Romaire, R. P. 1990. Crawfish culture in the southeastern USA. *World Aquaculture,* 21(4): 58–65.

Kim, M. K., and Lovell, R. T. 1995. Effect of overwinter feeding regimen on body weight, body composition and resistance to *Edwardsiella ictaluri* in channel catfish, *Ictalurus punctatus. Aquaculture,* 134: 237–246.

Lovell, R. T., Shell, E. W., and Smitherman, R. O. 1978. Progress and prospects in fish farming. In

A. M. Altschul and H. Wilke (eds.), *New Protein Foods,* p. 262. New York: Academic Press.

National Research Council. 1993. *Nutrient Requirements of Fish.* Washington, D.C.: National Academy of Sciences.

Robinson, E. H., Jackson, L. S., and Li, M. H. 1996. Supplemental phosphorus in practical channel catfish diets. *J. World Aquacult.* Soc., 27:303–308.

Rosenberry, R. 1990. World shrimp farming 1990. *Aquac. Digest,* Sp. Rep., 40 pp.

Schuster, W. H. 1952. Milkfish farming in southeast Asia. In *Proc. of Indo-Pacific Fish Council, Southeast Asian Fish,* Dev. Ctr., Spec. Pub.

USDA. 1991. National Aquaculture Statistical Service, Sp. Ctr. Washington, D.C.: U.S. Dept. of Agriculture.

USDA. 1997. National Aquaculture Statistical Service, Sp. Ctr. Washington, D.C.: U.S. Dept. of Agriculture.

Villaluz, D. K. 1953. *Fish Farming in the Philippines.* Manila, the Philippines: Bookman Co.

CHAPTER TWENTY
PET DOGS AND CATS

D. P. LAFLAMME AND S. S. HANNAH
RALSTON PURINA COMPANY
ST. LOUIS, MO

DOGS AND CATS IN AMERICAN SOCIETY
CAREERS IN THE PET INDUSTRY
NUTRITIONAL REQUIREMENTS OF DOGS AND CATS
BASIC HEALTH CARE
REPRODUCTION IN THE KENNEL OR CATTERY
DEVELOPMENT AND SOCIALIZATION OF PUPPIES AND KITTENS
SUMMARY

About one of every three households in the United States owns dogs or cats, such that there are approximately 55 million dogs and 65 million cats in the United States. Pet ownership is also popular in Europe, with over 70 million pet dogs and cats. The role of pets has evolved within the past century such that many are now considered to be family members; thus the philosophy and objectives of companion animal care and nutrition differ from that of production animals. For example, production animal nutrition focuses on a good economic return by seeking maximum production, whether that is rapid growth, high milk production, or litter size, at the lowest cost. Pet nutrition focuses on maximizing the long-term health and well-being of the pet, for which there are few short-term measures, and on the emotional ties between pets and owners.

Nutritional needs are strongly influenced by the animal's lifestage. Lifestages of concern for production animals include growth, maintenance, and reproduction. For companion animals, these also apply, although "maintenance" describes a much higher percentage of companion animals than production animals. In addition, the geriatric lifestage is unique to companion animals—production animals rarely live to a geriatric age. Those that do tend to be serving as companion animals despite their species!

In addition to lifestage, lifestyle is quite different between production and companion animals, as well as being quite variable between individual pets. Production animals within a geographic area tend to live under conditions that are similar for a particular production function, such that their level of exercise, exposure to the elements, lifestyle, and general husbandry are similar. Pets, on the other hand, can vary widely in lifestyle. In the United States, the majority of dogs and cats are housepets and relatively few hunt or work for a living. However, there are exceptions and these animals' nutritional needs will differ from the relatively inactive housepet. Further, the variation in energy requirements of dogs appears to be much greater, even within a given breed, gender, and age group, compared to the variation seen in production animals.

A diet which provides optimum nutrition for long-term health, rather than simply meeting minimum nutrient levels, can be important to companion animals. Frequent monitoring of productivity and profitability may provide a signal of the adequacy of nutrition for production animals. Such immediate feedback is rarely available for pets; thus indicators of nutritional adequacy are less readily available. Pet owners must trust that commercial diets provide the desired nutrition for their pet. Indeed, most manufacturers of high-quality pet foods maintain research facilities where they conduct nutrition research and product adequacy testing.

This chapter will provide a brief overview of dogs and cats in current society; discuss basic health care; introduce some of the unique aspects of canine and feline nutritional requirements; and look at the pet care industry.

DOGS AND CATS IN AMERICAN SOCIETY

Unregistered purebred or mixed-breed dogs make up the vast majority of the 55 million dogs in the United States. The American Kennel Club (AKC), the largest official canine registry organization in the United States with well over one million dogs, recognizes over 140 different breeds of dogs. The most popular purebred dogs, based on AKC registration in 1996 and 1997, are the Labrador Retriever, Rottweiler, German Shepherd Dog, and Golden Retriever (Table 20-1). The AKC divides the breeds into seven groups, according to the uses for which the breeds were originally developed. These groups are: Sporting; Hound; Working; Terrier; Toy; Nonsporting; Herding; and Miscellaneous. The breeds within any given group can differ widely in terms of body size, conformation, behavior traits, and other characteristics, although they generally share those characteristics important to the group's original function, such as a natural instinct to point or to herd.

While the primary role of dogs in the United States today is family pet, many serve various other functions. Sporting dogs and hounds are often used as pointers, retrievers,

TABLE 20-1

THE MOST COMMON BREEDS OF DOGS AND CATS REGISTERED WITH THE AMERICAN KENNEL CLUB AND THE CAT FANCIERS ASSOCIATION

Dog Breed	Number, in 1997	Cat Breed	Number, in 1995
Labrador Retriever	158,366	Persian	44,735
Rottweiler	75,489	Maine Coon	4,332
German Shepherd Dog	75,177	Siamese	3,025
Golden Retriever	70,158	Abyssinian	2,468
Poodle	54,773	Exotic	1,610
Beagle	54,470	Scottish Fold	1,327
Dachshund	51,904	Oriental Shorthair	1,191
Cocker Spaniel	41,439	American Shorthair	1,050
Yorkshire Terrier	41,283	Birman	990
Pomeranian	39,357	Burmese	896
Shih Tzu	39,075	Ocicat	868
Chihuahua	38,926	Tonkinese	780
Boxer	38,047	Cornish Rex	736
Miniature Schnauzer	32,351	Russian Blue	609
Shetland Sheepdog	32,086	Devon Rex	590
Siberian Husky	24,432	Somali	585
Dalmation	22,726	Manx	575
Miniature Pinscher	22,297	Colorpoint Shorthair	507
Pug	20,082	British Shorthair	485
Boston Terrier	18,185	Ragdoll	390

Source: Internet listings, American Kennel Club and Cat Fanciers Association, 1998.

or pack hounds for hunting. Herding dogs, such as Border Collies and Australian Cattle Dogs, are used to work cattle and sheep. Labrador Retrievers and Golden Retrievers are popular breeds for use as support dogs to assist people with various disabilities, although other breeds and mixed-breed dogs are also used (Figure 20-1). Beagles and other hounds with keen noses are popular with Customs agents and drug enforcement agencies, while German Shepherd Dogs and Doberman Pinschers have found work with military, police forces, and disaster rescue teams. The Siberian Husky and similar breeds are used in northern climates to pull sleds. Whippets and English Greyhounds, once used for hunting, are now used in dog racing. Dogs (and cats) of all kinds are used in medical research for the benefit of both pets and humans.

Like dogs, cats originally served a specific purpose other than companionship—protection of the granaries from rodents. Today, cats continue to protect their habitations against rodents, but primarily serve as pets and companions. Their popularity has soared in recent years and, with over 65 million cats in the United States, they outnumber dogs. Similar to the situation with dogs, the vast majority of cats are either mixed-breed or unregistered purebreds. The Cat Fanciers Association (CFA), the feline counterpart to the AKC, recognizes 33 breeds for showing in their Championship Class, and two additional breeds each in the Provisional and Miscellaneous Classes. The most popular breeds of

FIGURE 20-1

Canine assistants for people with disabilities. (Photo by Peter Skinner/Photo Researchers.)

In addition to companionship, dogs can play an active role is assisting people with many types of disabilities. Perhaps the best known of these are guide dogs for the blind, but there are many other ways that dogs can provide support for people with disabilities. For example, dogs can be trained to aid the deaf, alerting those individuals to sounds made by the telephone, alarm clock, doorbell, or fire alarm. For individuals with physical disbilities, service dogs can help with practical tasks such as picking up dropped items, turning on lights, or pulling wheelchairs.

Dogs to be used in these programs usually are specially raised and trained. Volunteers often raise the puppies until they are old enough to enter training programs. For example, Canine Companions for Independence (CCI), one of the organizations that trains and places assistance dogs, selectively breeds Golden Retrievers, Labrador Retrievers, or crosses between these breeds, then places them with volunteers. The volunteers care for the puppies until they are 13 to 18 months of age. The adult dogs then return to a CCI center and undergo six to eight months of training appropriate to their special task before being placed into service.

cats, based on CFA registration in 1995, are the Persian, Maine Coon, Siamese, and Abyssinian (Table 20-1).

CAREERS IN THE PET INDUSTRY

The production and care of these millions of dogs and cats creates a range of career opportunities.

The pet industry offers career choices in many different areas ranging from practicing veterinarian or academic researcher to marketing associate or sales representative. The choice any individual makes in deciding which career path is best for that individual depends on many factors, including personal and professional interests. Do you want to work "hands on" with animals or do you prefer the business end of the field? Are you motivated toward health and science or do you prefer product development and sales?

For those with an interest in biological and health science research, there remains much research to be done in the field of companion animal nutrition, physiology, and health care. The research is conducted at the private laboratories of major pet food and pharmaceutical companies as well as at many universities. Those with advanced technical training in many related areas such as nutrition, pharmacology, immunology, veterinary medicine, physiology, or molecular biology may find interesting career opportunities in companion animal-related industry or academia.

The pet industry also includes manufacturers and distributors of pet foods, nutritional supplements, veterinary medical supplies, and pet products such as litter, leashes, and grooming aids; service providers such as breeders, groomers, trainers, and kennel operators; and pet health care including the veterinary profession. Careers in nontechnical areas of the pet industry offer opportunities in business such as sales and marketing, creative advertising, and management positions.

Veterinary medicine is a very popular career choice for students studying in the animal sciences. In the United States, approximately 75% of all veterinarians are in private clinical practice. However, other veterinarians engage in careers in teaching and research, government or military jobs, or positions in industry. Nearly 4,000 veterinarians are employed at schools and colleges of veterinary medicine in the United States. In addition to teaching, faculty members conduct basic and clinical research, provide various services to the public, contribute to scientific publications, and develop continuing education programs to help graduate veterinarians acquire new knowledge and skills.

Veterinary technicians also serve an important role in veterinary medicine. Technicians must be knowledgeable in the care and handling of animals, in the basic principles of normal and abnormal life processes, and in routine laboratory and clinical procedures. The technician is primarily an assistant to veterinarians, biological research workers, and other scientists. In addition to veterinary practices, veterinary technicians are employed in a number of other facilities including biological research laboratories, drug or feed manufacturing companies, animal production facilities, zoos, and meat packing companies.

NUTRITIONAL REQUIREMENTS OF DOGS AND CATS

Canine Nutrition

To many, dogs are considered carnivores. In reality, dogs are omnivores, easily capable of acquiring much of their essential nutrition from vegetable matter. Wild canids, such as wolves, coyotes, and jackals, consume fruits, roots, grasses, and other vegetable matter in addition to animal tissue. Domestic dogs are easily able to digest and utilize nutrients from properly processed plant sources. In fact, a nutritionally complete and balanced dog food can be developed without any animal tissue, although this would not be a natural diet for dogs.

Dogs have maintenance nutrient requirements that are similar to other omnivores, such as humans or swine, although there are some differences. For example, they require the same ten essential amino acids. They also require many of the same preformed vitamins, although they do not require a dietary source of vitamin C.

Maintenance energy needs (kilocalories of metabolizable energy) for dogs can be estimated by the equations $132(Kg\ body\ weight)^{0.75}$ or $144 + 62.2(Kg\ body\ weight)$. Either of these can provide an estimate of maintenance energy requirements (MER); however, these equations are based on average calorie needs. Most dogs will vary somewhat from the calculated MER, due in part to individual metabolic rate and other differences. Environmental factors also may influence energy needs. Dogs housed outdoors require approximately 7.5% more energy to maintain energy balance for every 10 °F drop in ambient temperature.

For most animals, a subcommittee of the National Research Council (NRC) has provided a listing of minimum nutrient requirements for that species based on available published and unpublished information. Dogs are no exception, with publications from the NRC in 1974 and 1985. More recently, however, the Association of American Feed Control Officials (AAFCO) established an independent listing of nutrient requirements which has become the official standard for the pet food industry (Table 20-2). This guideline is intended to take into account the estimated bioavailability of nutrients from common feed ingredients. A unique aspect of this nutrient profile is the inclusion of maximum safe levels for those nutrients for which adequate data exist to establish such levels.

Pet food companies may utilize the AAFCO nutrient guidelines to formulate pet foods, although some of the larger companies have established their own profiles, based on their proprietary data. There are some limitations to the AAFCO guidelines. The guidelines address the classic lifestages of growth, reproduction, and maintenance, but do not address the unique companion animal lifestage of "geriatric." There is a growing body of evidence from human and companion animal studies that indicate aging can affect nutrient requirements. For example, older dogs appear to require more protein compared to young dogs. No allowances are made in the AAFCO profiles for effects of lifestyle, breed effects, or other differences. As noted below, these effects can be considerable. In addition, since minimum nutrient needs may not be synonymous with optimum nutrient needs, many pet foods are formulated to include a "margin of safety," often based on their own research.

One unique aspect of canine nutrition is the extreme variability in nutritional needs induced by differences in lifestyle. Many dogs are housepets that get very little exercise. These dogs truly require maintenance levels of energy and other nutrients, and may tend to grow fat due to overconsumption of pet food, supplemental treats, and table scraps. Obesity is a common problem in both dogs and cats, as described in Figure 20-2. On the other hand, a smaller number of dogs are highly active and have special nutritional needs. Examples include working dogs, such as dogs used by police or U.S. Customs agents; hunting dogs; and racing dogs including greyhounds or sled dogs. These working dogs will require more energy and other nutrients compared to the housepet, yet each of these activities may influence nutritional needs differently.

Another unique aspect of dogs is the extreme variation in breed size, which influences nutritional requirements. Adult dogs in good condition can weigh less than 2 kg or

TABLE 20-2
NUTRIENT PROFILES FOR DOG AND CAT FOODS ESTABLISHED BY THE ASSOCIATION OF AMERICAN FEED CONTROL OFFICIALS (AAFCO)

Nutrient	Units, Dry Matter	Dogs			Cats		
		Growth and Reproduction, Minimum	Adult Maintenance, Minimum	Maximum	Growth and Reproduction, Minimum	Adult Maintenance, Minimum	Maximum
Protein	%	22.0	18.0		30.0	26.0	
Arginine	%	0.62	0.51		1.25	1.04	
Histidine	%	0.22	0.18		0.31	0.31	
Isoleucine	%	0.45	0.37		0.52	0.52	
Leucine	%	0.72	0.59		1.25	1.25	
Lysine	%	0.77	0.63		1.20	0.83	
Met + Cys	%	0.53	0.43		1.10	1.10	
Met	%				0.62	0.62	1.5
Phe + Tyr	%	0.89	0.73		0.88	0.88	
Phenylalanine	%				0.42	0.42	
Threonine	%	0.58	0.48		0.73	0.73	
Tryptophan	%	0.20	0.16		0.25	0.16	
Valine	%	0.48	0.39		0.62	0.62	
Taurine, canned food	%				0.20	0.20	
Taurine, dry food	%				0.10	0.10	
Fat	%	8.0	5.0		9.0	9.0	
Linoleic acid	%	1.0	1.0		0.50	0.50	
Arachidonic acid	%				0.02	0.02	

TABLE 20-2 (CONTINUED)
NUTRIENT PROFILES FOR DOG AND CAT FOODS ESTABLISHED BY THE ASSOCIATION OF AMERICAN FEED CONTROL OFFICIALS (AAFCO)

Nutrient	Units, Dry Matter	Dogs			Cats		
		Growth and Reproduction, Minimum	Adult Maintenance, Minimum	Maximum	Growth and Reproduction, Minimum	Adult Maintenance, Minimum	Maximum
Minerals							
Calcium	%	1.0	0.6	2.5	1.0	0.6	
Phosphorus	%	0.8	0.5	1.6	0.8	0.5	
Ca:P ratio		1:1	1:1	2:1			
Potassium	%	0.6	0.6		0.6	0.6	
Sodium	%	0.3	0.06		0.2	0.2	
Chloride	%	0.45	0.09		0.3	0.3	
Magnesium	%	0.04	0.04	0.30	0.08	0.04	
Iron	mg/kg	80	80	3000	80	80	
Copper	mg/kg	7.3	7.3	250	15	5	
Manganese	mg/kg	5.0	5.0		7.5	7.5	2000
Zinc	mg/kg	120	120	1000	75	75	
Iodine	mg/kg	1.5	1.5	50	0.35	0.35	
Selenium	mg/kg	0.11	0.11	2	0.10	0.10	
Vitamins & Others							
Vitamin A	IU/kg	5000	5000	250000	9000	5000	750000
Vitamin D	IU/kg	500	500	5000	750	500	10000
Vitamin E	IU/kg	50	50	1000	30	30	
Vitamin K	mg/kg				0.1	0.1	
Thiamin	mg/kg	1.0	1.0		5.0	5.0	
Riboflavin	mg/kg	2.2	2.2		4.0	4.0	
Pantothenic acid	mg/kg	10	10		5.0	5.0	
Niacin	mg/kg	11.4	11.4		60	60	
Pyridoxine	mg/kg	1.0	1.0		4.0	4.0	
Folic acid	mg/kg	0.18	0.18		0.8	0.8	
Biotin	mg/kg				0.07	0.07	
Vitamin B$_{12}$	mg/kg	0.022	0.022		0.02	0.02	
Choline	mg/kg	1200	1200		2400	2400	

Source: Association of American Feed Control Officials, Inc. (1998), pp. 133–142.

FIGURE 20-2

Obesity. (Photo courtesy of Ralston Purina Company, St. Louis, MO.)

Obesity is the most common nutrition-related problem in dogs and cats in developed countries. While approximately 25% of dogs and cats of all ages are overweight or obese, nearly 50% of middle-aged animals are overweight. Obesity is associated with a number of health problems, such as diabetes mellitus (sugar diabetes) and arthritis.

Many factors contribute to obesity, such as genetics, lack of exercise, and consumption of high-fat foods. Neutering of dogs and cats results in a reduced metabolic energy requirement. If not fed appropriately, this can increase the risk for obesity. The feeding of treats, snacks, or table scraps may contribute to weight gain. Ultimately, obesity is caused when a dog or cat consumes more calories than it uses. Therefore, controlling calorie intake and calorie expenditure are important in the management or prevention of obesity. Food intake should be monitored and adjusted up or down to keep the animal at an ideal body condition.

Animals that are significantly above or below optimum should be examined by a veterinarian to assure that no other health problems are present. Too-rapid weight loss can lead to Fatty Liver Syndrome in cats, which can be fatal. Dogs that lose weight too quickly may tend to regain the lost weight. Because there are health implications, severely obese animals should undergo weight loss under the supervision of a veterinarian.

more than 60 kg. Large-breed dogs require less energy per kilogram of body weight than small-breed dogs due to relative differences in body surface area. Since energy is a controlling factor for intake for dogs, like other species, nutrients must be balanced to the expected energy intake of the dog. This suggests that a complete and balanced food which is minimally adequate for small-breed dogs may not provide adequate amounts of protein, calcium, or other nutrients for large-breed dogs, due to the larger dogs' lower intake per unit body weight. These differences can be addressed by formulating diets with sufficient excess of nutrients to meet the needs of all breeds of dogs rather than to simply meet minimum requirements. It also suggests the need to use multiple breeds of dogs in establishing nutrient requirements or when testing products for nutritional adequacy. From the pet food consumers' perspective, it illustrates a need for commercial pet foods with different energy densities and nutrient profiles to meet the needs of these various dogs.

Feline Nutrition

Cats are unique among domestic animals. They are true carnivores and, therefore, must receive at least a portion of their nutrients from animal sources or from synthetic replacements. However, they also are able to utilize nutrients, such as carbohydrates, amino acids, and fats, from properly processed plant sources. Like dogs, the MER of individual cats varies considerably. However, average MER can be estimated as 70 to 80 Kcal/kg body weight (30 to 35 Kcal/lb).

Cats require more dietary protein than any other domestic animal. While the exact amount necessary will vary with protein quality and other aspects of the diet, one report cites the adult cat's mimimum protein requirement as 29% of the diet dry matter, compared with 12% for adult dogs and rats, and 8% for humans. In addition to higher total protein requirements, cats also have unique amino acid requirements. For example, they are extremely sensitive to diets deficient in the amino acid arginine. Arginine is involved in the urea cycle within the liver, which incorporates potentially toxic ammonia into relatively nontoxic urea. Arginine-deficient diets can result in excesses of ammonia in the blood, which can interfere with normal brain function.

Cats require a dietary source of the amino acid taurine, which is found abundantly in animal tissue. Most mammals synthesize taurine *in vivo* from the amino acids methionine or cysteine. However, cats have competitive pathways that divert cysteine to other metabolites and have other unique requirements for taurine. Taurine deficiency can contribute to blindness, heart failure, reproductive failures, developmental abnormalities in kittens, and compromised immune function in adult cats. In order to maintain normal plasma taurine levels above 50–60 nmol/ml, dry extruded cat foods should contain approximately 1000 ppm (0.1%) taurine, while canned cat foods must contain at least 2000 ppm (0.2%) taurine on a dry-matter basis.

Cats require the fatty acids arachidonic acid and linoleic acid in their diet. Arachidonic acid is a metabolically active fatty acid that is found within the cell membrane of every mammalian cell. Most animals are able to convert linoleic acid into arachidonic acid, so do not require a dietary source of arachidonic acid. Cats, however, lack sufficient enzyme activity necessary to make this conversion effectively. Inadequate arachidonic acid can cause reproductive failures in cats.

Other unique metabolic features of cats include an inability to convert the amino acid tryptophan to the B-vitamin niacin, leading to an increased requirement for niacin. Likewise, cats have higher requirements for thiamin, pyridoxine, and other B vitamins compared with other species. Cats cannot convert beta-carotene to vitamin A and, therefore, require a source of preformed vitamin A.

Given the opportunity, most domestic cats will eat 10 to 20 small meals distributed throughout the 24-hour day. This feeding pattern is not influenced by the form of the diet, nor is it affected by feeding several cats together. Feral cats would need to eat 10–12 mice per day to meet their nutrient requirements, suggesting that 10–20 meals per day is natural for cats. However, cats can adapt to eating one or two meals daily.

Commercial Pet Foods

Commercial foods that provide complete and balanced nutrition (defined as containing all the nutrients the animal needs in correct proportion to one another) are widely available for dogs and for cats. Commercial dry dog foods were introduced in the late 1800s in the form of baked biscuits. Today, worldwide pet food manufacturing and sales is a $25 billion industry, with over $10 billion spent in the United States alone (Table 20-3). Seven companies dominate the sales, accounting for approximately 70% of pet food sold in the United States in 1996. However, there are thousands of different pet food companies, distributing well over ten thousand brands of dog or cat food.

Commercial pet foods are generally classified into categories on the basis of their moisture content: dry foods (<12% water), semidry (<18% water), semimoist (<35% water), and canned (<82% water). Foods in each of these categories can be manufactured to provide complete and balanced nutrition.

Nutritional adequacy of pet foods can be documented using one of the two methods described by AAFCO. The first involves comparison of the nutrient content of the food, determined by laboratory analysis, to the nutrient profile established by AAFCO (Table 20-2). This method of determining adequacy does not specifically account for nutrient bioavailability. The other method for substantiating nutritional adequacy involves animal feeding tests using protocols consistent with those described by AAFCO (Figure 20-3). Feeding trials are considered superior to laboratory analysis since they provide an indication that the nutrients not only are present in adequate quantities and proportions in the food, but are available to the animal.

Unlike livestock feeds, commercial pet foods are cooked. Proper cooking of pet foods is important. Cooking makes the carbohydrates more digestible, but overcooking can destroy amino acids and make proteins less digestible. The majority of dry, semidry, and semimoist foods are produced by extrusion. This is a process of cooking that uses both steam and friction for heat, plus pressure, to quickly cook the ingredients and form them into the desired shapes. Retorting is a means of cooking and sterilizing canned foods using a pressure-cooking process similar in principle to that used in home canning.

TABLE 20-3

PET DOG AND CAT POPULATION ESTIMATES AND SIZE OF PET FOOD INDUSTRY FOR SELECTED COUNTRIES

	France	Germany	Italy	Japan	United Kingdom	United States
Dogs, millions	9	5	6	10	7	55
Cats, millions	8.2	6	7	7	7	66
US Dollars, millions	2,140	2,994	870	7,069	2,610	11,724

Source: Petfood Industry Magazine (1997).

FIGURE 20-3

AAFCO procedures for nutritional adequacy testing. (Photo courtesy of Ralston Purina Company, St. Louis, MO.)

Animal feeding protocols to substantiate nutritional adequacy of foods for the lifestages of reproduction, growth, or adult maintenance have been established by AAFCO. In order to substantiate a claim that a product provides complete and balanced nutrition for all lifestages, the product must successfully pass both reproduction and growth protocols sequentially. For a food to successfully pass any of these tests, the performance results from the animals fed the test diet must equal or exceed those from animals fed a control diet or predetermined colony standards.

Reproduction: At least eight females must be used to test each diet. The diet is fed as the sole source of nutrition, except that water is also freely available, beginning at or before the time of breeding and continuing until the puppies or kittens are 4 or 6 weeks of age, respectively. Observations include daily food intake, weekly body weight of female, number and weight of young born and weaned, veterinary examination, and key blood values.

Growth: At least eight puppies or kittens from at least three different litters must be used to test each diet. The diet is fed as the sole source of nutrition, except that water is also freely available, beginning at six to eight weeks of age, respectively. The study lasts for 10 weeks. Observations include daily food intake, weekly body weight, veterinary examination, and key blood values.

Adult Maintenance: At least eight adult animals must be used to test each diet. The diet is fed as the sole source of nutrition, except that water is also freely available, for a period of 26 weeks. Observations include daily food intake, weekly body weight, veterinary examination, and key blood values.

Standardized regulatory guidelines have been prepared by AAFCO regarding pet foods and pet food labels; however, it is up to the individual states to adopt and enforce pet food regulations. Under the AAFCO guidelines, pet food labels must provide a nutritional adequacy statement that indicates whether the product provides complete and balanced nutrition and, if so, for what lifestage(s) and how the nutritional adequacy was determined. The label also must indicate the guaranteed minimum concentration of protein and fat, and maximum concentration of crude fiber and water; and it must list all the ingredients used in the food in descending order by weight.

Matching an appropriate dog or cat food to the needs of the individual pet requires knowledge of the pet's lifestage and lifestyle, including consideration for individual factors such as body condition, individual metabolism, activity level, and so on. It also entails consideration of feeding management, such as *ad libitum* feedings versus measured meals.

The majority of pets are fed commercial foods for a large portion of their intake. Many also consume supplements, either in the form of specific nutritional supplements, or in the form of treats or table scraps. Most supplements and treats do not provide balanced nutrition, so the addition of excess treats to the diet can interfere with the balanced nutrition provided by complete foods. To avoid this problem, and to reduce the risk for obesity associated with excess calorie intake, treats or scraps should be limited to about 10% of daily calorie intake.

BASIC HEALTH CARE

In pets, as in livestock, controlling infectious disease involves proper nutrition, environmental control, stress reduction, minimization of exposure to infectious agents, and use of effective vaccines. This section provides an overview of common infectious diseases and internal and external parasites affecting dogs and cats.

Infectious Diseases

Puppies and kittens are especially susceptible to infectious diseases as their immune systems do not mature for several months after birth. Often, the signs of disease are much worse in an affected kitten or puppy than would be seen in an adult animal. The immune system is a highly complex system of specialized cells, such as those that produce antibodies, which help protect animals from disease and infection caused by foreign invaders such as viruses, bacteria, and other foreign organisms.

As with other mammalian species, the intake of colostrum within hours after birth is critical to provide antibodies from the mother and protect the newborn puppy or kitten from infectious diseases. Between six and sixteen weeks of age, this passive immunity will begin to disappear. Consequently, it is critical to begin vaccination during this time.

Vaccines stimulate the immune system without causing disease. Their purpose is to prime the immune cells to produce antibodies upon subsequent exposure to the disease organism, helping to prevent infection or reduce the severity of disease. The most common infectious diseases for which vaccines are available are discussed in this section.

COMMON INFECTIOUS DISEASES OF DOGS.   *Rabies* is a viral disease affecting the central nervous system. The virus is transmitted in the saliva of infected animals.

Most often, transmission occurs when the rabid animal bites its victim, but any contact between infectious saliva and a break in the skin, such as a cut or scratch, can allow the virus to be transmitted. Airborne infections may also occur in confined areas, such as in bat caves. All warm-blooded animals are susceptible to rabies, including dogs, cats, and human. Certain species of animals are able to carry the virus for an extended period without becoming sick and, therefore, serve as natural reservoirs of the virus. Among these are the skunk, fox, racoon, and certain bats.

Early signs can include fever, listlessness, or altered behavior, followed later with paralysis, muscle tremors, convulsions, and death. Because rabies is usually fatal and can be transmitted to man, most states have laws requiring dogs to be vaccinated for rabies.

Canine distemper is another viral disease that can attack the central nervous system. Signs of distemper include fever, lack of appetite, diarrhea, drainage from the eyes or nose, depression, pneumonia, or seizures. Transmission of the distemper virus most commonly occcurs via airborne virus. Vaccination is critical and highly effective in controlling the disease.

Canine parvovirus is one of the most common and deadly viral infections of dogs. Puppies under five months of age are the most severely affected, but unvaccinated dogs of any age can be infected. The virus primarily attacks the gastrointestinal tract and may cause fever, vomiting, depression, severe diarrhea, dehydration, and death.

Parvovirus is spread through fecal contamination. The virus can survive for extended periods on contaminated surfaces. For this reason, infected animals must be quarantined. The premises must be thoroughly disinfected before introducing new animals. Introduce new puppies to such areas only after the puppies have been adequately vacccinated against parvovirus.

Infectious hepatitis is a viral infection that affects the liver, kidneys, or eyes. Dogs may die rapidly, or show signs similar to those of distemper: fever, loss of appetite, depression, vomiting, diarrhea, and bleeding disorders. Some dogs which survive the early disease may have permanent liver damage while others may make a full recovery. The virus is shed in the urine of infected dogs and can survive for days in the environment. Effective vaccines are available.

Canine respiratory disease, or "kennel cough," is caused by several organisms, including *canine parainfluenza virus, Bordetella bronchiseptica,* and *canine adenovirus-2.* This highly infectious condition primarily affects dogs living in close proximity, such as in a kennel or shelter, or those that are frequently exposed to other dogs, such as show dogs. Signs of kennel cough can include fever, nasal discharge, a dry, hacking cough or a moist, persistent cough, or pneumonia. Vaccines against these organisms provide only short-lived immunity. For high-risk dogs, vaccination should be repeated semiannually.

Leptospirosis is a bacterial disease that affects the kidneys and liver. These blood-borne bacteria usually are transmitted by direct contact, bite wounds, or ingestion of infected meat. Leptospiral organisms thrive in stagnant water or slow-moving streams, and can also survive within insects. Clinical signs of disease include fever, muscle soreness, vomiting, bloody discharge, and shock. Those surviving the acute disease may develop chronic kidney or liver failure in later years.

Control of rodents in kennels and external parasites in the environment, and isolation of infected animals, can help reduce the spread of leptospirosis. Bacterins are available to help protect against clinical disease, although these do not prevent animals from becoming carriers of the organism.

COMMON INFECTIOUS DISEASES OF CATS.   *Rabies* can affect cats as well as dogs. Some states require cats to be vaccinated against rabies. Unless a cat has absolutely no exposure to the outdoors or to other animals, vaccination should be strongly considered even if laws do not require it.

Feline panleukopenia, or feline distemper, is one of the most important viral infections of cats. It is transmitted by direct contact with infected cats or their secretions, or by fleas from infected cats. The virus is extremely hardy and may survive for extended periods in the environment. Kittens should not be brought into an area that was previously occupied by an infected cat until the kitten has been vaccinated.

The disease destroys many of the cat's white blood cells. Typical signs include fever, depression, loss of appetite, vomiting, and dehydration. If pregnant queens become infected, the developing fetuses may be aborted or mummified, or kittens may be born with brain lesions that affect their sense of balance and motor function.

Feline leukemia virus (FeLV) is a common cause of severe illness and death in domestic cats. Death may occur from the cancers caused directly by the virus or from secondary infections caused by immune-suppressive effects of the virus.

Transmission of FeLV occurs via exposure to the saliva or respiratory secretions from the infected cat. Urine and feces from infected cats may also carry the virus. Close contact between cats is necessary for transmission since the virus is rapidly inactivated when exposed to the environment. Infected cats may live many years without showing signs of disease, allowing them ample opportunity to spread the virus.

Some common signs of FeLV include anemia, decreased appetite, diarrhea or constipation, and enlarged lymph nodes. FeLV also interferes with the cat's immune system, predisposing infected cats to many severe, chronic illnesses, especially cancers. There is no cure for FeLV, but vaccines are available to reduce the risk of infection.

Feline immunodeficiency virus (FIV) can appear very similar to FeLV, although the viruses themselves are quite different from one another. The primary mode of transmission of FIV is through bite wounds. Transmission between cats within multiple-cat households does not appear to be a problem so long as the animals do not fight.

Infected cats may appear normal for years until immunodeficiency allows severe infections to develop. Infection and inflammation of the gums, mouth, skin, urinary bladder, and upper respiratory tract are common. FIV-infected cats have an increased risk of developing certain types of cancer although the cancer risk is greater with FeLV infection.

No vaccine against FIV is available. The best protection is to prevent cats from coming into contact with infected cats. Pets kept indoors and away from free-roaming cats are highly unlikely to contract FIV infection.

The two most common *feline respiratory viruses* are feline viral *rhinotracheitis,* also known as feline herpesvirus infection and commonly called "rhino" by cat breeders, and *feline calicivirus.* Both of these viruses are highly contagious and can be transmitted directly cat to cat, or via respiratory discharges from the sneezing cats. Clinical signs may include sneezing, fever, loss of appetite, and inflammation of the tissues around the eyes or even ulcers of the mouth and eyes. These diseases can be a significant problem in multiple-cat households and catteries. Vaccinations for both viruses are available in combination with each other.

Internal Parasites

Gastrointestinal and other parasites are a common problem in dogs and cats. The parasites can be wormlike (e.g., roundworms, hookworms, heartworms) or one-celled protozoa (e.g., *Giardia, Toxoplasma*) organisms. The signs associated with parasite infections are fairly nonspecific, such as a dull haircoat, coughing, diarrhea, loss of appetite, pale mucous membranes, or a pot-bellied appearance. Malnutrition or dehydration caused by severe parasitic infestation can weaken an animal, making it more susceptible to viral and bacterial infections and diseases.

Some parasites, especially roundworms and hookworms, have the potential of infecting humans. Some steps to prevent human infection with pet-associated parasites include:

- Deworm kittens, puppies, and dams with an effective parasiticide when the young are 2, 4, 6, and 8 weeks of age.
- Deworm newly acquired puppies or kittens at least twice, 2 weeks apart.
- Have a veterinarian examine the stool of all adult pets at least annually.
- Cover sandboxes when children are not playing in them.
- Prevent children from eating dirt.

GASTROINTESTINAL "WORMS."   *Roundworms (Toxocara canis, T. cati, Toxascaris leonina)* and *hookworms (Ancylostoma caninum* and *Uncinaria stenocephala)* are among the most common intestinal parasites of young dogs or cats. Roundworms can be transmitted to puppies even before birth, and to newborn puppies and kittens by their mother's milk. Eggs shed in the feces of infected dogs and cats require time to mature before they become infective, so frequent removal of waste and proper cleaning of the facilities help control infestations. Huge accumulations of infective larvae can build up in the soil if animals are confined to one place for long periods. Prevention of infection or reinfection of animals depends on maintaining a clean environment and regular treatment with an effective parasitacide.

In the small intestine, roundworms compete with the puppy or kitten for nutrients, resulting in malnutrition, stunted growth, poor health, and a "pot-bellied" appearance. Hookworms attach to the intestinal wall and suck blood, causing anemia. Clinical signs of hookworm infestation include lethargy, poor appetite, anemia, and black, tarry stools. With heavy infestation, blood loss can be severe enough to cause death.

Hookworm larvae also can penetrate human skin. As they migrate under the skin, they cause an extremely itchy condition called cutaneous larval migrans.

Whipworms (Trichuris vulpis, T. felis) are a common cause of chronic diarrhea in dogs.

While small numbers of these parasites may not cause noticable signs, larger numbers are associated with chronic or reoccurring diarrhea that may contain blood. Elimination of whipworm infestations may require multiple treatments.

Tapeworms' (Dipylidium caninum, Taenia taeniaeformis) long, flattened bodies, made up of many segments, resemble ribbon or tape. The mature segments, filled with eggs, break off and are passed in the feces. These segments, which resemble grains of rice, can be observed near the animal's tail and rectum, or in the feces. Tapeworm infections rarely cause significant disease in cats or dogs. Animals usually become infected with tapeworms by ingesting infected fleas or rodents. Fleas and rodents become infected by eating the tapeworm eggs that are in the environment. While tapeworms are easily treated, reinfection is common. Controlling the flea and rodent populations will reduce the risk of tapeworm infection in pets.

PROTOZOAN PARASITES. *Giardia* are protozoa (one-celled organisms) that can parasitize the small intestine of dogs and cats. Animals become infected by ingesting giardia-containing feces from another infected animal. Giardiasis is more common in multiple-pet households, kennels, and catteries due to its mode of transmission. Also, the infection rate is greater in young animals.

Diarrhea is the most common sign of giardia infection. Giardia may be present in animals without causing signs of disease; however, such animals remain potential sources of infection to other animals. Elimination of giardia infections from households of pets may be difficult and depends on proper treatment and sanitation. It is uncertain whether species of giardia that infect pets are contagious to humans or vice versa. Careful hygiene will eliminate the risk of transmission to humans.

Coccidia are extremely common in cats and dogs. Infections usually cause no problems in normal adults, but this protozoan can cause significant diarrhea in kittens or puppies, or in immune-compromised animals. Serious infections may develop in crowded environments. Good sanitation and hygiene will help control coccidia.

Toxoplasmosis, a disease of cats and other mammalian species, is caused by the protozoa *Toxoplasma gondii.* Although infection with *Toxoplasma* is fairly common, actual disease caused by the parasite is relatively rare. Cats usually become infected by consuming *Toxoplasma* in infected prey or in other raw meat. Transmission from an infected mother to her fetus occurs in sheep, goats, and humans, but is much less common in cats. Toxoplasmosis can be a problem in humans, as discussed in Figure 20-4.

Most cats show no clinical signs of infection with *Toxoplasma.* If signs are seen, they are more apt to occur in kittens. Depression, loss of appetite, fever, or pneumonia may be seen. Rarely, the liver, pancreas, eyes, or central nervous system may be affected. In some cases, coinfection with FeLV or FIV may predispose a cat to develop toxoplasmosis.

Cats that become infected but do not develop signs of disease typically shed *Toxoplasma* oocyts (eggs) in their feces only for a 2-week period, shortly after their initial infection. These require about 48 hours to mature before they become infectious, so daily cleaning of litter boxes can prevent this route of transmission. No vaccine is yet available against *Toxoplasma.*

HEARTWORMS. *Heartworms (Dirofilaria immitis)* are transmitted by mosquitoes, so heartworm disease is most prevalent in areas where mosquitos thrive, such as the South-

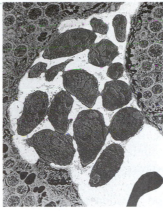

FIGURE 20-4

Toxoplasmosis in humans. (Photo by Moredum Animal Health LTD/SPL/Photo Researchers)

Toxoplasmosis is the disease caused by a microscopic parasite called *Toxoplasma gondii*. It has been found in virtually all warm-blooded animals including most pets, livestock, and human beings. Nearly one-third of all adults in the United States and in Europe have antibodies to *Toxoplasma,* which means they have been exposed to this parasite.

There are several ways *Toxoplasma* is transmitted in humans: directly from pregnant mother to unborn child when the mother becomes infected with *Toxoplasma* during pregnancy; consumption and handling of undercooked or raw meat, or unpasteurized dairy products from infected animals; inhalation or ingestion of oocyst-contaminated soil or feces. Pigs, sheep, goats, and poultry are sources of meat commonly infected with *Toxoplasma. Toxoplasma* in meat can be killed by cooking at 152 °F (66 °C) or higher or freezing for a day in a household freezer.

Developing fetuses of women who become infected with *Toxoplasma* during pregnancy are at risk of developing severe problems. Women who are in frequent contact with cats should be serologically tested for *Toxoplasma gondii* before becoming pregnant, because, if they are already seropositive, they are not at risk of acquiring a primary, acute infection during pregnancy.

The other population at high risk for infection with *Toxoplasma* consists of immuno-compromised individuals, such as those with Acquired Immune Deficiency Syndrome (AIDS) or those undergoing immunosuppressive therapy (e.g., for cancer or organ transplantation).

Knowledge of the *Toxoplasma* life-cycle can provide ways to reduce the risk of human infection. Cats usually shed *Toxoplasma* in their feces for only one to two weeks in their lives and oocysts are not infectious immediately after passage from the cat. Oocysts in meats can be destroyed by proper cooking and handling. Some steps that can be taken to reduced the risk of human *Toxoplasma* infection include:

- Change cat litter daily to prevent maturation of oocysts.
- Pregnant women should avoid handling of cat feces, litter, or litter pans.
- When cooking, avoid tasting meat before it is fully cooked.
- Cook meat thoroughly until the internal temperature reaches 152 °F (66 °C) in a conventional oven.
- Wash hands with soap and water after handling raw or undercooked meat.
- Cutting boards, knives, and the sink and counters should be washed well after cutting meat.
- Wear gloves while gardening and wash hands with soap and water after working with soil.

Because of the seriousness of these potential situations, medical doctors and veterinarians should be consulted by people in any of these conditions.

eastern United States. Although the disease has been recognized more frequently in dogs, both dogs and cats can be affected.

The infectious, immature heartworm larva (microfilaria) enter the skin via a mosquito bite. Over the next 6 months the larva make their way to the blood vessels in and around the lungs, mature, and begin to produce microfilaria. Clinical signs of heartworm disease are due to adult worms in the blood vessels in and around the lungs, and are related to the number of worms present. Clinical signs include coughing, shortness of breath, and decreased activity. A veterinary evaluation may identify an enlarged heart or changes in the lungs.

Heartworm infection can be prevented by daily or monthly administration of compounds such as diethylcarbamazine, ivermectin, or others. Adverse reactions to heartworm preventatives can occur if microfilaria are present in the bloodstream, so animals should be tested for heartworm prior to initiating a preventative program.

External Parasites

Fleas are tiny, wingless insects that can jump or crawl rapidly from one host animal to another. Fleas feed on the blood of the host animal. While extremely heavy flea infestations can cause sufficient blood loss to create severe anemia, especially in young or malnourished dogs, smaller numbers of fleas can also cause problems.

Fleas are among the leading causes of skin disorders in dogs and cats, both causing direct damage and inducing a potentially severe allergic reaction. Flea bite allergy occurs when the animal is exposed to flea saliva. The reaction can cause intense itching, hair loss, and secondary skin infections. Fleas also serve as carriers of other diseases and parasites. For example, fleas can transmit some species of tapeworms.

The life-cycle of the flea is about 30 days. Fleas feed on the host, then deposit eggs in multiple locations throughout the home and environment. The eggs are dormant in cold weather and hatch in warmer weather. Effective control of fleas requires eliminating fleas on the host animal and its environment. Organophosphates and pyrethrins can effectively kill adult fleas. Newer, safer compounds, such as chitin-inhibitors, insect growth regulators, and others that can interrupt the life cycle or kill flea larva are being introduced on an ongoing basis.

A variety of different *ticks* can parasitize dogs and cats. While most ticks have a preferred host species, many will feed on whatever animal species is available including dogs, cats, or humans. Tick bites are of concern for two reasons. A heavy tick infestation can cause severe blood loss. Of more frequent concern is the number of diseases that ticks can carry and transmit. Among the disease-causing organisms spread by ticks are *Borrelia burgdorferi* (Lyme Disease), *Ehrlichia canis* (Ehrlichiosis), *Rickettsia rickettsi* (Rocky Mountain Spotted Fever), and *Francisella tularensis* (Tularemia). All of these can affect humans as well as dogs or cats.

The tick drops off of the host animal after feeding, so elimination of ticks requires treatment of both the animal and its environment. Animals should be examined carefully for ticks whenever they return from outdoors. If ticks are found already feeding, they should be removed by gentle traction, using tweezers or a gloved hand. Cleaning with soap and water after handling ticks can reduce the risk of disease transmission.

There are several different types of *mites* that affect dogs or cats, causing various degrees of hairloss, or mange. Mites are easily transmitted from one animal to another. *Sarcoptes* cause sarcoptic mange or "scabies," typically visible as a crusting of the ear margins and elbows. *Demodex canis* lives in the hair follicle and causes intense itching and "red mange." It is usually localized to a small area, but can cover the entire body in malnourished or immune-compromised animals. Ear mites (*Otodectes cyanotis*) are more common in cats than in dogs. Signs of ear mites include redness and irritation of the outer ear, which can become severe if the animal has been scratching. The affected ears often contain an accumulation of foul-smelling, dark-colored exudate within the ear canal. The mites themselves are difficult to see with the naked eye, but may appear as small white specks on the background of this exudate.

All types of mites are hardy and are resistant to treatment. Several weeks of veterinary-prescribed treatments are often necessary to eliminate mite infestations.

REPRODUCTION IN THE KENNEL OR CATTERY

Production of puppies and kittens for commercial profit represents one aspect of companion animal husbandry which could be compared to similar operations in production animals. However, most breeders who provide pure-breed puppies and kittens operate on a relatively small scale compared to breeders of production animals. Many of the breeding animals are in fact pets and yield relatively few litters during their lifetime. Despite this, a sad truth about puppies and kittens, whether pedigreed or mixed-breed, is that more are born each year than can find good homes. An estimated 20 million dogs and cats were euthanized at shelters between 1991 and 1994. All pet owners should be strongly encouraged to have their puppy or kitten spayed or castrated unless a responsible breeding program is planned.

Similar to production animal operations, successful breeding programs in dogs and cats are basically a function of effective disease control, good nutrition and management programs, and proper selection of breeding stock. Most breeding of purebred animals involves attempts to match particular breed characteristics to produce superior offspring. As advances are made in genetic testing, further refinement in selective matings will be possible (Figure 20-5).

Canine Reproduction

Normal male dogs are capable of reproduction by age 10 to 12 months. Breeding males should receive a thorough veterinary examination at least twice yearly. Reproductive performance problems in males may be induced by heat, ischemia, age, overuse, and other causes. If infectious diseases, such as brucellosis, are identified, breeding should be halted until the situation is resolved.

Puberty in the bitch may occur at any time between 5 months and 2 years, and generally occurs earliest in small breeds. The interval between estrous cycles varies between individuals, but generally averages 5 to 12 months. Reproductive performance can be en-

FIGURE 20-5

Genetics in companion animal reproduction. (Photo by Kathi Lamm/Tony Stone Images.)

Recent advances in the technology of applied genetics make it increasingly likely that genetic testing will become a valuable tool in helping breeders eliminate hereditary diseases in companion animals. As researchers continue to identify disease genes, more genetic tests will become available. Incorporation of genetic testing into a responsible breeding program will allow breeders to identify and eliminate undesirable traits without expensive breeding studies and without compromising the expression of desirable traits. Many genetic diseases require the presence of two "affected" copies of a particular gene, one from the mother and one from the father, for the disease to be manifested. Since each apparently normal parent carries only one affected copy of the gene and one normal copy of the gene, the parent does not develop disease; thus each parent is considered a hidden "carrier" of the trait. Traditional genetic management strategy of such traits would require expensive breed testing to identify carriers and, once identified, suggest removal of both carrier parents from the breeding population. An advantage of genetic testing is the ability to identify those animals that do not carry the hidden gene and preferentially use them in breeding programs. An alternative is to retain breeding animals that carry one affected copy of a gene but also possess other desirable traits. Used properly, breeders can utilize genetic knowledge of their animals to match breeding pairs that will produce only nonaffected (clear) or carrier offspring while propagating desirable traits, and then use subsequent genetic testing to slowly dilute the undesirable genes out of the gene pool.

hanced if females enter productive service at about the second estrous cycle. Properly nourished, healthy females can be bred at every cycle, if desired.

Prior to breeding, the bitch should be in good body condition, free of internal and external parasites and infectious diseases. Vaccinations should be updated prior to breeding since many cannot be given during pregnancy. Any degree of obesity should be corrected before breeding to reduce the risks of problems in whelping or lactation which may accompany obesity.

For planned matings, multiple matings several days apart will increase the likelihood for success. Bitches may experience a "false pregnancy," and show all the symptoms of being pregnant without actually being pregnant. Suspected pregnancies should be confirmed by a veterinarian using palpation (feel) or ultrasound. The normal gestation period is 63 days, but can vary by breed and individual.

When the bitch approaches whelping time, she normally becomes restless and searches for a secluded spot. A whelping box sized to allow the brood female to lie down comfortably but not much larger, should be provided about a week before expected delivery date. Good bedding material is important for the comfort and well-being of the bitch and the pups. Soft carpeting, affixed to the whelping box to prevent pups from crawling under it, provides excellent results. Straw or other hard particles can cause eye and skin irritation to the pups and should be avoided. Finely shredded newspaper is an acceptable alternative to attached carpet.

As with other species, nutritional needs increase during pregnancy and lactation. Body weight gain occurs mostly in the last trimester. During this period nutrient requirements for a bitch can increase up to two times her normal requirements. This is best met by feeding a nutrient- and energy-dense, complete and balanced food, such as those formulated for growing puppies.

While the bitch will often fast during the period immediately prior to whelping, her appetite should return within 24 hours after whelping. Very attentive dams with large litters may be reluctant to leave their puppies to take care of themselves. They may need encouragement to seek food and water. One way to do this is to provide a highly palatable food, moistened with water, several times daily. By peak lactation at about 20 to 30 days after whelping, the dam's food requirements may be 3 to 4 times her normal intake.

Beginning when the puppies are about 3 weeks of age, they should be given access to moistened food. A shallow pan containing food moistened with warm water can be placed in the whelping box. Puppies should gradually increase their intake of solid food such that, by the time they are 4 to 6 weeks of age, they should be meeting most of their needs with the solid food. This practice facilitates weaning, which should occur at about 6 weeks of age.

Bitches should be fasted for 24 hours on the day of weaning, followed by 2 to 3 days of reduced food intake. This helps stop milk production and aids getting the bitch back onto a maintenance energy intake. Male dogs used infrequently as sires have no special nutrient requirements, but those used in heavy service may benefit from a nutrient-dense diet to maintain body condition.

Feline Reproduction

Most of the same principles discussed for dogs apply to cats as well. Cat breeding facilities must be kept free of infectious diseases. All cats should be regularly examined by a veterinarian and only healthy cats in good body condition should be used for breeding. Overcrowding contributes to the dissemination of disease in a cattery and should be avoided.

Normal male (tom) cats reach puberty at about 8 to 10 months of age, and may be used for breeding after about 12 months of age. Puberty in the female cat (queen) occurs between 5 and 12 months of age. Queens should not be used for breeding until they are 10 to 12 months of age. Queens are seasonally polyestrus, induced ovulators. This means that they will not ovulate until they have been stimulated to do so, such as by mating.

The probability of ovulation and a successful mating increases with multiple matings. Estrus in nonpregnant queens can last 6 to 10 days, with repeat cycles occurring every few weeks.

Because the domestic cat exhibits little physical evidence of estrus, behavioral aspects of estrus become important for timing of planned matings. Proestrus is accompanied by vocalization, decreased hostility toward males, treading of the hind feet, rolling, rubbing on objects, and behavioral changes toward humans. True estrus is characterized by acceptance of the male, with the female in a characteristic position with elevated hindquarters, lowered forequarters and tail displacement. Copulation is brief and is followed by an aggressive postmating response by the queen.

As the queen nears the end of her 63-day gestation period, she should be provided with a "queening" box that will provide privacy, as well as a clean, warm environment. Queening boxes should be lined with a removable, soft pad such as carpeting, cloth, or paper. Most queens will spend all of their time in the queening box with the kittens for the first few days after parturition. Providing a fresh litter pan while removing the kittens for 30 to 60 minutes each day helps avoid fecal and urine retention by the dam.

Food intake should be monitored to assure the queen is consuming adequate quantities to maintain milk production as well as body condition. Kittens should be monitored regularly for appropriate weight gain. Frequent, gentle handling of young kittens may aid both physical and social development. Kittens should be weaned at about 6 to 8 weeks of age. While some breeds may vary, most kittens should weigh at least 500 grams at weaning.

DEVELOPMENT AND SOCIALIZATION OF PUPPIES AND KITTENS

One aspect of animal behavior that is becoming increasingly important is the behavioral development of young animals. Socialization of young animals has a remarkable influence on subsequent adult behavior patterns.

Puppies experience four distinct periods of behavioral development: the neonatal period, the transition period, the socialization period, and the juvenile period. In most breeds, the neonatal period lasts for the first 2 weeks of the puppy's life, during which the puppy interacts primarily with its mother. The newborn is functionally blind and deaf but has a good sense of smell and has tactile senses. The newborn's motor capabilities allow it to crawl toward or away from warmth and to suckle. Urination and defecation occur reflexively upon stimulation by the dam.

During the transition period, between 15 and 21 days, the puppy's sensory, motor, and psychological capabilities mature. The eyes and ears become functional. The puppy learns to stand, walk, and chew. By the end of this period, adult behaviors, such as play and tail wagging, can be observed. The puppy develops control of urination and defecation and begins to eliminate outside the nest area.

The socialization period extends until the puppy is 12 weeks of age. Experiences during this period are thought to have dramatic effects on ultimate adult behavior. Interactions with littermates and humans are important during this period. Puppies begin chewing, growling, and biting while playing as they mimic activities important to establishing the social hierarchy critical to pack life. They begin to explore areas farther and farther outside their immediate nest area. Weaning occurs during the socialization period. This period also includes the ideal time to housebreak a puppy by taking advantage of the natural instinct to void away from the nest area.

From 12 weeks until sexual maturity is the juvenile period. Key human-animal and animal-animal interactions occur during this period. Puppies must establish their place in the dominance hierarchy with other dogs as well as their human "pack." Gently establishing the human family members as dominant is critical to assuring a well-behaved dog. Lack of appropriate socialization and discipline during this stage can contribute to the all-too-common problem of euthanasia or abandonment of unruly dogs.

Cats do not exhibit the high degree of sociability and dependency seen in dogs. They are not asocial creatures, however. Kittens develop more rapidly than puppies, with functional eyes and ears at an earlier age. The kitten brain is nearly mature by 5 weeks of age, although fine motor skills take a bit longer to develop.

Queens provide more prolonged attention to young kittens than is typical for bitches. Kittens learn to hunt, to use a litter pan, and other species-typical behaviors from their mothers. Play with other kittens leads to social attachments and the development of social relationships. Kittens deprived of play activity often demonstrate abnormal adult behaviors such as being easily upset and poor learning ability.

The sensitive period for kittens appears to be between 4 and 8 weeks of age. Frequent handling, exposure to different people, and exposure to children during this period produces cats that are more social and less fearful of strangers. Continued exposure to other cats or kittens remains important at this age. Kittens removed from the litter too soon tend to become aggressive toward other cats as adults.

The ideal age for placing a kitten with a family is between 8 and 12 weeks of age. As with puppies, it is important to teach the kitten what it is and is not allowed to do using positive reinforcement and gentle reprimands.

SUMMARY

There are approximately 55 million dogs and 65 million cats in the United States. The philosophy and objectives of companion animal care and nutrition differ from those of production animals. Production animals are managed on the basis of providing accepted feeding and husbandry practices compatible with an acceptable economic return, while decisions concerning companion animals are more often based on emotions as well as concern for the long-term well-being of the pet.

Nutritional needs are strongly influenced by the animal's lifestage and lifestyle. The majority of dogs and cats are housepets and relatively few hunt or work for a living. However, there are exceptions and these animals' nutritional needs can differ greatly from the relatively inactive housepet. Cats' nutritional requirements are unique compared to other species. In addition to greater dietary protein requirements, they require dietary sources of taurine, preformed vitamin A, and arachidonic acid.

Long-term care of pets involves good nutrition, good health care, and proper socialization. Providing the long-term care of pets provides many career opportunities. Some of these include careers in basic or applied research, veterinary medicine, pet grooming, pet product industry positions, and others. Responsible breeding programs in dogs and cats involve effective disease control, good nutrition and management programs, and proper selection of breeding stock. Early socialization of puppies and kittens is critical to establishing acceptable behavior in adults. Companion animals are susceptible to numerous infectious diseases and both internal and external parasites. Many of these can be controlled by vaccines and other preventive measures.

GLOSSARY

AAFCO   Association of American Feed Control Officials. Formed in 1909, it is an organization composed of the feed control officials from each state and Canada who are involved in regulation of all types of animal feed. They establish model pet food regulations that may be adopted and enforced by the individual states.

Ad libitum   Freely availiable or unrestricted. In feeding, *ad libitum*–fed animals are allowed unlimited quantities of food.

Ammonia   A compound composed of nitrogen and hydrogen. It is a byproduct of protein breakdown. Excessive quantities are toxic to the body so various metabolic pathways exist to incorporate ammonia into less-toxic or nontoxic compounds.

Antibodies   Proteins produced by cells of the immune system that bind to and help destroy foreign organisms such as viruses. There are five different types of antibodies produced that vary somewhat in function and location in the body. Antibodies are also known as immunoglobulins, abbreviated as Ig.

Arachidonic acid   A fatty acid with 20 carbons and four unsaturated double bonds. This fatty acid belongs to the omega-6 family in that the first double bond is located at the sixth carbon from the omega end of the fatty acid. Arachidonic acid

is used as a precursor to numerous metabolically active compounds within the body. Most animals can synthesize adequate quantities of arachidonic acid from other omega-6 fatty acids, such as linoleic acid.

Bacterin   Inactivated bacteria or portions of bacteria that are administered for the purpose of stimulating the immune system to recognize and react against the bacteria upon subsequent exposure. Similar to a vaccine except that a bacterin stimulates the immune system against a bacteria rather than a virus.

Beta-carotene   A pigmented hydrocarbon compound found in plants that is converted into vitamin A by most mammalian species. Beta-carotene is reported to have biological antioxidant activity independent of its role in vitamin A.

Bioavailability   The fraction of nutrients, drugs, or other active compound in a substance that is available for absorption and use by the animal consuming the substance.

Bitch   A female dog.

Carnivore   A flesh-eating mammal whose predominant diet consists of other animals.

Estrus   The fertile period during which a female is sexually receptive to males.

Extrusion/extruded   In foods, a process whereby

moist, mixed ingredients are rapidly cooked using the energy provided by steam, friction, and pressure as the mixture is forced through a barrel-like structure. This process is used to cook the majority of dry, semidry, and semimoist dog and cat foods sold in the United States, as well as many cereals, snack foods, and other foods for human consumption.

Induced ovulator A female that only ovulates upon stimulation such as that induced by copulation, rather than ovulating spontaneously.

Linoleic acid A fatty acid with 18 carbons and two unsaturated double bonds. This fatty acid belongs to the omega-6 family in that the first double bond is located at the sixth carbon from the omega end of the fatty acid. Linoleic acid is an essential fatty acid in monogastric animals and must be supplied by the diet.

Maintenance energy requirements The energy required to maintain body weight and normal activity in an adult animal that is not reproducing. Maintenance energy requirements (MER) can be highly variable between individuals.

Metabolizable energy That portion of the energy in food available to fuel metabolic processes within the animal. It is calculated as total (gross) energy of food less fecal and urinary energy.

Omnivore An animal that consumes both animal and vegetable matter in its normal diet.

Oocyst Fertilized, encapsulated egg of a parasite.

Passive immunity Protection from infectious diseases afforded to neonates by antibodies absorbed from colostrum. Passive immunity may last from a few weeks to four months. While it protects the young, it can also interfere with an effective immune response to vaccinations. Thus, it is important that final vaccinations are given at or after the age of four months. Passive immunity can also be provided by administering blood plasma to immune-compromised individuals.

Polyestrus Females that experience multiple estrous cycles. Seasonally polyestrus species have multiple estrous cycles only within a particular season of the year.

Proestrus The period immediately preceeding estrus, associated with increased hormonal activity.

Retort/retorting The equipment for or process of pressure-cooking canned foods. Adequate heat and pressure are applied to sterilize the contents of the cans, aiding in preservation of the contents.

Spay/spayed Surgical removal of a female's ovaries and uterus (spayed = past tense of spay).

Taurine A sulfur-containing amino acid that is produced within the body from methionine or cysteine. It serves many purposes, such as transmitting signals in the nervous system, binding bile acids from the liver, and others. Cats require a dietary source of taurine as they are unable to produce adequate quantities to meet their needs.

Queen A female cat.

Queening The act of giving birth to kittens, parturition.

Whelp/whelping The act of giving birth to puppies, parturition.

REFERENCES AND SUPPLEMENTAL READING

Association of American Feed Control Officials. 1998. *Official Publication Association of American Feed Control Officials, Inc.,* pp. 113–156.

Kelly N. C., and Wills, J. M. 1996. *BSAVA Manual of Companion Animal Nutrition and Feeding.* Ames, IO: Iowa State University Press.

Kilcommons, B. and Wilson, S. 1992. *Good Owners, Great Dogs.* New York: Warner Books.

National Research Council. 1985. *Nutrient Requirements of Dogs.* Washington, D.C.: National Academy Press.

National Research Council. 1986. *Nutrient Require-*

ments of Cats. Washington D.C.: National Academy Press.

Pedersen, N. C. 1991. *Feline Husbandry: Diseases and Management in the Multiple-Cat Environment.* Goleta, CA: American Veterinary Publications.

Ralston Purina Company. 1991. *Nutrition and Management of Dogs and Cats.*

Shojai, A. D. 1998. *The Purina Encyclopedia of Cat Care.* New York: Ballantine Books.

Contact Information for Important Resources:

Association of American Feed Control Officials
http://www.aafco.org
c/o Rodney J. Noel, Secretary
Office of the Indiana State Chemist
1154 Biochemistry Bldg.
W. Lafayette, IN 47907-1154

American Veterinary Medical Association
http://www.avma.org
1931 N. Meacham Road, Suite 100
Schaumburg, IL 60173-4360

American Kennel Club
http://www.akc.org
5580 Centerview Dr., Suite 200
Raleigh, NC 27606-3390

Canine Companions for Independence
http://www.caninecompanions.org
National Headquarters
P.O. Box 446
Santa Rosa, CA 95402-0446

Cat Fanciers' Association, Inc.
http://www.cfainc.org
P. O. Box 1005
Manasquan, NJ 08736-0805

CHAPTER TWENTY-ONE
OTHER ANIMALS, OTHER USES, OTHER OPPORTUNITIES

D. E. ULLREY AND J. BERNARD
MICHIGAN STATE UNIVERSITY
EAST LANSING, MI

ANIMALS FOR FOOD, HIDES, AND FIBER
ANIMALS RAISED FOR FUR
ANIMALS IN RESEARCH
ANIMALS AS TISSUE AND ORGAN DONORS
ANIMALS AS PETS AND COMPANIONS
ANIMALS IN ZOOS AND AQUARIUMS
SUMMARY

Dogs, cats, cattle, sheep, swine, horses, and poultry were domesticated by humans in a period beginning about 12,000 years ago (Clutton-Brock, 1987). Through this domestication, humankind acquired companions, means of transport, and sources of food and clothing that they did not need to hunt. As medical science advanced, rats, mice, guinea pigs, rabbits, and monkeys became surrogates for humans in studies of physiology and disease. Wild or unusual domesticated animals are now being reared as exotic pets, for the production of food, clothing, and ornamentation, or to provide unconventional recreational experiences. New developments in biotechnology are making possible the temporary or permanent substitution of animal tissues for failing parts of the human body.

As a consequence, animal scientists have a broadened opportunity to apply the principles of their profession, including the latest techniques of science and the traditional features of husbandry, to over 50 animal species in the United States, and even more, if animals that are important in other countries are included. Some of these species may be of long-term economic significance, whereas others may wane in importance as interest in them declines. Nevertheless, it is apparent that the future of animal science includes much more than food and fiber production with traditional farm animals. New species will be involved, new uses for traditional products are being developed, new products are being devised, and new opportunities for the well-trained and imaginative animal scientist abound in the United States and internationally.

ANIMALS FOR FOOD, HIDES, AND FIBER

There are well over 250 associations and registries in the United States and Canada that promote particular species or breeds and that maintain breeding records (Bixby et al., 1994). Some are concerned with the common breeds of farm animals. Others focus on uncommon breeds of domesticated animals and on wild species reared in captivity. Worldwide, there is interest in dozens of other species, hybrids, and breeds that have potential for commercial or subsistence levels of food, hide, and fiber production. Some of the more important of these are discussed in this chapter.

Microlivestock

In 1991, a panel established by the National Research Council published a treatise on microlivestock, a term coined for species that are inherently small, such as poultry and rabbits, and for breeds of cattle, sheep, goats, and pigs that are half the size or less of the common breeds (NRC, 1991). A survey of more than 300 animal scientists in 80 countries was conducted, and over 150 species were proposed for inclusion. Ultimately, discussions on about 40 species were developed, taking into consideration the ecological interdependence of animal, plant, and human life, the limited amount of the earth's surface that can be safely cultivated, and the innate advantages of small animals to the subsistence family with no refrigeration, and with limited cash, space, and animal feed.

Even without refrigeration, one small animal can be consumed by the immediate or extended family before the meat spoils. When cash is in short supply, small animals are individually less expensive to buy; several small animals pose less financial risk if one should die; small animals generally have a high reproductive rate and fast turnover; and they provide flexibility in matching the feed supply and the family's fluctuating needs for cash or food.

MICROCATTLE. Among the largest of microlivestock, microcattle are mostly small breeds of *Bos taurus* and *Bos indicus*. In the United States, there has been a selection trend for large cattle, resulting in breeds that are far too big to meet some of the major needs of the Third World. Many microcattle breeds are tolerant of heat and humidity and a variety of tropical diseases and parasites. They integrate well into large pastoral herds or serve as solitary family cows and have the ability to sustain themselves on marginal grazing lands. As with conventional breeds, their productivity can be increased by selective breeding and improved feeding. Representative examples of microcattle include the following:

The adult Dwarf West African Shorthorn cow weighs about 125 kg, the adult bull 150 kg. It is adapted to harsh, humid climates and has good resistance to trypanosomiasis. The Muturu, a slightly larger shorthorn subtype, with cows weighing 160 kg and bulls 210 kg, is found in Nigeria. It is very trypanosomiasis resistant, yields a high percentage of meat, and is widely kept as a village scavenger. N'dama, adults weighing 200–400 kg, are often the only cattle that remain productive in the least-hospitable, hot areas of West Africa.

Dwarf Zebu breeds are kept from Taiwan (Taiwan Black) to Malaysia (Kedah-Kelantan), Sri Lanka (Sinhala), Sudan (Nuba Dwarf), Somalia (Small Zebu), Ethiopia (Showa), Tanzania, Uganda, and Kenya (Mongalla), and Zimbabwe (Mashona). All have a low basal metabolic rate, resist heat well, and generally have a high resistance to ticks and other parasites. Researchers in Mexico have developed the Bonsai Brahman, a breed in which adult females average 150–180 kg and adult males 200–220 kg. Production of up to 4 L of milk per day has been reported, compared to 6 L per day by their full-sized counterparts, yet they can be maintained in a small space. A campesino with almost no land can have one or two Bonsais but could not maintain a single standard-sized cow.

Criollo are descendants of Spanish and Portugese cattle that were imported into Central and South America over 400 years ago. They have adapted to a wide range of harsh climates, and some varieties are quite small. The Chinampo is found in Baja California, Mexico, is docile, has a low basal metabolic rate and body temperature, is active at night, and feeds largely on scrub and cactus. Florida Scrub Cattle of Criollo origin, genetically isolated for 300 years, are hardy in harsh, subtropical conditions, have good resistance to ticks and screwworm, and can subsist on high-fiber forage.

Sanga are ancient crosses between longhorns or shorthorns and humped cattle that are found throughout eastern and southern Africa. Bavenda adults weigh 240 to over 300 kg and are found in Transvaal and South Africa. Ovambo cows weigh about 160 kg, bulls about 225 kg, and are found in northeastern Namibia. Nilotic adults weigh 180–300 kg and are found in southern Sudan.

Chad has "native" and Dwarf Black Cattle that are humped, very drought resistant, and graze the sparse savanna. Cows weigh 225 kg and bulls weigh 275 kg.

Other small types include "Arab" cattle in the Middle East, Hill Cattle in Nepal, Tibetan Dwarfs in Tibet, Yellow Cattle in southwest and south China, Cheju Hanwoo in Korea, Madura in Indonesia, and Dexter Cattle in Ireland and North America. This latter breed is popular among some city folk who have small country estates.

The banteng (*Bos javanicus*) is a small southeastern Asian cattle species that exists wild in remote areas from Burma to Indonesia. In Indonesia it is used as a farm animal for draft and meat. Under good conditions, it may be 50% bigger than the other microcattle, with males weighing 450–500 kg. Females commonly weigh 300 kg or less. Indonesia has over 1.5 million domesticated banteng, about 20% of the country's cattle population. Small numbers have been introduced into Sumatra, Malaysia, and northern Australia. Experimental herds have been established in Texas and in New South Wales, Australia (National Research Council, 1983a).

MICROGOATS. Of the world's half-billion domesticated goats (*Capra hircus*), more than 90% are raised in developing countries. The adults of many breeds weigh less than 35 kg, although common commercial goat breeds weigh 60–100 kg. Young grow rapidly, mature early, have high reproductive rates, and produce flavorful meat and rich milk. Angora and Cashmere goats (adults often weighing less than 30 kg) produce a very valuable hair fiber. Goats are easily handled, tolerate extremes of climate, and are selective browsers, feeding on tree leaves, shrubs, and forbs, often in preference to grass. Their resistance to trypanosomiasis is particularly valuable in many regions of Africa.

Goats are prominent multiuse animals in much of Asia, Africa, and Latin America. They are raised for food and fiber but may be sold for cash or used in payment of school fees, taxes, and the costs of marriages and funerals. Although they have strong territorial attachments, they are curious and independent, and may wander away if not watched. Males are malodorous during rutting season, and there is a common prejudice in industrialized nations against goats and goat meat. Although their preference for browse minimizes competition with cattle and sheep for grass pasturage, shrubs and trees may be severely damaged by goat overpopulation. The seeds of certain trees, such as *Acacia* and *Prosopis*, are scarified by passage through the goat's digestive system, and germination is promoted.

Representative breeds of microgoats include the West African Dwarf or Djallon (20–30 kg) in West and Central Africa; Nubian Dwarf (35–40 kg) in the United States; American Pigmy (15–25 kg) in the United States, derived from the West African Dwarf; Sudanese Nubian (25–30 kg) in northern Sudan; Sudanese Dwarf (11–25 kg) in southern Sudan; Small East African (20–30 kg) in Kenya, Uganda, and Tanzania; Mauritian (25–30 kg) in Mauritius; and the small, hardy Criollo (20–35 kg) of Iberian ancestry in Latin America. Hejazi (20 kg) are found in the Middle East; and Sinai or Black Bedouin (20–50 kg) are found in Sinai, Egypt, Israel, and the Negev Desert. Microgoat breeds found in Pakistan or India include Chapper (20–24 kg), Barbari (20–40 kg), Gaddi or White Himalaya (25–30 kg), Changthangi or Ladakh (20 kg), and Black Bengal (10–14 kg), also known as the Teddy or Bangladesh Dwarf. The Terai (8–12 kg) and Southern Hill Goat (12–16 kg) are found in the lowlands and mid-altitudes, respectively, of Nepal. The Chinese Dwarf (Tibetan, Jining, Fuyang, Chengdu Grey—20–40 kg) is well adapted to humid regions of China, and the Katjang (20 kg or less) is widespread in Southeast Asia, China, and the Pacific Islands. The Heuk Yumso (25–35 kg) is a prolific, cold-climate goat found in Korea.

The goat's wild ancestor is the bezoar (*Capra aegagnus*), a seriously endangered species with spectacular horns that was first domesticated over 9,000 years ago. Originally living in the region from Greece to Pakistan, the few remaining specimens are restricted to two small Greek islands, where they are known as agrimi.

Other wild relatives with the same chromosome number as domestic goats (2n = 60) have been shown to produce hybrid offspring that are frequently fertile. These are the

Nubian ibex (*Capra ibex*) and the markhor (*Capra falconeri*), the mountain goat of Pakistan. Hybrids, known as ya-ez, of the ibex and the Sinai Desert goat were created at Kibbutz Lahav in the northern Negev Desert, are fertile, and produce a mild-flavored meat that is in demand in the dining rooms of Tel Aviv hotels. Markhors live at high elevations in rugged mountains on diets that are inadequate to sustain domestic goats. They have an insulating underfur that is a soft, valuable raw material for Kashmiri shawls. Some markhors have been domesticated or used to produce domestic goat-hybrids that possess some of the markhor's desirable attributes.

MICROSHEEP. Domestication of sheep began in the Stone Age in the Middle East and Central Asia, about 8,000 to 11,000 years ago. It is likely that their principal wild ancestor was the mouflon (*Ovis orientalis*), with some genetic contribution from the urial (*Ovis vignei*) and the argali (*Ovis ammon*). These three species still exist in remote, rugged, upland areas of the mountains of Central Asia. Their meat is of excellent quality, without undesirable mutton flavor, but they have hair, not wool. They have been crossed with domestic sheep, and all hybrids are fertile, although only the mouflon has the same chromosome number (2n = 54) as domestic sheep, whereas the urial (2n = 58) and argali (2n = 56) are different. Mouflon-domestic sheep hybrids are hardy and have been quite effective in defending themselves against coyotes in southern Utah.

There are hundreds of breeds of sheep (*Ovis aries*), but most of those reared commercially have adult weights greater than 35 kg. Many of the smaller breeds are adapted to harsh environments and can sustain themselves in regions that are otherwise suitable only for goats or camels. Such sheep constitute the majority of livestock in arid regions of North Africa and the Middle East. Some have greatly enlarged rumps or tails that store large amounts of fat that are withdrawn during periods of food deprivation. Many tropical breeds have little hair and little or no wool, and provide principally meat and milk. Other breeds, particularly in temperate regions, also produce marketable quantities of hair or wool. Predators, such as feral dogs, can take a heavy toll on ewes and lambs, and some breeds are quite susceptible to internal parasites and other diseases.

Representative examples of microsheep breeds include the West African Dwarf (25–35 kg), found from Senegal to Nigeria and south to Angola. This breed is well adapted to warm, humid conditions, is prolific, has good disease resistance, and is a major source of meat in West Africa. The Landim (23–40 kg) is a prolific, long fat-tailed type found in East and Central Africa. The Berber (25–41 kg) and Arab (40–50 kg) breeds are found in North Africa, the former in the Atlas Mountains. Their wool is used for coarse cloth and carpets. The Southern Sudan Dwarf (15–25 kg) is one of the many small breeds found in eastern and southern Africa and has a short, fine fleece.

Hejazi (32 kg) are fat-tailed sheep found in the deserts of Arabia. They are highly adapted to drought and privation. Zel or Iranian Thin-Tailed (30–32 kg) are found in the Caspian region of northern Iran. They produce coarse wool, milk, and mild-flavored meat without the mutton taste and odor that some find objectionable in other breeds. The Greek Zackel (30–40 kg) is primarily a milk producer in the mountains and islands of Greece. The Sitia (25–30 kg), found in Crete, and the Common Albanian (25–35 kg) are triple-purpose animals, producing meat, milk, and wool. The Zeta Yellow (25–35 kg) of Yugoslavia is used for milk and some meat, but its primary product is wool. Not shorn every year, the long fibers are used in expensive carpets. The Pag (20–35 kg) of Yugoslavia and Roccia (Steinschaf) (30–35 kg) of northern Italy and Austria are adapted to poor pastures and rocky terrain. The Corsican (25–30 kg) is a hardy breed native to Corsica, with coarse wool that may be both black and white.

Entre Douro e Minho (15–25 kg) are found in the mountains of Portugal, whereas Churro do Campo (20–30 kg) are found in the dry interior, and are kept for milk and wool. Galician (18–25 kg) are kept in Spain, principally for milk, but they also produce a marketable wool.

Soay (25–30 kg) is probably the most primitive domesticated sheep in Europe. It is found in Scotland, and may be unchanged from Viking times. It has a short brown fleece that is shed annually. The North Ronaldsay or Orkney (27–32 kg), found in northern Scotland, appears to survive year-round on seaweed and is adapted to a high salt intake.

Criollo sheep in Latin America were derived from Spanish Churro and Merinos and tend to be small and hardy. The related Navajo-Churro (45–70 kg), found in the southwestern United States, is probably the oldest breed of sheep in this country. Believed to have been introduced by the Spanish explorer Francisco Vazquez de Coronado in 1540, it was a species never before seen by the local Native Americans. Nevertheless, it was adopted into the culture of the Navajo, whose shepherds and weavers produced (and still produce) colorful rugs from its wool. This breed can exist in the hot, dry desert of the American Southwest without supplementary feed and with little water. The ewes have a strong maternal instinct, a trait important in protecting lambs against coyotes. Virgin Islands White Hair (35–55 kg), also known as St. Croix, are hair sheep found on islands in the Caribbean. They are well adapted to heat and humidity, breed most of the year, commonly have twins, and also produce a palatable meat.

South Asia has many breeds of microsheep whose adult females weigh 25 kg or less. Two of the more important in northwest India are the Magra or Chokhla (20–25 kg), adapted to hot, dry areas and with a white, shiny fleece valued for carpet wool, but with poor reproductive efficiency, and the Marwari (25–30 kg), a widespread, white-fleeced sheep with high resistance to disease and parasites, and good fertility. The Mandya or Bandur (25–35 kg), found in southwest India, is an outstanding meat breed and adapts well to mixed farming. Hu (35–45 kg), also known as Huyang or Lake Sheep, are fat-tailed sheep found in China with a 6-month lambing interval. They are intensively managed to produce meat, wool, and lambskins. Javanese Thin-Tail (25–40 kg), found in Indonesia, are prolific and are raised for meat, manure, and skins.

MICROPIGS. The adults of most breeds of domestic swine (*Sus scrofa*) are too large to classify as microlivestock, but mature weights of the breeds that follow are generally less than 70 kg. These small swine are found most commonly in South Asia, the East Indies, West Africa, Latin America, and various oceanic islands. With appropriate shelter, there are few climatic limitations to their production, but they are best suited to warm, humid environments, although not necessarily the tropics. Pigs are omnivorous, rapid growing, and prolific, and adapt well to a variety of management systems, from scavenging to total confinement. They serve subsistence families by utilizing otherwise unused kitchen waste and by consuming roots, leafy trash, or bitter fruits and nuts that are not consumed by humans or ruminants.

In this treatise, the term micropig will be used in a generic sense, but the term Micropig® has been trademarked by Charles River Laboratories, Inc. of Wilmington, Massachusetts for the strain of Yucatan Miniature Swine they selected and bred for medical research. This is a subtype of the Black Hairless (Pelon, Tubasqueno, Birish) Criollo pig found in the hot, arid Yucatan Peninsula of Mexico. The parent stock is used for meat and lard, and is known for its docility, resistance to disease, and relative lack of odor. Following importation into the United States in 1960, mature weights of 75 kg have been lowered by selective breeding to 30–50 kg, with an ultimate goal of 20–25 kg. Another Criollo micropig is the Cuino (10–12 kg), found in the highlands of central Mexico. A century ago, it was a common household animal, but is now threatened with extinction. The Nilo (Macao, Tatu, Canastrinha) is a small, black, hairless Criollo pig of Brazil, often kept inside the house.

West African Dwarf (Nigerian Black, Ashanti) adults weigh 25–45 kg and are kept as village scavengers in the hot, humid, lowland forests of West Africa. They are relatively resistant to trypanosomiasis.

China and Southeastern Asian countries, such as Viet Nam, have long had small pigs (Chinese Dwarfs) as scavengers or as part of intensive agriculture. Crosses of small, black Chinese pigs with European types in the early 1800s provided the foundation for many modern Western breeds, and recent importations of other Chinese breeds are being evaluated for their potential contribution to the gene pool of North American swine. Vietnamese Pot-Bellied Pigs, while larger as adults than many microbreeds, have become popular as pets in the United States.

The Kunekune (Pua'a, Poaka) is a black-and-white spotted pig of New Zealand, late maturing at a weight of 40–50 kg and reported to fatten on grass alone. The Ossabaw (20–30 kg) has been feral on Ossabaw Island, South Carolina for over 300 years. It is well adapted to environmental extremes and sustains itself in coastal salt marshes. Other miniature laboratory pigs include the Goettingen, Hanford, Kangaroo Island, Ohmini, Pitman-Moore, and Sinclair (Hormel), maturing at less than 70 kg.

The smallest pig is the pigmy hog (*Sus salvanius*) of northeastern India. It has the same chromosome number ($2n = 38$) as the common pig but weighs less than 10 kg. It originally lived along the southern foothills of the Himalayas but is now among the twelve most endangered animal species on earth and is found only in the Manas National Park in Assam.

Rabbits

Domestic rabbits (*Oryctolagus cuniculus*) are easily maintained, require little space, are fast growing, reproduce rapidly, and can subsist on diets that are not competitive with the needs of humans. They may be raised in large intensive rabbitries or by subsistence farmers. The world population of rabbits raised for their pink, mildly flavored meat has been estimated to be about 708 million, resulting in an annual production of rabbit meat of about 1 million metric tons (NRC, 1991).

Intensive rabbit production tends to be concentrated in temperate, industrialized countries such as France, Italy, Spain, Germany, and Hungary. In the United States, about 200,000 producers raise 6–8 million rabbits each year, producing 3.6–4.5 million kg of meat for consumption in the home and in restaurants. Each doe will produce 25–50 live rabbits per year, yielding 57–113 kg of meat. Some rabbit breeds, such as the long-haired Angora, produce a wool fiber (about 450 g/year) that makes a luxuriant, soft, lustrous fabric. This fiber may be mixed with fine wool from Merino sheep to provide more substance and to improve wearing quality.

Domestic rabbits had their origin in the wild rabbit of Spain and Portugal. Now they are found worldwide, with nearly 160 breeds recognized by the American Rabbit Breeders Association. The most popular breed for commercial meat production in North America and Europe has been the New Zealand White, although hybrids are gradually replacing purebreds. Weight of a full-grown New Zealand White is 4–5 kg, with production of about 2 kg of meat at 8–10 weeks of age. Other meat breeds, popular in various locations, include Flemish Giants, Checkered Giants, Yellow Silvers, Dutch, Chinchillas, Japanese Large Whites, and Polish. The Rex has a high-quality pelt used in furs.

The gastrointestinal system of the rabbit is designed for fiber digestion by microorganisms in the cecum and colon, although rabbits are not as efficient as horses in this regard. Cecal pellets are voided separately from normal fecal pellets, the former being softer and smaller than the latter. The cecal pellets are consumed by the rabbit that voided them (coprophagy), allowing for recycling of the products of cecal fermentation through the stomach and intestine. Thus, components of microbial cells, such as proteins, may be digested to their constituent amino acids and made available for absorption. The absorption of other intra- and extracellular products of fermentation, such as volatile fatty acids and vitamins, also may be promoted by this recycling.

Rabbits begin to breed at 4–6 months, gestation is 28–32 days long, and reproduction may continue over 4 years. Small breeds typically have 4 young per litter, whereas large breeds may have 8 to 10. Housing facilities need not be expensive, but good husbandry and sanitation are important to control or avoid diseases such as coccidiosis that results in diarrhea or the virulent virus that causes hemorrhagic tracheo-pneumonitis.

Other members of the order Lagomorpha (69 species) also have potential as food producers. Wild European hares (*Lepus europaeus*), released in Argentina and New Zealand, are now being trapped and carcasses exported to Europe as game meat. The forest rabbit or tapeti (*Sylvilagus brasiliensis*) is adapted to hot humid regions of Central and South America and is commonly eaten, although not raised domestically. It tolerates tropical environments better than domestic rabbits but, in the wild, produces only 1–3 young after a 44-day gestation. The eastern cottontail (*S. floridanus*), the popular game rabbit of the eastern and southwestern United States, has a gestation period of about 28 or 29 days, and females may produce 3–7 litters per year with an annual potential of 35 young.

Rodents

Considering that the order Rodentia includes 1,814 species, it is not surprising that a number of them have been found useful to humans. The role of rats, mice, guinea pigs, hamsters, and gerbils in research laboratories and as pets is discussed elsewhere, but many rodent species have been used as food for centuries. The guinea pig (*Cavia porcellus*) is a domesticated cavy with an uncertain relationship to the five wild species within the *Cavia* genus still living in South America. Some contend the guinea pig was domesticated for food over 7,000 years ago by the prehistoric Andean peoples living in what is now the central highlands of Peru and Bolivia (Leonard, 1973). More certain are the Spanish records of the sixteenth-century invasions of South America that recount use of the guinea pig by Incas for food and in religious ceremonies (Clutton-Brock, 1987). Peru now has about 20 million guinea pigs, producing about 15 million kg of meat annually, just 3.6 million kg less than the meat produced by Peru's sheep flocks (NRC, 1991).

Despite aversion to the idea of rodents as food in many Western cultures, Abrams (1983) has estimated that 42 of 383 cultures eat rodents. Some are domesticated, whereas others are trapped or hunted in the wild. In Colonial America, squirrel meat (gray [*Sciurus carolinensis*] and fox [*S. niger*]) was relished, particularly in Brunswick stew, which was said to be highly favored by Thomas Jefferson. Today, squirrel is the second most widely hunted game animal, after deer, in the United States. City markets in Latin America offer capybara (*Hydrochoerus hydracgaeris*), guinea pig, paca (*Agouti paca*), and vizcacha (*Lagostomus maximus*). Asian markets may offer bandicoot rats (*Nesokia indica*), cloud rats (*Phloeomys* spp. and *Crateromys schadenbergi*), and rice rats (*Rattus argentiventer*). Bushmeats in the rural markets of Africa may include cane rats (*Thryonomys swinderianus*, known as grass cutters in Ghana), giant rats (*Cricetomys gambianus*), and other rodent species.

Some rodent species have been so heavily exploited, their wild populations are endangered in many areas. This is true for agoutis (*Dasyprocta* spp.) in much of Latin America and hutia (*Capromys*, *Geocapromys*, and *Plagiodontia* spp.) in the Caribbean.

Although native to South America, the coypu (*Myocastor coypus*) has been introduced into aquatic environments in many countries, including the United States. Known as nutria in the fur trade, it was said to be the most important furbearing species in Louisiana in 1995, despite the decline of the nutria fur market and concern for the damage this animal has done to the wetland habitat. Its meat is said to be mild and tender, but the carcasses of coypu trapped in Louisiana are used more often to feed farmed alligators than as human food.

Poultry

CHICKENS. Domestic chickens (*Gallus domesticus*) are the most universally accepted food animals on the surface of the earth, and those varieties that have been selected for their adaptability to commercial production are discussed in Chapter 15. Descended from one or more species of Southeast Asian junglefowl, chickens are found in a relatively unselected form in the yards and homes of the poor in nearly every country. They are hardy, self-sufficient birds, capable of converting weed seeds, insects, and kitchen wastes into high-quality food. A number of breeds exist, with distinguishing characteristics of body size and shape, growth rate, egg production, and feather color.

Through genetic selection, tailor-made hybrids, and development of highly technical nutrition and husbandry systems, they have been converted into industrial chickens that produce meat or eggs very efficiently; and most developing countries now have some intensively reared chickens in total confinement. Their meat and eggs are affordable to those in the cash economy, but concern remains for subsistence households, where the primitive chicken still has an important role. Although growth rates are slower and eggs produced are fewer, with low-cost modifications in management and a minimum of effort, the productivity even of household or village chickens can be greatly improved.

Some chickens, such as bantams, are of great interest to hobbyists, and they are frequently exhibited at poultry shows. Their origin is somewhat obscure but most appear to be miniature versions of standard breeds, weighing one-fourth to one-fifth as much. The hens tend to be "broody" and are quite successful as mothers. Not only will they incubate their own eggs but they will readily accept the eggs of other species. For this reason, they have been used to incubate the eggs of some game birds. If appropriately protected out-of-doors by fencing during the first few weeks after hatching, bantam hens have been observed training their game-bird chicks to avoid predators. As a consequence, postrelease survival of the game birds was higher than when they were artificially incubated.

TURKEYS. The turkey (*Meleagris gallopavo*) is native to North America and was domesticated in Mexico in about 400 B.C., prior to the Spanish Conquest. They are natural scavengers, range further than chickens, and can subsist on seeds, vegetation, and insects. Commercial turkeys are much less adaptable than their wild ancestors and have been so intensely selected for heavy muscling that they cannot mate naturally, requiring use of artificial insemination. As a consequence, these highly selected birds are not suitable for the less-sophisticated management systems typical of subsistence households. "Unimproved" turkeys are still raised as a cash crop and for food in their native range in Mexico and Central America.

QUAIL. The domestic quail (*Coturnix coturnix*), sometimes called the Japanese quail, is believed to have had its origin centuries ago in China. Migrating Chinese carried them throughout Asia, and millions are now raised in Japan, Hong Kong, Indochina, Indonesia, Malaysia, Thailand, Taiwan, and the Philippines, as well as in Spain, Brazil, and Chile. Smaller numbers are raised elsewhere, including the United States. Quail are very precocious, may start to produce eggs by 5–6 weeks of age, and may lay over 200 eggs a year. Incubation to hatching requires about 17 days. Quail eggs are sold fresh or boiled, shelled, and either canned or boxed like whole eggs. The meat is very palatable, and one company in Spain processes 20 million quail annually for meat.

GUINEA FOWL. Guinea fowl (*Numida meleagris*) are widely raised in Africa and in a few areas of Asia. They are hardy, relatively disease-free, require little water or attention, and are better able to use green feeds and to protect themselves against predators than farmyard chickens. The meat is dark with a delicate game-bird flavor, and egg production is substantial. They are also adaptable to intensive-rearing systems, and millions of guinea fowl are raised in commercial facilities in France, Italy, Hungary, and Russia.

PIGEONS. Pigeons (*Columba livia*) have been reared in North Africa and the Middle East for centuries. Young pigeons, squabs, grow rapidly, their meat is finely textured, and in North America and Europe, they have been raised for the gourmet market. The natural diet of adults consists mostly of seeds, but includes leaves, fruits, and some invertebrates. Parent birds produce "crop milk," a secretion from the crop lining, high in fat and energy, that is fed to their young for the first 4–5 days after hatching. Subsequently, for about 4 weeks, the young are fed by regurgitation of their parents' food. Commercial squab producers expect one breeding pair to produce 12–14 squabs per year. When harvested at 21–30 days of age, squabs weigh 340–680 g, depending upon breed, nutrition, and other environmental factors.

DUCKS. Domestic ducks (*Anas platyrhynchos*) have considerable potential as subsistence-level sources of food. In Asia, there is about 1 duck for every 20 humans, but in the rest of the world, their use is minor compared to chickens. Ducks can efficiently convert waste resources—fallen seeds, insects, weeds, and aquatic plants—into meat and eggs. In confinement, only the broiler is more efficient in conversion of feed to weight gain. The meat breeds vary in weight from <1 kg for the Call to 4.5 kg for the Pekin. The muscovy (*Cairina moschata*) is a ducklike bird that perches in trees and is native to the rainforests of Central and South America. They have dark, flavorful meat that accounts for 50% of the duck meat consumed in France—about 54 million kg per year. The muscovy was domesticated in pre-Columbian times, probably in Colombia. It was introduced into Europe in the early 1500s and from there into North America, Africa, Asia, and Oceania. Mature males weigh 5 kg, mature females about 2.5 kg. A hybrid of muscovies and common ducks, called the mule duck, produced by artificial insemination, is the major duck breed in Taiwan, where 30 million are consumed per year. Taiwanese exports of frozen breasts and drumsticks account for about 24% of the duck meat consumed in Japan (NRC, 1991).

GEESE. Domestic geese are descended from the greylag goose (*Anser anser*) and the swan goose (*Anser cygnoides*), which were domesticated in Europe and China, respectively. There are now at least nine recognized breeds. Geese are found worldwide but are particularly important in Asia and Central Europe. The natural diet consists of grasses, seeds, fruits, tubers, roots, and incidental invertebrates. Due to capacious ceca inhabited by anaerobic microorganisms, geese can digest 15–20% of the fiber in their diet. As a consequence, if green grass is available, geese can be raised on less grain than any other domestic fowl. If goslings are well fed, they may reach market weight of 5–7 kg in as little as 10 weeks, but most are marketed at 20–30 weeks.

Gamebirds

Dr. Gary S. Davis, Raleigh, NC, Executive Director of the North American Gamebird Association, has estimated that about 40 million gamebirds are produced in the United States each year. The majority of these are ring-necked pheasants, bobwhite quail, Chukar partridge, and mallard ducks.

PHEASANT. The ring-necked pheasant (*Phasianus colchicus*), whose wild ancestors came from Asia, was first successfully introduced into North America in 1881. It has adapted well to grain-growing areas in the northern United States and Canada, and has become an important gamebird. Pheasants breed well in captivity and are being produced for gourmet food markets, shooting preserves, and release into previously populated areas that have been depleted by hunting or poor reproductive success. Fertility is best when one cock is mated with 8–12 hens, about 1 month before natural egg production begins in April. The start and extent of the laying period can be regulated by controlling daylength with artificial light. If eggs are regularly removed after laying, a hen pheasant will produce 60–70 eggs in one season. Under normal incubating conditions, eggs hatch in 23–26 days (Scheid, 1986). Female pheasants to be marketed as dressed birds should reach a ready-to-cook weight of 0.9–1 kg by 16–18 weeks, and males should reach a ready-to-cook weight of 0.9–1.1 kg by 16 weeks. Birds sold to shooting preserves should be well feathered, muscular, alert, and not too fat. Birds that have been grown in outdoor flight pens to maximize flying ability are usually in appropriate condition at 16–20 weeks (Flegal, 1994).

BOBWHITE QUAIL. Bobwhite quail (*Colinus virginianus*) are small, chunky birds with tasty meat. Their preferred habitat is open pinewoods, brushy fields, and farm fence rows. They commonly travel on foot and stay in coveys of a dozen or more in a relatively limited area. They are quite omnivorous and eat leaves, buds, fruits, seeds, insects, and snails. Nests are built on the ground, often in high grass with an arch of woven grass over the top. Fourteen to sixteen white eggs hatch in about 23 days. The young grow rapidly and can fly in about 2 weeks. In commercial breeding pens, 10 hectares will provide space for an annual production of 8,000–10,000 birds. Breeders are paired off in mid-March, and egg production begins naturally in early April and persists into August if eggs are removed for artificial incubation. If birds are produced for release into shooting preserves, they must be conditioned to outside weather and allowed to develop flight capability in flight pens. When conditioned, they are usually ready for release by 17–18 weeks of age. If released 5–8 weeks before hunting, they will adapt to the wild and react like wild birds, but only 20–35% are commonly recovered due to predation and accidents.

PARTRIDGES. The chukar partridge (*Alectoris graeca*) is a native of dry regions of southeastern Europe and parts of Asia. There have been several attempts at introduction into the United States, with variable success. They favor semiarid, open, rocky country and have done best in the West. They are gray-brown with black eye-stripes that run down each side of the neck and join below the throat to form a bib. The bill, legs, and feet are bright red, there are heavy black/brown bars on each side of the breast, and the tail is rufous. They are intermediate in size between grouse and quail. Flocks of 10–40 birds are common, roosting on open ground or among rocks. They are strong flyers but may attempt to escape by running. Egg production begins naturally in mid-April to early May, 8–15 eggs are laid in a hollow near a rock or bush, and females incubate the eggs for 21–23 days. If removed daily for artificial incubation, 70–80 eggs will be produced annually.

MALLARD DUCKS. Mallard ducks (*Anos platyrhynchos*) are believed to be the ancestors of most domestic ducks except the muscovy. They are the premier sport duck in the

United States and Canada and favor freshwater marshes, ponds, rivers, lakes, and bays. They feed on aquatic plants, seeds, grass, insects, and small aquatic animals. They make a down-lined hollow nest among reeds or grass and lay 8–10 eggs. Incubation requires about 26–28 days; the ducklings are fully feathered at 7 weeks, and start flying at 52–60 days. If they are intended for release, it is important to minimize human contact to keep them shy and wary.

Deer

Some authors have speculated that reindeer (*Rangifer tarandus*) were among the first domesticated animals and have been used for draft for several thousand years. Clutton-Brock (1987) proposed that reindeer may have been used for food by Upper Paleolithic hunters but found no evidence of early domestication and stated that the harnesses and sledges used with reindeer appear to have been derived from those developed for cattle and horses. In Lapland and Russia, in the first millenium A.D. and since, reindeer have been ridden, driven, used as pack animals, milked, and eaten.

The red deer (*Cervus elephas*) was used for meat, hides, bone, sinew, and antlers for at least 5,000 years by the hunter-gatherers of northern Europe, and perhaps longer in more southern latitudes. The ancient Romans took along herds of fallow deer (*Dama dama*) for sources of meat on their military campaigns.

In recent years, deer farming has become important in many countries (Figure 21-1). Old World red deer (*Cervus elephas*) were released into the forests of New Zealand over 70 years ago. They adapted so readily that by the 1950s they were damaging the forests and causing erosion of pastureland (Mackintosh and Krzywinski, 1992). Thousands of tons of venison were harvested by commercial hunters, and the numbers of free-ranging deer dropped dramatically. To sustain the market that had been established for venison, deer farming was legalized in New Zealand in 1969. The numbers of deer farmers grew to over 2,000 by 1987, with a national herd of about 500,000 farmed red deer. Red deer are now being raised in New Zealand, Australia, Taiwan, Korea, Russia, China, Scotland, and the United States. The closely related, but larger, North American elk (*C. elephas*), or wapiti, is being raised in New Zealand, Canada, and the United States.

Fallow deer are being raised in New Zealand, Australia, England, Denmark, Sweden, Switzerland, Germany, and the United States. Sambar (*C. unicolor*) are being raised in Australia, Mauritius, New Zealand, and Papua New Guinea; sika deer (*C. nippon*) in Taiwan, New Zealand, and the United States; musk deer (*Moschus spp.*) in China and India; Pere David's deer (*Elaphurus davidianus*) in New Zealand; and white-tailed deer (*Odocoileus virginianus*) in New Zealand, the United States, and Canada. Even moose (*Alces alces*) are being raised in small numbers in Scandinavia and in Russia.

For the past 25 years, deer have been increasingly displacing sheep on New Zealand pastureland. Chilled or frozen venison is exported around the world, and velvet antlers are marketed in Asia for use in traditional medicines. There are now more than 5,000 New Zealand deer farms with over 1,000,000 animals, mostly red deer. As deer farming has grown, so has the supporting infrastructure, including shows, auctions, slaughter plants, professional associations, publications on care and management, and specialized veterinary care.

FIGURE 21-1

Red deer farming. (Photo by A.Walsh/Animals Animals.)

In the United States, except for Texas shooting preserves, deer were not farmed to any significant extent before 1985. Now there are approximately 50,000 fallow deer and 5,000 red deer (Jordan et al., 1994). Mature fallow deer weigh about 45 kg, whereas mature red deer hinds (females) weigh about 90 kg. Age at first breeding in both species is about 16 months. A mature stag (male) can breed about 35 females, although a 2-year-old is best limited to eight. The breeding season for fallow deer in north temperate regions is principally from October to November 15. The red deer breeding season begins a week or two earlier. Gestation is about 234 days for both, and normally there is one offspring per birth. Age at weaning is 90–125 days, with weaning weights of 16–18 kg and 36–45 kg for fallow and red deer, respectively.

Although farmed deer that are accustomed to the presence of humans are quieter than their free-ranging counterparts, most species are easily frightened by quick movements and loud noises. As a consequence, successful husbandry requires special facilities and careful, deliberate handling. The sides of passageways, and catching and holding pens, are usually made of solid planks or plywood because deer, when pressed, tend to look through wire fences and may charge into them, breaking their necks or legs. Because of their leaping ability, the fences confining deer must be higher than those required for confinement of traditional farm animals.

Antelope

Controlled harvesting of free-ranging antelope or deliberate herding of partially domesticated antelope in Africa and in Argentina and Texas, where several antelope species have been introduced, are alternatives to the farming and ranching of domestic cattle, sheep, or goats. Antelope ranching in East and South Africa is well established, and 20 years ago there were 3,000 ranches in the Transvaal on which wild springbok (*Antidorcas marsupialis*) ran with domestic cattle (Kyle, 1972). On the Galana River estate in Kenya, comparisons of the productive efficiency of farmed cattle, buffalo (*Syncerus caffer*), oryx (*Oryx beisa*), and eland (*Taurotragus oryx*) have been conducted. Both the oryx and eland are resistant to the endemic diseases of Africa and subsist on very little water. The eland may be the most suitable for domestication because its social system is based on dominance hierarchy rather than territoriality. Small herds of domestic eland have been farmed in Zimbabwe, Kenya, and the Ukraine. In the latter, eland are used for meat, and eland cows have been trained for milking.

The blackbuck (*Antilope cervicapra*) was the most common ungulate on the plains of India until the nineteenth century. Destruction of habitat and overhunting reduced an estimated population of at least 4 million animals to the point where the largest numbers are now found in Argentina, where they were imported into the southern pampas in 1906, and in Texas, where they were imported into the Hill Country in the 1930s and 1940s. Texas blackbuck readily reproduce on ranches where they mingle with cattle and other indigenous and exotic wildlife. They are selectively hunted for sport, meat, hides, and horns.

Bison

The American bison (*Bison bison*) is commonly called a buffalo but is not closely related to either the African buffalo (*Syncerus caffer*) or the Indian water buffalo (*Bubalus bubalis*). It was long the dominant ungulate on the Great Plains of North America and ranged from Canada to Mexico. As many as 60 million bison were said to have been present in 1860, having provided food, clothing, and shelter to prehistoric human hunters for thousands of years. The introduction of firearms, horses to carry the hunters, the movement of Euro-Americans westward, and a government policy intended to control the Plains Indian by destruction of this important food and hide resource reduced this massive herd to less than 1,000 bison by 1889 (Regelin, 1991). A few conservation-minded ranches, the Bronx zoo, and isolated pockets of public and private land provided a reservoir from which bison were reintroduced into state and national parks, reservations, and private ownership (Callenbach, 1996).

One of the reservoirs that harbored bison from prehistoric times is the area ultimately designated Yellowstone National Park (Meagher, 1973). Protection from hunting and earlier reductions of natural predators has allowed the Yellowstone herd to outgrow its year-round range. The normal behavior of bison in winter is to migrate to lower valleys in search of shelter from harsh weather and a more accessible food supply. Because the Park is partially surrounded by cattle ranches, migrating Yellowstone bison encroach on private lands whose owners fear spread of brucellosis (for which some bison test positive) to their livestock. Such transmission has not been documented, but to reduce the possibility, bison are being shot in both government-sanctioned and illegal hunts. As might be expected, this has led to conflicts between a number of individuals, agencies, and associations allied with different sides of the issue.

Although it has been estimated that there are now 11,000 bison in public preserves, the popularity of bison and bison meat has led to private herds totaling approximately 200,000 animals in North America (Albrecht, 1997) (Figure 21-2). To ensure product

FIGURE 21-2

Bison in a feed lot. (Photo courtesy of USDA-Meat Animal Research Center, Clay Center, NE.)

quality and to fulfill the demands of this niche market, the North American Bison Cooperative was formed in 1993. The Cooperative constructed a slaughter plant in New Rockford, ND, and 239 producer members from 4 provinces and 14 states now own or manage more than 100,000 bison (Anderson et al., 1997).

Systems of management are patterned after those successfully used for beef cattle, although fences and handling facilities must be constructed to accommodate the greater strength and agility of bison. There is extensive use of grass, but feedlot grain finishing for 90–120 days is common. About 3.4 million kg of meat from approximately 15,000 bison are produced annually in the United States. The USDA Meat and Poultry Inspection Directory lists about 100 slaughter facilities nationwide that process bison. Most of the meat comes from bulls slaughtered at 18–24 months of age, at weights of 500–550 kg. The meat tastes much like beef, particularly when the bison are finished on corn.

Water Buffaloes

It has been estimated that there are at least 130 million domesticated water buffaloes (*Bubalus bubalis*) in the world (NRC, 1981). Their images can be seen on seals struck 5,000 years ago in the Indus Valley, suggesting domestication in the region now known as India and Pakistan. Although in use in China 4,000 years ago, they were not found in the literature and art of the ancient Egyptians, Greeks, or Romans until Arabs brought them westward to the Near East (into modern Syria, Israel, and Turkey) in about 600 A.D. Pilgrims and crusaders returning from the Holy Land in the Middle Ages introduced them into Europe, where they are still found in Hungary, Romania, Yugoslavia, Greece, Bulgaria, and Italy (in the Pontine Marshes southeast of Rome, and south of Naples). Medieval Egyptian villagers also adopted the water buffalo, and it is now the most important domestic animal in modern Egypt, where it provides draft power, meat, milk, cheese, and cooking oil. Subsequent importations into South America and into Oceania have been very successful, with over 400,000 in the Amazon basin and 3,500 in Papua New Guinea.

There are two general types, the Swamp buffalo and the River buffalo. Swamp buffaloes are slate gray, droopy necked, have sweptback horns, wallow in clear or muddy water, and are found from the Philippines west to India. They are used mostly for draft but also produce meat. They are seldom used for producing milk, principally because they yield so little. River buffaloes are black or dark gray, have coiled horns or straight, drooping horns, prefer to wallow in clean water, and are found from India west to Egypt and Europe. They are used for draft but are a dairy-type water buffalo and produce about 70% of India's milk supply. Buffalo butterfat is a major cooking oil (ghee) in India and Pakistan. In Italy, buffalo milk is the source of Mozzarella cheese.

As in cattle, when old animals are killed, the meat can be tough. However, buffalo meat and beef are similar, and when water buffalo are fed appropriately and killed at a young age, buffalo steaks have rated at least as high as beef steaks in taste tests. Weights at 18 months of age are in the range of 350–400 kg. Buffalo fat is always white, and the meat is darker-colored than beef.

Although they enjoy wallowing, water buffaloes can be raised in upland areas if they have shade in hot climates. About 500,000 are found in the temperate regions of Georgia (Eurasia) and Azerbaijan. Unless injured or severely stressed, water buffaloes are gentle enough to be cared for by children. When providing draft power, buffaloes are not driven, but the herdsman walks alongside or ahead and the buffaloes follow. They respect fences less than cattle, and when determined, may be difficult to contain.

Camels and Llamas

Collectively, camels and llamas are known as camelids, with an even number of toes on each foot, and anatomical features that distinguish them from true ruminants. They have rudimentary central incisors in the upper jaw and canine teeth in both jaws. The muscle attachments of the hind legs allow them to rest on their knees when lying down. The feet do not have functional hooves, but the toe bones are embedded in a broad cutaneous pad on which they walk. Although they ruminate, the stomach has three rather than four compartments, and the hindgut is very long (Stevens and Hume, 1995).

The Old World camelids include the two-humped, Bactrian camel (*Camelus bactrianus*) and the one-humped, Arabian or dromedary camel (*Camelus dromedarius*). Domestic Bactrian camels are found principally in the cool, desert regions of Central Asia, with possibly a wild population on the Mongolian side of the Altai mountains (although these might be feral domestic camels). The dromedary is the domestic camel of the hot deserts of North Africa and western Asia, and there are no known extant wild populations.

The earliest evidence for camel domestication has been dated to about 2,600 B.C. in Iran, with indications that the Bactrian camel may have been domesticated before the dromedary. When Alexander the Great sacked Persepolis, the ceremonial center of the Persian Empire in 330 B.C., 5,000 Bactrian camels were ordered to carry away the treasure. Both the Bactrian and dromedary camels are used for transport, draft, meat, milk, fiber, and hides, and the dromedary camel is very important in the Middle East and North Africa.

Both species share the same chromosome number (2n = 70) and will interbreed, producing offspring that are usually fertile. When left on their own, camels tend to form herds of bachelor males, adult females with their newborns, and up to 30 adult females with their 1- and 2-year-old offspring led by one adult male. Females usually give birth to one calf every other year, after a gestation period of 370–440 days. Full size of 350–600 kg is attained at 5 years, and camels may live for 50 years.

The New World camelids include the wild guanaco (*Lama guanicoe*) and vicuna (*Vicugna vicugna*) and the domestic llama (*Lama glama*) and alpaca (*Lama pacos*). The guanaco is most common in semidesert and high plains but ranges from Andean highlands in Ecuador and Peru to the plains of Patagonia. The vicuna lives near the snow line at 4,000–5,000 m in the Andes. Vicunas have a highly prized, fine wool fleece, that may be harvested by driving wild vicunas into corrals, shearing them, and releasing them again.

Archaeological evidence suggests that South American camelids were exploited and domesticated as early as 5,500 B.C., before Old World camels were brought under man's control in western Asia. Llamas are used principally as beasts of burden, but their meat may be used for food, fleece for clothing, hair for rope, hide for leather, and dried feces for fuel. They are capable of carrying loads of 96 kg at 26 km/day over rugged mountain elevations of 5,000 m. Alpacas are bred principally for their wool, which was once woven into robes worn by Inca royalty (Nowak, 1991).

Guanacos weigh 100–120 kg, and females give birth to a single 6–16 kg young every other year after a gestation period of about 342–368 days. Vicunas are the smallest of the camelids, with an adult weight of 35–65 kg. The gestation period is 330–350 days, and the single newborn weighs 4–6 kg. Adult llamas and alpacas weigh about 130–155 kg and 55–65 kg, respectively, with usual gestation lengths of 335–360 days (Fowler, 1989). The four South American camelids all have the same chromosome number (2n = 74) and will interbreed (Clutton-Brock, 1987).

The fossil record indicates that the camel family evolved in North America about 40 million years ago. Subsequently, some species migrated southward across the isthmus of Panama to South America whereas others moved north across the Bering Straits from Alaska to Siberia. Subsequently, camels disappeared from North America until their evolutionarily altered descendents were reintroduced in modern times. Some dromedary camels were released into the deserts of the Southwest in a military experiment some years ago, but they soon disappeared. Recent interest in llamas and alpacas for pets, recreation, and production of fiber in the United States was documented by the International Lama Registry of Kalispell, MT in 1996, when they reported over 91,000 llamas, 8,800 alpacas, and small numbers of guanacos and crosses owned by 13,732 individuals.

Ratites

OSTRICHES. Ostriches are large, flightless birds (2–2.4 m tall, 110–150 kg)—along with emus, rheas, kiwis, and cassowaries—known as ratites. Until the 1980s, live ostriches (*Struthio camelus*) were seen mainly in zoos in the United States. They have an unusually long large intestine and capacious paired ceca that provide for efficient microbial fermentation of the high-fiber diets (grasses, seeds, leaves, flowers) that are regularly consumed in the wild. Breeding groups of free-ranging ostrich usually include one male per 3–4 females. One of these is a "major" female mated to the male in a monogomous bond. A nest site is selected by the male, and if accepted by the major female, her eggs plus those of the "minor" females will be laid in the same nest. Major females lay, on alternate days, an average clutch of 8 eggs. Minor females may add a total of another 10–15 eggs. Incubation to hatching requires 42–46 days. If eggs are continually removed for artificial incubation, a major female may lay 60 or more in one season (Ullrey and Allen, 1996).

Ostrich feathers were used widely by the fashion industry before World War I, and ostrich leather has been used in boots, shoes, and other leather goods for many years. The commercial ostrich industry began in the mid-nineteenth century in Africa, where ostrich are indigenous. South Africa was involved early, and still is a major international supplier of ostrich meat, leather, and plumes.

Commercial ostrich breeding began in the United States in the 1980s, and the American Ostrich Association of Fort Worth, Texas, was formed in 1987, with the objective of educating producers and promoting ostrich products. A survey conducted by this association in 1995 indicated that there may be 350,000–500,000 ostriches of all ages in this country. Four states accounted for over half of the total, with Texas first (26.2%), California second (11.2%), Arizona third (10.5%), and Oklahoma fourth (6%).

Although some ostrich meat is imported from South Africa, most of that marketed through restaurants and supermarkets in the United States is produced here (Figure 21-3). Approximately 1,500 ostriches are commercially processed per month, supplying more than 0.5 million kg of meat annually for American consumption. Most ostriches go to slaughter at 10–14 months of age, produce about 32 kg of meat, and are capable of producing 1.3 m^2 of leather and 1 kg of feathers. However, a marketing system for ostrich leather produced in the United States is just getting organized, and there is no vi-

FIGURE 21-3

Ostrich farming. (Matt Meadows/Peter Arnold, Inc.)

able market for U.S.-produced plumes, due to prohibitive costs. As a consequence, the ostrich leather market and the small plume market in the United States is dominated by South African imports. Some infertile eggs from ostrich and other ratites are used to produce decorative items or may be cut, hinged, painted, etched, and gem-encrusted to produce high-style purses.

EMUS. Indigenous to Australia, emus (*Dromaius novaehollandiae*) are 1.5–1.8 m tall, and weigh 50–65 kg when mature. They reach breeding age at 2–3 years, and females produce 30–40 eggs per year if the eggs are continually removed for artificial incubation. Time to hatching varies with incubation temperature, but 49–56 days is typical for optimum conditions. From hatching to 2 months, young emu are longitudinally striped. They gradually darken until mature, when they have mottled dark brown and beige body feathers and a bare blue upper neck outlined below with black feathers. Emu have two small ceca, a short large intestine, and a short digesta retention time (5.5 hours) compared to the ostrich (48 hours). However, a relatively capacious jejunum-ileum suitable for anaerobic microbial fermentation results in dietary fiber digestion sufficient to meet 50% of maintenance energy requirements. Thus, while not as efficient as ostrich and rhea, emu are able to use a moderately high-fiber diet (Ullrey and Allen, 1996).

Emu production in the United States has a short history, and marketing systems are still being developed. When killed for processing, plumage is plucked first, followed by skinning for production of garment leather, removal of subcutaneous fat for rendering into oil, and separation of muscle from the carcass for gourmet restaurants (Minnaar and Minnaar, 1992).

Alligators and Crocodiles

The natural habitat of the free-ranging American alligator (*Alligator mississippiensis*) is the southeastern United States where it lives primarily in fresh to brackish water areas, from the Virginia border with North Carolina to Georgia, Florida, Alabama, Mississippi, Louisiana, southern Arkansas, McCurtain County, Oklahoma, and Texas (Ross, 1989). After mating in the spring, the female constructs a nest mound of sticks, mud, and vegetation. An average of 40–45 eggs are laid, covered, and guarded until they hatch about 65 days later. The mother protects her young against predators for an extended subsequent period, and it is not unusual to see hatchlings lying on their mother's back.

Natural foods include fish, turtles, snails, crabs, frogs, insects, snakes, waterfowl, small mammals, and other alligators. The teeth of an alligator are made for grabbing, tearing, or holding, so food is not chewed, but swallowed whole. If food is plentiful, alligators grow rapidly, may live 35–50 years, and reach lengths of 4 m or greater and weights of over 270 kg.

The alligator is prized for its hide and meat, and was first hunted commercially in Florida during the late 1800s. This harvest was unregulated until 1943, when population declines led to imposition of a 1.2-m minimum size limit. However, alligator numbers continued to decline, even after raising minimum size limits to 1.8 m in 1954; and in

1962, the legal harvesting of alligators was closed. An interstate network of illegal hide dealers continued to function until the 1969 inclusion of the American alligator on the first Endangered Species List and introduction of more effective federal regulations in 1970. Alligator numbers rebounded, and in 1977, the alligator was reclassified from endangered to threatened.

Alligator management systems were instituted by the State of Florida, allowing for controlled hunting and the collection of eggs and hatchlings for rearing on licensed alligator farms. Subsequently, systems of producing eggs and hatchlings in captivity were developed in Louisiana and in Florida. In 1996, there were over 30 alligator farms in Florida, generating approximately 136,000 kg of meat and over 15,000 skins a year. The wholesale price of meat averaged $11–$15/kg and of skins about $82/m². Louisiana's alligator farms produced 245,000 kg of meat and 122,800 skins with a total value of $9.6 million.

There are 20–22 other species of alligators, crocodiles, caimans, and gavials found in the warm waters of the world. At least 18 of these are endangered or threatened with extinction. Habitat destruction is a major problem, but so is illegal poaching because of the market value of hides and meat. The belly skin is the most prized part of the hide due to its smaller scales and suitability for items such as shoes, handbags, and wallets, as well as for larger items, such as luggage. Species preferences (in order) in the international market are for hides from saltwater crocodiles (*Crocodylus porosus*), Morelet's crocodiles (*C. moreletii*), American alligators, Siamese crocodiles (*C. siamensis*), and Nile crocodiles (*C. niloticus*) (NRC, 1983b).

Iguanas

The green iguana (*Iguana iguana*), a tree-dwelling herbivorous lizard with a natural range from Mexico to Brazil, has been a highly prized source of food in Central and South America for at least 7,000 years. Overhunting and habitat destruction has nearly eliminated this species in many areas, and in the 1980s, the Smithsonian Tropical Research Institute in Panama funded a study of the green iguana by Dr. Dagmar Werner, a German herpetologist. The Green Iguana Management Project evolved out of this study, and Dr. Werner has developed a system of successfully raising these iguanas in captivity. The system includes artificial egg-laying sites, controlled incubation, and protection of the hatchlings from environmental extremes and from predators. Special diets support rapid growth, early sexual maturity, and nearly 100% survival, in contrast to a 95% loss of wild hatchlings to predators in their first 2 years.

Critical features of natural iguana habitat also have been identified, and through education and by enlisting the self-interest of local peoples, Dr. Werner has devised successful means of restoring habitat and returning captive-born iguanas to the wild. This has provided campesinos with a food and cash resource that is less environmentally destructive than the slash-and-burn agriculture practiced in some areas. Surplus captive-reared iguanas from the Management Project have been used to generate interest in iguanas as food among those who have not previously tasted this chicken-like meat. The legacy of this Project is the Pro Iguana Verde Foundation in Costa Rica, whose conservation objectives remain the same as originally proposed by Dr. Werner, and whose methods have been adopted to meet the increasing demand for iguanas as pets.

ANIMALS RAISED FOR FUR

Much of the early exploration of North America by Europeans was stimulated by the demand for furs and the discovery that beaver, muskrat, mink, otter, fox, raccoon, and lynx were widely available on this continent. At that time, fur bearers were acquired by hunting and trapping. By the end of the nineteenth century and the beginning of the twentieth, systems of fur farming were being developed that helped meet demand and prevented extirpation of wild populations. Farm rearing of silver fox, a color phase of the red fox (*Vulpes vulpes*), was particularly lucrative, and a silver fox pelt sold for over $1,000. Shortly thereafter, fashions shifted from long-haired to short-haired dense furs such as those of mink (*Mustela vison*), and commercial mink farming developed rapidly from the 1920s into the 1960s, with peak production of 6 million pelts in 1968. In contrast to 1938, when 80% of the pelts were from wild mink, by 1970, 95% of mink pelts were from farm-raised animals.

Natural mutations or selective breeding have resulted in over 20 different mink pelt colors. Natural dark mink pelts comprise about half of those produced on farms, with the mix of other colors dependent upon market demand. Mink produce young in the spring, and the pelts are taken in November and December. In the United States, raw pelts or tanned skins are marketed at auctions, primarily through the Hudson Bay Company and the Seattle Fur Exchange. World production of mink pelts in 1989 was over 41 million, with the United States producing 4.6 million, in fourth place behind Denmark, the former USSR, and China.

World production of fox pelts in 1989 was nearly 5 million, with Finland producing about 60% of the total. U.S. production was about 38,000. Approximately 68% were blue fox, a color phase of the arctic fox (*Alopex lagopus*), 13% were silver, and the rest were other color mutations.

Fur farming is a cyclical and risky business, with pelt prices fluctuating wildly in response to variations in fashion, pelt supply, and the amount of disposable income available for luxuries. In the early 1990s, the animal-rights movement attempted to disrupt the fur industry through boycotts and by acts of terrorism, including assaults, animal release, arson, burglary, and destruction of records and property. Market forces resulted in some contraction in the number of fur farms and total pelts produced, but production per farm increased, and in 1995, 2.7 million mink pelts were produced with an average pelt price of $53.10, higher than in any year since records were first kept by the USDA in 1975.

In the United States and Canada, mink and foxes continue to be most important, with appreciably less demand for other species. The short-tailed chinchilla (*Chinchilla brevicaudata*), native to the South American Andes, whose skins were imported into the

United States in great numbers before 1920, is now raised here principally as a pet. Although it has a particularly thick, soft, warm fur, few of the specimens currently raised in this country have pelts of the high quality demanded by the fur trade.

ANIMALS IN RESEARCH

The use of animals as surrogates for man or other animals in biomedical research has a long history. Nearly every advance in human and veterinary medicine over the last 100 years had its foundation in animal research. Metabolic processes were defined, and the effectiveness and safety of consumer products, drugs, medical devices, and medical procedures were established. Some of the advances of direct benefit to man include immunizations against polio, mumps, measles, diphtheria, rubella, and hepatitis; broad-spectrum antibiotics and other anti-infective drugs; anesthetics and analgesics; diagnostic techniques, such as the electrocardiogram, electroencephalogram, angiogram, and endoscopy; organ transplantation; artificial joints; cataract removal and lens replacement; and thousands of medications.

Many of these same products and techniques are also of direct benefit to animals, having been developed with them in the first place. In addition, vaccinations against distemper, rabies, parvovirus, anthrax, tetanus, and feline leukemia; treatments for parasites; orthopedic surgery for horses; detection and control of tuberculosis and brucellosis; and control of heartworm infections in dogs are a result of animal research.

Continuing research on new surgical techniques to repair congenital heart defects, control of cancer, cure of diabetes, reversal of Alzheimer's disease, treatment of cystic fibrosis and multiple sclerosis, and prevention of HIV and many other infectious and non-infectious diseases requires use of animals, if solutions to these serious problems are to be found. The possibility of ill-advised restrictions on appropriate uses of animals in research is of such concern that persons afflicted with these diseases have formed iiFAR, an acronym for the "incurably ill For Animal Research," to inform the general public of the costs and benefits of such research. The National Association for Biomedical Research was organized by scientists with similar goals. It is relevant that of those discoveries considered sufficiently meritorious to win the Nobel Prize in medicine between 1980 and 1991, nine of the twelve winners used animals in their studies.

Reports required by the Animal Welfare Act of 1966, as amended by Congress in 1970, provide a perspective on which species and the numbers of animals that are involved (Crawford, 1996). This reporting requirement does not apply to laboratory rats (*Rattus* spp.) and mice (*Mus* spp.), birds, and cold-blooded species, although very large numbers of rats and mice are used. In 1983, the U.S. Congress Office of Technology Assessment estimated that, of the 17–22 million animals used in research and testing annually, 90% were rats, mice, and other rodents.

There has been a downward trend, for approximately 20 years, in the use of dogs and cats, with 89,420 dogs and 29,569 cats used in 1995. The use of primates has held steady at about 50,000 annually. Use of guinea pigs, hamsters, and rabbits has gradually declined to about 333,000, 248,000, and 354,000, respectively. Farm animals (mammals only) were added to the reporting requirement in 1990, and nearly 164,000 were used in research in 1995. Other animals used in research, such as squirrels, ferrets, bats, exotic ungulates, carnivores, marine mammals, and other rodents totaled about 126,500.

Because of their close relationship to man, nonhuman primates are particularly useful surrogates in biomedical research. For the same reason, great concern for their welfare has been engendered. Although they constitute only 0.3% of the laboratory animals used in the United States, nonhuman primates are invaluable because of their similarity to humans in nearly all aspects of anatomy, physiology, and behavior (King and Yarbrough, 1995). About 30 nonhuman primate species are used, with Old World monkeys, native to Asia (rhesus and long-tailed macaques) and Africa (baboons), most common. The squirrel monkey is the most widely used New World species. Most nonhuman primate research is conducted at universities, seven of which have National Institutes of Health-designated Regional Primate Research Centers.

Despite the lack of a reporting requirement when used in biomedical research, there are many nonmammalian models that have proved useful (Woodhead and Vivirito, 1989). Included are species as diverse as protozoa, leeches, houseflies, sea urchins, sharks, octopuses, frogs, toads, salamanders, newts, snakes, and fish. The National Research Council (1974) has published guidelines for the breeding, care, and management of amphibians as laboratory animals.

Responsible scientists use tools that they believe are least likely to be harmful and most likely to be effective in solving research problems. In some cases, use of animals is neither necessary nor appropriate. The "Three Rs" guide researchers in meeting their needs and in responding to the concerns of the animal welfare community. The Three Rs stand for *reduction, refinement,* and *replacement.* Reduction is the use of as few animals as possible by sharing research animals among studies with similar objectives or by using more powerful statistical methodology. Refinement is the use of procedures to minimize discomfort or the use of more effective analgesics. Replacement involves use of computer modeling or cell or tissue culture instead of animals. If animals must be used, the National Research Council (1996) has prepared a guide to assist scientists and institutions in fulfilling their obligation to plan and conduct animal experimentation in ways that are scientifically, technically, and humanely appropriate.

ANIMALS AS TISSUE AND ORGAN DONORS

The first open-heart surgery was performed in a human patient in 1952, using techniques perfected with the dog (Mrachek, 1995). A congenital defect in the septum separating the two upper chambers of the heart was closed. However, attempts to correct more severe malformations in the ventricles of other patients were not very successful until a system was devised for oxygenating the blood while bypassing the heart. After a risky, but successful, use of cross-circulation to oxygenate the blood of a young patient by passing it through the lungs of the patient's father, a bubble oxygenator and bypass machine was developed. Open-heart surgery quickly became routine, and in 1994, an average of about 2,000 open-heart surgeries were performed in the United States every day.

Cardiac diseases that were previously incurable and were expected to lead to certain death are now responsive to surgical intervention. But there continues to be a need for implantable devices, such as cardiac valves, to replace those that were congenitally malformed in children or damaged by scarlet fever, or otherwise, in adults. The first valve was a ball-and-cage design developed with dogs. Subsequent designs were tested in pigs, calves, sheep, and nonhuman primates, with the sheep becoming the standard experimental species.

Today's cardiac valves are either mechanical or bioprosthetic. The mechanical valves have two hinged, carbon-plated leaflets in Dacron cuffs that allow them to be sewn into place. They make up about 65% of the valve market. Bioprosthetic valves make up the rest. They are derived from natural valve tissue mounted in a fabric sewing cuff. Aortic valve tissue from pigs is most often used, although pericardial tissue may be used as well.

Technically more difficult and ethically more troubling is the issue of organ transplantation. The first human-to-human heart transplant was made about 30 years ago, but the recipient lived only 28 days. Further research led to transplant procedures that were so successful that insurance companies now cover their cost, and there are waiting lists for donor organs. Unfortunately, human hearts, lungs, or livers become available only after death of the donor. If the potential donor or the potential donor's family do not plan for or agree to transplantation of the donor's organs, then those organs, though technically suitable, will be wasted. The result is a large disparity between the numbers of individuals waiting for an organ transplant and those who get one. In late 1994, there were 37,123 persons on the UNOS (United Network for Organ Sharing) national patient waiting list, whereas the number of organ transplants performed in 1993 were 18,164 (Nasto and McLaughlin, 1995).

This disparity in the availability of organs for allotransplantation (transplanting an organ from the same species) has led to interest in xenotransplantation (transplanting an organ from a different species). Attempts were made to graft slices of rabbit kidney into a child with renal insufficiency as early as 1905. Unfortunately, this attempt and others with kidneys from pigs, goats, sheep, and nonhuman primates made into the 1940s were equally unsuccessful. In the 1960s, coincident with development of drugs that suppressed the recipient's immune system and impeded tissue rejection, xenotransplantation began to progress. A 23-year-old woman with serious renal disease was kept alive for 9 months with a chimpanzee kidney. Baboon kidneys were successfully used for short times in other patients. Unfortunately, the high levels of immunosuppressive drugs also interfered with the ability to fight infections, which then became lethal.

By the 1990s, considerable progress in understanding the mechanisms of tissue rejection had been made. At the 1996 annual meeting of the American Heart Association in New Orleans, Dr. Jeffrey Platt of the Duke University Medical Center in Durham, North Carolina, predicted that within a year, a pig heart would be transplanted into a human (News-Press, 1996). He suggested that the first use of pig hearts would be temporary, enabling the recipient to live for a few weeks or months, while they awaited permanent transplantation of a human heart. Prior to the xenotransplant, a human gene would be implanted into the donor pig, suppressing production of sugars that identified the pig heart as a foreign organ. Examination of Dr. Platt's scientific papers indicates that, while one year may have been an optimistic timeline, such a transplant will undoubtedly be made very soon (Lawson and Platt, 1996).

Although the use of nonhuman primates for xenotransplants would seem more promising than use of pigs, nonhuman primates are available only in small numbers, and the organs of those species that are most readily available are too small to be used in adult humans. Nonhuman primates also may harbor viruses or other infective agents that pose an epidemiologic risk. In addition, social opposition to the use of nonhuman primates, as compared to pigs, has been expressed. By contrast, the risk of transmission of infections from pigs to humans is minimal and could be largely obviated by maintenance of specific pathogen-free swine herds. Ethical issues relating to use of pigs as organ donors are somewhat diminished by the widespread use of this animal for food. Research currently underway at the University of Missouri and elsewhere may result in strains of transgenic pigs whose organs are less likely to be rejected.

ANIMALS AS PETS AND COMPANIONS

Although American households have over 12 million pet birds, 6 million pet ferrets, and millions of pet hamsters, gerbils, fish, snakes, iguanas, and other small creatures, dogs and cats continue to be the most popular pets in the United States, with populations of about 55 million and 65 million, respectively (Pet Food Institute, 1996). Over 4.5 billion kg of manufactured foods are consumed each year by these dogs and cats, with a value of over $9 billion. Pet-food ingredients from plants are important sources of nutrients, but over 20% of the ingredients in dog and cat food are byproducts from the meat, poultry, and seafood processing industries.

The taming of wolves (*Canis lupus*), thought to be the ancestors of domestic dogs (*Canis familiaris*), probably began over 12,000 years ago. Through selection, these prehistoric companions of man were transformed into more than 400 currently recognized breeds. Presumably, wolf pups, caught in the wild, were reared in a human community where their descendents were bred for appropriate behavior and desired physical traits, generation after generation. In addition to providing companionship, some of these early dogs assisted in the hunt, just as certain breeds do today. Some were harnessed to pull sledges and have done so in Arctic and Subarctic regions for centuries. Their keen sense of smell has proven useful in tracking fugitives from the law, locating the injured in collapsed buildings and under avalanches, and in detecting illegal drugs and explosives.

The benefits provided by pets to the ill were recognized in the nineteenth century by Florence Nightingale, the famous nursing pioneer (Hines and Bustad, 1986). Formal training of guide dogs for the blind began about 65 years ago (Eames and Eames, 1989), and there are now 16 major guide dog training facilities in the United States. In 1975, the concept of service dogs for the disabled was pioneered by Canine Companions for Independence, and there are now over 100 centers training service and hearing dogs (Henderson, 1996). Service dogs can operate light switches, retrieve items, pull wheelchairs, and open doors. Hearing dogs alert the hearing impaired to ringing telephones, crying infants, smoke alarms, and people calling them by name. Unfortunately, there are at least 9 million Americans with significant physical or sensory impairment, whereas there are only 10,000–12,000 working assistance dogs, 7,000 of which are guide dogs for the blind.

The association between man and cats is thousands of years old, but except for relatively small numbers of a few special breeds, reproduction of cats is seldom controlled by man. As a consequence, most domestic cats (*Felis catus*) closely resemble their wild progenitor, *Felis silvestris*. This wild cat is commonly divided into a European subspecies, *F. silvestris silvestris*, and *F. silvestris libyca*, a subspecies from Arabia and Africa. Interbreeding of these two subspecies produces a cat with pelage resembling the striped tabby. The three principal variations of the striped tabby are believed to be the result of mutations. These are the blotched tabby, the black, and the sex-linked orange. Breeds such as the Manx, Persian, Siamese, and Abyssinian are not thought to be of ancient origin, and their unique characteristics are probably the result of selection for those characteristics by man.

Cats are highly territorial, solitary, and, at least partly, nocturnal hunters. Although willing to accept food, lodging, and affection from humans, they are quite capable of living a feral existence, and many do. The Ancient Egyptians considered cats to be sacred animals, and large numbers were embalmed and mummified in the city of Bubastis after death. Huge quantities of these were excavated from tombs at Gizeh early in this century, and representative specimens now reside in the British Museum in London (Clutton-Brock, 1987).

Although dogs and cats are classified in the order Carnivora, wild dogs tend to be more omnivorous than wild cats, which are almost totally carnivorous. These differences in dietary habits are supported by differences in digestive tract morphology. Dogs have more premolars and molars, with those in the rear designed for crushing, which assists in breaking bones and in masticating plant material. Cats have an upper premolar that occludes with a lower molar to cut animal flesh like shears, but do not have crushing molars. The cat also has a smaller cecum and shorter intestine in proportion to body length than the dog, consistent with a carnivorous diet. In addition, cats exhibit a number of differences in metabolism that are characteristic of carnivory, and in requirements for nutrients that are found regularly in animal tissues but rarely in plants (see Chapter 20).

ANIMALS IN ZOOS AND AQUARIUMS

Wilson (1992) has estimated that 1,032,000 living animal species are known (not including microorganisms, such as protozoa). Included are 4,000 mammals, 9,000 birds, 6,300 reptiles, 4,200 amphibians, and 18,000 fishes and lower chordates. The remaining 990,500 are invertebrates, 75% of which are insects. Somewhat more than 3,000 species of mammals, birds, reptiles, and amphibians are found within the world's zoos, representing about 13% of the known terrestrial vertebrates. Increasingly, there are special collections of invertebrates in zoos, and freshwater and marine mammals, fish, and invertebrates in aquariums, as well. Although the number of species in captivity (and requiring the care of man) is not large compared to the total, the development of adequate diets and application of appropriate husbandry techniques is a daunting task.

Fortunately, the principles of animal science, so effective in meeting the needs of traditional domestic animals, also work well when caring for wild animals in captivity. In addition to providing a safe environment in which rare animals can be sustained and may reproduce, many institutions maintain banks of frozen sperm and embryos as insurance against unforeseen catastrophies. Of course, it is helpful to this preservation to know as much as possible about the normal physiology of wild animals, the essential features of their natural habitat, and how they behave within that habitat. If information is available specific to their care, or can be derived from studies of domestic animal models, captive wild animals have been shown to thrive, and zoos and aquariums can truly serve as arks for the conservation of threatened and endangered species. If natural habitat can be preserved or restored, captive populations of wild animals can be used to repopulate that habitat.

SUMMARY

Animal species and breeds that are not commonly included among traditional farm animals raised in the United States may be of importance elsewhere in the world or have undeveloped potential as sources of food and fiber, particularly in countries or cultures with limited economic resources. Current numbers, uses, and details of biology that are relevant to their potential are included in this chapter. Many of these animals are smaller than conventional livestock and require less expensive inputs. They also are commonly less productive, but are responsive to improved husbandry and to genetic selection for increased productivity.

Many animals are of economic or social importance for other purposes. Mink and foxes are the primary species raised for fur. Dozens of species are raised for pets and as companions. Dogs have proven useful not only as companions but as service animals in assisting the handicapped. These and other species are vital to medical research, as the causes and control of disease are explored and vaccines and treatments are developed. Exciting progress has been made in tissue and organ transplantation, and introduction of human genes into animals may significantly enlarge the donor pool without problems of tissue rejection that have been so troubling in the past. Zoos and aquariums are increasingly important as arks of last resort for animal species whose very existence is threatened by loss of critical habitat. Habitat destruction and species extinctions not only reduce the variety and beauty of our environment, but can destroy, before discovery, plants with medicinal potential in the treatment of disease. Respect and concern for wild animals may encourage preservation of critical ecosystems that, as a consequence, would benefit us all.

Animal scientists have a critical role to play in all of this activity. If well trained in the principles of science and the skills of husbandry and communication, the opportunities in production agriculture, specialized animal care, research, extension, and teaching are greater than ever before. A solid education, an internship including relevant work experience, a broad perspective, and an optimistic and responsible attitude can provide entree to an exciting career in animal science and a lifetime of satisfaction and happiness.

GLOSSARY

Allotransplantation Transplantation of an organ or tissue from one animal to another of the same species.

Amino acids Organic compounds that constitute the basic building blocks of proteins.

Anaerobic microorganisms Microscopic organisms which live in a low-oxygen or oxygen-free environment.

Artificial insemination The introduction of semen into the female reproductive tract by a technique other than natural breeding.

Basal metabolic rate The energy required to sustain life processes of a resting animal in a thermoneutral environment, and in a postabsorptive state.

Bioprosthetic A device derived from a living organism, used to replace a body part.

Biotechnology The application of technology to biological science.

Brucellosis A contagious bacterial disease characterized by abortion and infertility.

Carnivore An animal whose diet is primarily comprised of animal tissue.

Chromosome A strand of DNA and associated proteins in a cell nucleus that carries genetic information.

Chromosome number A species-specific number of chromosomes located in each cellular nucleus.

Coccidiosis A protozoan infection characterized by the invasion and destruction of the intestinal lining.

Coprophagy Intentional ingestion of fecal matter.

Crop milk The high-fat, high-energy secretion produced from the lining of the pigeon crop.

Cutaneous Related to the skin and associated tissue.

Epidemiologic Relating to the development, incidence, and spread of disease.

Herbivore An animal whose diet is primarily comprised of plant tissue.

Hind An adult, female red deer.

Ileum The final segment of the small intestine.

Indigenous Originating in or native to an environment.

Jejunum The middle segment of the small intestine, between the duodenum and ileum.

Microbial fermentation The conversion of complex organic compounds into relatively simple substances by microorganisms.

Microlivestock Domestic livestock that is inherently small, e.g., breeds of cattle, goats, sheep, and pigs that are half the size or less of common breeds.

New World The western hemisphere.

Old World The eastern hemisphere.

Omnivore An animal whose diet is comprised of both animal and plant tissue.

Pathogen A specific cause of disease.

Ratites Large, flightless birds such as ostriches, emus, rheas, and cassowaries; kiwis are also ratites but are much smaller.

Screwworms Larvae of the blow fly, which develop in the tissues of living animals; severe infestations may cause death.

Squab A young or unfledged pigeon.

Stag An adult, male deer.

Tracheo-pneumonitis   Inflammation of the upper respiratory tract; often due to a viral infection.

Transgenic   Transfer or crossover of genetic material between species.

Trypanosomiasis   A protozoan infection transmitted by insect vectors.

Ungulate   Any hoofed mammal.

Venison   The meat from deer (sometimes, meat from antelope).

Volatile fatty acids   Short-chain fatty acids produced from microbial action in the gastrointestinal tract.

Xenotransplantation   Transplantation of an organ or tissue from an animal of one species to an animal of a different species.

REFERENCES

Abrams, H. L. 1983. Cross cultural survey of preferences for animal protein and animal fat. Presented at *Wenner-Gren Foundation Symposium No. 94,* October 23–30, Cedar Key, FL.

Albrecht, S. 1997. Personal communication from Executive Director of National Bison Assoc., 4701 Marion, #100, Denver, CO 80216–2140.

Anderson, V., Metzger, S., and Sexhus, D. 1997. Additional research needed as bison popularity grows. *Feedstuffs,* 69(20; May 19): 54, 56–57.

Bixby, D. E., Christman, C. J., Ehrman, C. J., and Sponenberg, D. P. 1994. *Taking Stock: The North American Livestock Census.* Blacksburg, VA: The American Livestock Breeds Conservancy, McDonald & Woodward, 182 pp.

Callenbach, E. 1996. *Bring Back the Buffalo! A Sustainable Future for America's Great Plains.* Washington, D.C.: Island Press, 280 pp.

Clutton-Brock, J. 1987. *A Natural History of Domesticated Mammals.* Austin, TX: Univ. Texas Press, 208 pp.

Crawford, R. L. 1996. A review of the Animal Welfare Report data: 1973 through 1995. *Natl. Agr. Library, Animal Welfare Information Center Newsletter,* 7(2; summer): 1–11.

Eames, E., and Eames, T. 1989. A comparison of the guide dog movements of England and United States. *J. Visual Impairment Blindness,* 83: 215–218.

Flegal, C. J. 1994. Managing game birds. *Ext. Bull. E–692* (revised). E. Lansing, MI: Michigan State University, 19 pp.

Fowler, M. E. 1989. *Medicine and Surgery of South American Camelids.* Ames, IA: Iowa State University Press, 391 pp.

Henderson, K. 1996. No dogs allowed? Federal policies on access for service animals. *Anim. Welfare Info. Center Newsletter,* 7(2): 13–16.

Hines, L. M., and Bustad, L. K. 1986. Historical perspectives on human-animal interactions. *National Forum,* 66(1): 4–6.

Jordan, R. M., Anfang, C., Sheaffer, C., and Wolf, C. 1994. *A Deer Production Primer.* St. Paul, MN: R. M. Jordan, 69 pp.

King, F. A., and Yarbrough, C. 1995. Nonhuman primates in research: A review of their critical role. *Lab Animal,* 24(1): 28–32.

Kyle, R. 1972. *Meat Production in Africa: The Case for New Domestic Species.* Bristol, Great Britain: Univ. Bristol.

Lawson, J. H., and Platt, J. L. 1996. Molecular barriers to xenotransplantation. *Transplantation,* 62: 303–310.

Leonard, J. N. 1973. *The Emergence of Man: The First Farmers.* New York: Time-Life Books, 160 pp.

Mackintosh, C. G., and Krzywinski, A. 1992. Farming and ranching: Convenors' report. In B. Bobek, K. Perzanowski, and W. L. Regelin (eds.), *Global Trends in Wildlife Management* (Vol. 2, pp. 471–472). Krakow-Warszawa, Poland: Swiat Press.

Meagher, M. M. 1973. *The Bison of Yellowstone National Park.* U.S. Natl. Park Serv. Monogr. No. 1, 161 pp.

Minnaar, P., and Minnaar, M. 1992. *The Emu Farmer's Handbook.* Groveton, TX: Induna, 178 pp.

Mrachek, J. P. 1995. Prosthetic cardiac valves: The impact of animal models on cardiovascular surgery. *Lab Animal,* 24(1): 33–35.

Nasto, B., and McLaughlin, C. 1995. Cross-species transplantation. *Lab Animal,* 24(1): 22–27.

National Research Council. 1974. *Amphibians: Guidelines for the Breeding, Care, and Management of Laboratory Animals.* Washington, D.C.: National Academy of Sciences, 153 pp.

National Research Council. 1981. *The Water Buffalo: New Prospects for an Underutilized Animal.* Washington, D.C.: National Academy Press, 116 pp.

National Research Council. 1983a. *Little-Known Asian Animals with a Promising Economic Future.* Washington, D.C.: National Academy Press, 131 pp.

National Research Council. 1983b. *Crocodiles as a Resource for the Tropics.* Washington, D.C.: National Academy Press, 59 pp.

National Research Council. 1991. *Microlivestock: Little-Known Small Animals with a Promising Economic Future.* Washington, D.C.: National Academy Press, 449 pp.

National Research Council. 1996. *Guide for the Care and Use of Laboratory Animals.* Washington, D.C.: National Academy Press, 125 pp.

News-Press (Ft. Myers, FL). 1996. Researcher: Pigs to supply needed parts. Monday, November 11, p. 3A.

Nowak, R. M. 1991. *Walker's Mammals of the World* (Vol. 2, 5th ed.). Baltimore, MD: Johns Hopkins University Press, 1629 pp.

Pet Food Institute. 1996. *Pet Food Institute Fact Sheet.* Washington, D.C.: Pet Food Institute, 7 pp.

Regelin, W. L. 1991. Wildlife management in Canada and the United States. In B. Bobek, K. Perzanowski, and W. L. Regelin (eds.), *Global Trends in Wildlife Management* (Vol. 1, pp. 55–64). Krakow-Warszawa, Poland: Swiat Press.

Ross, C. A. 1989. *Crocodiles and Alligators.* New York: Facts on File, 240 pp.

Scheid, D. W. 1986. *Raising Game Birds.* Brookfield, WI: Farmer's Digest, 111 pp.

Stevens, C. E., and Hume, I. D. 1995. *Comparative Physiology of the Vertebrate Digestive System* (2nd ed.). Cambridge, Great Britain: Cambridge University Press, 400 pp.

Ullrey, D. E., and Allen, M. E. 1996. Nutrition and feeding of ostriches. *Anim. Feed Sci. Technol.,* 59: 27–36.

Wilson, E. O. 1992. *The Diversity of Life.* Cambridge, MA: Harvard University Press, 424 pp.

Woodhead, A. D., and Vivirito, K. 1989. *Nonmammalian Animal Models for Biomedical Research.* Boca Raton, FL: CRC Press, 619 pp.

CHAPTER TWENTY-TWO
MEAT AND MEAT PRODUCTS

MARKUS F. MILLER
TEXAS TECH UNIVERSITY
LUBBOCK, TX

EFFECTS OF COOKING
WHY MEAT RETAIL CUTS DIFFER IN PRICE
SUMMARY

The modern meat industry joins other segments of the vast U.S. agriculture industry as one of the success stories of increasing efficiency. The main task of the meat industry is to convert live animals into wholesome, nutrient-dense meat cuts that provide high-quality proteins, fats, vitamins, and minerals needed for growth, development, maintenance, and well-being of the human body. Byproducts of these slaughtering and dressing operations provide us with hundreds of finished products, such as leather, gelatin, pharmaceuticals, and pet food, that otherwise would not be available.

This chapter is concerned with only the red meats—beef, lamb, and pork. Information about poultry, fish, and other meats is provided in other chapters.

MODERN METHODS OF PROCESSING CARCASSES

As late as the early 1970s, major cattle slaughterers used skinning cradles in which they laid bled cattle on their backs to laboriously skin them by hand. They used skinning knives with a curved blade to reduce cuts and scores in the valuable hides. Development of the on-the-rail dressing system by Canada Packers, Ltd., keeping the bled animal suspended by its hind legs throughout the dressing operations, greatly increased the efficiency of converting an animal into a carcass and byproducts. This new system reduced the chances of microbial contamination. Today, mechanical, air-driven, rotary knives are used for hide removal from the shank, head, belly, and side regions. The hide then is mechanically pulled from the back with a hide puller, greatly reducing the time and labor required for hide removal and providing a more valuable hide with fewer defects for leather production. Such systems allow modern slaughterers to slaughter and dress up to 425 cattle, 325 sheep, and 1,250 hogs per hour.

Compared with cattle, relatively little change has occurred in both pig and lamb slaughter in the last 50 years. Slaughter pigs can be skinned like cattle, but pigs are more difficult to skin because of a tighter attachment of the skin to the subcutaneous fat. Most pigs are dressed with their skin on after the bled pig has been immersed in hot water (137–143 °F) to loosen the hair so that dehairing machines with metal-tipped paddles can remove it. Hot water in the scalding vat loosens the hair by solubilizing the proteins around the hair root. The most prominent recent changes in the hog slaughter industry concern reduction of antemortem stress on the pig by improving handling facilities and procedures. Most alleys through which pigs are driven have rounded instead of sharp corners, easing movement of the pigs. Research shows that the less preslaughter stress a pig receives, the less likely it is to have low muscle quality (pale color, soft, and exudative—PSE). PSE muscle is unattractive in the retail display case and excessively shrinks during processing and cooking.

Slaughter lambs require more hand labor during dressing than cattle or pigs. Most of the pelt is loosened from the body by fisting—forcing a closed hand between the skin and the body. Fisting is possible in lamb slaughter because sheep have a prominent fell, which is a layer of connective tissue separating the skin and the underlying muscle and fat tissues.

In all three red meat species much more attention is paid to sanitation during slaughter, dressing, and processing than formerly was paid. For example, on the kill floor, tails of cattle are bagged in plastic to reduce transfer of microbes to the carcass. In all three species, organic acid rinses are being successfully used on carcasses to reduce the level of microbial contamination. A lower population of microbes should increase the shelf life of meat products and reduce the chances of illness from eating meat. However, a reduction in total number of microorganisms may not have the desired effect of reducing the number of pathogenic microbes on the meat, if any are present. Microbes compete with each other. A large population of friendly microorganisms may prevent pathogenic ones from becoming sufficiently numerous to be harmful. Without this competition, pathogens may grow and multiply more rapidly.

The general belief among people is that pigs are much dirtier animals than cattle or sheep. However, if pigs are fed in confinement and then scalded in hot water after death to remove their hair, few, if any, viable microorganisms remain on the surface of the skin. Their carcasses actually have a less numerous population of microbes than cattle or sheep carcasses. The hide and hair of cattle, the skin and wool of sheep are major sources of carcass contamination and many steps are taken by slaughterers to prevent transfer of these microorganisms to the carcass.

DISTRIBUTION OF MEAT AND MEAT PRODUCTS

Great changes also have occurred in the distribution of meat products to consumers. The cattle drives that started about 1780 and continued for over 100 years were necessary to move cattle from the sparsely populated, southwestern United States (where cattle grazed the vast grasslands) to railroads that transported them to packinghouses for slaughter near population centers in the Midwest. Some were trailed to the Louisiana Territory. Sheep, hogs, and even turkeys also were trailed in some parts of the country. Development of the rail car refrigerated with ice and salt ended the cattle drives because less expense was incurred in shipping the lighter-weight carcasses than live cattle. Development of the mechanically refrigerated rail car and then truck (reefer) allowed the packinghouses to be moved to the location of the live animals. For the cattle industry, this move in large part was from the East and Midwest to the Plains states from the Texas Panhandle northward. In the 1960s, most carcass beef was shipped as carcasses to distribution centers or directly to retail markets where carcasses were broken into wholesale cuts. By 1980 the boxed beef method of merchandising primal and subprimal cuts of meat was developed. After carcasses were chilled to remove the animal heat and reduce microbial growth, carcasses were broken in the packinghouse into primal and subprimal cuts along fabrication lines equipped with conveyers. The cuts were trimmed of excess fat, bone, and connective tissue, placed in cardboard boxes, further chilled in large coolers, and shipped to distribution centers or to retail markets for fabrication of retail cuts. By the mid 1990s, more than 90% of beef, almost 100% of pork, and over 80% of lamb was shipped from slaughter plants in boxes.

PACKAGING OF RETAIL MEAT CUTS

The fabrication and packaging of retail cuts in the packinghouse has been minimal because consumers are accustomed to seeing red meat cuts displayed in the supermarket showcase showing bloom. When normal muscle is first exposed to the air, the principal muscle pigment, myoglobin, has a much darker color than after it is exposed to oxygen in the air for 15 to 20 minutes. This color change when myoglobin is oxygenated to the brighter-red oxymyoglobin pigment form is called blooming. If animals are exposed to a prolonged stress that depletes their muscle glycogen supply before slaughter, the myoglobin to oxymyoglobin pigment conversion does not fully occur. These carcasses are known as dark cutters, receiving a considerable discount on the meat market. Because most consumers will not buy a darker-colored muscle, associating it with advanced age of animal or a lengthy storage period after slaughter, the change to fabrication of retail cuts in the packinghouse has been slow. Although packaging films are available that allow oxygen to penetrate the film and convert myoglobin to oxymyoglobin in the muscle, this exposure of the meat to oxygen during cold storage isn't desirable. It increases the rate of oxidation of meat fats, producing off odors and flavors known as rancidity. Oxidation of fats may be the greatest problem in the meat industry. Therefore, while in cold storage, meat should be packaged so that its exposure to oxygen is minimal.

In 1990s, a new packaging system for fresh meat was developed that allows retail cuts to be fabricated in the packinghouse, reducing exposure to microbial contamination, and taking advantage of the efficiency of the labor force. The retail cuts are placed on trays and wrapped in a packaging film that is oxygen permeable. Then the top of the package is capped with a layer of packaging material that is oxygen-impermeable. The cuts are boxed, refrigerated until needed, and then shipped to retail markets. Before the packages of meat are placed in the retail display cases, the oxygen-impermeable layer of packaging material is peeled off, oxygen penetrates the film, surrounds the meat, and it blooms. In a similar packaging system, packaged retail cuts are placed in an oxygen-impermeable bag that reduces oxygen exposure until the packages are removed from the bag for retail display. These packaging systems for retail cuts may greatly increase the fabrication of retail cuts in packinghouses, increasing labor efficiency and lessening microbial contamination. The future of the meat industry may well depend on improved packaging of fresh and cooked meats and the development of ready-to-heat, precooked meat dishes that consumers can heat and serve. Increased demands on the time in people's lives require that the meat industry become more friendly and provide more easily prepared menu items.

THE DIET/HEALTH "SCARE" FOR RED MEATS AND THE RESPONSE BY THE LIVESTOCK INDUSTRY

A serious problem for the industry during the 1980s and 1990s was the health scare surrounding red meats. The poultry industry took advantage of this scenario and fostered a great increase in poultry consumption at the expense of red meats. Before more strict rules were enforced, the Food and Drug Administration allowed health claims for foods in advertising that were not substantiated by reliable research. One of these claims was that chicken was more healthy than red meats in the human diet, particularly from a heart disease viewpoint. No such advertising claims are allowed today because we now know that chicken is no more nutritious or healthy in the human diet than red meats. In fact, a study published by the National Academy of Sciences (Table 22-1) showed that beef is more deserving of a "health food" label, if such labels were allowed, than chicken. Cooked Choice grade beef (the second-highest-quality grade), compared to lean, skinned chicken, has fewer calories and is a richer source of protein, heme iron that is more readily available than iron from vegetable sources, zinc (a component of many enzymes), and vitamin B12 (helps prevent anemia).

Contrary to popular belief, cooked beef, pork, lamb, chicken, and dark-meat turkey have very similar concentrations of cholesterol (Table 22-2), implicated in increasing incidence of heart diseases in that segment of the population whose tissues cannot properly metabolize cholesterol. Light-meat turkey and some fishes have about 20% less cholesterol than the above-mentioned meats. If Select grade beef was compared with chicken, it would have less saturated fats than chicken, while Choice grade beef has slightly more. Choice beef grade has more of the monounsaturated fatty acid, oleic acid, which is con-

TABLE 22-1

COMPOSITION OF 100 G (3.5 OZ.) OF COOKED USDA CHOICE GRADE BEEF AND LEAN, SKINNED CHICKEN

Trait	Trimmed, Choice Grade Beef	Lean, Skinned Chicken
Calories/100 g	225.0	239.0
Protein, g	30.4	27.3
Monounsaturated fatty acids, g	4.6	3.0
Saturated fatty acids, g	4.1[a]	3.8
Iron, mg	3.2	1.3
Zinc, mg	7.1	1.9
Vitamin B12, mcg	2.0	.3
Cholesterol, mg	90.0[b]	88.0[b]

[a]If Select rather than Choice grade was analyzed, the saturated fatty acid content was 3.6 g.

[b]Cholesterol concentration of meat is increased by cooking because water content is reduced (see Appendix I for cholesterol concentrations of raw animal products).

Source: National Academy of Sciences.

sidered a "good" fatty acid that does not increase the chances of increasing heart diseases as do some saturated fatty acids. If the chicken is fried, its fat content is much higher than shown in Table 22-1 because foods absorb fat during frying. Thus, chicken is no more a healthy dietary component than red meats. A healthy diet should include a variety of foods, including meats of various kinds.

A considerable shift in fat consumption in the U.S. population has occurred in the last 40 years. In the late 1950s, about 70% of our dietary fats were from animal fats. By the 1990s, the consumption of animal fats had fallen to about 55% of the total, while our total consumption of fat had risen. Thus, we are eating more fat than our parents ate and much more of it is from vegetable sources. During the same time span, deaths from heart diseases have decreased, but little change has occurred in deaths from cancers. Some research links consumption of unsaturated fats with cancer incidence. Only about one-fourth of both total fat and saturated fatty acids in our diets are directly obtained from red meat, poultry, and fish entrees. We get about 35% of dietary cholesterol directly from the same meats, but all of our dietary cholesterol has animal sources because plant foods do not contain cholesterol.

LOW FAT MEATS

Because over one-third of the U.S. population is considered overweight and because a substantial segment of the population is "watching their weight," low-fat foods have become more popular choices because of their lowered caloric content. If the fat content of a meat product is reduced below usual levels, something must replace the fat. Water is the usual replacer. Alkaline phosphates or animal or plant products may be added to hold the needed extra water in the product. Fats impart desirable flavoring, textural, and mouth-feel properties to foods. If fat content of a food is reduced or eliminated, serious palatability problems may arise. Much research is being done on producing and improving low-fat and no-fat foods. A high proportion of low-fat or no-fat foods do not survive in the marketplace, mainly because consumers don't like their taste compared to their full-fatted counterparts. The best example may be the demise of the McDonald's McLean Burger in 1996. Another problem with reduced-fat foods is that some consumers believe they can eat all they want without gaining weight. Because our weight is determined by amount of exercise and other physical activity versus the total number of calories consumed, people prone to be overweight can easily reach that state on low-fat or no-fat foods.

"THE OTHER WHITE MEAT"

To take advantage of the good dietary image of chicken, the pork industry started a successful advertising campaign in the 1980s touting pork as "The Other White Meat." Although pork is classed as a red meat, its muscle is a much lighter color than beef or lamb because of a lower myoglobin content and because pigs are slaughtered at a much younger age (about 6 months) than cattle (18–24 months) or lambs (12–15 months). As an animal ages, its muscle myoglobin content increases. Great strides have been made in reducing the fat content of pork by selecting leaner boars and sows to produce the next generation. However, much of the modern pork has too little intramuscular fat (marbling) for optimum palatability.

The greatest success story in meat production has been the poultry industry with vertical integration allowing a company to control all segments of the industry from setting of eggs to sale of the myriad finished poultry products. This control has allowed vast improvements in meat-producing birds so that they reach market at a young age (5–6 weeks) when they very efficiently convert feedstuffs to body tissues and cheaply produce a pound of marketable product. These great strides in efficiency and the much shorter generation interval (the average age of parents when their offspring are born) of poultry compared to red meat animals allow poultry to be sold at a much lower price than red meats. The swine industry is experiencing this same vertical integration, allowing it to also become much more efficient.

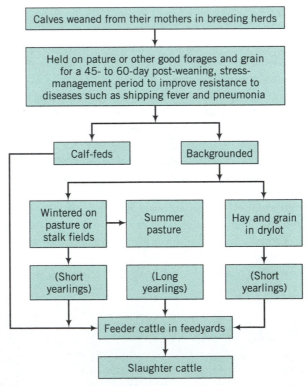

FIGURE 22-1

Routes that calves can take to the slaughter market.

The cattle industry lags far behind in vertical integration and may never reach the same degree of integration as the broiler and pork industries. The majority of feed for cattle and sheep with their four-compartment, ruminant stomach consists of pastures and forages while poultry and swine require mainly grains in their diet. Many people live on a small farm but work in town. They own a few cows to eat the forages their land produces and sell feeder calves in the fall to a stocker cattle owner who grazes them on winter pasture or stalk fields or sends them directly to a feedlot. The cattle then may be sold to someone else for feeding in drylot or one of the other owners may retain ownership of them during the feedlot phase. When ready for slaughter, the feeder cattle become slaughter cattle and are sold to a slaughterer (Figure 22-1). Thus, cattle usually have multiple owners before they are slaughtered for meat and none of the owners has much control over the actions taken by the other owners. However, cattle processing and beef marketing cooperatives organized with the intent of taking animals all the way to marketing of their products, and returning profits from processing and marketing to their members have been developed. Two such organizations are Northern Plains Premium Beef, and U.S. Premium Beef. Other alliances target the natural/implant-free beef market. Three organizations of this kind are B3R Premium Beef Program, Maverick Ranches Beef, and Coleman Natural Products.

Like the cattle industry, the sheep industry has little vertical integration. Coyotes and other predators, as well as other production constraints, have been associated with the steady decline in U.S. production of lamb meat. These factors have created U.S. markets for lamb produced in countries with abundant grassland such as Australia and New Zealand. However, their sheep numbers also are decreasing as some farmers turn to more profitable enterprises.

SLAUGHTER PLANT SIZE

The size of slaughter plants for meat animals has been steadily increasing. In the mid 1990s the four largest cattle slaughterers killed over 80% of all fed steers and heifers. The four-firm concentration in slaughtering of hogs was about 50% and in sheep and lambs about 75%. This concentration within the slaughter industry has some other segments of the industry worried about insufficient competition in buying of live animals. The main reason that such concentration exists is that larger slaughter plants are more efficient. As the daily slaughter capacity increases, the per-head cost of slaughter and processing dramatically decreases from about $25 for a slaughter capacity of 300 head per hour to about $45 for 25 head per hour. A large unit also can more efficiently process byproducts of the slaughter and fabrication operations than a smaller unit. In the modern slaughter plant, a carcass can be sold for a lower total value than the live animal cost because of the efficient recovery of byproducts. Most byproducts have much less value per pound than carcasses. However, the sum of the values of these byproducts provides sufficient revenue that the packer can sell carcasses for less total value than the live animal cost. This byproduct value commonly is termed drop value and results in the profit that packers can make on each head slaughtered. Hides and fats from slaughter and fabrication operations usually are the most valuable byproducts of cattle. Pharmaceuticals also are very valuable byproducts and include gland extracts, serum for research and health studies, and components of cosmetic creams. It has been said that hog slaughterers use everything but the squeal. Most hides are shipped overseas for manufacture of leather goods that U.S. consumers buy back. Two main reasons for this practice are that U.S. environmental protection laws are more strict than those of some countries, creating a large expense of disposing of water containing chemicals used in hide tanning, and that less industrially developed countries have a much cheaper labor supply than the United States.

FOOD SAFETY

The 1990s brought much consumer concern and worry about the safety of our food supply. Of note is the food poisoning organism *Escherichia coli* O157:H7, a virulent strain of bacteria that causes significant mortality among the infected, particularly the very young, the old, and those whose competing, friendly gut microbes have been killed by antibiotic treatment. However, 1% or fewer of foodborne illness outbreaks are caused by *E. coli* O157:H7. In contrast, *Salmonella enteritidis,* a food infection organism that grows and produces toxin in the digestive tract, causes one-fifth to one-fourth of the foodborne illness outbreaks. Some illnesses caused by the *E. coli* strain have been attributed to undercooked ground meat. For safety from this organism and others that might cause illness, it is recommended that ground meats be cooked to an internal temperature of 160 °F. Another recommendation is to cook ground meats until the juices run clear during cooking. However, juices lose their pink tint at different temperatures in various meats. Therefore, the 160 °F internal temperature, determined with a meat thermometer, is the safer recommendation. Steaks and roasts are much less likely to harbor microbes that cause illness because muscle tissue of healthy animals is sterile or nearly so when the animal is slaughtered. If microbes gain access to the meat during processing of carcasses and cuts, most will be on the surface of meat cuts like steaks and roasts. The meat surface will become sufficiently hot during cooking to kill the offending microbes. However, if the meat is ground, the microbes are mixed throughout the product, not residing just on the surface. Therefore, ground products have to be cooked more thoroughly to ensure their safety. Most (about 60%) foodborne illness results from improper handling and cooking of meat at foodservice establishments or in homes. Meat produced in the United States is the safest in the world and has the lowest incidence of pathogenic bacteria.

The incidence of pesticides and other residues in food products is a major concern to many consumers. However, until researchers develop better methods to control insects that devour crops, farmers and ranchers will have to use pesticides to allow production of enough food for human needs. Some progress is being made in developing strains of crops that are resistant to pests.

The use of growth promotants and antibiotics in the production of livestock also is a major concern to some consumers. However, the use of these substances results in only parts per billion in animal tissues and should not be a concern for consumers' health. For example, estrogenic implants used to increase daily gain and improve feed efficiency of cattle barely raise the very low levels of estrogenic substances in meat. Some vegetables (mostly green leafy) humans routinely consume contain more of these substances than does meat.

"Mad cow" disease (Bovine spongiform encephalopathy—BSE), so named because afflicted cattle appear nervous and have difficulty walking, is a brain disease that received much publicity in the 1990's. About 37,000 cases of BSE were recorded in the United Kingdom in 1992, and rapidly declined to about 4,000 cases in 1997. Scrapie is a similar disease in sheep and goats and Creutzfeldt-Jakob Disease produces similar symptoms in humans. No evidence has been presented that consumption of meat causes Creutzfeldt-Jakob Disease in humans. However, as a safeguard, the USDA has banned all animal imports from the United Kingdom since 1989, and in 1998 banned the feeding of animal byproducts from ruminant animals to other ruminants. BSE has not been detected in the United States. This issue is discussed further in Chapters 11 and 18.

U.S. MEAT PRODUCTION

Today's meat industry contributes greatly to the U.S. and world economies. According to USDA statistics, world meat production is about 48 million tons with U.S. producers contributing about one-fourth of the total. U.S. meat sales are about $70 billion annually, making it the largest food industry. The United States leads other countries in production and consumption of beef and veal, broilers, and turkey, is third in pork, and tenth in lamb, mutton, and goat. Despite our lofty world rankings, our average per-capita consumption of cooked meat averages only about 4 oz. per day.

The world population is increasing about 1 billion every 10 years (see Chapter 1). Sufficient food to feed a rapidly growing population is a major challenge for the twenty-first century, as discussed in other chapters. Ruminant animals can graze on lands not suitable for direct production of human food. The meat from these animals is greatly needed to provide nutrient-dense meat products to feed people. About two-thirds of the agricultural land in the world is pasture, range, or meadow. We need animals to graze these land areas to produce meat and other animal products.

MEAT INSPECTION

The federal meat inspection service in the United States is reputed to be among the best in the world. Inspection is provided by the Food Safety and Inspection Service of the U.S.D.A. Established in 1906, the service was developed to ensure that animals used for meat production are healthy and that slaughter and processing plant conditions allow production of wholesome meat. Packing plants that do not ship product across state lines may elect to have state inspection if available. About 3,000 plants in 26 states had state inspection in 1996. State inspection regulations are supposed to be equal to federal regulations. Inspectors observe the animals in the holding pens before slaughter, checking for signs of illness or injury that could render the meat unfit for human consumption. Detection of any condition that could make the meat unwholesome causes either condemnation of the animal or a more thorough postmortem inspection. If condemned, it will be sent to the rendering plant where the tissues will be tanked (cooked under pressure at a temperature and for a time that will kill any microorganisms) and cannot enter the human food chain. Tankage, a supplement for animal diets, was named after this tanking process. During the postmortem inspection, parts of the animal body are visually inspected after they are removed during the dressing procedures. If a localized condition is found that could make the meat unfit for human consumption, that part is tanked. If the abnormal condition is generalized, all of the body will be tanked. About 1 in 200 cattle, 1 in 260 sheep, and 1 in 430 swine are condemned and tanked during federal inspection.

Procedures and formulas for production of processed meat products also are subject to inspection regulations at any point along the production line before the product is shipped. Carcasses and edible byproducts that pass inspection are marked with a round stamp similar to Figure 22-2. The abbreviations represent U.S. Inspected and Passed. The number is the code number for the packing plant, allowing traceback of the meat. This stamp shows the consumer that the meat was federally inspected and is wholesome as far as the inspectors can determine. State inspection systems use different insignia.

In addition to inspection of live animals, carcasses, and processed meats and their ingredients, federal inspectors are concerned with plant and equipment sanitation, and labeling of retail meat products prepared in that plant. Labels must show meat cut names that are descriptive of that cut, the species name, the cut's wholesale or primal cut origin, the net weight, the company producing it, and the company's address. If the meat has

FIGURE 22-2

Federal meat inspection stamps placed on carcasses (left) and processed meat products (right). The number is the code for the slaughter or processing plant, allowing meat to be traced to its processing plant origin.

been further processed, an ingredient list must be part of the label, listing ingredients in their order of predominance.

Federal inspection is provided by the federal government during a normal 8-hour shift. If the shift goes beyond 8 hours or work is done on a federal holiday, the establishment using the service must pay for it on an hourly basis. The weak links in our meat inspection scheme are after the products leave the slaughter and processing plants. Retail markets, restaurants, and other foodservice establishments are not subject to federal inspection. They receive often sporadic inspection from city or state inspectors who may use inspection regulations less stringent than federal regulations. Because only about 10% of food poisoning outbreaks are traced to a processing plant origin, 40% to foodservice establishments, and 20% to consumers' homes, better inspection procedures are needed in retail markets and foodservice establishments, and consumers need more education about safely handling food in their homes. Practicing the three C's for handling of meats can prevent most outbreaks of food poisoning—keep it *clean* (don't allow contamination), *cold* (inhibit microbial growth and reproduction), and *covered* (to prevent contamination).

HAZARD ANALYSIS CRITICAL CONTROL POINTS

In 1997, the Hazard Analysis Critical Control Points (HACCP) system became a part of standard operating procedures for slaughter and processing plants. The critical points at which meat might become unwholesome along the line that meat travels during slaughter, dressing, and processing into meat items must be identified and procedures developed for controlling these critical steps. The first phase of this process was implemented in 1997 with the initiation of Standard Operating Procedures (SOPs). This system shifts to the slaughterer and processor more of the responsibility of ensuring that a wholesome product is produced. Experiences of progressive meat processors who already use the HACCP system and of other industries show that this move to a HACCP-based system is a desirable move to further ensure that our food supply is wholesome. The new inspection system employs both the usual visual evaluation for contamination from the hide, hair, and viscera, and the tracking of unseen microbes that may cause foodborne illnesses.

CARCASS COMPOSITION

The three major tissues in a carcass are muscle, fat, and bone. Across red-meat animal species, fat percentage, with a practical range from 15 to 55%, varies by far the most from carcass to carcass. Bone varies the least (10 to 24%). Muscle, the most valuable component, ranges from about 40 to 70%. As an animal fattens, its percentage of muscle and bone decreases. Fat is the latest developing of the three tissues. Therefore, most animals fed high-energy diets in preparation for slaughter will have higher percentages of muscle

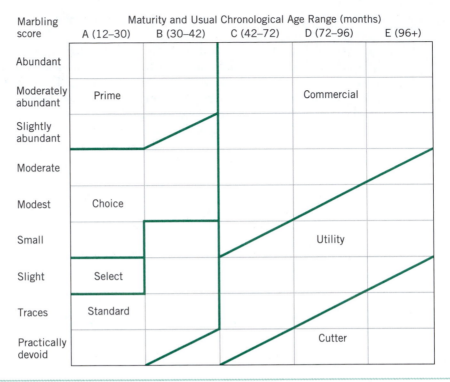

FIGURE 22-3

Relationships among marbling score, maturity, and quality in beef carcasses. (Adapted from Meat Evaluation Handbook.)

when going on feed than when deemed ready for slaughter. Fat will be deposited faster than muscle while the animal is on the high-energy feedlot diet. Unfortunately, the fat depot that tends to be deposited last is intramuscular fat (marbling), which is the major determinant of beef carcass grades (Figure 22-3). As marbling scores increase, quality grades are increased and the carcasses are more valuable from a quality standpoint. However, as an animal fattens, its carcass contains more total fat and is less valuable per pound because of this excess fat.

The United States is one of the few countries that can afford to feed animals just to increase the palatability of the meat. Research shows that 50 to 60 days of drylot feeding of steers and heifers raises the eating quality of the meat and little change occurs with longer feeding. However, most young cattle will not grade Choice with this short feeding period. Therefore, they are fed much longer to deposit more marbling so that a higher percentage will grade Choice and return a higher price per pound when slaughtered. Choice grade beef carcasses generally bring from $6 to 7 more per hundredweight than Select grade. Also, relatively low grain prices and the added value associated with increased carcass weight of animals result in continued feeding of cattle in feedyards.

Unfortunately, other fat depots also are increasing in size as marbling is deposited, creating much fat to trim from carcasses during fabrication of wholesale and retail cuts.

Fat was needed during World War II because it had many uses in the war effort in the 1940s and animals were selected for small frame size and fatness. Fats still are needed for use in a wide array of consumer and industrial products, but we have a large surplus of fat. Animal breeders are selecting herd replacements that are larger-framed and less fat than during the era when fats were more valuable than today.

Some animals will deposit marbling without a large amount of the other fat depots. Animals with this genetic propensity should be identified and used as sires and dams of future generations if their meat has acceptable eating quality.

COMPOSITION OF MUSCLE

Muscles in the animal body vary widely in size, quality, and price received from retail cuts fabricated from them. The longissimus muscle is the largest muscle, comprising about 10% of muscle weight. This ribeye (cattle) or loineye (hogs and sheep) muscle is the longest muscle with an origin at the second or third rib and insertion at the hip bone. It is one of the most tender muscles, making it the most valuable one. Contrast the longissimus with the tenderloin muscle composed of two loin muscles—Psoas major and Psoas minor. The tenderloin may be the most tender muscle but is small, comprising about 2% of total muscle weight. Its tenderness and small size create a high price per pound. Toward the other end of the spectrum of major muscles is the semitendinosus, located in the rear limb. It contributes less than 2% of muscle weight and is one of the less tender muscles. It courses from the hip bone to the tibia and provides beef eye of round steaks, which often are tenderized to become minute steaks. It is the round-shaped muscle in ham and leg-of-lamb slices.

Muscles vary widely in composition, mainly because of variations in fat content. Water, the most abundant component, comprises about 75% of muscle and varies inversely with fat content. It contributes to the initial juiciness effect we experience when we first chew a bite of meat. Protein is the least variable but most valuable component from a nutritional viewpoint and the one that is in shortest supply in world food for humans. Proteins supply amino acids needed by animal bodies for growth, maintenance, and repair of tissues. About 18.5% of muscle is protein. About one-half of the total protein is composed of myofibrillar proteins, principally myosin and actin, which function in muscle contraction. About one-third of muscle protein is composed of sarcoplasmic proteins, mainly enzymes and pigments such as myoglobin, which stores oxygen and affects muscle color most. The last kind of protein is stromal, the connective tissues of which collagen, reticulin, and elastin are examples. They form the "skeleton" for muscles.

Lipids (fats) average about 3% in muscle, varying from .5 to over 30%. Neutral lipids are one-third of the total amount and are composed of triglycerides, three moles of one or more fatty acids attached to a glycerol molecule. Phospholipids, compounds containing phosphorus and lipids, are another one-third of the total lipid and function in rancidity development in meat. Cholesterol comprises about .5% of muscle weight and is a necessary component of cell walls and many enzymes and hormones. Contrary to pop-

TABLE 22-2

CHOLESTEROL CONTENT OF SELECTED COOKED MEATS[a]

Kind of Meat	Cholesterol (mg/deciliter)
Beef	76
Dark-meat chicken	79
Dark-meat turkey	73
Flounder	58
Lamb	78
Light-meat chicken	73
Light-meat turkey	59
Pork	79

[a]Cholesteral concentration of meat is increased by cooking because water content is reduced (see Appendix I for cholesterol concentrations of raw animal products).

Source: Agriculture Handbook No. 8, Composition of Foods, Raw, Processed, Prepared. Washington, D.C., USDA.

ular belief, cholesterol content of meat varies little between leaner and fatter cooked meat cuts (Table 22-2). Likewise, fowl and red meats differ little in cholesterol content. Our bodies need a daily supply of cholesterol. If it is not supplied in the diet, it will be manufactured. In about 30% of the population, increased dietary cholesterol increases serum cholesterol levels. Little change in serum cholesterol level occurs with dietary changes in the other 70%.

Lipids are important from both positive and negative standpoints. They positively contribute to both sustained juiciness and flavor of meat. The species flavor components are in fats. If we add fat from one species to muscle from another species, we will identify the meat with its source of fat. However, lipids contain 2.25 times as many calories as carbohydrates and proteins, oxidize to form off odors and flavors of rancidity, and consumption of saturated fats (whether from plant or animal sources) has been implicated as a contributor to heart diseases. Although fats from beef, lamb, and pork are classified as saturated fats, unsaturated fatty acids predominate in pork fat (Table 22-3), about half of beef fatty acids are unsaturated, and about 46% of lamb and mutton fatty acids are unsaturated. Chicken fat is more unsaturated—about 69%. Research shows that stearic and oleic acids, two of the three most prevalent fatty acids in red-meat fats, do not contribute to heart disease.

About 1.5% of muscle is nonprotein nitrogen (NPN). These compounds contain nitrogen but are not proteins, as the name indicates. Some of these compounds contribute to meat flavor. One very important NPN compound is ATP (adenosine triphosphate), a high-energy compound that supplies energy for muscles and other tissues to do their work.

Only about .8% of muscle is carbohydrate, but these compounds are very important in both the live animal and its muscles postmortem. Glycogen is the principal readily

TABLE 22-3

FATTY ACID COMPOSITION OF SOME ANIMAL FATS EXPRESSED AS A PERCENTAGE OF TOTAL FATTY ACIDS

Kind of Fatty Acid	Lard (Pork)	Beef Tallow	Mutton Tallow	Chicken Fat
Saturated	38.8	50.6	53.8	31.1
Monounsaturated	48.2	42.1	35.8	48.1
Polyunsaturated	13.0	7.4	10.4	20.8

Source: Adapted from *Designing Foods: Animal Product Options in the Marketplace.* Washington, D.C., National Academy Press, 1988.

available energy store for the living animal. After death, muscle glycogen is converted to lactic acid, which lowers the muscle pH to a desirable 5.4 to 5.6 and aids in the development of desired muscle colors. If glycogen stores are deficient at death, such as would result from a prolonged antemortem stress, the dark cutting muscle condition results. A sudden change in weather and lengthy periods of exercise are examples of stressors.

Inorganic compounds comprise about 1% of muscle. To determine this mineral content, the meat sample is ashed—burned in a muffle furnace. Minerals do not burn and are the ash. Meats are significant dietary sources of iron, phosphorus, and magnesium. We get over 40% of our dietary iron from animal sources. Meat's heme form of iron is two to four times more absorbable from the gut than non-heme iron from other sources. Beef is the best muscle dietary source of iron because of its greater content of myoglobin, the pigment that gives beef its characteristic bright-red color. Iron is a component of the molecule of both myoglobin and hemoglobin. Adequate dietary iron helps prevent anemia.

AGE, SEX, WEIGHT, FATNESS, GRADE, AND BREED EFFECTS ON MEAT QUALITY AND VALUE

Age, sex, weight, fatness, and grade of meat animals have large effects on their value and meat's desirability at our dinner tables or in foodservice establishments.

Age Effects

The federal carcass-grading standards are designed to penalize older animals by assigning them a lower-quality grade, because research shows that muscle becomes less tender as animals age. As animals age, connective tissue surrounding muscle fibers becomes less soluble and does not break down to gelatin during cooking. Meat from older animals has more insoluble connective tissue, commonly called gristle, than meat from younger animals. Most meat of sires and dams culled from breeding herds is ground and manufactured into sausage products because it is not sufficiently tender to be sold as steaks or chops and roasts. However, boning beef from bull and cow carcasses is in great demand because it has a lower fat content than steer and heifer beef and because its dark color from increased myoglobin content with advancing age is desirable for sausage production. Boar meat usually has a strong, unpleasant odor and flavor that limits its use to highly spiced products. However, only about one-half of the human population can taste this boar flavor. Mutton (meat from sheep over about 20 months of age) likewise has a strong flavor that is not liked by the large majority of U.S. residents. It too can be used in sausage products, but must be mixed with other meats to dilute the strong flavor. Of the three red-meat species of mature animals, mutton is the least demanded.

The age at which a male is castrated greatly affects meat characteristics. If bull calves are castrated at a weight of less than 550 lb., two-thirds of them may grade Choice, depending on their genetic constitution for marbling deposition. If castration is delayed until they weigh 700 lb, only about a third of them may grade Choice. If castration is further delayed until they weigh 900 lb, only a tenth of them may grade Choice. The shorter the time that androgens produced by the testes are allowed to act in the animal body, the higher will be the meat quality and fatness and the lower will be muscle production.

Sex Effects

Sex of young animals affects carcass composition more than it affects meat palatability. Bullocks (intact males under 2 years of age) are less tender and deposit less marbling than either steers or heifers similar in age, but their percentage of muscle is higher than for steers because they deposit more muscle and less fat than the castrates under the influence of their greater supply of androgens from the testes (Table 22-4). Beef from steers and heifers usually differs little in palatability, but heifers are fatter than steers because of their greater supply of estrogens from the ovaries. Similar differences are found when ewe and wether lambs are compared. However, gilts are less fat than barrows and a slight differ-

TABLE 22-4

COMPARISON OF SIMILAR-AGE TRIOS OF HALF-SIB BULLOCKS, STEERS, AND HEIFERS FROM NINE HEREFORD AND ANGUS SIRES FED THE SAME DIET FOR THE SAME LENGTH OF FEEDING PERIOD

Trait	Bullocks	Steers	Heifers
Marbling score	Slight	Small	Modest
USDA quality grade	Low Select	Low Choice	Average Choice
Fat thickness, inch	0.25	0.41	0.56
USDA yield grade	2.1	2.8	3.7
Tenderness	6.2	7.3	7.5
Juiciness	7.2	7.2	7.3
Flavor	7.4	7.7	7.9

Source: Williams, John, II. Performance, carcass characteristics, and ultrasonic estimates of changes in muscle and fat of bulls, steers, and heifers. Ph.D. dissertation, Univ. of Tennessee, 1965.

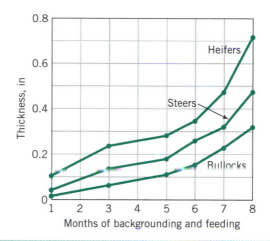

FIGURE 22-4

Ultrasonic estimates of subcutaneous fat thickness of half-sib, Angus, and Hereford bullocks, steers, and heifers fed alike during 8 months of backgrounding and drylot feeding.
Source: Williams, John, II, Performance, carcass characteristics and ultrasonic estimates of changes in muscle and fat of bulls, steers and heifers. Ph.D. Dissertation, Univ. of Tennessee (1965).

ence in palatability sometimes is found. A low percentage of pork from gilts, barrows, and sows has the undesirable boar odor and flavor.

The primary difference in sexes across species is in composition, which determines the yield of lean meat. Heifers and ewes generally yield more fat and less muscle than steers and wethers. Gilts are leaner and higher yielding than barrows. Differences in palatability among castrated cattle, sheep, and hogs are minimal.

The effects of sex of cattle on fat deposition are shown in Figure 22-4. If cattle are similar in genetic composition and age and are fed alike, at any time during the backgrounding and feeding period, steers will have about twice as much subcutaneous fat thickness as bullocks. Heifers will have about twice as much fat thickness as bullocks. Thus, sires must be much leaner than their steer or heifer offspring. For example, if a breeder wants to produce steers with .4 inch of fat thickness over the ribeye, the sire, if bred to cows of similar genetics, must have no more than .25 inch of fat thickness at the same age.

Weight Effects

Weight has similar effects across species. As an animal becomes older, it becomes heavier and fatter if adequate feed is available. Muscle and bone tissues reach a plateau at maturity, but adipose tissue still is deposited after maturity if caloric intake exceeds body needs for maintenance and production. Higher-energy diets produce more fatness than lower-energy diets if the animals are fed for the same time period. Genetic makeup of the animal also has a large effect on carcass composition. For example, most breeds of cattle from the continent of Europe tend to be larger and heavier at maturity than British breeds. Larger-framed animals mature later and have leaner carcasses at a given age than smaller-framed animals.

In addition to the penalty for increased fatness of animals imposed by marketing systems, weight above certain limits is undesirable because the primal and subprimal cuts are too large for the boxes used in their distribution. Retail cuts, when fabricated by traditional methods, are too large for the desired serving size. Weights of slaughter animals have risen steadily for several years because the cost of slaughtering, dressing, and fabricating cuts from a larger animal is similar to that of the same operations on smaller animals. Thus, meat packers make more profit killing heavier animals because they have more to sell. We are producing much more meat with fewer animals than we did a few years ago. Unfortunately, heavier animals have to be fed longer and deposit more fat, adding to our oversupply of fat.

Grade Effects

Table 22-5 shows the relationships among beef carcass grades, meat palatability factors, and fat content of the loin muscles. As the degree of marbling within the ribeye muscle

TABLE 22-5

SENSORY PANEL RATINGS AND FAT PERCENTAGE OF THE MUSCLE OF BEEF LOIN STEAKS BY MARBLING SCORE

Grade and Marbling Score	Tenderness	Juiciness	Flavor	Fat (%)
Prime				
Moderately abundant	6.45[a]	5.56[a]	6.13[a]	10.4
Slightly abundant	6.29[a]	5.39[ab]	5.96[a]	8.6
Choice				
Moderate	6.21[a]	5.30[b]	5.92[a]	7.3
Modest	6.21[a]	5.00[c]	5.73[b]	6.0
Small	5.86[b]	4.98[c]	5.67[b]	5.0
Select				
Slight	5.70[b]	4.79[d]	5.37[c]	3.4
Standard				
Traces	5.10[c]	4.72[d]	5.17[d]	2.5
Practically devoid	4.65[d]	4.81[cd]	4.68[e]	1.8

[a,b,c,d,e]Means in a column with different superscripts differ (P < .05). N = 678 carcasses. A higher score is more desirable.

Sources:

1. Smith et al., Relationship of USDA marbling groups to palatability of cooked meat. *Journal Food Quality,* 7: 289 (1984).
2. Savell et al., Percentage ether-extractable fat and moisture content of beef longissimus muscle as related to USDA marbling score. *Journal of Food Science,* 51: 838 (1987).

declines, the eating quality of the muscle and the fat content determined chemically also decline. If the muscle has at least Modest marbling, additional marbling has little effect on tenderness. These data were the basis for setting the lower limit of marbling for Certified Angus Beef at the Modest marbling score. Tenderness varies the most across marbling scores and juiciness varies the least. The differences in tenderness, juiciness, and flavor scores are greater among beef carcasses with the lower marbling scores that represent Select and Standard grade beef with Slight or less marbling than those with more marbling.

Most of the beef qualifying for the various low-fat labels will grade either U.S. Select or Standard. The American Heart Association guidelines allow fat contents up to 7.3% for meats in diets of heart patients. Table 22-5 shows that beef carcasses grading average Choice (Modest marbling) and lower would qualify for diets of heart patients under these guidelines. Consumers have a better chance of obtaining beef with higher palatability if they choose steaks with more marbling. However, the fat content increases about 1.2% as marbling is increased one degree. Thus, caloric value of the muscle increases as grade increases toward Prime. Similar relationships exist in pork and lamb.

Breed Effects

Table 22-6 illustrates that breeds of red-meat animals differ in muscle tenderness and their ability to deposit marbling, the grading factor influencing carcass quality grade

TABLE 22-6

CATTLE BREED EFFECTS ON MARBLING SCORE, PERCENTAGE OF CARCASSES GRADING CHOICE, AND MEAT PALATABILITY

Breed Group[a]	Marbling Score	Choice Grade (%)	Tenderness	Juiciness	Flavor
Chianina X	Slight[10]	24	6.9	7.2	7.3
Limousin X	Slight[35]	37	6.9	7.3	7.4
Brahman X	Slight[45]	40	6.5	6.9	7.2
Gelbvieh X	Slight[55]	43	6.9	7.2	7.4
Sahiwal X	Slight[60]	44	5.8	7.1	7.0
Simmental X	Slight[65]	60	6.8	7.3	7.3
Maine Anjou X	Slight[70]	54	7.1	7.2	7.3
Tarentaise X	Slight[75]	60	6.7	7.0	7.3
Charolais X	Slight[80]	63	7.3	7.3	7.4
Brown Swiss X	Slight[80]	61	7.2	7.2	7.4
Pinzgauer X	Slight[95]	60	7.1	7.2	7.4
South Devon X	Small[10]	76	7.4	7.4	7.3
Hereford-Angus X	Small[10]	76	7.3	7.3	7.3
Red Poll X	Small[15]	68	7.3	7.1	7.4
Jersey X	Small[75]	85	7.4	7.5	7.5

[a]Breed of sire bred to Hereford and Angus or F_1 cross dams.

Source: Cundiff, Larry V., et al., Breeding for lean beef (Germ Plasm Evaluation Program). Beef Research Progress Report No. 3. Fort Collins, CO: Roman L. Hruska Meat Animal Research Center and Univ. of Nebraska Agricultural Experiment Station, USDA, ARS-71 (1988).

most. These data are from crossbred calves; therefore, breed differences would be greater if purebred animals were tested. Tenderness of meat varies more than juiciness and flavor and is rated the most important palatability factor by the majority of consumers. Miller et al. (1995) showed that 50% of consumers rated tenderness the most important beef palatability trait, 40% rated flavor first, and only 10% rated juiciness at the top. Thus, tenderness and flavor of meat are very important factors in the consumer perception of meats.

Cattle with Zebu breeding have more problems with less tender meat than most other breeds. However, the majority of these cattle have acceptable meat palatability and some individuals have excellent palatability. Differences between individuals within a breed are greater than the differences between breed averages. Thus, all breeds contain individuals that range from acceptable to unacceptable in meat palatability, which is a highly heritable trait. Individuals in all breeds in all species that are low in meat palatability should be culled from breeding herds regardless of their other attributes because the main reason for raising meat animals is to produce meat. Because the average consumer eats red meat because he or she likes it, we need much more effort in identifying those strains of animals that are high in meat palatability to use in breeding herds. Several such efforts were started by progressive breeders in the 1990s.

Fatness Effects

Fatness greatly influences the value of carcasses. Beef carcasses having more than about 35% fat are penalized because too much fat must be trimmed during fabrication of wholesale and retail cuts, producing low yields of trimmed retail cuts. However, more fatness usually enhances meat quality. Deposition of intramuscular fat (marbling) tends to increase as subcutaneous and intermuscular fat depots increase in size. While differences in amount of marbling may have no more than a 10 to 15% association with meat palatability factors, this effect is positive—more marbling results in greater palatability. Marbling is the only trait presently measurable that tends to increase all three major palatability factors—tenderness, juiciness, and flavor. In all consumer studies, more marbling increases customer satisfaction of meats if other factors are equal.

Fatness may have additional beneficial effects by preventing cold shortening of muscles. If a muscle is chilled too quickly after death, its muscle fibers will contract and be tougher than if cold shortening did not occur. Cold shortening is more prevalent in muscles of carcasses that have a thin layer of subcutaneous fat and in parts of the carcass that are least thick, such as the rib. If cold shortening occurs in the longissimus muscle that is exposed when a beef carcass is ribbed, the ribeye will have a dark ring around it that is called heat ring, a misnomer because the change in color was caused by the ribeye being chilled too quickly. If a beef carcass has less than about .3 inch and a lamb carcass less than about .1 inch of subcutaneous fat thickness, they may cold shorten if chilled at usual chill cooler temperatures (about 25 °F or −3 °C for beef carcasses). Muscles of pork carcasses generally do not cold shorten.

EFFECTS OF FATNESS ON MEAT PALATABILITY

Since Biblical times, the fatted calf has been a symbol of a feast of tender, juicy, flavorful meat. Consumers still desire meat with high palatability, but because of the costs of producing fatter animals and the concern about fat and cholesterol in the human diet, many consumers now buy low-fat or no-fat fresh and processed meats. A 1987 study by the National Livestock and Meat Board (Knop, *Drover's Journal* 20:1) showed that about one-half of consumers made an effort to avoid foods high in cholesterol content and over one-half were trying to reduce fat in their diet. Less concern now is expressed about cholesterol content of foods, but low-fat food concerns were stronger in the mid-1990s than 10 years earlier. The meat industry has responded by providing leaner products under branded beef names or "Lite," "Lean," or "Low Fat" labels.

Will decreasing the caloric content of meat be compatible with maintaining the meat's tenderness, juiciness, and flavor? Table 22-7 shows results from 471 "A" and "B" maturity beef carcasses. Most U.S. steers, heifers, and bullocks that supply steaks and roasts fall within this maturity range. If the carcasses had at least a Slight degree of marbling, at least 93% were rated desirable in tenderness, 99% in flavor, and 92% in overall palatability. At least twice as many carcasses with Traces or less marbling were rated undesirable in the palatability traits as those with more marbling. Flavor presented the least problems in these cattle with at least 97% of the steaks with any marbling score being rated desirable.

The chances of beef being high in palatability are greater if more marbling and a higher-quality grade are present. Therefore, restaurants that take pride in serving highly palatable meat (and discriminating consumers who wish to eat the better meat) will buy the high and average Choice and Prime grades although the fat content and caloric value of these products is considerably higher than for Select or Standard grade beef. Despite considerable research evidence that a minimal amount of marbling generally is associated

TABLE 22-7

PERCENTAGE OF BEEF RIB STEAKS RATED DESIRABLE[a] FOR OVERALL TENDERNESS, FLAVOR DESIRABILITY, AND OVERALL PALATABILITY STRATIFIED BY MARBLING SCORE

Marbling Score	Overall Tenderness	Flavor Desirability	Overall Palatability
Moderate or more	93	100	100
Modest	98	100	100
Small	96	99	94
Slight	93	99	92
Traces or less	86	97	80

[a]Desirable indicates that the steaks were rated at least 4.5 on an 8-point scale.

Source: Tatum et al., Interrelationships between marbling, subcutaneous fat thickness and cooked beef palatability. *Journal of Animal Science,* 54: 777-784 (1982).

TABLE 22-8

SENSORY PANEL RATINGS OF BEEF STEAKS BY FAT THICKNESS OVER THE RIBEYE

Thickness (inch)	Tenderness	Juiciness	Flavor
<.25	6.8[a]	7.1[a]	7.2[a]
.25–.50	7.2[b]	7.2[a]	7.5[b]
.50–.75	7.4[b]	7.3[a]	7.5[bc]
.75–1.00	7.4[b]	7.3[a]	7.5[bc]
>1.00	7.8[b]	7.6[a]	7.9[c]

[a,b,c]Means in a column with different superscripts differ (P < .05).

Source: Dikeman, M.E., Fat reduction in animals and the effects on palatability and consumer acceptance of meat products. *Proceedings Reciprocal Meat Conf.*, 40: 93 (1987).

with lower meat palatability, the majority of consumers at the retail meat display case select meat with lower amounts of marbling, citing its lower caloric value as the reason. Thus, they are selecting meats that tend to have lower palatability.

Fatness of the whole carcass also affects meat palatability (Table 22-8). Those cattle of many breed crosses from the Germ Plasm Evaluation Study at the Roman L. Hruska U.S. Meat Animal Research Center, Clay Center, NE, were significantly less tender and flavorful if they carried less than .25 inch of subcutaneous fat over the ribeye muscle. These thin rind cattle fit best into a lean beef merchandising program. Those cattle carrying between .25 and 1 inch of fat thickness differed little in palatability, but those over 1

TABLE 22-9

PERCENTAGE OF BEEF RIB STEAKS RATED DESIRABLE[a] FOR OVERALL TENDERNESS, FLAVOR DESIRABILITY, AND OVERALL PALATABILITY STRATIFIED BY FAT THICKNESS OVER THE RIBEYE

Fat Thickness (inch)	Overall Tenderness	Flavor Desirability	Overall Palatability
.1	67	100	75
.2	92	99	86
.3	97	99	96
.4	93	99	95
.5	96	100	96
.6	94	100	90
.7	97	100	97
.8	93	100	97

[a]Desirable indicates that the steaks were rated at least 4.5 on an 8-point scale.

Source: Tatum et al., Interrelationships between marbling, subcutaneous fat thickness and cooked beef palatability. *Journal of Animal Science*, 54: 777–784 (1982).

inch tended to be superior. The reduced tenderness of the carcasses with less than .25 inch of fat thickness probably was due in part to their more rapid chilling rate, causing cold shortening of the muscle, and not solely to their thin fat cover. Research with lambs and pigs shows similar effects as found in beef of both marbling and carcass fatness on meat palatability.

Table 22-9 shows the percentage of beef carcasses that were rated desirable by thickness of their subcutaneous fat layer over the ribeye muscle. If the carcasses had at least .3 inch of fat thickness, at least 93% were rated desirable in tenderness, 99% in flavor, and 90% in overall palatability. Carcasses with less than .2 inch of fat thickness had considerably more tenderness and overall palatability problems.

EFFECTS OF COOKING

Cooking method and doneness can have as much effect on meat palatability as any other factor. Research on pork chops (Table 22-10) shows that cooking by broiling causes the meat to be more tender and as juicy and flavorful as meat cooked by frying and microwaving. Frying reduces tenderness and juiciness but greatly increases flavor because of the absorption of fat that carries flavoring components. People who are trying to limit their caloric intake should not fry meats or other foods. When all three palatability factors were combined by sensory panelists to determine an overall acceptability score, broiling and frying produced superior scores to microwaving. Thus, microwave ovens can be used to cook meat, taking advantage of their cooking speed and economy of operation, but the meat will have slightly lower palatability than if it is broiled or fried. Cooking methods such as these that don't use added moisture during cooking help the meat retain its flavor but have little or no tenderizing effect. Therefore, we should use these dry heat methods to cook meat cuts that already are tender. Meat cuts that lack tenderness must be cooked by moist-heat methods, such as braising and cooking in liquid, which tenderize them during cooking.

TABLE 22-10

EFFECT OF COOKING METHOD ON PALATABILITY[a] OF PORK LOIN CHOPS

Cooking Method	Tenderness	Juiciness	Flavor	Overall Acceptability
Broiling	6.5	6.5	6.6	6.6
Frying	5.9	5.7	7.5	6.6
Microwaving	6.0	6.4	6.5	6.3

[a]A higher score is more desirable.

Source: Kersh, Ronald, Effect of cooking method and chop thickness on cooking losses and palatability of pork loin chops. M.S. thesis, Texas Tech University (1978).

TABLE 22-11

EFFECT OF DONENESS (INTERNAL TEMPERATURE) OF GRILLED PORK CHOPS ON COOKING YIELD AND PALATABILITY[a] DETERMINED BY A SENSORY PANEL

Trait	Rare (140 °F)	Medium (158 °F)	Well Done (176 °F)
Cooking yield, %	73.8	67.0	58.3
Tenderness	11.3	10.8	9.1
Juiciness	11.4	9.4	6.1
Flavor	9.8	10.1	10.2

[a]A higher score is more desirable.

Source: Simmons et al., Effects of internal temperature and thickness on palatability of pork loin chops. *Journal of Food Science,* 50: 313 (1985).

How done the meat becomes during cooking also has large effects on its cooked yield and palatability. Cooking yields decrease dramatically as doneness increases. Therefore, if you cook meat to a more done state, you will have to buy more raw meat to have the same amount of cooked meat to eat. When cooking with dry-heat methods, the more done the meat is cooked, the drier and less tender it becomes (Table 22-11). Juiciness usually decreases more than tenderness as meat is cooked longer, but flavor usually improves with longer cooking times.

Moist-heat cookery methods cause a toughening of muscle fibers but a tenderizing of collagen, the principal connective tissue. If meat is cooked too long with moist heat, it will fall apart because collagen (that holds the meat together) is converted to gelatin, but the muscle fibers become less tender as cooking time increases.

Do thicker steaks and chops have higher palatability than thinner ones? If the internal temperature (doneness) of the meat is the same, thickness of the meat cut has little effect on palatability. Thinner meat cuts will show a less browned surface than thicker cuts at the same internal temperature because they had to be cooked a shorter time. If external appearance, rather than internal temperature determined with a meat thermometer, is used as the endpoint of cooking, thinner cuts will be overcooked, less tender, and less juicy compared to thicker cuts; thick cuts generally will be undercooked. Therefore, a meat thermometer should be used to determine meat doneness when dry-heat cookery methods are used.

WHY MEAT RETAIL CUTS DIFFER IN PRICE

Why do meat cuts within a species differ so much in price in the supermarket display case? A difference of at least 1,000% is not unusual. The demand for a meat cut determines in large part its price. At least four factors influence demand and these price differences. First, muscles within a carcass vary in tenderness with the most tender ones located near the center of the back. Tenderloin cuts from the Psoas major muscle are high priced and very tender in young animals. This cut, even from sires and dams culled from a breeding herd, may be tender enough to sell as steaks, rather than becoming grinding meats for sausages. Tenderness generally decreases in the anatomical locations farther from the center back. The meat palatability factor that varies the most in meat is tenderness and this factor also is the most important to consumers. If a meat cut is more tender, consumers are willing to pay more for it.

A second factor is amount of plate waste—fat, bone, and gristle, that part left on the dinner plate. With other factors equal, meat cuts with less waste bring a higher price per pound. Marketing changes to more boneless retail cuts and closer trimming of fat from primal and subprimal cuts, translating to retail cuts with less fat cover, have reduced plate waste and the effect of this factor on meat prices.

A third factor is the amount of convenience the meat cut offers. In times when both parents in the majority of two-parent families work outside the home and single-parent families are common, much less time is available to prepare meals compared to a generation earlier. We expect this trend toward more heat-and-serve and table-ready food items to continue. Because more time and labor are required to provide this convenience, such retail items must bring a higher price.

A fourth factor is the supply of and demand for a meat cut. Flank steaks of beef are among the least tender muscles in the body, but have no waste, and only two are contained in a carcass. They bring prices comparable to the tender steaks from the loin mainly because of their short supply.

Differences in comparable retail cut prices across species are very large. Poultry is least expensive, pork is next, beef third, and lamb is most expensive. This ranking is a result of the cost of production, dressing percentage (the percentage of a live animal that is carcass), and how the meat cuts are retailed. Production costs are about two times greater for pork and three times greater for beef than for chicken. Average retail prices reflect these production cost differences—pork is about twice as expensive as chicken and beef is about three times as expensive. Part of this production cost difference is caused by the differences in feed conversion. A pound of live broiler can be produced with less than 2 pounds of feed. Comparable feed conversions for feeder pigs and feeder cattle are about 2.5 and 7.5, respectively.

Dressing percentage (carcass weight/slaughter weight $\times$ 100) averages about 62% for fed steers and heifers, 72% for barrows, gilts, and broilers, and 50% for ewe and wether lambs. The amount of fill in the gastrointestinal tract has the most effect on dressing percentage—more fill causes a lower percentage because the carcass is a lower percentage of the heavier live weight. Fatter animals dress higher than leaner ones. As an animal fattens, relatively more of the fat is deposited in the carcass depots (subcutaneous, perirenal, intermuscular, and intramuscular) than is deposited on and around the internal organs that are not part of the carcass.

SUMMARY

The meat and food industry is a dynamic, fast-paced, ever-changing industry. The current industry is changing so rapidly that many companies have ongoing education and training programs for their employees.

The implementation of food safety programs using space-age technology to remove and eliminate pathogens from meat will make future packing plants look more like hospital environments. The implementation of organic acid washes, laser beam sterilization, and electrical charges for bacteria removal will allow meat to become even safer.

The push for higher-quality meats will continue with the search for a machine that will sort tough beef from tender as well as high-quality pork from low-quality pork. In any event, the meat industry will continue to be a place of high-paying, fast-paced jobs for graduates from colleges of agriculture.

GLOSSARY

Background calves   Weaned calves grazed on forages or forages with some grain to prepare them for entry into a feedlot.

Beef   The meat from cattle over about 1 year of age.

Byproducts   All of the parts of an animal except its carcass.

Calf-feds   Weaned calves going into a feedlot without first being wintered on pastures or other roughages.

Certified Angus Beef   The first large-scale, successful branded beef program. Major entry criteria are a black coat color, at least 51% Angus blood, at least a Modest marbling score, and no evidence of Zebu breeding.

Cold shortening   Shortening of sarcomeres (contractile units) on muscle fibers caused by chilling a carcass too rapidly. May cause toughening of the muscle fibers.

Dark cutter   Dark-colored, gummy muscle produced by subjecting an animal to prolonged stress.

Fisting   Removing the hide of sheep and goats by pushing the closed hand between the skin and the carcass.

HACCP   Hazard Analysis Critical Control Points.

Loineye   The cross-section of the longissimus muscle in sheep and hogs. The area of the muscle is called loineye area.

Mutton   The meat of sheep over about 20 months of age.

Pork   The meat of swine of all ages.

PSE muscle   Pale, soft, and exudative muscle that is caused by antemortem stress and/or a genetic defect.

Reefer   Refrigerated truck for transporting meat.

Ribeye   The cross-section of the longissimus muscle in cattle at the 12th rib. The area of the muscle is called ribeye area.

Saturated fatty acids   Fatty acids that do not have a double bond in the carbon chain.

Unsaturated fatty acids   Fatty acids that have at least one double bond in the carbon chain.

Veal   The meat from young calves under about 3 months of age.

Viscera   The organs and associated tissues in the abdominal and thoracic cavities of an animal.

SUPPLEMENTAL REFERENCES

Judge, M., Aberle, E., Forrest, J., Hedrick, H., and Merkel, R. 1989. *Principles of Meat Science.* Dubuque, IA: W. H. Freeman.

Kinsman, D. M., Kotula, A. W., Breidenstein, B. C. 1994. *Muscle Foods.* New York: Chapman and Hall.

Lawrie, R. A. 1979. *Meat Science.* New York: Pergamon Press.

Miller, M. F., Huffman, K. L., Gilbert, S. Y., Hamman, L. L., and Ramsey, C. B. 1995. Retail consumer acceptance of beef tenderized with calcium chloride. *J. Anim. Sci.* 73: 2308–2314.

Romans, J. R., Costello, W. J., Carson, C. W., Greaser, M. L., and Jones, K. W. 1994. *The Meat We Eat.* Danville, IL: Interstate Publishers.

CHAPTER TWENTY-THREE
MILK AND MILK PRODUCTS

R. L. BRADLEY
UNIVERSITY OF WISCONSIN
MADISON, WI

COMPOSITION OF MILK AND DAIRY FOODS
MILK MICROBIOLOGY
MILK PROCESSING
PROCESSING OF BYPRODUCTS
OTHER PRODUCTS
DEFECTS
CLEANING AND SANITATION OF DAIRY PLANT SYSTEMS
OPERATING EFFICIENCIES
IN-PLANT QUALITY AUDITS
SUMMARY

The fluid milk industry has been revolutionized in this country. This is exemplified by the transition from the time milk was sold door-to-door daily (it was dipped from a 10-gallon can on a horse-drawn wagon and placed in the purchasers' own container) to today, when milk is sold in many different containers, even in flexible-plastic pouches, with at least 14 days shelf-life. Consider that in 1908 the first compulsory pasteurization law was introduced in Chicago for all milk not from tuberculin-tested cows. In 1914 tank trucks were first used to transport milk, with the first bulk farm tank replacing milk cans in 1938. The first homogenized milk was sold in 1919 and prior to that time it was illegal to use a homogenizer in manufacturing fluid milk. In 1932 the paper carton was intro-

TABLE 23-1

PER-CAPITA SALES OF FLUID MILK PRODUCTS[a]

Year	Whole Milk	Lowfat Milk	Skim Milk	Flavored Milk & Drinks	Buttermilk	Half & Half	Light Cream	Heavy Cream	Sour Cream & Dips	Eggnog	Yogurt
1975	168.0	53.2	11.5	9.7	4.7	2.4	0.4	0.6	1.6	0.4	2.0
1980	137.5	70.1	11.6	10.0	4.1	2.4	0.2	0.7	1.8	0.4	2.5
1985	116.7	83.3	12.6	9.7	4.4	3.0	0.4	1.0	2.3	0.5	4.0
1990	85.6	98.3	22.9	9.4	3.5	3.0	0.4	1.3	2.5	0.5	4.0
1991	82.7	99.7	23.9	9.5	3.4	3.1	0.3	1.3	2.6	0.4	4.2
1992	79.5	99.2	25.0	9.6	3.2	3.2	0.3	1.3	2.7	0.5	4.2
1993	75.8	96.7	26.9	9.6	3.0	3.2	0.4	1.4	2.7	0.4	4.4
1994	74.2	95.5	28.6	9.8	2.9	3.1	0.3	1.4	2.7	0.4	4.7
1995	71.8	92.7	32.0	10.0	2.8	3.2	0.4	1.6	2.9	0.4	5.2

[a]In pounds.

Source: Data from Milk Industry Foundation (1995).

duced to consumers, with the blow-molded plastic container appearing in 1964. About 1974 nutritional labeling of dairy foods was accepted. Finally, in 1988 lower-fat dairy foods gained considerable acceptance.

Data in Table 23-1 show consumption per capita over the last few years. There are some geographic variations, particularly with cultured products.

COMPOSITION OF MILK AND DAIRY FOODS

The nutritional value of milk is well known. The following affirms its nutritional quality (Table 23-2). In addition to high-quality protein, milk is an excellent source of calcium, vitamin B2, phosphorus, and vitamin B12. The milk protein, casein, representing about 80% of total protein, is the reference standard against which all other protein is compared. Whey protein has a Protein Efficiency Ratio (PER)[1] of 133 compared to casein with a PER of 100.

Milk is defined in the Code of Federal Regulations (CFR) as the normal lacteal secretion, practically free from colostrum, obtained by the complete milking of one or more healthy cows. It shall contain not less than 3.25% milkfat and 8.25% solids-not-fat. Addition of vitamin D is optional. Other milk and cream products are defined in the CFR Title 21, Section 131.

Milk Products

According to the CFR, pasteurized whole milk must contain 3.25% milkfat and 8.25% milk solids-not-fat. When the milkfat amount is reduced, the label will read: reduced-fat milk (2%), low-fat milk (1%), or fat-free milk (skim milk with <0.5% milkfat). Only the milkfat content is altered, not the milk solids-not-fat. If any of these milks are acidified or cultured, the level of acidity as lactic acid is not <0.5%. Lactose fermenting bacteria must be used to ferment milks labeled "cultured," but either bacteria or food grade acidulants may be used for "acidified" milks. Vitamin A at 2000 IU/quart must be added to reduced-fat, low-fat, and fat-free milks; however, vitamin A addition is optional in cultured and acidified milks. Vitamin D addition is optional in all milks, but if added shall be at the 400-IU level/quart.

In order to be labeled "cream" the minimum milkfat content must be 18%. In this category there is a light cream (18% milkfat), light whipping cream (30–36% milkfat), and heavy cream (36% milkfat). Sour cream is light cream cultured or acidified to at least 0.5% acidity expressed as lactic acid. "Half-and-half" is a mixture of milk and cream such

---

[1]PER is by definition the number of grams of body weight gain of an animal per unit of body protein consumed. Conventionally, this index is obtained by feeding laboratory rats the test protein as the sole source of protein in the diet.

TABLE 23-2

COMPOSITION OF BOVINE MILK

A. Gross Composition	(%)
Water	87.5
Milkfat	3.7
Protein	3.3
Lactose	4.8
Ash	0.7
Total Solids	12.5

B. Vitamins and Minerals	(per 100 grams)
Calcium	119 mg[a]
Magnesium	13 mg[a]
Phosphorus	93 mg[a]
Potassium	151 mg[a]
Sodium	49 mg[a]
Thiamin	.038 mg
Riboflavin	.161 mg[a]
Niacin	.084 mg
Pantothenic acid	.313 mg
Vitamin B6	.042 mg
Folacin	5 µg
Vitamin B12	.356 µg[a]
Vitamin A	138 IU

[a]An excellent source.

that the milkfat is between 10.5 and 18%. Also, this product may be cultured or acidified to 0.5% lactic acid.

Finally, yogurt is whole milk by definition fermented with typical yogurt bacteria, *Lactobacillus delbruekii* ssp. *bulgaricus* and *Streptococcus thermophilus*. Reduced-fat, low-fat, and no-fat yogurts must fit the corresponding milk definition.

Low-Fat and No-Fat Substitutes

The fat-reduction emphasis is prevalent in these products and represents misnomers. Two examples are typical of this category: low-fat sour cream and no-fat sour cream. Low-fat sour cream contains <6% milkfat or 1/3 of original milkfat. If there were a reduced-fat sour cream it would be classified as sour half-and-half. All other requirements for acidity, vitamins, optional ingredients, and methods of analysis are identical to those for sour cream.

Filled and Substitute Products

Filled products have milkfat replaced by vegetable fat; however, all other composition requirements are the same as for the milkfat-containing product.

Substitute products require a total replacement of all dairy ingredients. An example is "coffee whitener." An examination of an ingredient declaration will show that sodium caseinate, a casein derivative, is used. Caseinate is defined as a chemical and not a dairy-derived protein as cheese whey protein would be. Vegetable oil is added as the fat source.

Byproducts of Processing

Several dairy byproducts are in high demand in the food industry. For example, butter-milk is the byproduct from churning butter. It has a composition similar to skim milk except for a high concentration of phospholipids from the fat globule membrane. This byproduct, when dried, has high demand in cake mixes, pancake mixes, and ice cream formulations.

The cheese industry has sweet whey and acid whey as byproducts. Acid whey has limited uses in sherbet and frozen yogurt formulations. However, with pH adjustment and demineralization, a substitute for sodium caseinate can be manufactured. Sweet whey, a byproduct from Cheddar and Mozzarella manufacture, again has innumerable uses. It is spray-dried after concentration to "spray-dried sweet whey," and as such finds use in frozen desserts and as a filler in many proprietary food blends. If sweet whey is ul-trafiltered, a whey protein concentrate is generated that has the same general composition as nonfat dry milk (e.g., 35% protein, 55% lactose, 10% ash, and 4% moisture). With demineralization and lactose removal a high (90%) protein concentrate is produced. Again, this has many uses, particularly when a Protein Efficiency Ratio of 133 is considered. While about 50% of cheese whey in various forms is used, the remainder is used in animal feed, awaiting discovery of higher-priced human outlets.

MILK MICROBIOLOGY

Microorganisms found in milk are very important because they include potential pathogens which can make humans ill or even bring on death. These microorganisms include milk spoilage organisms, as well as beneficial organisms. Milk is a low-acid, perish-able food; therefore we should consider its microbiology very important.

What do these bacteria look like? They are either rods of about a micrometer (μm) in diameter and 2 to 5 μm in length, or cocci. Cocci are spheres and are about one μm in diameter. In addition, these milk bacteria may take stain in different ways and are called gram positive or gram negative, depending on this differential staining. A further classifi-cation of bacteria is psychrotrophic, mesophilic, and thermophilic. The psychrotrophic bacteria will reproduce at 7 °C. Thermophilics will reproduce at 55 °C. There is a further subclassification of thermophilics called thermodurics. These will survive a heat treat-ment but will not multiply at 55 °C. Mesophilics multiply in the midrange and are the largest category of bacteria.

Bacteria can be divided in other ways; for example, those that cause spoilage in foods, such as in milk. These are principally, as far as milk and dairy products are concerned, the psychrotrophic bacteria. They either cause proteolysis or lypolysis or ferment lactose to lactic acid. If they cause illness they are pathogens. A number of them are associated with diseases of cows and therefore find their way into the milk supply (e.g., *Listeria monocytogenes, Mycobacterium tuberculosis, Escherichia coli).*

The value of milk decreases with time due to microbial growth and enzymatic activity. This is a very important consideration, for the quicker the milk is processed from the raw state to a pasteurized state and gets to the consumer, the better the flavor of that milk will be. Delay allows time for bacterial growth and multiplication and this can cause off-flavors in milk.

Psychrotrophic bacteria are the principle bacteria that cause spoilage when milk is refrigerated. These bacteria produce enzymes as all bacteria do. The major problem with these enzymes is that they are heat resistant, and are unaffected by pasteurization and ultimately will trouble the manufacturer of products like butter and cheese, which are stored for many months. Also, off-flavors can be developed by these bacteria and these off-flavors are of innumerable varieties. However, populations in excess of $.5 \times 10^6$ are needed to generate enough flavor material so that it is perceptible by the consumer. Thus, psychrotrophic bacteria can cause off-flavor problems directly if the initial population is great enough and indirectly over a length of time in stored dairy foods that contain enough heat-tolerant enzyme.

Where do these bacteria come from? What are their sources? The first source might be the cow. Milk coming from a cow is usually sterile. The streak canal of the teat has many bacteria residing in it, the number and type of which depends upon where that cow has been during the time between milkings. Other contaminating bacteria can come from the skin of the animal. Most of these bacteria are harmless but many spoilage organisms and pathogens could be here. This is the principle reason why proper cleaning of the cow before milking is absolutely imperative. Milking equipment is the next possible source of bacteria to invade the milk supply. Bacteria can attach themselves to stainless steel as well as rubber parts of the milking equipment. This stresses the need for efficient cleaning as well as proper sanitizing of milking equipment before and during use. When raw milk is put into the bulk storage tank or when it is transported by truck, other bacteria may be in these two vessels if not properly cleaned and sanitized and will contaminate the milk. Flies are an important bacterial source and their omnipresence during the milking practice has to be controlled.

Types of Microorganisms Found in Milk

A number of bacteria find their way into raw milk. Pasteurization was initially developed by Louis Pasteur to remove tuberculosis (TB) organisms from the milk supply. TB in raw cows' milk has long been absent, but we review other pathogenic bacteria here because their presence signifies trouble in the milk supply.

Psychrotrophic bacteria are able to grow in milk at cold temperatures. They produce heat-stable enzymes, which subsequently can be troublesome in products such as cheese and butter that are stored for lengthy periods of time. Also, by producing bacterial populations in excess of $.5 \times 10^6$, off-flavors will develop as a result of their metabolic activity.

Lactic acid bacteria principally ferment lactose to lactic acid, causing "developed acidity," as it is termed. Lactic acid bacteria are either *Lactococcus* or *Lactobacillus* genera and can be beneficial in the production of all fermented dairy foods. However, their presence is undesirable when no fermentation is needed, such as in fluid milk.

Coliform bacteria are another group of microorganisms that are present in the gastrointestinal tract of all mammals. Thus, coliforms are found in and around cows as well as humans. Their presence in raw milk indicates a lack of cleanliness of the animal at milking time. The Pasteurized Milk Ordinance (PMO) gives the maximum bacterial populations allowed in the milk supply. Raw milk may contain not more than 100,000 microorganisms/ml per farm or per patron. When the milk from more than one farm is mixed or comingled then this number cannot exceed 300,000/ml. This population is termed an aerobic plate count or standard plate count. Pasteurized milk, however, must contain no more than 20,000 microorganisms/ml as an aerobic plate count within its shelf-life. Another pasteurized milk standard listed in the PMO is for coliform bacteria. Coliform bacteria in pasteurized milk are an index of contamination after pasteurization, because these bacteria do not survive pasteurization. No dairy product except for cheese may contain more than 10 coliform bacteria per gram or per milliliter of sample. Coliform bacteria are looked upon as an excellent sentinel for the quality of milk. While there is no federal or state standard for coliform bacteria in raw milk, their presence in pasteurized milk is indeed an excellent indicator of the quality of handling of that milk supply. One particularly troublesome type of coliform bacteria today is *E. coli* 0157:H7. It is found in about 2% of the raw milk supply and again is easily destroyed by pasteurization.

About 3% of all raw milk is contaminated with *Listeria monocytogenes*. It is a troublesome microorganism that is destroyed by pasteurization. However, it may invade somatic cells and gain added heat protection. When milk is in its raw state, numerous somatic cells are present. If *Listeria monocytogenes* is also present, these bacteria can and will invade the somatic cell and change the D-value of that milk from 1 second to 5 seconds. The D-value is the time to destroy 90% of the population at 72 °C. If this were the case, 1 in 1,000 organisms would survive a minimal, high-temperature, short-time pasteurization process of 72 °C for 15 seconds. This further emphasizes the need during processing for the discharge from a standardizer/clarifier to be directed into a floor drain so that no one will walk into it or through it, or transport it around the dairy plant.

Yersinia enterocolitica and *Campylobacter jejunii* are two pathogenic microorganisms that are often found in raw milk. These also can be eliminated by proper pasteurization. Another pathogen is *Salmonella*. About 5% of all raw milk contains *Salmonella* of one species or another. *Salmonellae* are very susceptible to heat treatment, and are thus destroyed by pasteurization.

To minimize pathogenic bacteria in the milk, that milk must have a low bacterial count, come from healthy cows, pass through and be stored in equipment that was properly cleaned and sanitized, and a Hazard Analysis Critical Control Points (HACCP) plan should be in daily use. Bacteria double their numbers at regular time intervals, depending upon the temperature at which they are living and the abundance of the food supply. In addition, bacteria grow in several phases that can be designated on a standard unimodal curve (Figure 23-1). There is a lag phase in which bacteria are struggling to gain or adapt

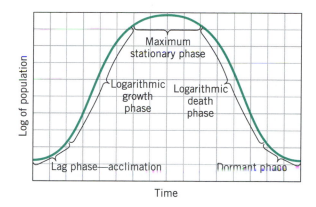

FIGURE 23-1

Typical bacterial growth curve.

to the environment. Next there is a logarithmic growth phase where numbers are increasing rapidly, resulting in an overpopulated medium where the curve plateaus. Eventually the curve declines, showing a log-death phase. Problems caused by bacteria can be innumerable. One such problem is off-flavor: bitter, fruity, rancid, sour, and unclean are typical of off-flavors developed.

The process of pasteurization, a time- and temperature-dependent thermal process, destroys microorganisms. Heat treatment inactivates the many enzymes present in bacterial cells, thereby destroying the bacteria. Pasteurization must destroy all of the pathogenic bacteria present, and in doing this, numerous other bacteria are also destroyed. Bacteria are destroyed according to their D-value (the time, in seconds, necessary to destroy 90% of their population). Obviously, the higher the bacteria numbers the longer the time to reduce the population to a satisfactory level. Some bacteria, termed thermoduric and thermophilic, may survive pasteurization. From a stored dairy product point of view, these are harmless bacteria since they usually do not grow unless there is thermal abuse of the finished dairy product. These heat-tolerant bacteria are nonpathogenic and present no problem; however, they may constitute part of the aerobic plate count.

Sources of Microorganisms

Microorganisms in pasteurized milk come from many sources. Some survive pasteurization (thermophilic bacteria and thermoduric bacteria). These are harmless and grow very slowly, if they grow at all in stored dairy products held below 7 °C. Pathogenic bacteria may be present on equipment surfaces and packaging material. Contaminated equipment used in fluid milk handling and processing must be cleaned and sanitized to prevent spread of the pathogens. The one piece of equipment in a fluid milk operation that is most difficult to clean appears to be the filler (that piece of equipment which fills the containers of fluid milk and other products). Compressed air, vacuum foam breakers, and the general air in the dairy plant are often excellent sources of bacteria. Finally, packaging material must be considered. While large numbers or even small numbers of bacteria on packaging material properly held in storage areas is uncommon, packaging supplies that are improperly stored or handled are probable sources of bacteria.

Storage Stability

Dairy product processors need to assess the shelf-life or storage stability of their products. A test on pasteurized milk to determine the adequacy of pasteurization is a chemical test for residual phosphatase enzyme. The destruction of the enzyme, alkaline phosphatase, in milk is used to determine pasteurization efficiency since its destruction closely parallels the pasteurization curve for destruction of *Mycobacterium tuberculosis*. A microbiological assay used to determine the numbers of coliform bacteria is highly desirable and can be completed in 18 hours of incubation. It serves as an indicator of the sanitary quality of the processing equipment. Freshly pasteurized milk should have no coliform bacteria. Presence of any coliform bacteria on day one is the basis for corrective action. However, absence of coliforms at best is a strong indicator of adequate pasteurization and proper handling. Several shelf-life prediction tests have been used. Bishop, Mosley, and the PI (preincubation) tests are all adequate. These tests are all described in *Standard Methods for the Examination of Dairy Products* (SMEDP; Marshall, 1992).

It may be necessary to determine the number of psychrotrophic organisms in a milk supply. This can be quite troublesome, in that the standard procedure for determining the population of psychrotrophic bacteria requires 10 days of incubation at 7 °C. To wait that long for a result is of little value because by then the milk analyzed would have been sold and consumed.

Several methods can be used to prevent recontamination. Obviously, thorough examination of the equipment used in the processing of milk is needed to determine if pitting, corrosion, or cracked stainless steel is present. Nonmetal parts on processing equipment, gaskets, O-rings, and plastic tubing need to be replaced at a regular interval (usually 3 or 6 months) depending upon where that nonstainless material, the gasket, or the plastic part is located. Hot contact surfaces usually require 3-month replacement and cold contact surfaces require 6-month replacement. All processors of dairy products must clean and sanitize all product contact surfaces between uses. This requires a solution with the correct cleaning chemical, at the correct concentration, at the right temperature, and for the appropriate length of time to get the surface clean. Regular examination of product contact surfaces for adequate cleaning and sanitation are mandatory. While formerly only product contact surfaces were cleaned; today, the requirements are increased. In addition to cleaning product contact surfaces, all non-product contact surfaces of equipment used in the plant must be cleaned: floors, walls, ceilings, and, in addition, the floor drains down to the trap. After proper cleaning, all of these surfaces are sanitized to destroy bacteria that survived.

This exemplifies the need for an adequate Hazard Analysis Critical Control Points (HACCP) plan in the dairy processing facility. That HACCP plan will spell out the frequency of inspection of equipment, and the frequency of cleaning and sanitizing walls, floor drains, and non-product contact surfaces. Both product and non-product contact surfaces can be swabbed to determine numbers of residual bacteria using the procedure shown in SMEDP. Product contact surfaces should have very few microorganisms, less than 10 per 50 cm². Non-product contact surfaces should have less than 100 organisms per 50 cm² depending upon the location of that non-product contact surface.

MILK PROCESSING

The first line of inspection for raw milk is the milk transport driver. In some states these truck drivers must be licensed because they are official samplers of raw milk. When arriving at the dairy farm the truck driver undertakes a series of steps to determine whether the milk supply to be picked up is of satisfactory quality. He also measures and records the volume in the tank, records the temperature, dates the receipt, and leaves a copy for the dairy farmer. Next he must agitate the contents of the tank mechanically for five minutes minimum, after which time he takes a legal sample. This sample is the official sample that is used as the basis of payment, for bacteria count, and for other tests that the dairy plant may wish to do. After all of these steps are completed, the milk is pumped from the bulk tank in the milk house to the tank truck. Depending upon the volume, the milk from one or many farms may be used to fill the truck. At the dairy plant the weight of the milk delivered is measured and the milk is sampled for antibiotic testing. No detectable antibiotics are allowed in the milk supply. Once passing the test, the milk is pumped into the plant through a metering device to measure volume, through a filter in-line to remove extraneous debris, and then into a horizontal or silo storage tank. Tests are performed on the sample of milk collected at the farm to determine its bacteriology and its fat, protein, lactose, and total solids content, usually with an infrared analyzer. Milk is generally priced on the basis of its fat and protein content. Other tests include freeze point and somatic cell numbers, which may influence the amount paid as premiums. Grade A raw milk may be stored no longer than 72 hours in the dairy plant. For manufacturing purposes the best raw milk is in the plant less than 24 hours before it is used.

In-Plant Processing

Milk is pumped from a storage tank through several essential pieces of equipment before it is packaged. First of all, the milk is pumped through a high-temperature short-time pasteurizer (HTST) (Figure 23-2). The first section where milk is preheated by hot pasteurized milk is the regenerator. This short residence time in the regenerator section warms the milk by heat transfer from the pasteurized milk on the opposite side of thin stainless steel plates. Thus it can be efficiently separated or standardized in a centrifugal separator, or standardizer-clarifier, located in the pasteurizer loop (Figure 23-3). The whole milk rises through holes located in a stack of the conical-shaped plates. Centrifugal force moves skim milk outward to the edge of the bowl because of its density. Skim milk fraction warmed to about 66 °C in the regenerator has a density of 1.036 whereas the milkfat has a density of .9. Thus the milkfat goes to the center and the skim milk portion goes to the outside. The debris that may be in milk, a minor amount of the protein, and somatic cells then become the sludge (separator bowl debris) that lines the outside

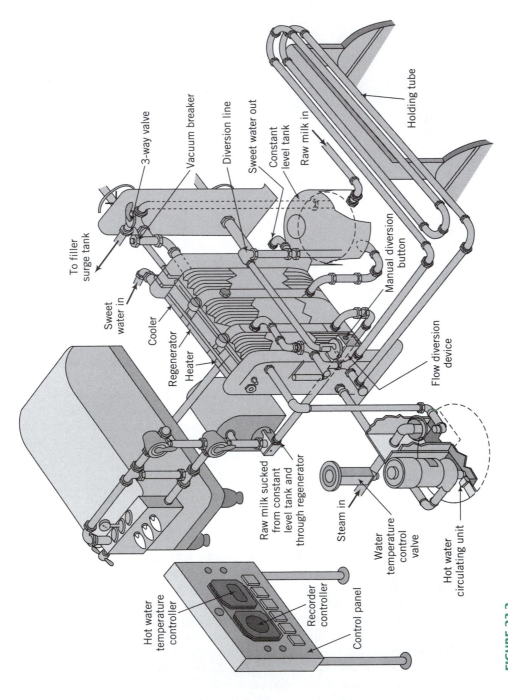

3-way valve

Vacuum breaker

Diversion line

Sweet water out

Constant level tank

Raw milk in

To filler surge tank

Sweet water in

Cooler

Regenerator

Heater

Manual diversion button

Flow diversion device

Holding tube

Raw milk sucked from constant level tank and through regenerator

Steam in

Water temperature control valve

Hot water circulating unit

Hot water temperature controller

Recorder controller

Control panel

FIGURE 23-2

HTST pasteurizer.

Source: Pasteurized Milk Ordinance.

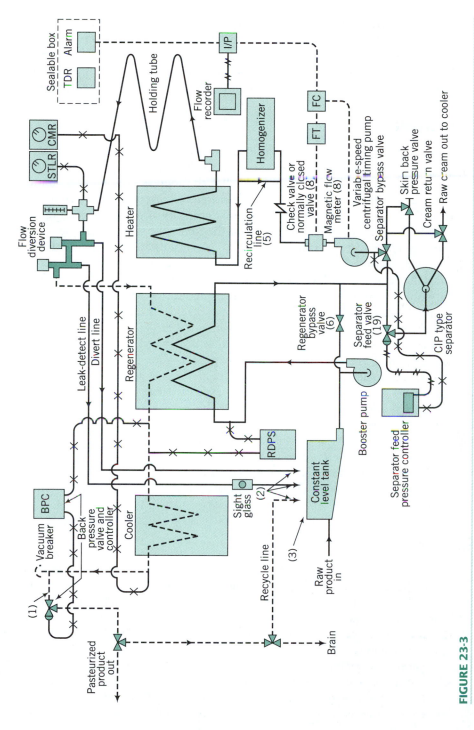

FIGURE 23-3

Separator in an HTST pasteurizer loop.

Source: Dairy Food Environ. Sanit., 12: 457 (1992).

perimeter of the bowl. With an automatic centrifuge, the bowl opens automatically at timed intervals to discharge the accumulated debris. This debris must be discharged to the floor drain (as indicated in the microbiology section since *Listeria monocytogenes* may be contained in this debris within the somatic cells). About 50% of the somatic cells are removed by this centrifugal action within the separator or standardizing clarifier.

Homogenization

Another piece of equipment within the pasteurizer arrangement is the homogenizer. In this equipment configuration (Figure 23-2) the homogenizer is located between the timing pump and the flow diversion valve. Not all products need homogenization, such as whipping cream and chocolate milk, so there is a bypass or recirculation line to allow their flow outside the homogenizer. This is necessary also because fluid milk processors do not synchronize the pumping rate of the timing pump with the homogenizer, thus some product will get rehomogenized. If the chocolate milk is stabilized with carrageenan, that product must not be homogenized because separation of the cocoa particles will occur. Also with whipping cream, if it is homogenized it will not whip. An intact fat globule membrane is necessary before cream can be whipped. When these products are produced the homogenizer is shut off and the flow is through the bypass.

Homogenization is the process of making a solution homogeneous. In order to do that with a milk product, the fat globules must be reduced in size so that they will not rise to the surface as in normal creaming by gravity. Going through the homogenization valves within the homogenizer, fat globules are broken apart and their surface area increases about six times. Homogenization makes the fat globule size much smaller. The normal nonhomogenized size of a milkfat globule is between 6 and 14 micrometers (μm). When properly homogenized 85% of the globules are in the 1-to-2-μm range. Using a light microscope to view these globules in a hanging drop slide, one can see globules as small as 1 μm. However, many smaller globules are present also. The Pasteurized Milk Ordinance (PMO) has a standard of identity for homogenized milk which defines it on a basis of <10% increase in the fat content in the top 100 ml of milk after quiescent standing for 48 hours.

Pasteurization

Pasteurization is the process of heating every particle of milk to a defined temperature for a fixed period of time as shown in Table 23-3. These are minimum times and temperatures with industry practices using higher temperatures and longer times. Since the pasteurization process is defined to heat every particle, foam must also be heated and will be discussed under vat pasteurization. Pasteurization must be done in properly designed and approved equipment (PMO).

Vat pasteurization (LTLT) is where milk is heated as a batch (Figure 23-4). The minimum time and temperature for milk is 63 °C and is held at that temperature for 30 minutes (Table 23-3). Also as part of the batch pasteurization system, a space heater is located above the surface of the product to assure pasteurization of the foam. This space heater is

TABLE 23-3

MINIMUM PASTEURIZATION TIMES AND TEMPERATURES

Milk Product	Vat or LTLT (Low temperature, long time)	HTST (High temperature, short time)	HHST (Higher heat, shorter time)	UHT (Ultra high temperature)
All fluid milks	63 °C (145 °F) for 30 min	72 °C (161 °F) for 15 sec	88 °C (191 °F) for 1 sec 90 °C (194 °F) for 0.5 sec 94 °C (201 °F) for 0.1 sec 96 °C (205 °F) for 0.05 sec 100 °C (212 °F) for 0.01 sec	138 °C (280 °F) for 2 sec
Any milk product with increased viscosity, added sugar, or milkfat at 10% or more	66 °C (150 °F) for 30 min	74 °C (166 °F) for 15 sec	same as above	same as above
Frozen dessert mixes and egg nog	68 °C (155 °F) for 30 min	79 °C (175 °F) for 25 sec or 82 °C (180 °F) for 15 sec	same as above	same as above

fed only with culinary grade steam. Because culinary grade steam is expensive to produce, many manufacturers simply raise the product temperature to comply with the requirement for the space temperature. Space temperature must be 3 °C above product temperature. If product temperature is increased so that the space above that product is 3 °C above minimum pasteurization temperature or 66 °C, then the legal requirement has been met.

Continuous pasteurization or HTST pasteurization requires a minimum heat treatment for milk of 72 °C for 15 seconds. This pasteurizer (Figure 23-2) (also called plate pasteurizer) is the system most frequently used in the United States.

Higher-heat shorter-time, and ultra-high-temperature (HHST and UHT) pasteurization can be accomplished in a plate pasteurizer or a tubular heat exchange unit. Some manufacturers use UHT processing to give increased shelf-life for their products.

Since a properly conducted pasteurization process is the key to public health, many controls are in place to guarantee this. Recorder controllers record the temperature as a function of time on a chart. Federal and state inspectors focus on its operation during inspections and validate its operation quarterly.

During the pasteurization process some milk is fortified with nonfat milk solids to boost consumer acceptability and also to increase its palatability. Usually 1 to 1 1/2% added milk solids are used. These solids, as a liquid slurry, are added to the milk supply as it is fed into the balance tank on the pasteurizer.

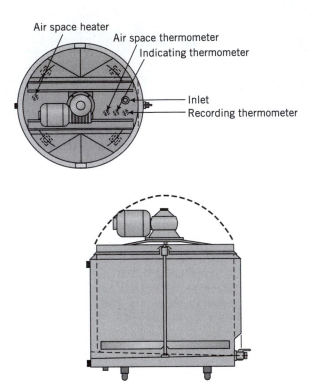

FIGURE 23-4

Batch pasteurizer.
Source: Pasteurized Milk Ordinance.

Vitamins A and D are required in low-fat, reduced-fat, and skim milks, whereas added vitamin D is optional for whole milk. Vitamin A and D concentrates to be supplemented are added to milk at pasteurization at some point in the pasteurizer loop. Some manufacturers continuously add vitamins at the balance tank or just before the homogenizer. Addition involves metering with a peristaltic pump so that the correct amount of vitamin solution is added to the milk supply as it travels past the injection point.

Pasteurized milk flows directly to the packaging equipment or is pumped to a pasteurized product storage tank to await packaging.

Packaging

Packaging of milk involves the possibility of many different types of containers. The least expensive container is a simple plastic pouch. These are finding greater and greater acceptance. The consumer must, however, have a pitcher designed specifically to hold the plastic pouch and must crimp the top when the bag is not in use.

Many dairies have blow-molding equipment in plant with which gallon jugs and half-gallon jugs are made on demand. Some of these jugs are pigmented to prevent the penetration of harmful radiation from the sun and from incandescent and fluorescent light, which diminishes the amount of some vitamins and alters milk flavor to give the classic off-flavor, sunlight oxidation. Paperboard containers are still used for much of our dairy products; however, plastic is less expensive and plastic pouches are even less expensive. Consequently, paperboard is being used less and less. Glass and returnable plastic containers are minor considerations today.

Once milk is packaged in its final container, these containers are cased either in cardboard or the standard wire or plastic dairy case. Containers are cased either manually or automatically and then the cases are stacked and may even be automatically conveyed to a refrigeration unit where product is held at 4 °C or less to protect flavor. Also, this refrigeration is necessary to give good shelf-life to the product. Distribution of the product to consumers is either directly from the refrigerated storage area at the dairy plant, or through distribution centers, which are now involved with more and more product. The demands of distribution center involvement are such that product must have excellent shelf-life and stability, otherwise there will be consumer rejection. Distribution centers increase the length of time required to get product to the consumer and as a result increase quality requirements.

PROCESSING OF CULTURED BYPRODUCTS

The manufacture of fermented dairy products is practiced by many fluid milk plants as well as those that specialize only in fermented products. These products are described in this section.

Buttermilk

Buttermilk can be made from skim milk, or partially skim milk (1% or 2%), or whole milk. The more fat in the product the less harsh is the acid generated from the lactose fermenting bacteria. Milk used for buttermilk production is pasteurized between 82 and 88 °C for 10–20 minutes, homogenized, cooled to 22 °C, and inoculated with active cultures of *Lactococcus lactis* ssp. *lactis* and *Lactococcus lactis* ssp. *cremoris*. These should be in a concentration ratio of 9 to 1. The latter organism provides the flavor generation while the former organism ferments lactose to lactic acid. A final titratable acidity of .8 to .85% is necessary to yield a desirable buttermilk with appropriate flavor, viscosity, and mouthfeel. When the vat of buttermilk is fully cultured, the milk is gently stirred to break the coagulum until it becomes homogeneous and then it is pumped to the filler. This pumping action must be gentle and without air incorporation, otherwise separation will occur in the finished product container. Most sections of the country use about 2 pounds of buttermilk per person per year; however, the consumers in Georgia double that consumption. This is not the product which is the byproduct of butter manufacture but it resulted from growth of natural contaminants in milk set out at room temperature to incubate. Today's technology and product safety preclude former manufacturing practices.

Yogurt

Yogurt has caught the public fancy and its consumption is still increasing. Yogurt is made from either skim milk or low-fat milk with 1 to $1\frac{1}{2}$% milkfat. Very little yogurt with a higher milk fat content is in the U.S. marketplace. Again, it is unfortunate that the low-fat craze has caught this product because even a 3 to 3.5 milkfat content will give a smoother mouthfeel and a less harsh acid bite. The nonfat dry milk fortification of yogurt depends upon the marketplace and ranges from 0 to about 4% added milk solids-not-fat (nonfat dry milk). Yogurt is stabilized with about 0.2% gelatin, pectin, or a starch-based additive. Yogurt milk, like buttermilk, requires an excessively high heat treatment (82–88 °C) for a long period of time (10–20 minutes) to completely denature the whey proteins. Denatured whey proteins absorb water and prevent or control syneresis (wheying off) which might occur as the product sits in the grocer's refrigerated display cabinet. There are two styles of yogurt made in the United States; one has fruit on the bottom and one has fruit mixed throughout the yogurt.

YOGURT WITH FRUIT ON THE BOTTOM. Milk containing any added solids-not-fat (dried skim milk) and stabilizer is pasteurized at 82 to 88 °C for 10 to 20 minutes, homogenized, and cooled to inoculation temperature of about 46 °C. An active culture of *Streptococcus thermophilis* and *Lactobacillus delbrueckeii* ssp. *bulgaricus* in a 1:1 ratio is added to develop the necessary acidity, flavor, and viscosity. The appropriate milk, with or without added solids, is pumped to a tank, temperature adjusted to 46 °C, and the culture is added. After sufficient mixing to assure that the culture is well distributed, the inoculated milk is pumped to the filler. A fruit mixture is added to the cup representing approximately 10 to 20% of the capacity of the cup and then the inoculated milk is added over the top of the fruit. A cap is placed on the container. Then the containers are boxed and placed in a hot room at 46 °C until the milk clots (approximately 6 hours). The pH at this time would be approximately 4.6. Containers with the clotted milk are quickly removed and placed in a cooler with forced air movement at 4 °C or less. When the product is cooled, it is ready for distribution and sale.

PRESTIRRED YOGURT. Prestirred yogurt is the product with the fruit stirred into the partially fermented milk base. Again, milk is pasteurized at 82 to 88 °C for 10 to 20 minutes with added solids-not-fat and stabilizer. The mixture is homogenized, cooled to 46 °C, and inoculated with the desired culture as mentioned above. However, the yogurt milk is allowed to ferment in the vat. When the titratable acidity has reached .85%, the product is cooled while stirring to 29 °C to slow the fermentation. At this time, the yogurt mix is pumped to a flavor tank where the appropriate fruit and flavoring material are added at the right percentage and blended. In pumping to the flavor tank, this yogurt milk may be passed through a wire maze valve. This valve will reduce any graininess or inconsistent texture to one that is smooth and homogeneous. The yogurt mixture has enough viscosity so that the fruit, when stirred in, will remain suspended. Next, the yogurt mix is pumped to the filler, and the cups are filled and placed in boxes and cooled. During the cooling, the stabilizer in this mixture, gelatin or starch, causes a reset of the yogurt.

Both kinds of yogurt are readily found in the marketplace. Currently, there appears to be a much higher use of starch as a stabilizing agent than gelatin or pectin. Use of other common stabilizers is not generally practiced because these do not function in low pH products.

Sour Cream and Others

Cultured dairy product also includes sour cream, sour half-and-half, and products containing lesser amounts of fat and even no fat. When sour cream is prepared it contains a minimum of 18% milkfat. In order for a dairy food to be labeled a "cream," it must contain 18% milkfat, minimum. Cream with 18% milkfat is pasteurized, again to a high temperature, 82 to 88 °C for 20 minutes. The product is cooled to an inoculation temperature of 22 °C whereupon an active culture of *Lactococcus lactis* ssp. *lactis* and *Lactococcus lactis* ssp. *cremoris* in a 9:1 ratio is added. This product can be fermented in a vat and then pumped to the filler or it can be "direct set" in the final container. Homogenization of this product at 2,000 + 500 or 2,500 pounds pressure, two-stage, is absolutely necessary to get the viscosity and smoothness in the finished product. About 0.2% vegetable gum stabilizer or starch is added to allow the appropriate viscosity to develop on culturing. Sour half-and-half and lesser-fat products require the blending of cream and whole milk or cream and skim milk and additional solids-not-fat to get the necessary body and texture in the finished product. When fat is removed solids-not-fat must replace it at about 1 pound per 2 pounds of fat removed. Vegetable gum stabilizers and starch or both are used to make these lesser-fat products acceptable to the consumer. The culturing technique is exactly the same as with sour cream. Cooling to 4 °C is required after these products reach a pH of 4.6 to 4.8.

OTHER PRODUCTS

Low-Lactose Milk

Low-lactose milk is produced by many dairy plants to compete for consumers in the milk beverage market who are lactose intolerant. These milks require the addition of β-galactosidase or lactase enzyme to milk. This enzyme, sold as a proprietary product, converts lactose to glucose and galactose. Thus those who have experienced lactose-intolerance problems in the past usually can consume this product without gastrointestinal distress. Some manufacturers direct lactose hydrolysis to a definitive end point, for example, 95% hydrolysis, then pasteurize to stop the hydrolysis. Others allow the β-galactosidase to remain active in the milk until there is no lactose remaining. Pasteurization of this product was before the addition of β-galactosidase enzyme.

Extended-Shelf-Life Products

There are a number of these products in the marketplace today. Manufacturers and buyers of milk together have defined a need for these products. For example, fast-food restaurants do not want frequent deliveries of fluid milk. They would prefer to get milk once a week or once every other week. In order to do this and have a milk product with no off-flavor, processors use UHT treatment. In other words, the milk is processed at a minimum temperature of 138 °C for 2 seconds. This equipment has been presterilized at 2 to 5 °C above minimum processing temperature. This milk product is filled into conventional 3-layered paperboard containers, plastic-paper-plastic. Shelf-life is approximately 45 days. The consumer may identify this product easily by two factors: it is refrigerated and the carton display panel shows the word "ultra-pasteurized."

Also, a minor amount of milk is processed so that it may be stored in containers that are unrefrigerated. While this style of milk is common in Europe, it is uncommon in the United States. This milk is given the ultra-high-temperature treatment of a minimum of 138 °C for 2 seconds in sterilized equipment. The sterilization process extends from the pasteurizer through the filling operation. The container used to hold the finished sterile product is a five-layered board: plastic, paper, plastic, aluminum foil, plastic. This paper board allows no oxygen to permeate to the finished product. The inner surface against the aluminum foil is sterilized with hydrogen peroxide which is dissipated with hot air before the milk is filled into the container. Fluid milk so processed has a minimum shelf-life of 90 days unrefrigerated. The consumer refrigerates the container before opening. Shelf-life is the usual two weeks after opening.

Half-and-Half

This product is manufactured mostly for coffee drinkers and a little for breakfast cereal needs. It is made to contain a minimum of 10.5% milkfat and 12.5% milk solids-not-fat. It is a high-fat milk, not a cream. To make this product blend cream, skim milk, and non-fat dry milk or condensed skim milk to bring the solids and milkfat to the appropriate level. This product is usually UHT processed and put into aseptically handled containers holding one-half ounce of finished product. Other containers, half-pint, pint, and quart, of conventional paper board makeup may be used for half-and-half. As with the extended-shelf-life milk, this milk product must be refrigerated.

Whipping Cream

In order for whipping cream to whip, the product cannot be homogenized. If this cream, containing a minimum of 30% milk fat, is pasteurized at 77 to 82 °C for 20 seconds and then cooled and packaged, it will whip successfully. However, many manufacturers prepare this finished product by giving it a UHT or HHST pasteurization treatment. When this is done the fat globules are broken during the heat treatment. As a consequence, the finished product will not whip unless the manufacturer adds about 0.1% glyceryl mono-stearate (GMS). The addition of this monoglyceride emulsifier coats the fat globules and allows whipping as if the product had been prepared at a lower heat treatment without homogenization. As with other UHT- or HHST-heated milk products, refrigeration is necessary.

DEFECTS

While the subject of defects in all dairy products should not be minimized, there are other resources that more fully and adequately define these defects, their causes, and prevention. This section will focus on commonly found defects and their control in the mentioned dairy products.

Flavor

A number of off-flavors plague dairy products. The principal off-flavor, light-induced oxidation, is caused by light: either fluorescent, incandescent, or sunlight. When the free amino acid, methionine, in the presence of riboflavin, the catalyst, is contacted by light at the appropriate wavelength, methional is principally generated among other off-flavors. Methional has a flavor threshold of 50 parts per billion in fluid milk. It has a flavor and odor resembling burnt hair, burnt chicken feathers, cabbagey, or somewhat skunky. This flavor can be commonly found in fluid milk and also in ice cream, cheese, butter, and cottage cheese. In fact, it can be found in any dairy product that is exposed to the sun, or incandescent or fluorescent light for a short period of time.

When milk or other dairy products are heated by conventional pasteurization, a slight cooked flavor is developed. This cooked flavor is undesirable at a more intense level and will resemble scalded milk in flavor and intensity.

Feed flavors in milk in most sections of the United States are contributed by alfalfa or corn silage but may come from such foods as cabbage, turnips, wild onion, and garlic. Such flavors in milk can be decreased in intensity or completely removed by vacuum treatment. Vacuum treatment requires direct steam injection to raise the temperature of milk to about 121 °C instantaneously whereupon the milk is flashed into a vacuum chamber and swirled down the wall to generate a near-monomolecular layer in the chamber. The higher the temperature, the thinner the milk film, and the more efficient the vacuum treatment on that milk.

Rancid flavor occasionally is found in the milk supply. This is primarily caused by freeze-thaw of milk on the bottom of the farm bulk tank and the use of high-speed centrifugal pumps to move milk. These physical abuses cause stripping away of the membrane surrounding the fat globule, which then allows lipase, native to milk, to attack and generate free fatty acids. The fatty acids in milk are of wide carbon number composition from C_4 to C_{22}. However, it is the fatty acids, C_4 through C_{10}, that give milkfat its characteristic flavor. This off-flavor is easily controlled by pasteurization to inactivate lipase and by reducing the physical forces that cause the fat globule membrane to be broken or stripped away in raw milk. If this rancidity is generated by heat-stable lipase from psychrotropic bacteria the onset of flavor will be delayed such that only products like stored butter and cheese will show the defect.

Most of the other off-flavors that can be found in milk supplies are of microbiological origin. These flavors are fruity, fermented, unclean, malty, and acid. As a consequence, these flavors can be controlled by keeping milk clean and cold in the raw state, pasteurizing to a temperature above minimum and holding for a time longer than minimum, then finally holding this pasteurized milk cold, <7 °C.

With good quality control, the flavor of all dairy products can be kept within a narrow spectrum of desirability.

Body and Texture

This is an attribute of fermented dairy foods, frozen desserts, and cheese. Only the fermented dairy foods yogurt and sour cream are considered. Quality of manufactured dairy products is easily controlled by the addition of vegetable gum stabilizers or starch where needed and when permitted, and by the use of a wire maze valve to minimize the grain or lumpiness of sour cream and yogurt. If the body is weak, additional stabilizer or additional milk solids are needed. If the body is too thick or too heavy, the amount of stabilizer or added solids-not-fat should be reduced. Too high or too low a homogenization pressure has a slight effect.

Appearance

YOGURT. In yogurt that has been mishandled, in which acidity has continued to develop, free whey will show on the surface. In extreme cases the clotted mass may shrink from the side walls of the container. The control measure is to shorten the shelf-life, minimize the heat damage because of improper storage conditions, and use a temperature for pasteurization where all whey proteins are denatured. This is required so that the whey proteins will bind as much water as possible and minimize the appearance of free whey. The appearance of some cultured products is not smooth, where tiny flecks of coagulated protein (called grain) show. This product must be passed through a wire maze valve to control the defect.

WHIPPING CREAM. A defect found primarily in whipping cream is "churned fat." If whipping cream after pasteurization is mishandled by high-speed pumps (3,500 rpm) or by malfunctioning pumps used to move that cream to the filter, partial churning of that cream may occur (the defect is called "cream plug").

COFFEE CREAM. The defect found in coffee cream is termed "feathering." When coffee is too hot, or when coffee has developed a large amount of caffeic acid, cream may feather. Feathering is when chunks of clotted cream rise to the surface or when a grayish flaky scum forms on the coffee surface. Feathering may also occur if acidity has developed in the cream or if the cream has a high bacteria count and is near spoilage or if it has been improperly homogenized or its salt balance is wrong. If calcium and magnesium are in higher concentration than phosphate and citrate, the product will feather in hot coffee. All manufacturers of half-and-half test their products to determine if they will feather. As a preventative measure most manufacturers add a minimum of 3 ounces of disodium phosphate or sodium citrate to half-and-half before pasteurization. The product must be correctly labeled to show the addition of this feathering preventative.

CLEANING AND SANITATION OF DAIRY PLANT SYSTEMS

The Pasteurized Milk Ordinance (PMO) states that all dairy product contact surfaces will be cleaned and sanitized between uses.

Automated Compared to Disassembly of Systems

The dairy industry has found that cleaning in place (CIP) is the most satisfactory cleaning procedure when performed correctly. Formerly all dairy equipment was disassembled daily, manually cleaned with relatively mild chemical cleaners, tepid water that one could put one's hands in, and a brush. Today, this has been replaced with CIP, where strong corrosive chemical solutions are used at relatively high temperatures, for example, 60 to 80 °C, at velocities of approximately 5 linear feet per second. Such systems are either pipeline circuits that are one piece welded with other pieces of equipment in between or pipelines that are sealed together with gaskets and clamps.

Two chemical types (alkaline and acid) are used for cleaning in CIP systems. The first is either alkaline cleaner or chlorinated alkaline cleaner. The base material of either of these is sodium hydroxide. It is the OH^- that supplies the cleaning power. Wetting agents, such as polyphosphates, may be added to efficiently wet the soil on the stainless steel or food product contact surface. Other additives such as chelators bind Ca^{++} and Mg^{++} so cleaning is not hindered. Chlorine may be added at a use level of 200 ppm to improve cleaning power. This chlorine does not function as a sanitizer, but only to improve the cleaning power. The pH at use dilution is approximately 11; thus chlorine will be inactive as a sanitizer. Alkaline cleaner is used to render two components of the milk system water soluble. These components are protein and milkfat. Protein is digested to make it more water soluble and milkfat is saponified to make it water soluble. The chemical concentration at use level is usually 0.5%, with higher concentrations used for tough cleaning problems.

The other chemical type that is used is acid. It is a 1:1 mixture of phosphoric and nitric acids. The purpose of this acid mixture is to remove minerals from the system being cleaned. Together with water rinses and the use of alkaline cleaner and the use of acid cleaner, the entire food contact surface can be freed of residual food materials. The temperature of cleaning is specified by the chemical supplier. This is in the range of 60 to 80 °C with the temperature measured at the end of the cleaning cycle. The cleaning time is usually up to 60 minutes.

In a normal CIP wash sequence, the first step is to rinse the surface free of residue as much as possible. The second step is to circulate chlorinated or conventional alkaline cleaner at 75 °C for 20 minutes, or longer. The third step is to drain the system, flush with hot water, then acid wash at 75 °C for 20 minutes or longer. The acid solution is drained from the system and hot water is used to rinse. The entire system is left to air dry until next used.

Different combinations of cleaners, different time sequences, and different temperatures may be needed to clean equipment that is particularly fouled with milk residue. For example, an evaporator may require 2% caustic soda for several hours with brushing to make sure that the tubes in that evaporator are clean. The technical representative from a cleaner company is a valuable resource.

Chemicals Needed to Sanitize

Chlorine as sodium hypochlorite has been the reference sanitizer for decades in destroying spores, bacteria, yeasts, and molds. Currently, it is under question from the U.S. Environmental Protection Agency and may be lost for use as a sanitizer in the food industry. In that case, sodium hypochlorite and perhaps dichloro- and trichloroisocyanurate and chlorine dioxide will be lost to the food industry. Chlorine as sodium hypochlorite is an outstanding sanitizer. Its use level is 100 to 200 ppm. The use pH should be between 6 and 7 for its most active state. At pH >7, chlorine has markedly reduced activity as a sanitizer and at a pH much below 6 it will produce chlorine gas. Chlorine has a negative side, in that it will corrode stainless steel. Thus the corrective action is to apply this sanitizer no longer than 20 minutes before product comes in contact with the surface.

A sanitizer commonly used in CIP systems is acid anionic sanitizer. It is usually phosphoric acid plus a wetting agent such as alkylbenzenesulfonate (ABS). At use dilution of 200 ppm of ABS, the pH is approximately 3.5. This is a very hostile environment for all bacteria that the sanitizer contacts. It is a very efficient sanitizer and it is broad spectrum but not quite as fast as chlorine.

The newest sanitizer in the dairy industry in the United States is peracetic acid, a mixture of acetic acid and hydrogen peroxide, a potent oxidizing system. The maximum use dilution is .35%. It is expensive, but is highly effective against psychrotrophic bacteria. Those who have used this as a sanitizer claim it is far more effective in destroying psychrotrophic bacteria than other sanitizers. Also, it is broad spectrum and quick to act. One major problem is its nauseating odor, which is troublesome in a closed environment.

A quaternary ammonia compound (quats) is an affective sanitizer, but it should not be used in the dairy industry on product contact surfaces. When used at the 200 ppm level, it is at its no-rinse dilution. At concentrations above this, one must rinse with potable water, which diminishes the efficiency of sanitizing, or with 200 ppm quats to bring the surface to a final concentration of 200 ppm. Quats has a great residual property. For this reason it was delisted some time ago and then brought back at the 200 ppm level. Because of the residual property, quats is valued as an environmental santizer. Many dairy plants use quats at 1000 ppm to sanitize walls, floors, ceilings, and floor drains. It is highly efficient against *Listeria monocytogenes*, but less effective against gram negative bacteria. *E. coli* and psychrotrophs will survive exposure to 200 ppm quats and cheese cultures will be slowed with 20 ppm quats. However, with the other sanitizers mentioned above, one should have no shortage of effective, efficient chemicals to destroy bacteria left on food product contact surfaces.

Hot water is also an effective sanitizer. Water at 80 °C requires a contact time of 5 minutes to effectively destroy bacteria, yeasts, and molds. This time and temperature requires that the entire contact surface be raised to 80 °C and held at that temperature for five minutes. This is particularly difficult if the equipment is not designed to allow the thermal expansion that comes as a result of using water at this temperature. However, it is more expensive to heat water to 80 °C compared to chemical costs. Also, water at 80 °C is a hazard.

OPERATING EFFICIENCIES

With today's demands for low-cost dairy foods, owners and operators of dairy plants have found that the need can be fulfilled by high-speed manufacturing of a limited number of products per plant. For example, one plant may make only Cheddar cheese. One plant may process only fluid milk. Another plant may make only frozen desserts. Because of greater efficiency and economy of scale, operating costs and production costs are minimized. As an end result, many fluid milk plants handle in excess of 1.5 million pounds of milk a day. Some cheese plants handle 2 to 6 million pounds of milk a day. Ultrafiltration plants near plants manufacturing cheese handle 4 to 5 million pounds of milk or whey a day. With well-trained, efficient operators and personnel, and appropriate equipment and plant layout, these plants are pacesetters.

IN-PLANT QUALITY AUDITS

The food industry, including the dairy industry, is coming into a new era of quality control. This phase of quality control will be driven by HACCP. HACCP is a proactive management tool that can provide the necessary safeguards and quality control to protect the consumer. Further, an HACCP plan in full effective operation will minimize the need for regulatory inspectors within the facility. The larger the facility, the more control is needed to assure no errors in daily production operation. While the operation itself may be quite simplistic, the necessary controls to guarantee day-to-day operating efficiency and control are mandatory. Like preventative maintenance throughout the system, quality control must be performed on a regular and routine basis.

SUMMARY

In the high-speed, efficient dairy processing industry only a few processors deviate from manufacture of a single product. Such is the handling of fluid milk from its raw state through pasteurization, standardization, vitamin fortification, and packaging. Discussion is given to show the efficiencies of pasteurization as well as the defects caused by surviving organisms and improper handling of raw and pasteurized milk. Cleaning and sanitation are legally required and must be effective to control bacterial survival and subsequent multiplication.

No coverage is given herein to other segments of the dairy processing industry. Specific treatises are published which cover these, such as *Ice Cream,* by R. T. Marshall and W. S. Arbuckle; *Cheese and Fermented Milk Foods,* by F. V. Kosikowski and V. V. Mistry; *Process Cheese,* by V. L. Zehren and D. D. Nusbarum, and *Concentrated and Dried Dairy Products,* by M. D. Caric.

GLOSSARY

D-Value A time at fixed temperature (e.g., 161 °F) needed to destroy 90% of a specific bacterial population. This is the time to decrease the population by one logarithm.

Demineralization A process of removing minerals either by ion exchange, manofiltration, or electrodyalysis.

HACCP (Hazard Analysis Critical Control Points) A proactive, voluntary (so far, for dairy) program which generates paper documentation to all quality control within a processing plant. Each processing point where a chemical, physical, or microbiological hazard exists is designated with control programs and assigned responsible leadership.

HTST pasteurizer A sectioned (usually 3) series of rippled, gasketed plates compressed together so that milk can flow through to reclaim thermal energy (regenerator) or be heated or cooled. Circulation of fluids is through gasket openings at the top and bottom of the plates.

Pasteurized Milk Ordinance A set of raw and pasteurized Grade A milk and dairy product recommendations prepared by FDA which form the basis of all state laws dealing with this subject.

Ultrafiltration A process of separating proteins from lactose and minerals using a pocysulfone membrane with 5–10,000 dalton exclusion because of pore size.

SELECTED REFERENCES

Bodyfelt, F. W., Tobias, J., and Trout, G. M. 1988. New York: Van Nostrand Reinhold.

Bylund, G. 1995. *Dairy Processing Handbook.* Lund, Sweden: Tetra Pak Processing Systems AB.

Code of Federal Regulations, Title 21, Parts 131–135. 1996. Washington, D.C.: Office of the Federal Register, National Archives and Records Administration.

Marshall, R. T. (ed.). 1992. *Standard Methods for the Examination of Dairy Products* (16th ed.). Washington, D.C.: American Public Health Assn.

Milk Industry Foundation. 1995. *Milk Facts.* Washington, D.C.: International Dairy Foods Assn.

USDA. 1976. *Composition of Foods, Dairy and Egg Products,* Ag. Handbook 8-1. Washington, D.C.: Supt. of Documents, U.S. Government Printing Office.

CHAPTER TWENTY-FOUR
POULTRY AND POULTRY PRODUCTS

ALAN SAMS
TEXAS A&M UNIVERSITY
COLLEGE STATION, TX

POULTRY MEAT
EGGS
LIQUID EGGS
SUMMARY

While the production of poultry and eggs for human consumption has been covered previously (Chapter 15), this chapter will be devoted to a discussion of the conversion of these birds and eggs into edible foods. Studies in this field are a complex combination of biology, chemistry, engineering, and economics. While human food is the main objective of poultry processing and products, related fields include waste management, nonfood uses, and pet and livestock feeds. The presentation of specific, numeric processing conditions is for guideline purposes only, and it should be remembered that different poultry processors will vary in their procedures.

POULTRY MEAT

Poultry Processing

INTRODUCTION. Commercial poultry is extremely uniform in appearance and composition. Tightly managed breeding, incubation, rearing, and nutritional regimens have

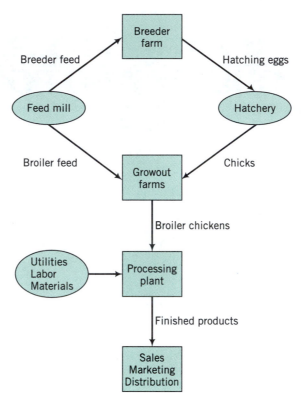

FIGURE 24-1

Components and material flow in a vertically integrated broiler company.

created a bird that is a virtual copy of its siblings. This uniformity has allowed poultry processing plants to develop into highly automated facilities with an efficiency that is unmatched by other livestock processors. With line speeds of 70 to 140 chickens/minute, uniformity, automation, and efficiency are recurring themes and have been keys to the success of poultry processing.

Poultry companies are vertically integrated. This is a system in which the same entity (e.g., company, cooperative, etc.) owns several (or all) steps of the production process from breeding through processing (Figure 24-1). This ensures maximum efficiency and uniformity. Except for some minor differences, broiler and turkey processing are quite similar. Because of this similarity and the fact that far more head and kilograms of broilers are produced annually in the United States, broiler processing will be the focus of this chapter and is diagrammed in Figure 24-2.

The poultry industry is rapidly becoming global. A growing percentage of the U.S. poultry industry revenues come from exports of poultry products, particularly the ones such as dark meat and feet that do not have strong markets in the United States. As a result, the industry in the United States has become keenly aware of the politics and eco-

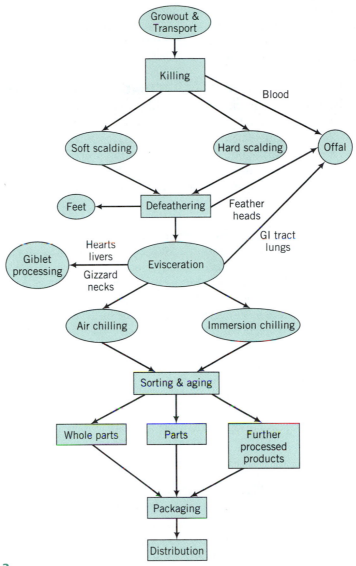

FIGURE 24-2

Steps and material flow through a broiler processing plant.

nomics of its major customer countries, the Russian Federation, Hong Kong/China, Japan, Canada, and Mexico. Although the United States is the world leader in poultry production, its industry is still concerned about conditions and any developments in poultry-producing nations with which it competes. Examples of important, competitive advantages in other producer countries include the large grain production in Brazil and the massive potential consumer market developing in China. In an effort to capitalize on some of the production and marketing advantages in various parts of the world, poultry companies based in the United States and other countries are establishing production operations in other regions of the world.

FEED WITHDRAWAL, CATCHING, AND TRANSPORTING. Chickens are grown on farms to a market weight of 1.5–2.5 kg live weight at 6–8 weeks of age, depending on the sex and intended use of the carcass. Feed is withdrawn from the birds 8–10 hours prior to slaughter to allow clearance of intestinal contents from the gut, which prevents fecal contamination of the carcass during processing. It is important that the birds continue to have full access to water to prevent dehydration and the associated loss in body weight and carcass yield. Excessive fasting can cause the accumulation of fluid and watery feces in the gut once it is empty. This would restore the potential for carcass contamination.

Following the feed-withdrawal period, the birds are caught by hand and placed in coops which are loaded on a truck for transport to the processing plant. Coops are manufactured as fixed stacks or as individual coops which are stacked during loading on a truck for the 1-to-3 hour ride to the processing plant. Once at the plant, most processors use mechanized unloaders which dump an entire stack of coops simultaneously onto a conveyor belt. The conveyor transports the birds into a room where they are hung by their feet on a shackle conveyor line to be slaughtered. A common problem with both manual and mechanized catching and unloading is inducing carcass defects such as bruising and broken bones. This problem can be minimized with proper training and supervision of personnel.

Bird transportation needs to be closely synchronized with the processing schedule to avoid excessive feed and water withdrawal that may occur if the birds are not processed as soon as possible after arriving at the plant. Scheduling considerations become even more important during hot weather when the weekly evaporative weight loss by birds can be extreme.

SLAUGHTER. Slaughter is the series of events involved in humanely killing the bird. The first step in humane slaughter is "stunning" to render the bird unconscious prior to killing. While hanging by their feet, the heads of the birds are dragged through a saline solution that is charged so that an electrical current of 10–40 mA flows for 7–12 sec through the bird to the shackle line which serves as the ground. A proper stun will produce 1–2 min of unconsciousness during which the legs are extended, the wings are tight against the body, and the neck is arched. In addition to humane slaughter, there are other benefits to be gained from proper stunning such as immobilization for improved killing machine efficiency, more complete blood loss, and better feather removal during picking. Inadequate stunning can result in carcass defects such as incomplete bleeding, while excessive stunning can cause broken clavicles (wishbones) and ruptured arteries.

Within seconds after stunning, the shackle conveyor moves the bird to the killing machine. The killing machine uses a rotating circular blade to cut the jugular veins in the neck of the bird. If the cut is too deep and the spinal nerve cord is cut, the resulting nervous stimulation "sets" the feathers and makes picking more difficult. Conversely, if the cut is too shallow there will be insufficient bleeding and the residual blood will cause engorged vessels and can discolor the skin. Once the neck has been cut, the bird is allowed to bleed for 2 to 3 minutes. During this period the bird loses about 30–50% of its blood, which eventually causes brain failure and death. If the blood loss is insufficient to cause death or if the neck cut is missed altogether, the bird may be still alive at the end of the bleeding period when it enters the scalder. In this case, the blood rushes to the skin surface in response to the scald water heat, imparting a bright-red color to the carcass.

SCALDING AND PICKING. Feathers are difficult to remove in their native condition due to their attachment in the follicles. To loosen them, the carcasses are submersed in a bath of hot water which serves to denature the protein structures holding the feathers in place. Two particular combinations of time and temperature have become industry norms and have quite different effects on the carcass. Scalding at 128 °F (53.35 °C) for 120 sec is called "soft scalding" and loosens the feathers without causing appreciable damage to the outer skin layers. Because it leaves the waxy, yellow-pigmented layer of the skin intact, soft scalding is the preferred scalding method for producing fresh poultry with a yellow skin exposed. If the skin will not be exposed or is not pigmented with carotenoids from the feed, the carcasses are usually scalded at 145–148 °F (62–64 °C) for 45 sec, a process called "hard scald." Because it loosens the outer skin layers, this is a harsher procedure than soft scalding. However, it allows easier feather removal than milder scalding conditions. Once loosened, the outer skin layer and its associated pigmentation is removed by the abrasion of the mechanical pickers. This is a major concern in poultry markets where the yellowness of chicken skin is desired by consumers. The loss of the waxy, outer skin layer may be beneficial for the processor whose product is destined to be coated and fried. Coatings generally adhere to the skin better in the absence of the waxy layer.

Picking machines consist of rows of rotating clusters of flexible, ribbed, rubber "fingers." While rotating rapidly, the fingers rub against the carcass and the abrasion pulls out the loosened feathers. By combining a series of these rotating clusters of fingers, each directed at a different region of the carcass, the whole carcass is picked. Picking machines adjusted too close to the bird may cause skin and bone damage while those machines that are too distant may not adequately remove the feathers.

EVISCERATION. Evisceration, the removal of inedible viscera, has become a coordinated series of highly automated operations. While the specifics of evisceration vary from plant to plant and from one equipment manufacturer to another, three basic objectives are accomplished: (1) the body cavity is opened by making a cut from the posterior tip of the breastbone to the cloaca (anus); (2) the viscera (primarily the gastrointestinal tract and associated organs, reproductive tract, heart, and lungs) are scooped out; and (3) the edible viscera or "giblets" (heart, liver, gizzard) are harvested from the extracted viscera, trimmed of adhering tissues, and washed with water. Although not technically part of the viscera, the feet (or "paws") have become a valuable product, primarily for export to cultures which use them for human food. The overall dependence of the evisceration process on machinery underscores the importance of machinery maintenance and adjustment for bird size. Poorly adjusted machines are frequent causes of torn skin, broken bones, and ruptured intestines with the resulting fecal contamination of the carcass.

INSPECTION AND GRADING. No discussion of poultry processing would be complete without a mention of inspection. Although this inspection process varies between countries, it generally involves inspection of: (1) the processing environment for sanitation, (2) both the exterior and interior of the carcass for freedom of disease, and (3) the packaging for accuracy of labels. While these objectives are maintained, the governmental and corporate inspection agencies and systems are dynamic and in a constant state of evolution to ensure the maximum degree of safety in the food supply. It will suffice here to say that in addition to constant monitoring of the carcasses being killed and eviscerated, corporate quality control and government inspectors sample the finished product (whole carcass, individual part, or fabricated products) on a regular basis (e.g., hourly) for compliance with existing regulations.

An emerging philosophy being incorporated into inspection/surveillance systems is the Hazard Analysis and Critical Control Point (HACCP) approach. In an HACCP system, inspection (through frequent and stringent sampling) is focused on those areas of production and processing either where the greatest risk (hazard) exists or where performance to some standard will essentially eliminate previous risks. An additional improvement in the inspection for wholesomeness (safety of the food) is the incorporation of microbial sampling into the inspection standards. This differs from the traditional visual examination, which is not a reliable indicator of the presence of harmful bacteria.

In addition to the required wholesomeness inspection, most processors also choose to have their fresh poultry products graded for uniformity and eating quality (broken bones, fleshing, discoloration, etc.) by federal government representatives. Some states and companies also have their own grading systems. Despite its voluntary nature, the virtual universality of grading by the poultry industry has made this reassuring marketing tool practically required for widespread product sale. Consumers will readily pay for the added assurance of quality and uniformity imparted by grading. This allows processors to recover the relatively small cost paid to have their product graded, making grading an effective means of adding value to their product.

CHILLING. The primary objective of chilling poultry is to reduce microbial growth to a level that will maximize both food safety and the time for marketing. Generally, a temperature of 4 °C or less is achieved as soon as possible after evisceration (1–2 hours postmortem). The two most common methods used for chilling poultry are immersion chilling, in which the product is placed in chilled (0–4 °C) water for about 45 minutes, and air chilling, in which the product is sprayed with water and then exposed to circulating chilled air (for about 90 min), which absorbs heat as it evaporates the water. While immersion chilling is used almost exclusively in the United States, air chilling is used almost exclusively in Europe.

To maximize both chilling rate and water uptake, immersion chillers are usually countercurrent flow, in which the carcasses and water flow in opposite directions. This system bathes the carcasses in water of an ever-decreasing temperature and increasing cleanliness. The amount of water uptake by each carcass usually approaches the governmentally regulated limit of from 6 to 12% of the pre-chill carcass weight, depending on the country and product. Because this water uptake is allowed to offset any drip loss that will occur during storage and shipping, the higher uptake limits are used for products packaged in drainable containers while the lower limits are used for products in sealed packaging. A frequent problem is that the actual amount of drip loss incurred varies with marketing practices (i.e., temperature, time, location) and results in inaccurate label weights with drainable containers. The added water from immersion chilling also adds to shipping costs and can interfere with the use of the product in further processing.

The two chilling systems have very different effects on the microbial quality of poultry carcass. The exposure to water flushes bacteria from the skin but the greater washing action achieved with immersion chilling results in a greater reduction in total bacterial load. However, the extensive bird-to-bird contact via the water results in more spreading of pathogenic bacteria to other carcasses in the community immersion chiller than occurs in an air chiller, where the carcasses are relatively isolated from each other. This cross-contamination results in immersion-chilled carcasses generally having a greater incidence rate of pathogen contamination than air-chilled carcasses, as determined by post-chilling inspection.

PACKAGING. By definition, all packaging systems for fresh poultry involve a container which protects the product from external contamination. The simplest form of packaging is to place the product in a cardboard or plastic box, fill the box with ice, cover the box, and store it below 4 °C. This "ice-packed" poultry has the problem that shelf-life is short (7 days) and drip losses can be excessive. A more prevalent packaging system involves placing the product on a styrofoam tray, wrapping the tray and product with a clear film, crust freezing the surface of the product in a blast freezer, and storing it at −2 °C. This "chill-packed" poultry has the advantages of a longer shelf-life (about 21 days) and less drip loss. A modified-atmosphere packaging system involves vacuum sealing the product in a plastic bag, injecting antibacterial gases into the sealed bag, placing the bag in a box, filling the box with dry ice snow, covering the box, and storing the product at −2 °C. Although this system is expensive, it has a very long shelf-life (about 28 days).

Poultry Meat Characteristics

CHEMICAL COMPOSITION AND PALATABILITY.
One of the main reasons poultry meat has enjoyed an increasing trend of consumption is because of its nutritional value, low fat content, and unsaturated fat type. Poultry meat is rich in high-quality protein and low in total fat and saturated fat (Table 24-1). Furthermore, because it is mainly associated with the skin, most poultry fat can be easily removed by removing the skin. In contrast, a greater proportion of the fat in red meats is found dispersed throughout the lean, making it harder to remove. While the composition of the cooked product varies with method of preparation, broiling and roasting are becoming more popular due to the lower fat content they yield.

Although currently being deemphasized in importance for the general consuming

TABLE 24-1

FAT, SATURATED FAT, AND CHOLESTEROL CONTENTS OF RAW POULTRY

Meat	Total Fat (%)	Saturated Fat (%)	Cholesterol (mg/100g)
Poultry[a] lean and skin	15.1	4.3	75
Poultry[a] lean only	3.1	0.8	70

[a]Composite of all retail broiler parts. Skin includes adhering fat.
Source: U.S. Department of Agriculture (1979).

public, cholesterol also is lower in poultry meat than other meat types. This is largely due to the ease of fat separation with poultry. In raw meat products, cholesterol is associated with fat so the higher fat content of a meat product translates into more cholesterol. It should be noted that there are very lean cuts of beef and pork being marketed. While these products sometimes suffer in palatability, their similar raw fat content also gives them a raw cholesterol content similar to that of skinless poultry meat.

Important differences exist in chemical composition between parts of a poultry carcass. Because broiler chickens are normally processed prior to the deposition of significant intramuscular fat (marbling), the majority of their body fat is outside of the muscles with much of it associated with the skin. This makes the fat easy to separate from the meat prior to preparation and has further improved the appeal of poultry meat. Another difference between tissues is the greater fat content of the dark (leg) meat compared to the light (breast) meat, making the dark meat juicier and more flavorful.

While all chickens are similar in most respects, differences exist in tenderness that greatly impact the ultimate use of the meat. Broiler chickens are hatched, grown, and processed by 7 weeks of age because their sole function is meat production. The chickens (hens) that are used for egg production are generally processed after their egg production abilities are exhausted (>1 yr of age). The meat from these older birds is much tougher than broiler meat because as an animal matures, the connective tissue holding the muscle together becomes very heat resistant and no longer breaks down easily during cooking. As a result, meat from these older birds is used in products receiving extreme heat treatments such as canned soups or stewing hens.

MICROBIOLOGICAL QUALITY. Increasing public concern about food safety has caused the poultry and other food industries to closely examine the microbiological quality of their products. While the loads of spoilage bacteria are generally an indication of general plant sanitation and marketing efficiency, pathogen incidence is also inherent to the production and slaughter of living animals for food. Depending on the pathogenic organism, the initial contamination usually comes either from the breeder (an infected hen lays an infected egg which hatches into an infected chick) or from the chick's environment. Sources of environmental contamination include previously infected birds in an inadequately sanitized house, rodents and exogenous birds carrying the organism, and feed containing inadequately cooked animal byproducts. An emerging concern is that the use of antibiotics in poultry feed to increase bird growth may also promote the development of bacteria that are resistant to the antibiotic. This would cause concern for human health because the antibiotic in question would be ineffective against the bacteria in question should that bacteria ever infect a human. One last source of contamination is by contact of a cooked product with an unclean surface (tabletop, utensil, raw product, or human). This type of contamination is generally prevented with controlled product flow in a plant and proper sanitation practices by workers and consumers.

Once present in a flock on the farm, the organism can spread by bird-to-bird contact. At the processing plant, the primary sites of spreading are the community bath environments of the scalder and the immersion chiller. Considerable spreading occurs in the plant with incidence rates rising approximately tenfold. It should be stressed that flocks and plants vary dramatically in their pathogen incidence and the types of bacteria present. Despite all the efforts to reduce contamination and spreading, it is not likely that pathogenic organisms will ever be completely eliminated from poultry production and slaughter. Therefore, methods of reducing bacteria on finished products have received much attention. In addition to a small collection of antibacterial chemical dips and sprays that are commercially available for use in processing plants, irradiation of raw or cooked products has proven quite effective in eliminating bacteria from poultry meats. Although irradiation has been approved for use on poultry in the United States, negative consumer perception of its safety has prevented its rapid adoption by the poultry industry.

Processed Poultry Meat Products

MARKETING CONCEPTS. The importance of food convenience and versatility has caused the poultry industry to shift from producing fresh, whole carcasses to marketing that carcass in the form of parts or highly processed, precooked products. Because the intangible property of convenience is added to the product during this "further processing," these products are called "value-added products." These products are profitable because consumers are not only willing to pay for the added production costs and convenience, but these products also are frequently made from relatively low-value parts of the carcass (e.g., leg meat). While the simplest form of further processing is cutting a carcass into parts, this topic is usually concerned with products undergoing more drastic changes in form, such as deboning, chopping, forming, coating, and cooking.

FORMED PRODUCTS. Formed products are products in which deboned meat is formed into some desirable shape and held there while being cooked to retain the shape. These products are of two general types: (1) those in which the meat is left as whole muscles or only cut into large pieces to retain the texture of intact muscle tissue, or (2) those in which the meat is finely chopped to the extent that it no longer resembles intact muscle tissue. Seasonings, skin and adhering fat, and water-holding binders such as salt or phosphates are usually added to the meat pieces prior to forming into the desired shape (e.g., loaf, patty, nugget). Loaves may have a browning glaze applied and are generally roasted or smoked. Whole-muscle patties may be grilled while formed patties and nuggets are generally coated with batter and/or breading and partially or completely cooked by frying.

EMULSIFIED PRODUCTS. Emulsified products are meat products in which the meat has been thoroughly chopped into a thick, pasty batter. During chopping, the muscle proteins coat (i.e., emulsify) the droplets of fat, preventing their coalescence and making them stable while dispersed in the surrounding aqueous environment. Curing agents and seasonings are other possible ingredients, depending on the product. The resulting batter is stuffed into a tubular casing which may then be divided into segments or links. Frankfurters and bologna are the most common examples of these products, which are generally cured, smoked, and cooked.

MECHANICALLY DEBONED POULTRY. Regardless of how efficiently a carcass is deboned, substantial meat remains on the skeleton such as between small bones. The relatively low meat:bone ratio, combined with the difficulty in harvesting this meat, makes these skeletal remains cheap byproducts of meat production. Mechanical deboners are machines designed to harvest this meat. Demeated skeletons (called "frames"), backs, and necks are coarsely ground and then forcefully squeezed against a sieve with pores approximately 0.05–0.1 cm in diameter. Soft tissue (mainly meat, fat, and bone marrow) is squeezed through the pores while hard tissue (mainly bone) is retained by the sieve. The pressure needed to separate the soft and hard tissues generates heat; which, when added to the unsaturated fat of poultry and the iron content of the marrow, makes mechanically deboned poultry (MDP) susceptible to lipid oxidation and rancidity. Therefore, MDP is usually used or frozen immediately after production. Its paste-like texture and highly functional protein make MDP useful as a binder in formed products and as the main ingredient in emulsified products.

EGGS

Structure and Composition

INTRODUCTION. The avian egg is a complex system whose primary purpose is reproduction. However, understanding the properties of the egg allow it to be used as a versatile and functional food source. It is important to make the distinction between "table eggs," which are infertile and produced by a specific type of chicken (a "layer"), and "hatching eggs," which are fertile and are produced by a different type of chicken (a "breeder"). Table eggs are used for human food while hatching eggs are incubated and hatched to produce chickens for the production of meat or more layer/breeders. The three main components of the eggs are the yolk, the albumen, and the shell. The egg's structure and composition are provided in Figure 24-3 and Table 24-2, respectively.

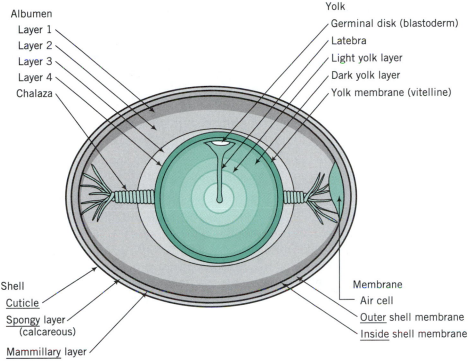

FIGURE 24-3

Components of a chicken egg.

YOLK. The yolk is essentially a bag of food material for the development of the embryo, if it were present. The yolk material is produced in concentric spheres and is contained within a flexible, porous membrane called the vitelline membrane. Because the yolk material is produced around the clock but the hen only eats carotenoid pigment–containing feed during the day, the yolk layers produced at night will be lighter than those produced during the day. The yolk material itself is a complex, highly structured mixture of fat, protein, and water (Table 24-2). The fat droplets are coated with a layer of protein which prevents their coalescence when dispersed in the water component of the yolk.

The yolk has a considerable amount of fat, a good energy source for any potential embryo. As with all animal fat, yolk fat contains cholesterol. The high cholesterol content of eggs has been a major limitation to their consumption. However, two recent factors have reduced this barrier. First, improved analytical methods have revealed that the cholesterol content of one large egg is 213 milligrams, down from the previously reported 260. Second, it is now thought that the type and amount of fat in the diet of most normal humans is more important to their health than the cholesterol content. In response

TABLE 24-2

COMPOSITION (%) OF THE EGG

	Egg Mass	Water	Protein	Fat	Carbohydrates	Minerals
Whole Egg	100	73.6	12.8	11.8	1	Tr
Yolk	31	47.5	17.4	33	Tr[a]	1
Albumen	58.5	88	11	Tr	Tr	Tr
Shell & Membranes	10.5	1.7	6.4	Tr	Tr	91.1

[a]Trace

Source: U.S. Department of Agriculture (1976).

to this second factor, some producers have fed the laying hens diets which contain fat types (such as those rich in omega-3 fatty acids from fish or algae) that are known to be beneficial to human health. Because she is a monogastric animal (has "one stomach"), the hen deposits these beneficial fats into the yolk, making the egg more healthy. Packaging these recommended fats in a more appealing food product (the egg) may increase their consumption by consumers who do not normally like to eat fish. The omega-3 egg is an example of a "designer food," a concept of using biological characteristics of an animal to improve the nutritional quality of the food it produces. Similar modifications of fat composition have been achieved in the meat of other monogastric animals like chickens and swine.

ALBUMEN. The albumen (or "white") of an egg is almost completely composed of protein in water (Table 24-2). These proteins have many specific functions, summarized in Table 24-3. These proteins are also largely responsible for the high nutritional quality of eggs, which are commonly used as the standard against which the nutritional quality of other foods is judged.

The albumen has four layers. When the hen forms the albumen around the yolk, she

TABLE 24-3

MAJOR PROTEINS IN EGG ALBUMEN

Protein	Amount of Albumen (%)	Functions
Ovalbumin	54	Foaming ability
Ovotransferrin	12	Binds metals to reduce bacterial growth
Ovomucoid	11	Inhibits bacterial proteases to limit their growth
Ovomucin	3.5	Foam stability
Lysozyme	3.4	Kills gram-positive bacteria
Ovoinhibitor	1.5	Inhibits bacterial proteases to limit their growth
Avidin	0.05	Binds biotin to reduce bacterial growth

Source: Adapted from Osuga and Feeney (1977) and Stadelmen and Cotterill (1986).

secretes only the thick albumen (layer 2 in Figure 24-3). As the yolk and surrounding albumen move down the oviduct, the albumen rotates around the yolk causing the ovomucin fibers surrounding the yolk to twist into a sling-like structure that suspends the yolk in the center of the egg. These twisted protein fibers are called the chalazae and form the chalaziferous layer (layer 4 in Figure 24-3). The water squeezed out during the twisting and the water that leaks out of the yolk both dilute the inner surface of the thick albumen and form the inner thin layer (layer 3 in Figure 24-3). Finally, water from the oviduct dilutes the outer surface of the thick albumen, forming the outer thin layer (layer 1 in Figure 24-3).

SHELL. The hen secretes a collagen layer, called the inner shell membrane, around the albumen during egg formation. The ovomucin fibers in the albumen attach to this membrane. She then forms another, similar membrane (the outer shell membrane) around the first one. To this outer membrane she secretes another organic layer (the mammilary layer) onto which she secretes calcium carbonate crystals (the spongy layer). The tightly packed, tall, columnar crystals have small pores between them that traverse the shell to allow gas exchange for the potential developing embryo. However, this gas exchange is also critical in the quality of the egg during storage. During laying (oviposition), she secretes a final protein layer (the cuticle) onto the shell surface to seal the pores against bacterial invasion and water loss. The shell and membranes are diagrammed in Figure 24-3.

Shell Egg Processing

QUALITY DETERIORATION. When an egg is laid, it exits the hen's body at about 40 °C (104 °F) into a much cooler chicken house or processing plant environment of about 30 °C (85 °F) or less. The cooling causes thermal contraction of the egg contents, which causes the liquid egg material to pull away from the inner surface of the shell. When this happens, a gap, called the air cell, is formed between the two cell membranes, usually at the large end of the egg. Once formed, the air cell enlarges as water vapor and carbon dioxide evaporate from the albumen through the shell pores. The size of the air cell is therefore proportional to the length of the storage of the egg, a relationship that is the basis for grading shell eggs. The quality grades assigned to eggs based on air cell size are indicated in Table 24-4. Methods of reducing air cell growth are to place a thin layer of food-grade oil over the pores to seal them or to keep the eggs in a cool, humid environ-

TABLE 24-4

AIR CELL SIZE RANGES FOR USDA GRADES OF INTERIOR EGG QUALITY

USDA Grade	Air Cell Size
AA	1/8-inch or less in depth
A	3/16-inch or less in depth
B	Over 3/16-inch in depth

TABLE 24-5

USDA WEIGHT CLASSES FOR CONSUMER GRADES FOR SHELL EGGS

Size or Weight Class	Minimum Net Weight Per Dozen (ounce)
Jumbo	30
Extra large	27
Large	24
Medium	21
Small	18
Peewee	15

ment. All these steps serve to reduce evaporation. Certainly, the quality grade of an egg can also be reduced by such defects as stained, dirty, or misshapen shells. Also, eggs are classified on size, using the categories in Table 24-5.

TABLE EGGS. To prepare table eggs for marketing, they must undergo a series of cleaning steps in addition to being graded and sorted. The eggs are first washed by spraying them with a detergent/sanitizing solution and scrubbing them with brushes. The eggs are rinsed with a water spray, which also may contain sanitizers. It is important to note that the wash solution should be slightly warmer than the eggs being washed. Likewise, the rinse water should be warmer than the egg and wash water. These temperature differences prevent the wash/rinse solution from being drawn into the egg through the cell pores by contraction of the egg contents if they were exposed to cooler temperatures. Another important point is that the washing process does not remove bacteria from inside the shell pore channel or the interior of the egg. Both of these can be significant sites of bacterial contamination.

Following washing and rinsing, the eggs are briefly dried and then candled. Candling is a process in which a bright light is passed through the egg to illuminate its contents. This reveals inclusions such as pieces of oviduct tissue ("meatspots"), drops of blood from a ruptured vessel during ovulation ("bloodspots"), or a cracked shell; all of which are rejectable defects. After candling, the eggs are oiled, packaged, and placed into a cooler to await distribution. Cooling should occur as rapidly as possible and it is important in preventing the growth of any possible pathogenic bacteria that might be present.

LIQUID EGGS

Although the majority of eggs (about 70%) in the United States are sold in the shell, a growing percentage (about 30%) are marketed in a liquid or other further processed form. The main reason for this is that many consumers view shell eggs as inconvenient. Liquid egg provides more convenience, versatility, and safety assurance since this material is usually pasteurized. Traditionally, excess table egg production was sent to plants called "breakers" where the liquid egg contents were separated from the shell and membranes. Now, the demand for liquid egg has increased to the point where eggs are being specifically produced for the breaker market.

The egg contents can be left in a mixture of natural proportions, blended to increase the yolk or albumen, or separated into just albumen or yolk. In commercial operations, this liquid egg material is almost always pasteurized (60 °C for 3.5 min.) to inactivate any pathogenic bacteria. Although safe to eat, this material still contains some other bacteria that make the liquid egg prone to rapid spoilage. For this reason, liquid egg is usually preserved by either drying or freezing.

Egg Products

GELATION. The most common use of eggs for human food is for their gelation property. Gelation is a chemical reaction that occurs when a protein solution is heated. The large protein structure unfolds and then forms strong, new bonds with neighboring protein molecules. In doing this, a strong network is formed that traps water inside. This network and water are responsible for the rubbery texture of a fried, scrambled, or hard-cooked egg. Also, one of the functions of egg in baked goods is to provide elasticity through the rubbery nature of their cooked gels.

SURFACE ACTIVITY. Compounds that have a part of their structure that is soluble in water and another part that is soluble in oil are said to be polar. Polar compounds can serve as emulsifiers by stabilizing mixtures of immiscible material such as oil and water or air and water. They do this by reducing the energy at the interface surface between these immiscible materials. These compounds are therefore said to have "surface activity." An example of this is the protein coat on the yolk fat droplets that prevents their coalescence. The yolk is particularly rich in these surface active compounds with phospholipids (fat-soluble lipids with water-soluble phosphates attached); these yolk compounds are used any time a stable, homogenous mixture of fat and water is desired (e.g., mayonnaise or chocolate).

The proteins of albumen are also good surface active agents, but for air-in-water mixtures ("foams"). The thickness, or viscosity, of the albumen as well as its ability to coat the air bubbles with protein both help to keep the trapped air bubbles stabilized. Foams are the basis for angel cakes and meringues. After the foam is formed by whipping air bubbles into the albumen, the foam is heated to gel the proteins and to set the shape of the product.

COLOR AND FLAVOR. Color and flavor are obviously two very distinct food characteristics. However, when eggs are used to contribute to these characteristics, they almost always go together. The laying hen consumes yellow pigments called carotenoids and deposits them in fat tissues of her body (including the yolk fat). These pigments give egg yolk its bright-yellow color, which is used to contribute the distinctive color of egg noodles, sponge cake, and custard desserts such as flan. The use of egg yolk as a colorant is so valuable that eggs destined for this use can have the carotenoid content of their yolks easily increased by modifying the hen's diet to contain more of the yellow pigments found in feedstuffs such as alfalfa or flower petals.

Flavor is one of the least-understood and -characterized aspects of food. However, most consumers would be able to identify an "eggy" flavor. The sulfur-containing compounds in egg are at least partially responsible for the unique flavor of eggs. Fortunately, in the products using egg yolk as a colorant, the egg flavor contribution is welcomed because that is the expected flavor of these products.

SUMMARY

The poultry meat industry is dynamic and rapidly growing. Through the concept of vertical integration, producers have also become processors. Additionally, because of a shrinking world and reduced trade barriers this industry is making the transition to a global one. This shift in marketing, combined with efforts to appeal to the ever-changing consumer demand and willingness to pay for convenience, variety, nutrition, and safety, will all keep the industry growing.

After decades of decline, the egg industry is showing signs of revitalization. This is partly because of the reduced concern about cholesterol and partly because of the increasing demand and production of convenience-oriented egg products. This and the strong role of eggs in the American culture give this industry a bright future too.

GLOSSARY

Albumen The "white" of an egg. It is comprised almost exclusively of protein and water and functions in foods in gelation and foaming.

Chickens Chickens are called Cornish hens, broilers (or fryers), roasters, and hens at 4, 6–8, 9–16, and 52+ weeks of age, respectively; the predominant commercial form is a broiler.

Eggs The reproductive package for birds and other animals. As a human food, they are a nutritious source of high-quality protein. They also are very useful in food processing by forming foams and gels.

Emulsion A stable mixture of two immiscible materials. An additional material such as a protein (an emulsifier) is needed at the interface to reduce the surface tension and stabilize the mixture. Ex-

amples are egg albumen foams (air-in-water) and meat frankfurters (oil-in-water).

Gelation The process of forming a rubbery gel by heating a protein (such as in meat or an egg) to rearrange its molecular structure into a strong network. Useful in binding food particles and in shaping foods.

HACCP Hazard Analysis and Critical Control Point is a quality assurance system which emphasizes the monitoring of specific critical or risky factors such as cooking temperature to prevent problems.

Poultry Any domesticated avian species used for food: chickens, turkeys, ducks, geese, quail, pigeons, and pheasant. Chickens are the only type of poultry with a significant commercial egg industry.

Scalding Technique of soaking a freshly killed bird in hot water to loosen the feathers for easier picking.

Stunning Process of rendering an animal unconscious prior to killing.

Surface activity The characteristic of a compound that reduces surface tension in an emulsion by being partially soluble in both immiscible materials (see emulsion).

Turkeys Commonly called fryers, roasters (or "young" hen/tom), and hens/toms at 9–16, 16–24, and 52+ weeks of age, respectively; the predominant commercial form is a roaster.

Value-added products Products which involve some form of additional processing beyond the whole ready-to-cook carcass. The consumer convenience imparted by the additional processing is an intangible asset for which consumers are willing to pay.

Viscera Gastrointestinal tract and associated organs, reproductive tract, heart, and lungs. Some viscera are edible by humans (heart, liver, gizzard).

Yolk The yellow center of an egg. It is composed of fat, protein, and water and functions in foods in gelation, emulsification, and coloring/flavor.

REFERENCES

Austic, R. E., and Nesheim, M. C. 1990. *Poultry Production* (13th ed.). Philadelphia, PA: Lea & Febiger.

Bailey, A. J., and Light, N. D. 1989. *Connective Tissue in Meat and Meat Products.* New York: Elsevier Applied Science.

Henrickson, R. L. 1978. *Meat, Poultry, and Seafood Technology.* Englewood Cliffs, NJ: Prentice-Hall.

Lawrie, R. 1979. *Meat Science* (3rd ed.). New York: Pergamon.

Mead, G. C. 1989. *Processing of Poultry.* New York: Elsevier Applied Science.

Mountney, G. J. 1976. *Poultry Products Technology* (2nd ed.). Binghamton, NY: Haworth.

North, M. O., and Bell, D. D. 1990. *Commercial Chicken Production Manual* (4th ed.). New York: Van Nostrand Reinhold.

Osuga, D. T., and Feeney, R. E. 1977. Egg proteins. In J. R. Whittaker and S. R. Tannenbaum (eds.), *Food Proteins.* Westport, CT: AVI.

Parkhurst, C. R., and Mountney, G. J. 1998. *Poultry Meat and Egg Production.* New York: Van Nostrand Reinhold.

Stadelman, W. J., and Cotterill, O. J. 1986. *Egg Science and Technology* (3rd ed.). Westport, CT: AVI.

Stadelman, W. J., Olson, V. M., Shemwell, G. A., Pasch, S. 1988. *Egg and Poultry Meat Processing.* Chichester, England: Ellis Horwood.

U.S. Department of Agriculture. 1976. *Composition of Foods: Dairy and Egg Products,* Handbook 8-1, Washington, D.C., 20402.

U.S. Department of Agriculture. 1979. *Composition of Foods: Poultry Products,* Handbook 8-5, Washington, D.C., 20402.

CHAPTER TWENTY-FIVE
AQUACULTURE PRODUCTS

R. T. LOVELL
AUBURN UNIVERSITY
AUBURN, AL

Several aquaculture species and product forms are becoming available to consumers. The most popular to U.S. consumers are shrimp, channel catfish, rainbow trout, and Atlantic salmon. Others are available in various world markets and will inevitably be offered to consumers in this country. Because of the variation in sources, morphological characteristics, and market forms, a general description of aquaculture products and processing procedures would be difficult to provide. Therefore, this chapter focuses on nutritional and other quality characteristics of aquaculture products, and presents a brief description of the market forms of shrimp, channel catfish, rainbow trout, and Atlantic salmon.

IMPORTANCE OF AQUACULTURE PRODUCTS

Shrimp from cultured sources presently account for 43% of the world supply. Ten years ago farm-raised shrimp made up only about 10% of the total shrimp harvest. Total production of farm-raised channel catfish in the United States has more than doubled in 10 years, increasing from 106,000 tons in 1986 to 230,000 tons in 1996. It presently ranks fourth in seafood consumed in the United States, behind canned tuna, shrimp, and fish cakes (cod and haddock). Because fish is considered a healthful food, primarily because of the low ratio of fat to muscle, it will gain in importance in the diet of American consumers. As the demand for fishery products increases, aquaculture will play a more important role in food production nationally and worldwide. Reasons why aquaculture will become a major source of fishery products are discussed in Chapter 19.

NUTRITIONAL VALUE OF FISH

The percentage of edible, lean tissue in fish is higher than that in beef, pork, or poultry because fish contain less bone, adipose tissue, and connective tissue. Table 25-1 compares the yield of lean edible tissue in the dressed carcass in different food animals. Using channel catfish as an example, 81% of the dressed carcass (less head, skin, and viscera) is edible muscle tissue and only 14% is waste, which consists primarily of bone with relatively little trim fat or connective tissue.

The caloric value of cultured fish is related to fat content and varies with species, size, diet, and season. For example, fillets from channel catfish ranging in live-weight size from 0.4 to 2.0 kg may vary in fat content from 6 to 10% (Li, 1991). Fillets from channel catfish harvested in fall (end of feeding period) contained 24% more fat than those harvested in spring (fasted over winter) (Nettleton et al., 1990), and fillets from channel cat-

TABLE 25-1

DRESSING PERCENTAGE AND CARCASS CHARACTERISTICS OF VARIOUS FOOD ANIMALS

Source of Flesh	Dressing Percentage[a]	Characteristic of Dressed Carcass		
		Refuse[b] (%)	Lean (%)	Fat (%)
Channel catfish	60	14	80	6
Beef	61	15	60	25
Pork[c]	72	21	54	25
Chicken	72	30	65	10

[a]The marketable percentage of the animal after slaughter.

[b]In fish, bones only; in beef and pork, bones, trim fat, and tendons; in poultry, bones only.

[c]Pork composition data reported in 1998 (USDA Food Composition Tables) revealed a reduction in average carcass fat content to about one-half of previously reported values.

Sources: Channel catfish, Lovell (1979); beef, Browning et al. (1988) and U.S. Department of Agriculture (1986); pork, Prince et al. (1987) and U.S. Department of Agriculture (1983); poultry, Moran (personal communication, 1989).

fish fed a high-energy diet (6% supplemental fat) contained 40% more fat than those fed a traditional catfish feed (Mohammed, 1989). Shrimp contain < 1% fat in the tail muscle because depot fat is stored in the hepatopancreas, which is in the head region. Tilapia, which are indigenous to the tropics, contain only 1 to 1.5% fat in the flesh, which is much less than freshwater fish from temperate regions such as catfish and carps. Cultured salmon at a marketable size of 5 kg may contain 20% or more of muscle fat. Thus, the caloric value of fish flesh will vary from less than 100 to over 200 kcal/100 g.

Protein percentage in fish flesh ranges from 14 to 18%, varying inversely with fat content. Essential amino acid content of fish muscle has a favorable profile for the human diet. It is relatively similar to that of muscle protein of other animal species; however, Lovell and Ammerman (1974) reported that the sulphur amino acid (methionine and cystine) content of channel catfish was lower than that of poultry, which coincides with a lower dietary requirement for these amino acids by channel catfish (2.3% of the dietary protein) as compared with poultry (3.3% of the protein) (National Research Council, 1993, 1995).

Fatty acid composition of fish varies with diet. Lipids from ocean-caught fish contain 15 to 27% omega-3 (n-3) highly unsaturated fatty acids (HUFA) (Bimbo, 1987). Cultured fish, such as salmonids, that are fed diets containing a high concentration of marine fish oil would also have relatively high amounts of n-3 HUFA in their lipids. Conversely, lipids of grain-fed freshwater fish like the channel catfish contain only about 2.5% n-3 HUFA (Nettleton et al., 1990). This difference is because n–3 HUFA comes primarily from marine algae and moves through the food chain to the fish, whereas grain-based catfish feeds are very limited in n-3 HUFA. Nettleton et al. (1990) reported that the average percentages of saturated, monounsaturated, and polyunsaturated fatty acids in farm-raised channel catfish were 24, 56, and 18, respectively, which compares with 32, 31, and 31 in menhaden fish oil (Bimbo, 1987). Most of the polyunsaturated fatty acids in farm-raised catfish is 18:2 n-6, while in marine fish oil it is n-3 HUFA (Nettleton et al., 1990).

The n-3 HUFA composition of fish flesh can be enhanced by feeding marine fish oil.

TABLE 25-2

FAT AND HIGHLY UNSATURATED FATTY ACID (HUFA) CONTENTS OF CULTURED CHANNEL CATFISH FED A PRACTICAL FEED SUPPLEMENTED WITH THREE CONCENTRATIONS OF MENHADEN FISH OIL, AND OF SEA-CAUGHT SALMON

| | Cultured Channel Catfish | | | | |
| | Control | Fish Oil Supplement | | | Sea-Caught |
Lipid	Feed	2%	4%	6%	Salmon
Total fat, g/100 g flesh	8.6	10.5	11.5	12.1	15
n-3 HUFAs, g/100 g lipid	3.0	5.7	8.4	10.1	15
n-6 HUFAs, g/100 g lipid	12.3	10.4	9.8	9.0	5
n-3/n-6 ratio	0.2	0.5	0.9	1.1	3

Source: Lovell and Mohammed (1989).

TABLE 25-3

VITAMIN AND MINERAL CONTENTS OF RAW FILLETS OF CULTURED CHANNEL CATFISH[a]

Vitamin	Content (mg/100 g)	Mineral	Content (mg/100 g)
Vitamin A	< 100 IU	Sodium	33
Vitamin E	< 1 IU	Potassium	315
Thiamin	0.34	Iron	0.34
Riboflavin	0.07	Copper	< 0.06
Niacin	2.3	Manganese	< 0.83
Vitamin B6	0.19	Chromium	< 1
Pantothenic acid	0.57	Selenium	0.013
Ascorbic acid	< 1	Calcium	7.1
		Phosphorus	1.84
		Magnesium	23
		Zinc	0.57

[a]Fish size was 0.45 to 0.68 kg. Values represent means of four collections made at different times during the year.
Source: Nettleton et al. (1990).

Channel catfish fed practical feeds supplemented with 0, 2 , 4, and 6% menhaden oil showed a marked increase in n-3 HUFA in the fillets as the amount of menhaden oil in the diet increased (Lovell and Mohammed, 1989) (Table 25-2). Adding 6% menhaden oil to catfish feed increased n-3 HUFA in the lipids to 67% of that of ocean salmon but greatly increased the total fat content. Sensory tests revealed that channel catfish fed 4% or more of menhaden oil had a "fishy" flavor, which was considered undesirable for the normally mild-flavored freshwater catfish.

Cultured fish are useful sources of several B vitamins, phosphorus, and trace minerals. Table 25-3 shows vitamin and mineral contents for farm-raised catfish. Fish flesh is low in calcium, vitamin C, and vitamins A and E. Table 25-4 shows typical caloric content and proximate and lipid composition of farm-raised channel catfish fillets.

PROCESSING AND MARKETING OF AQUACULTURE PRODUCTS

Most aquaculture animals enter the processing plant alive. This is because processing plants are generally in close proximity to the production source, and the animals are harvested alive and transported directly to the processing line.

Processing procedures vary considerably among aquaculture products. In the case of shrimp, the animals are beheaded and the tails are iced in a processing facility on the farm, then transported to another facility for further processing. Further processing of shrimp usually consists of freezing the tails in some form, such as cooked or raw, shell on or off, or various ready-to-eat products.

TABLE 25-4

PROXIMATE AND LIPID COMPOSITION OF CULTURED CHANNEL CATFISH FILLETS[a]

Item	g/100 g Raw Fillet
Calories	128.0
Protein	15.6
Water	76.4
Ash	1.0
Total lipid	6.9
Saturated fatty acids	1.51
Polyunsaturated fatty acids	1.22
Total n-3 fatty acids	0.16
Highly unsaturated n-3 fatty acids	0.10
Cholesterol	33.4

[a]Fish size was 0.45 to 0.68 kg. Values represent means of four collections made at different times during the year.

Source: Nettleton et al. (1990).

The main consumer products from catfish processing is fillets, where the yield is 36 to 40% of total fish weight. Next is whole, dressed fish, where the yield is 60 to 64%. Large fish (>1.5 kg) may be cut into vertical steaks. Over 80% of processed catfish products are marketed frozen while less than 20% are marketed in ice-pack.

Rainbow trout raised for food in the United States are harvested at a pan-size weight, between 250 and 450 g. The processing plant is usually near the production facility. The fish are gutted and frozen for marketing with heads and skin intact. Processing loss is 20% or less. Atlantic salmon are harvested at weights of 2.5 to 5 kg and can be processed into several market products. The fish may be gutted and frozen intact for further processing. It can also be filleted or cut vertically into steaks and frozen. Smoked salmon is a popular product worldwide. This involves soaking the fish in a light brine solution to enhance preservation, and holding in a smoking chamber with heat to cook and reduce moisture in the product.

QUALITY

Aquaculture provides opportunity for a high level of quality control over the processed fish. Time intervals between harvest and slaughter and between death of the animal and preservation of the processed product are relatively short. For example, rainbow trout and channel catfish enter the processing line alive and are slaughtered, chilled, and frozen within minutes. Farm-raised shrimp are removed alive from the ponds and ice-packed on the pond bank to immediately reduce temperature. At the pond-site the shrimp are beheaded, washed in chlorinated water, and iced again for transfer to a freezing plant. Time from harvest to freezing is less than 24 hours and temperature of the product is continuously low.

Cultured fish have not been recognized as major sources of microorganisms that cause foodborne illness, although, as in the case of other food animals, environmental contamination (feeds, water, personnel) could occur. Wyatt et al. (1979) found incidences of *Salmonella* in processed catfish but the source could not be ascertained. Byrd (1973) surveyed processed catfish from plants in the southern United States and found relatively low total surface bacteria counts (10^2 to $10^3/cm^2$) on the fish.

Aquaculture products, like seafoods, are not processed under mandatory inspection as are meat and poultry products. Like all food products processed or sold in this country, they are under FDA scrutiny. Processors of aquaculture products are subject to regulations of local and state health agencies for plant design and operation. Most aquaculture industries have their own HACCP programs and processing guidelines. For example, processed catfish products state on the label that they are processed under guidelines of the Catfish Institute, which is the industry marketing organization. Also, the National Marine Fisheries Service (U.S. Department of Commerce) provides a voluntary inspection service for processed seafoods and aquaculture products. Many buyers, especially for state and federal agencies, require a statement on the label that the product was processed and graded by the National Marine Fisheries Service. The processor pays for the service.

A serious quality problem in some aquaculture systems is off-flavors, which can be absorbed from the culture environment by the fish in freshwater or low salinity (< 3 ppt) seawater. Most notable is the musty, muddy flavor that is usually caused by geosmin (trans-1,10-dimethyl-trans-(9)-decanol) or MIB (2-methylisoborneol) (Lovell, 1983; Martin et al., 1987). These compounds are synthesized by species of blue-green algae and actinomycetes. Fish absorb these compounds through the food chain and directly from the water through the gills and skin. Sensory thresholds of geosmin and MIB in fish flesh are 8.4 and 0.8 ppb, respectively (Chan, 1989). Lelana (1988) found that sensorily detectable amounts of geosmin could concentrate in the flesh of channel catfish with 15 minutes exposure to 2.5 ppb of geosmin in the surrounding water (this concentration is often found in water when off-flavor occurs). Although the off-flavor culture ponds usually return to normal within several weeks, off-flavor is a serious inconvenience to the industry. There is no satisfactory control for the odorous compounds in the culture system; however, off-flavor can be purged from the fish relatively quickly by holding the fish in clean water for 3 to 7 days, depending upon temperature and flavor intensity (Lovell, 1983). There are no objective tests for off-flavor, so processors use trained personnel to taste the fish prior to processing. Environment-related off-flavor has been found worldwide with many species and under a variety of conditions, including warmwater, coldwater, and marine species. Lovell and Broce (1985) reported intense musty flavor and high geosmin concentration in cultured shrimp that occurred during a decrease in salinity in the shrimp ponds to < 3 ppt, which allowed geosmin-producing algae to grow.

Other than fish oils, commonly used feed ingredients have negligible effect on fish flavor. Johnson and Dupree (1990) evaluated a variety of commercial feed ingredients for effect on flavor of channel catfish. They added each ingredient singly to a purified diet and found that none had an important effect on the flavor of the fish.

Color of flesh is an important marketing attribute for many fish. Salmon must have a deep-pink color. In wild salmon this pigment is provided by the carotenoid, astaxanthin, that comes through the food chain from microcrustaceans in the marine environment. However, in culture systems a source of astaxanthin or canthaxanthin must be included in the diet. Interestingly, consumers object to any amount of pigment in light-fleshed fish, such as channel catfish. Dietary sources of xanthophylls (zeaxanthin and lutein), commonly found in yellow corn and corn gluten meal, cause objectionable concentrations of yellow color in catfish muscle. Lee (1987) found that the maximum concentration of xanthophylls in catfish feed that would not cause sensorially detectable yellow color was 11 mg/kg.

Aquaculture products have an advantage over many wild-caught fishery products in that they are produced and harvested under controlled conditions. This fact alone does not ensure quality, but does provide opportunity to monitor and control the environment from which the fish were harvested and the quality of the fish prior to final processing. Aquaculture products, as with all fishery products, are highly perishable and require the same high level of quality control to preserve quality and ensure safety.

FUTURE OF AQUACULTURE PRODUCTS

Aquaculture is one of the fastest-growing food-producing industries in the world today. It will continue to grow as an industry and to provide a higher percentage of the world's needs for fishery products. Reasons for this are increasing demand for fish worldwide, especially in the more developed countries; diminishing supplies and increasing costs of sea-caught fish; greater consistency in supply and quality of cultured fish; utilization of resources unsuitable for other types of food production; and attractive investment opportunities in aquaculture.

SUMMARY

The most popular aquaculture products available to U.S. consumers are marine shrimp, channel catfish, rainbow trout, and Atlantic salmon. These products vary in origin (freshwater, marine), nutrient composition (primarily lipids), quality characteristics (such as color), and market form. Compared with meat and poultry products, fish muscle has similar nutritional quality; however, the dressed fish carcass has less waste because of a smaller amount of bone, connective tissue, or trim fat. Compared with wild-caught fish, cultured fish have the advantage that they are produced and harvested under controlled conditions and they enter the processing scheme alive. Aquaculture will grow as an industry and provide a higher percentage of the world's fishery products.

GLOSSARY

Aquaculture   Culture of aquatic animals for productive or commercial purposes in a controlled environment.

Astaxanthin   A pigmented carotenoid that gives pink-to-red color to skin or flesh of fish, especially salmon. Natural source is micro- and macrocrustaceans.

Crawfish   Freshwater crayfish of the genus *Procambarus*.

Finfish   True fishes, as distinguished from crustaceans or mollusks.

Off-flavor   A foreign, undesirable flavor in fish. Of economic concern is a musty, muddy flavor sometimes found in intensively cultured fish in freshwater or low salinity seawater. Microorganisms growing in the culture environment are the source.

Omega-3 highly unsaturated fatty acids (HUFA) Fatty acids with three or more unsaturated bonds (double bonds between carbon atoms), one double bond being at the number-3 carbon from the terminal carbon in the fatty acid chain. Source is oil from marine fishes.

Pen culture   The process of culturing fish in net pens or cages suspended in the sea, lakes, rivers, or other large bodies of water.

Penaeid shrimp   Shrimp of the genus *Penaeus*, which includes most commercially cultured marine shrimp.

Pond culture   The process whereby young fish are stocked and fed to marketable size in earthen ponds that are constructed especially for the culture and harvest of a particular fish species.

Shellfish   Technically, crustaceans and mollusks; however, penaeid shrimp and, to a lesser extent, lobster and crayfish are the shellfish of commercial importance in the United States. Oyster harvesting is not considered aquaculture.

Tilapia   Tropical, freshwater fish of the genera *Tilapia* and *Oreochromis*.

REFERENCES

Bimbo, A. P. 1987. Marine oils. *J. Amer. Oil Chem. Soc.,* 64(5), 9 pp.

Browning, M. A., Huffman, D. L., Egbert, W. R., and Jones, W. R. 1988. Composition of beef. *Recip. Meat Conf.,* Chicago, Illinois, pp. 166–168.

Byrd, L. A. 1973. The microbiology of pond-raised catfish. Master's thesis, Auburn University, Alabama, 63 pp.

Chan, C. M. 1989. Taste threshold and consumer response to geosmin and 2-methylisoborneol in farm-raised channel catfish. Master's thesis, Auburn University, Alabama, 51 pp.

Johnson, P., and Dupree, H. K. 1990. Least-cost ingredients work well in catfish feeds. *Feedstuffs,* 62(54): 15–17.

Lee, P. 1987. Carotenoids in channel catfish. Ph.D. dissertation, Auburn University, Alabama, 74 pp.

Lelana, E. 1988. Geosmin and off-flavor in channel catfish. Ph.D. dissertation, Auburn University, Alabama. 73 pp.

Li, M. 1991. Response of channel catfish to various concentrations of dietary protein under satiate and restricted feeding regimes. Ph.D. dissertation, Auburn University, Alabama, 78 pp.

Lovell, R. T. 1979. Fish culture in the United States. *Science,* 206: 1368–1372.

Lovell, R. T. 1983. Off-flavor in pond-cultured channel catfish. *Wat. Sci. Tech.,* 15: 67–73.

Lovell, R. T., and Ammerman, G. R. 1974. Processing farm-raised catfish. *So. Coop. Ser. Bull.,* 193. 59 pp.

Lovell, R. T., and Broce, D. 1985. Cause of musty flavor in pond cultured shrimp. *Aquaculture,* 50: 169–174.

Lovell, R. T., and Mohammed, T. 1989. Content of

omega-3 fatty acids can be increased in farm-raised catfish. Highlights of *Agr. Res., Ala. Agric. Exp. Stat.,* 35: 16.

Martin, J. F., McCoym, C. P., Greenleaf, W., and Bennett, L. 1987. Analysis of 2-methylisoborneol in water, mud and channel catfish from commercial ponds in Mississippi. *Con. J. Fish. Aquat. Sci.,* 44: 909.

Mohammed, T. 1989. Effect of feeding menhaden oil on fatty acid composition and sensory qualities in channel catfish. Master's thesis, Auburn University, Alabama, 47 pp.

Moran, E. T., Jr. 1989. Personal communication. Poultry Sci. Dept., Auburn University, Alabama.

National Research Council. 1983. *Nutrient Requirements of Warmwater Fish and Shellfish.* Washington, D.C.: National Academy of Sciences.

National Research Council. 1993. *Nutrient Requirements of Fish.* Washington, D.C.: National Academy of Sciences.

National Research Council. 1995. *Nutrient Requirements of Poultry.* Washington, D.C.: National Academy of Sciences.

Nettleton, J. A., Allen, W. H., Jr., Klatt, L. V., Ratnayake, W. M. N., and Ackman, R. G. 1990. Nutrients and chemical residues in one-to-two-pound Mississippi farm-raised catfish. *J. Food Sci.* 55: 954–958.

Prince, T. J., Huffman, D. L., Brown, P. M., and Gillespe, I. R. 1987. Effects of ractopamine on growth and carcass composition of finishing pigs. *J. Am. Sci. Suppl.* 1, Vol. 65.

USDA. 1983. Composition of foods: Pork products. *Agric. Handbook,* No. 8-10, p.23.

USDA. 1986. Composition of foods. Pork products. *Agric. Handbook,* No. 8-13, p. 41.

Wyatt, L. E., Nickelson, R., and Vanderzart, C. 1979. Occurrence and control of Salmonella in freshwater catfish. *J. Food Sci.,* 44: 1067–1069.

CHAPTER TWENTY-SIX
WOOL, MOHAIR, AND OTHER ANIMAL FIBERS

D. E. HOGUE
CORNELL UNIVERSITY
ITHACA, NY

WOOL
MOHAIR
OTHER ANIMAL FIBERS
PELTS, SKINS, AND HIDES
SUMMARY

The worldwide production of wool, mohair, and other animal fibers, as well as hides, skins, and pelts, for use in clothing, carpets, tapestry, and industrial applications represents a significant contribution to society. Wool, mohair, alpaca, hair, feathers, and other fibers from a range of animals and birds and pelts from various animal species are used to improve the quality of life in diverse cultures everywhere. The production, characteristics, and uses of these animal products are briefly described in this chapter.

WOOL

The wonders of wool were vividly captured in a *National Geographic* article entitled Wool: Fabric of History (Hyde and Wolinsky, 1988). Hyde writes,

For 12,000 years, since man realized that with sheep he could roam and prosper on the windswept mountains and plains of southwest Asia, wool has been a civilizing force. Man almost certainly discovered the food value of sheep before wool, but when he began to fashion garments to protect his body from hot or freezing temperatures, he learned that sheep could be worth more alive than dead.

A symbiotic relationship developed—man protected sheep from predators, sheep provided man with food and clothing. Man, whose body is least suited of all the animals to live in inhospitable climates, has made use of the natural material ever since.

The fascinating history of wool and its use since ancient times is beautifully depicted in text (by Nina Hyde) and photography (by Cary Wolinsky) in *National Geographic* tradition.

Definition

Wool is generally considered to be the fleece obtained from sheep, normally by shearing the sheep at annual intervals. The broader definition, based on the Wool Products Labeling Act passed by the U.S. Government in 1939, defines wool as "the first fiber from the fleece of the sheep or lamb or hair of the Angora or Cashmere goat (and may include specialty animal fibers from the hair of the camel, alpaca, llama, and vicuna) which have never been reclaimed from any woven or felted wool product." The term *wool*, as used in this chapter, pertains only to the wool obtained from sheep. Fibers, pelts, hides, and skins from other animals are described in separate sections of this chapter.

Historical Perspective

Historians have provided evidence that wool fabrics were used as early as 10,000 to 20,000 years ago. Woolen clothing was worn by the Babylonians about 4,000 years ago. Babylonians, Egyptians, Greeks, and Hebrews spun and weaved wool fabrics in the home during ancient times.

The use of wool as a principal fiber for clothing and textiles was drastically changed with the invention of the cotton gin, which provided a major boost in the supply of cotton fabrics for clothing, tapestry, and other uses formerly dominated by woolen goods. In more recent times, synthetic fibers, including nylon and many plastics-based fabrics, have resulted in a gradual decrease in world demand for wool and a decline in wool production.

World production of wool reached an all-time high of 7.4 billion pounds in 1990. Since then, annual production has trended downward, due not only to competition from other natural and synthetic fibers, but also to drought conditions in some of the leading wool-producing areas of the world (e.g., Australia and New Zealand), and political changes in Eastern Europe and other regions.

World and U.S. Production

Major wool-producing countries are Australia (29% of world total), Russia, New Zealand, China, Argentina, Uruguay, United Kingdom, Pakistan, and South Africa. The

United States produced 77.3 million pounds of grease wool (weight before processing) in 1993, or 1.25% of the world total. Grease wool refers to that as shorn from the sheep; clean (scoured) wool refers to that resulting from a cleaning process to remove grease (lanolin) and foreign material. (Lanolin is the natural oil secreted by the sheep skin and deposited in the wool; clean wool represents about 60% of the weight of grease wool.)

The amount of wool produced annually in the United States is less than the total demand. For example, in 1995, 32 million pounds of clean wool were produced in the United States (27% of the total used), whereas 85 million pounds (73%) were imported. Of the total wool used, 91% was for apparel (worsted and woolen fabric) and 9% for carpets and rugs. Worsted wool is made from longer fibers and is combed so that garments wrinkle less than those made from other wool fabrics made from shorter, uncombed fibers (about half of garment wool is worsted and half is woolen fabric).

General Chemical and Physical Properties

The unique properties of wool make it well suited for both clothing and carpets. Wool fibers have minute overlapping scales or plates, all pointing in the same direction. These scales interlock into felt under moisture, heat, and pressure. The number of these scales in a wool fiber may be as large as 2,000 per inch. The surface of wool is water resistant and its interior is highly absorbant; it may absorb up to 30% of its weight without feeling wet to the touch. Compare this with 5% for synthetics and less than 10% for cotton. Wool absorbs perspiration and releases it slowly through evaporation. This makes one feel less chilled in winter and in summer gives an evaporative cooling effect. Air trapped between fibers gives wool its insulating property (light weight but great warmth). Part of the feeling of warmth is due to the fact that fewer fibers touch the skin than with other fibers, so less heat is conducted away from the skin. Wool is also fire and acid resistant; it requires a higher temperature to ignite than other natural fibers, and it burns more slowly. (In fact, a wool blanket smothers an out-of-control flame.) Wool is very elastic, which makes clothes wrinkle resistant. The wool fiber is highly crimped and absorbs noise and can be bent many more times without breaking than is the case with other natural fibers such as silk and rayon.

Types of Fibers

The general structure of the wool follicles and the three types of fiber are shown in Figure 26-1. Sheep skin contains two types of follicles, primary and secondary, and produces three types of fibers: true wool fibers, med fibers, and kemp fibers. True wool fibers can originate from both follicle types, whereas kemp and med fibers grow only in primary follicles. True wool fibers represent the products used in worsted and woolen goods. Med fibers (also called hair, gare, and heterotype fibers) are long and fine and lack crimp; they are not easily seen with the naked eye. Kemp fibers are short, coarse, and brittle. Kemp is undesirable as a component of the fleece of sheep raised for wool production, but is a desired component of the fleece of "carpet wool" breeds and is an essential constituent in the production of tweed fabrics.

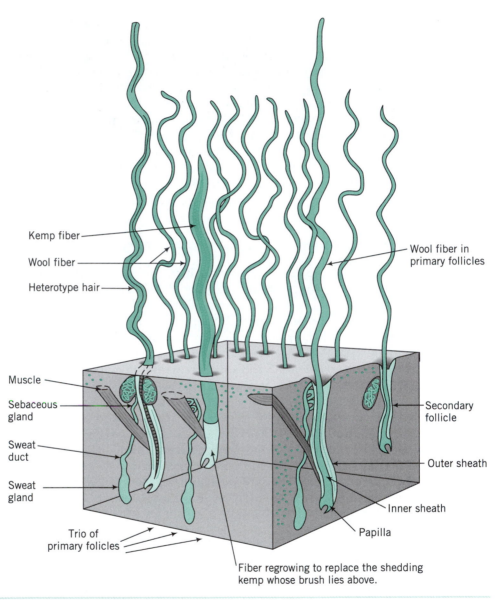

Kemp fiber

Wool fiber

Heterotype hair

Wool fiber in
primary follicles

Muscle

Sebaceous
gland

Sweat
duct

Sweat
gland

Secondary
follicle

Outer sheath

Inner sheath

Papilla

Trio of
primary folicles

Fiber regrowing to replace the shedding
kemp whose brush lies above.

FIGURE 26-1

Dimensional drawing showing a wool follicle group with the three types of fiber and the two types of follicles in the skin.

Source: Sheep Production Handbook, American Sheep Industry Assoc. (1997).

Fiber Growth

Wool and hair fibers have in common a thin outer layer (cuticle) surrounding the inner layers, the adjacent cortex, and the central core, the medulla (generally present mainly in medium and coarse wool breeds; medulla occupies more than half of the cross-sectional area of kemp fibers). The cuticle is covered by a thin outer membrane (epicuticle), which protects the wool fiber from damage and promotes the water-repellent property of wool. The cells within the cortex give wool its unique properties of durability, elasticity, and resiliency.

The wool fiber grows continuously by processes of cell proliferation and migration in the follicle. Figure 26-1 shows a drawing of a wool follicle group with the three types of fiber and the two types of follicles in the skin. A cross-sectional drawing of a medullated wool fiber is shown in Figure 26-2. The follicle consists of several zones, including: bulb zone (site of active cell division), keratogenous zone (protein synthesis, cell elongation, and final keratinization of the fiber), and sloughing zone (degraded sheath cells are sloughed into the fiber canal). The length of the wool fiber continues to increase as new cell growth and maturation proceeds in the follicle. The amount of wool produced in a year depends on the number of follicles on the body surface of the sheep and on the rate of growth of individual fibers. Fibers grow to a certain cross-sectional diameter (determined largely by genetics), but continue to grow in length indefinitely. Sheep are normally shorn yearly to produce fleeces with fiber length sufficient to meet demands of the woolen industry.

Fiber Elasticity

Wool fibers have important elasticity properties due to their unique chemical composition and arrangement of molecules (molecular spring) and to the specific cellular arrangement within the cortex, giving the fiber its characteristic crimp (tight curls or waves). The

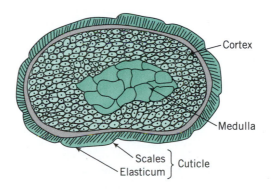

FIGURE 26-2

Cross-sectional representation of a medullated wool fiber.
Source: Sheep Production Handbook, American Sheep Industry Assoc. (1997).

Amino acids (the "building blocks" of wool)
Alanine, Rginine, Aspartic acid, Cystine, Glutamiic, Glycine,
Histidine, Hydroxylysine, Isoleucine, Leucine, Lysine,
Methionine, Phenylalanine, Serine, Threonine, Tryp-
tophan, Tyrosine, Valine.

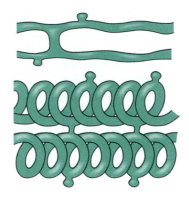

These are linked up in polypeptide chains.

Chains are arranged in spring-action fold, or coils.

FIGURE 26-3

The amino acids in wool.
Source: Sheep Production Handbook, American Sheep Industry Assoc. (1997).

protein of wool fiber is keratin, made up of 19 amino acids (Figure 26-3) and particularly rich in the sulfur-containing amino acid, cystine. The molecular chains of wool keratin take two forms, alpha (relaxed state of the molecule) and beta (stretched state).[1] There is no difference in chemical composition of the two forms; alpha keratin is unique to wool, beta is not. Beta keratin configuration returns to the alpha configuration (relaxed) when stress is removed from the wool fiber, in effect creating a molecular spring.

Fiber Strength

Wool fibers must be able to resist breakage when exposed to the rigors of processing. Tensile strength (measured in Newtons/kilotex) is generally divided into the following ranges

---

[1]Beta keratin is not to be confused with beta carotene. The former is a protein, the latter is a precursor of vitamin A.

of acceptable values: >30, increasingly sound as value increases; 20 to 30, part tender; 10 to 20, tender; <10, rotten. The tensile strength of various wools and hairs compared with that of human hair, expressed as a standard (100%), are: long wools, 80%; medium wools, 70%; Merino wools, 62%; mohair, 90%; camel hair, 90%.

Fiber strength is affected not only by genetics, but by nutrition, disease, and other environmental factors. These factors are discussed in a later section of this chapter.

Value-Determining Characteristics

As discussed in Chapter 18, the dual-purpose nature of sheep production (i.e., meat, or milk in some cultures, and wool), has an impact on the emphasis placed by the individual sheep producer on the breed of sheep and therefore on the type of wool produced. Nonetheless, the characteristics of wool that determine its market value are subject to the same considerations, regardless of the production setting. The major characteristics of the fleece that determine its value include those affecting the value of the individual wool fiber in addition to those affecting the value of the entire fleece or clip.

The first U.S. grade standards for wool, introduced in 1926, were based entirely on subjective, visual appraisal of fiber diameter. Revised grading standards were introduced by the United States Department of Agriculture (USDA) in 1966 and in later years through 1971, based on advancing technology in fiber sampling and objective measurements. The current USDA wool grades and specifications are shown in Table 26-1. The grading system is based on the "spinning count." The USDA grade number refers to the

TABLE 26-1

USDA WOOL GRADES AND SPECIFICATIONS

USDA Grade		Average Fiber Diameter (microns)	Blood System Grade	Breeds Corresponding to Approximate Wool Grades
Finer than	80	18.1 or less	Fine	Merino
	80	18.1–19..59	"	"
	70	19.6–21.09	"	"
	64	21.1–22.59	"	Rambouillet
	62	22.6–24.09	$\frac{1}{2}$ blood	Targhee
	60	24.1–25.59	"	Southdown
	58	25.6–27.09	$\frac{3}{8}$ blood	Montadale, Shropshire,
	56	27.1–28.59	"	Corriedale, Hampshire, Columbia, Panama
	54	28.6–30.09	$\frac{1}{4}$ blood	Dorset, Suffolk, Cheviot,
	50	30.1–31.79	"	Oxford
	48	31.8–33.49	"	
	46	33.5–35.19	Low $\frac{1}{4}$ blood	Romney, Leicester
	44	35.2–37.09	Common	Cotswold
	40	37.1–38.99	Braid	Lincoln
	36	39.0–41.29	"	
Coarser than	36	41.3 and up	"	

Source: USDA Market. Bull., 53 (1971); American Sheep Industry Assoc. (1996).

hanks (one hank = 560 yards of yarn) of yarn that can be woven from one pound of clean wool. The older "blood system" of grading, based on the approximate fiber diameter typical of breeds and their crosses with fine wool, medium wool, and coarse wool, has gradually been replaced by the use of average fiber diameter in microns. The micron designation is the preferred and prevalent system. Both systems of specification are shown in Table 26-1, along with breeds typical of each category.

Characteristics that Affect the Value of the Individual Fiber

DENSITY. Density refers to the number of fibers per unit area of the skin surface. The number of wool fibers per fleece varies from about 16 million in some animals of medium and coarse wool breeds to about 120 million in some fine wool sheep. The main factors affecting the value of wool fibers are diameter, length, strength, and color.

FIBER DIAMETER. Fiber diameter varies from about 18 microns (μm) in fine wool breeds to 40 or more in some coarse wool breeds. Fiber diameter has a major effect on wool quality and value. Coarse fibers (large diameter) decrease price. In carding and combing, increased fiber diameter increases breakage and is associated with increased fabric harshness, rigidity, and abrasion resistance.

FIBER OR STAPLE LENGTH. Fiber or staple length refers to the average fiber length in a shorn fleece. Fiber length varies in different body areas, longer on body than on head. Long fibers are desirable and generally range from one to three inches, depending on interval since the animal was last shorn, breed, nutrition, and other environmental variables. Several special terms which are related to fiber length and fineness are used by the wool processing industry. Carpet wool can be of any fiber length, but is too coarse to be used for other purposes. Clothing wool is too short to be processed with specialized combing machinery and its use is therefore limited to tweeds and other similar clothing products. Combing wool is sufficiently long to be used in combing machines which sort and straighten the fibers for worsted yarn used for high-quality cloth. French combing wool is similar to combing wool, but requires special combing machines due to its shorter fiber length. The relationship between fiber length and diameter in determining into which of the above categories a given wool sample will fall is shown in Figure 26-4.

FIBER OR STAPLE STRENGTH/POSITION OF BREAK. Fiber growth is a continuous process. It can be interrupted by acute illness caused by infectious agents or by sudden nutritional insults, resulting in a weak point in the fiber corresponding to the time of the interrupted fiber growth. This weak point, like a defective link in a chain, results in a break in the fiber at that point when the wool is processed for yarn manufacture. Thus, fleeces from sheep whose wool growth has been interrupted in this way are reduced in value. If sick animals are shorn immediately after recovery from an illness that has resulted in interrupted wool growth, the position of the break in the fiber will be near the skin, so that the loss in fleece value will be minimized. New wool growth will proceed

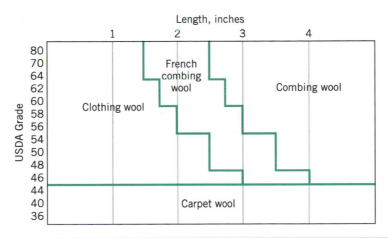

FIGURE 26-4

Length designations often used for wool, according to fineness.
Source: USDA.

normally so that the fleece removed at the subsequent shearing will be normal. In some areas of the world, annual abrupt changes in climate and feed supply cause a predictable break in fleeces. Producers shear at that time and refer to it as "shearing on the break."

COLOR. Wool from most sheep produced for wool is composed of almost all white fibers. However, some breeds of sheep, such as the Barbados Blackbelly, Black Welsh Mountain, California Red, Karakul, Navajo-Churro, and Shetland, produce colored wool or hair (see Chapter 18). Most sheep grown for wool produce white fleeces and the world market is based largely on white wool. The presence of black or dark fibers in a white fleece detracts from its value. Therefore, sheep producers generally select breeding stock relatively free of dark fibers in the wool. The natural color of wool fibers cannot be removed by processing. Therefore, wool from colored breeds has a market niche of its own, based on consumer preference for colored breeds, as in the case of the Karakul. Yarn is often treated with color-fast dyes to produce woolen garments and other woolen goods in an array of colors.

Characteristics that Affect the Value of the Entire Fleece or Clip

YIELD. Value of a fleece of a given grade is based on the yield of clean wool. Yield of clean wool is expressed as a percentage of clean wool fibers present (CWFP) in a grease wool sample. By definition (American Sheep Industry Association, 1997,) CWFP is the weight of the wool base present in the grease wool, adjusted to a moisture content of 12%, an alcohol-extractives content of 1.5%, and a mineral matter content of 0.5%. Wool base is bone-dry, extractives-free, wool fibers. Prices paid to producers for grease wool are dependent on yield. Often this value is subjectively assessed by the wool buyer. However, there is an increasing trend for this important characteristic to be objectively measured at a commercial testing laboratory. Objective measurement of yield reduces the producer's risk in marketing wool. The yield of clean wool averages about 60%, but breed differences exist, providing an incentive for genetic selection for high wool yield (yield is the opposite of shrink).

CONTAMINATION. Grease wool is often contaminated with a variety of foreign materials including animal manure, vegetable matter, plastics, and other materials. Each contaminant must be removed during processing into clean wool. Pricing of a fleece is based on clean wool yield, so it is in the interest of the producer to minimize sources of contamination.

Animal matter—The natural secretions from the skin (yolk or lanolin and sweat or suint) are inherent to wool production and represent the major portion of the animal matter fraction. Urine and feces (dung) may contribute a significant amount of contamination, depending on the production setting and environment. Sheep housed in confinement with inadequate bedding may accumulate large amounts of dung (referred to as tags) in the wool. Feces and urine stain the fleece, increasing the cost of cleaning the wool.

Vegetable matter—Straw, burrs, seeds, hay, and other debris from pasture or feedlots are easily entrapped by the fleece (removed by carbonizing).

Mineral matter—Dust, sand, dirt, and mud may contaminate the fleece to varying degrees, depending on the climate and management system.

Plastics—Polypropylene and other plastics are often used to manufacture string for tying hay bales and for other farm uses. Broken or fragmented string often clings to the wool and must be removed during cleaning.

Applied contaminants—Sprays, marking chalk, branding fluid, ointments, various parasite-drenching liquids, copper sulfate solutions used for treating foot rot, and other materials applied to the animal during the year may adhere to the fleece and must be removed, or permanently stained portions of the fleece discarded, during wool processing.

Marketing

Major factors in determining wool price are average fiber diameter and length of fibers in a given quantity of wool. Conventional methods of pricing, based on visual estimates of fineness, length, and other quality factors, are gradually being replaced by more objective measurements of quality. For example, core samples removed from bales of wool may be subjected to measurement of average fiber diameter and its distribution in the sample using an instrument consisting of a projection microscope equipped to measure individual fibers. Electrooptical laser instrumentation and other new techniques are in developmental stages. Other important factors are uniformity of grade, fiber strength, color, softness, and freedom from colored fibers and contaminants.

MARKETING AGENTS AND METHODS OF SELLING. In the United States, most producers sell their wool through "wool pools" and cooperatives often organized within a given state boundary and operated under laws of the state. These organizations, in turn, consign their wool to private or cooperative warehouses for marketing to processors. Methods of selling, whether by the individual producer, pool, cooperative, or warehouse, may be by private treaty, sealed bid, or auction.

Processing

The *Sheep Production Handbook* (American Sheep Industry Association, 1997) describes wool processing as follows:

> Wool processing plants operate with wool purchased from throughout the world. Inventories are built on the basis of diameter, length, color, the presence of colored fibers, and contamination-free wools. Wools are blended for specifications that may vary from the production of designer suits to blankets.
>
> Textile manufacturing in the wool industry consists of two major divisions, apparel and carpet. Apparel wool is usually of smaller fiber diameter than carpet wool, but carpet wool generally is suitable for use in some apparel. Most wool produced in the United States is apparel wool.
>
> There are two systems used in the manufacture of apparel wool fabrics. The two systems, known as worsted and woolen, differ with respect to raw materials used, manufacturing processes, and the types of yarn and cloth produced. Although the processing principles have changed little over the years, modern processing machinery uses high-tech components that permit higher running speeds and production. Because of this, fiber diameter uniformity, staple length, and staple strength are today more critical to the process than ever before.
>
> The worsted system uses virgin wool, that is, wool not previously processed. The woolen system uses, in addition to virgin wool, large amounts of other wool materials, including the short-fiber by-product of the worsted mills known as noils, wool waste, and recycled wools. In general, the woolen system uses shorter wools than are used by the worsted branch. Both systems use certain other textile materials in the form of fiber or yarn, including cotton, silk, and synthetics.

The typical system of processing wool from the grease wool stage (Figure 26-5) to the finished fabric is diagrammed in Figure 26-6. Scouring is the removal of impurities from grease wool using a water washing procedure involving detergents and/or a mild alkaline wash. Carbonizing is a process involving aqueous acid followed by heating to remove excess contamination with vegetable matter. The process weakens and shortens the fibers and makes them more brittle. Carbonizing reduces value of the wool.

After scouring, loose wool is dried with hot air blowing and then may be dyed, fol-

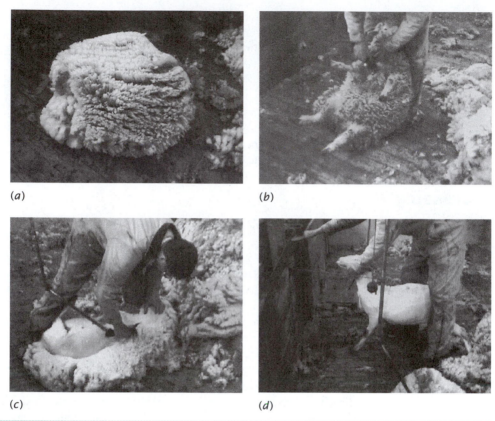

(a)   *(b)*

(c)   *(d)*

FIGURE 26-5

Newly shorn wool fleece (a) and sequential photographs during the shearing process (b, c, d). (Courtesy Michael L. Thonney, Cornell University.)

lowed by carding. The carding process involves passing wool through a series of cylinders and rollers covered with short wires that disentangle and separate wool fibers. Carded wool is used for spinning, weaving, and dyeing, and is further processed through steps not described here, to produce finished woolen fabrics and felts.

MOHAIR

Mohair is the fleece of the Angora goat. The fibers are pure white, smooth, and grow in ringlets but the fibers have very little crimp. Mohair fibers resemble wool fibers in general structure. They have an average diameter midway between fine and coarse wool. Mohair fibers grow in follicle groups of three primary follicles. As in the case of wool, kemp and medullated fibers reduce the value of the fleece because these fibers do not dye well. Fiber

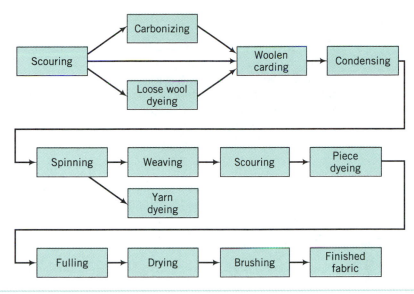

FIGURE 26-6

Typical woolen system for yarn manufacturing, weaving, and finishing.
Source: Sheep Production Handbook, American Sheep Industry Assoc. (1997).

length after one year of growth may be nearly 10 inches; however, it is customary in warm climates to clip the fleece twice a year. Fleece yield per year averages about 7 pounds. Mohair is noted for its durability, affinity for dyes, luster, and fine quality. Undercoat fibers are short, dull, and chalky and must be removed by combing the higher-quality mohair fibers. Undercoat fibers may make up 10 to 30% of the fleece weight. High-quality mohair is used in making clothing and for cloth and carpets.

Annual world production of mohair is about 60 million pounds, of which nearly half is produced in the United States (90% in Texas). Other leading countries in mohair production are Turkey, South Africa, Argentina, Australia, and New Zealand.

OTHER ANIMAL FIBERS

Several animal species in South America and other regions of the world contribute significantly to the supply of natural fibers for use by humans. Characteristics of some of these animals are briefly described.

Alpaca

This mountain animal lives at high altitudes and produces a soft, fine, lustrous wool in various shades of tan, brown, gray, and black. Average annual production per animal is 2.5 to 3 pounds; moisture and grease content is less than that of sheep wool.

Cashmere

This fiber is produced by some breeds of goats raised primarily for meat production. The fiber diameter is only 11 to 18 microns. Cashmere is a highly valued luxury fiber used in sweaters and other garments; it brings a much higher price than wool or mohair. The amount of cashmere harvested from a typical fleece averages only 0.2 to 0.3 pounds.

Afghanistan, China, Iran, and Outer Mongolia are leading cashmere producers. Some cashmere is produced in Texas and other southwestern states.

Llama

The fleece of the llama is coarser and contains more kemp than that of the alpaca or guanaco. An attribute of llama wool is its durability.

Guanaco and Vicuna

These animals are smaller than the llama. The guanaco resembles the llama but has a finer fleece with a fawn-to-brown color. The vicuna produces a soft, fine fleece that yields only about 0.5 pound of wool annually.

Other Animals

A surprising number of other animals provide hair useful for spinning into clothing, blankets, and other fabrics. Bactrian camels are said to produce some of the finest down for spinning. Arabian camels are also used. Deer, horses, musk ox, American bison, yak, Highlander cattle of Scotland, rabbits (notably Angora), racoons, beavers, opposum, and even cats and dogs (some breeds more than others) provide hair for spinning (Knoll, 1981; Crolius and Montgomery, 1994).

Birds

Feathers and down (underfeathers) from ducks, geese, and other species of birds are used as fillers for pillows, blankets, cushions, and in the lining of jackets. Even colorful feathers of peacock, pheasant, and ostrich can be removed from the shaft and cut into tiny pieces and carded with wool and other fibers for spinning. Feather quills are used for making pens, painting equipment, and fishing lures.

It has been estimated (McDowell, 1991) that half of the population of southeast Asia, the Andes mountains of South America, and the Himalayan mountains of Asia are dependent for income on the sale of handicrafts made from animal and bird fibers.

PELTS, SKINS, AND HIDES

The sale of pelts, hides, and skins of animals as byproducts of the meat processing industry represents a substantial contribution to the viability of animal agriculture. Often, the value of byproducts sold determines the difference between profit and loss to the meat packer. In addition, the production of furs from mink, fox, chinchilla, rabbit, and other commercial enterprises, some of which are based on the use of slaughterhouse byproducts (as in the case of carnivores such as the fox and mink), and some based on plant resources (as in the case of rabbits), is significant.

Pelts

Pelts are a major byproduct of the lamb meat packing industry. Pelts from North American sheep are larger than those from most other regions, averaging about 9 square feet. Most (perhaps 80%) of the U.S. lamb pelts are exported for tanning. Lambskins are classified as wooled skins or wool-free skins. Unblemished wooled skins are used to make "sheepskin" coats, footwear, and other accessories. Wool-free (pulled wool) skins are used for garments, purses, and accessories. Pelts of mink, fox, rabbits, and other fur animals are used for coats, neckpieces, and many other garments.

Skins and Hides

The term *skin* is applied to pigs, sheep (wool removed), and small cattle (hide weighing less than 30 pounds). The term *hide* is applied to beef skins weighing 30 pounds or greater. Pig skins, cattle skins and hides, horse hides, and buffalo hides are tanned and used for a wide variety of leather goods ranging from shoes, gloves, and coats to an array of sporting goods (baseballs, footballs, baseball gloves, basketballs, and soccer balls). Leather from 14 million cattle hides, 10 million pig skins, and 4 million sheep skins is produced annually, largely exported for tanning, from U.S. animal slaughter. The five leading countries in fresh hide and skin production are shown in Table 26-2.

TABLE 26-2

RANKING OF LEADING COUNTRIES IN CATTLE AND BUFFALO HIDES AND IN SHEEPSKIN AND GOATSKIN PRODUCTION[a]

Cattle/Buffalo Hides		Sheepskins		Goatskins	
Country	Weight	Country	Weight	Country	Weight
India	2,013	Australia	380	China	358
United States	1,972	China	358	India	241
USSR (former)	1,530	USSR (former)	282	Pakistan	96
Brazil	924	New Zealand	243	Nigeria	42
Argentina	792	Turkey	143	Ethiopa	32
World Total	14,872		2,888		1,147

[a]In millions of pounds.

Source: FAO Production Yearbook (1992).

SUMMARY

Production of animal fibers, including wool, mohair, alpaca, hair, and feathers from an array of animal species, and of hides, skins, and pelts, represents a significant contribution to society. In this chapter we define and describe each of these resources. The production of wool, its physical and chemical characteristics, and its uses are emphasized. Parallel information is provided on other animal fibers and on the importance and uses of hides, skins, and pelts.

GLOSSARY

Apparel wool That suitable for manufacture into apparel fabrics.

Belly wool That which grows on the belly of the sheep; it is usually coarser, shorter, weaker, and less dense that the remainder of the fleece.

Bale A compressed pack of wool in a convenient form for transit, varying in weight from 150 to 1000 pounds.

Blood grade Denotes the fineness of wool as compared with pure Merino, which is called full or fine blood.

Break Due to illness or poor nutrition at some time during the growth of the wool, it is weak at one particular point of the staple but sound above and below the break.

Britch wool Wool from the hind quarters of the sheep, usually the coarsest on the body, often approaching hair in its characteristics.

Burry wool Wool containing vegetable impurities.

Carbonizing The extracting of vegetable matter impurities from wool by treatment with acid.

Carding A step during the processing of wool in which it is fed into a machine which opens up the wool into an even layer to form a single continuous strand of fibers called a "sliver."

Carpet wool Coarse wool used in manufacture of carpets.

Chemical shearing Removal of the fleece from the live sheep by a single injection of a chemical, epidermal growth factor, which results in a break

in the wool fibers, allowing easy removal of the fleece a few weeks later (presently being tested for commercial application).

Clean basis Refers to the pricing of the clean, scoured wool, excluding loss and costs due to scouring.

Clean wool Wool after it has been scoured or cleaned, removing grease, dirt, and other foreign material (synonymous with scoured wool).

Clip One season's yield of wool (usually one year).

Clothing wool Short fibers used in the manufacture of woolens.

Combing Process by which the short fibers, entangled fibers, and vegetable matter are separated from the long fibers and the latter are straightened out and laid parallel to each other.

Core sample Sample extracted from a bale of wool by inserting a sharpened hollow tube the length of the bale.

Cotted fleeces Those in which the fibers are excessively matted or tangled.

Crimp The natural waviness of the wool fiber.

Crutching Shearing of wool from around the dock and udder, often done before lambing (sometimes called "dagging" or "tagging").

Density The number of fibers produced on a given area of the sheep's body.

Felt A textile structure entirely composed of fibers physically interlocked and consolidated by the utilization of mechanical work, chemical action, and moisture, not by weaving, knitting, or stitching.

Fiber diameter   Cross-sectional diameter of individual wool fibers.

Fiber fineness distribution analyzer   Machine that measures the diameter of several thousand individual wool fibers and both average diameter and variability in diameter.

Finishing   Everything that happens to wool fabric after leaving the loom until it is ready for the cutter.

Fleece   The entire coat of wool shorn from a sheep at one time.

Frowsy wool   A lifeless-appearing wool with fibers lying in random directions.

Graded wool   Fleeces that have been individually handled and visually classed according to fiber diameter, length, and other characteristics.

Grease price   Price paid for grease wool; determined by multplying yield by price of clean wool.

Grease wool   Wool in its natural state.

Half-blood   American designation of wool compared in fineness to the full-blooded Merino as standard.

Hank   A unit of measurement used to estimate the USDA grade or the amount of yarn that can be spun from one pound of clean wool; 1 hank = 560 yards of yarn.

Heavy wool   Wool with a high shrinkage in scouring.

Keds   Blood-sucking ticks that pierce the skin, causing serious damage to sheep pelts.

Kemp   An opaque, brittle fiber present in some fleeces which appears not to absorb dye and consequently is prominent in the finished fabric unless specially treated.

Keratin   Protein found in wool fiber.

Lanolin   Purified wool grease; the natural oil of wool.

Loom   Machine for producing clothing by weaving.

Matching   Made by sorting fleeces and putting together those portions of different fleeces which correspond in quality.

Med fibers   Medullated fibers that tend to be finer than kemp fibers, longer than true wool fibers, and generally lacking crimp.

Medium wools   Refers to the wools that grade high quarter-blood, three-eighths-blood, and low half-blood.

Medullated fiber   An animal fiber that in its original state includes an open core.

Medulla   Central core of medium and coarse wools, kemp, and heterotype fibers.

Micron   Linear unit of measure (one-millionth of a meter) used to describe wool fiber diameter.

Noil   The short and tangled fibers which are separated from the long fibers, known as top, by a worsted comb (sometimes used to stuff teddy bears and other toys).

Open wool   Refers to fleece not densely grown on the sheep and often parted down the spine.

Pelt   the skin of a sheep (or other small animal), including the wool or other fiber.

Position of break (POB)   Indicates the location of the weakest part of the fiber in a staple.

Pulled wool   That pulled from the pelt of a slaughtered sheep after the flesh side of the skin has been painted with a depilatory agent.

Quality number   The spinning count by which wools, tops, noils, and yarns are known, this originally based on the count of yarn to which the material will theoretically spin.

Quarter-blood   American designation of wool compared in fineness to the full-blooded Merino as standard.

Range wool   Wool shorn from sheep raised under ranching conditions; in the United States, better known as territory wool.

Reprocessed wool   The fiber resulting when wool has been woven or felted into a wool product, which, without ever having been utilized in any way by the consumer, subsequently has been made into a fibrous state (as defined in the Wool Products Labeling Act of 1939).

Reused wool   The fiber resulting when wool or reprocessed wool has been spun, woven, knitted, or felted into a wool product which, after having been used in any way by the ultimate consumer, has been made into a fibrous state (as defined in the Wool Products Labeling Act of 1939).

Scoured wool   Wool from which the bulk of impurities have been removed by an aqueous or solvent washing process.

Scouring   The removal of grease, soil, and suint from wool by washing with water, soap, and alkali.

Secondary/primary ratio (S/P ratio)   The ratio of primary to secondary wool fibers.

Seedy   A term applied to wools containing grass seeds and other vegetable impurities of various descriptions that are difficult to remove.

Shearing   The removal of wool from sheep.

Shearling   Wooled lambskins.

Sliver   A ropelike strand of fiber produced by carding.

Sorting   The classification and division of wool fibers in a fleece into groups or sorts, according to fineness, length, soundness, elasticity, spinning, and other properties.

Spinning count   Term which denotes the degree of fineness of the wool fiber; the count number originally indicated the number of hanks of yarn which could be spun from a pound of clean wool.

Staple length   The length of a wool fiber from tip to base.

Staple strength   The force or pull required to break a staple of a given thickness; staple strength is expressed in Newtons/kilotex.

Suint   Excretions deposited in the wool from sweat glands.

Tagging   See Crutching.

Tags   Trade term for dung, floor sweepings, or stained pieces of wool.

Tender fleece   Wool having a moderately weak place in the fibers. See Break.

Tex   The direct decimal system based on metric units used to describe the linear density of fibers, slivers, or yarns.

Top   A continuous untwisted strand of combed wool in which the fibers lie parallel, with short fibers having been combed out as noil.

Vegetable matter base (VMB)   Percentage of burrs, seeds, straw, and other vegetable impurities in a grease wool core sample.

Virgin wool   Wool shorn from live sheep or pulled from sheep skins and not previously manufactured.

Wool base (WB)   The oven-dry weight of wool fiber that is free from all impurities (expressed as a percentage of the weight of the grease wool core sample).

Wool Products Labeling Act   Legislation requiring every wool product (except upholstery fabrics and floor coverings) to bear a label listing the type and percentage of fibers as well as the registered number of the manufacturer.

Woolen system   Manufacturing process that produces a relatively bulky, low-twist yarn with low linear density; the resulting fibers are criss-crossed and do not lie in any general order.

Worsted system   Manufacturing system that produces yarn spun from top; the resulting fibers are parallel and smooth compared to woolen yarns.

Yield   The amount of clean wool obtained from a definite quantity of grease wool.

Yolk   A combination of suint and grease deposited on the wool fibers from the sweat and sebaceous glands of the sheep.

REFERENCES

Acker, D. E., and Cunningham, M. 1998. *Animal Science and Industry* (5th ed). Upper Saddle River, NJ: Prentice Hall,

American Sheep Industry Association. 1997. *Sheep Production Handbook*. Denver, CO: C&M Press, wool chapter, pp. 1101–1175.

Botkin, M. P., Field, R. A., and Johnson, C. L. 1988. *Sheep and Wool Science, Production and Management.* Englewood Cliffs, NJ: Prentice Hall.

Crolius, K., and Montgomery, A. B. 1994. *Knitting with Dog Hair.* New York: St. Martin's Griffin.

Ensminger, M. E. 1971. *Sheep and Wool Science.* Danville, IL: Interstate Printers and Publishers.

Hyde, N., and Wolinsky, C. 1988. Wool: Fabric of history. *National Geographic,* 173(5): 552-591 (May).

Kammlade, W. G., Sr., and Kammlade, W. G., Jr. 1955. *Sheep Science.* New York: J. B. Lippincott.

Kroll, C. 1981. *The Whole Craft of Spinning.* New York: Dover Publications.

McDowell. R. E. 1991. *A Partnership for Humans and Animals.* Raleigh, NC: Kinnic Publishers.

Taylor, R. E. 1995. *Scientific Farm Animal Production* (5th ed). Upper Saddle River, NJ: Prentice Hall.

CHAPTER TWENTY-SEVEN
THE FUTURE: ANIMALS AND SOCIETY IN THE TWENTY-FIRST CENTURY

DEMAND FOR ANIMAL PRODUCTS

FEED RESOURCES

TRENDS AND EXPECTATIONS OF THE NATURE OF U.S. ANIMAL AGRICULTURE

OPPORTUNITIES IN ANIMAL AGRICULTURE

SUMMARY

Important goals in preparing this textbook, *Introduction to Animal Science,* were to provide a comprehensive description of the role of animals in contemporary society, an appreciation for the complexities of animal agriculture in an increasingly crowded world, and a glimpse of the nature and scope of individual animal industries and their products. Whether students head toward careers in animal agriculture or not, all will have a stake in the future of agriculture as consumers and citizens. That being the case, this closing chapter of *Introduction to Animal Science* briefly considers some of the trends and directions that food production and animal-human interrelationships may take in the new millennium.

The twenty-first century promises to bring many changes in the way animals are raised and the way their products are processed, marketed, and consumed. These changes are the result of major advances in scientific knowledge, in communication, transportation, and other technologies, of the increased concern and awareness of population growth and the environment, and of dynamic economic development around the world.

We now live in a world interconnected like never before and in which food shortages due to floods, drought, and other natural disasters in one place are known instantaneously around the globe, so that help can be mobilized quickly. On the other hand, despite modern technologies, humanity has not yet fully addressed the constraints confronting us on a global scale to provide adequate food for future generations. During the 1980s, Sir Kenneth Blaxter, the late distinguished British animal scientist, contemplated the future as follows:

> On the average we will survive; on the average we will have enough to eat; on the average the wealth of the world will increase; globally, animal production will continue to develop and sufficient animal production will be provided to supply enough of the nutrients from animal products to satisfy the needs and also the wants of average man. What should concern us is not, however, this statistical mean, but the obscenity of its standard deviation,[1] which no properly civilized world should tolerate.

Those engaged in animal agriculture, from farm to dinner table, now and in the future, should take seriously the admonition of Blaxter as they pursue their own role in society.

DEMAND FOR ANIMAL PRODUCTS

Trends now underway in animal agriculture in the United States and worldwide are complex and will be driven by factors both within agriculture and extrinsic to it. Many of these factors are not easily assessed and some are not even predictable. Trends in the United States probably are to be expected to occur in other countries, but the vast differences among countries in demographics, population growth, natural resources, cultural traditions, and economic conditions make it difficult to predict, let alone evaluate, long-term trends. However, one thing is certain. The human appetite for animal products has persisted throughout recorded history.

Increased economic status of a country or region is historically associated with greater per-capita demand for animal products. Per-capita consumption of animal products in the United States and other economically affluent societies has reached a peak, suggesting a saturation point in per-capita consumption in high-income societies. The principle appears to be one of increased demand for animal products as purchasing power of a population rises, followed by a plateau in appetite for meat, milk, and eggs. This principle suggests that exports of animal products from the United States and other exporting countries will continue to grow as domestic supply exceeds demand. Animal production in the developing countries can be expected to expand in response to increased purchasing power and increased population.

---

[1]Here he refers to the wide range in food availability and affordability and the large proportion of humans who fall far below the average and are therefore in danger of malnutrition.

The expansion of animal production in the less-developed countries can be expected to occur in larger and more efficient production facilities. A smaller proportion of animals will be raised by subsistence-farming methods. However, to be sure, animal products originating on small farms for home and local consumption will continue to contribute significantly to the maintenance of rural cultures and to farm income and rural economies in all parts of the globe for the foreseeable future. CAST (1999) published an excellent summary of present and future global animal production.

FEED RESOURCES

In most areas of the world abundant supplies of animal feed resources that do not compete with production of crops used for direct human consumption are available to support expansion of food animal populations and output of animal products. Some estimates indicate the potential for doubling of the arable land (8 billion additional acres) and increasing by more than 20% (9.2 billion acres) the land area in the world devoted to permanent pasture and meadow. Such increases in utilization of available land for animal production, coupled with improved efficiency of crop and animal production on these lands, could extend the food supply to meet the needs of a world human population of the magnitude predicted within the foreseeable future.

This optimistic view can only become reality with prudent stewardship of natural resources and the environment.

TRENDS AND EXPECTATIONS OF THE NATURE OF U.S. ANIMAL AGRICULTURE

As agriculture has become more complex and internationally driven, the nature of animal agriculture in the United States has changed and new trends have emerged. In the United States, the following trends are underway and can be expected to continue:

- Fewer and larger farms and an increase in corporate farming.
- Feeds (grains and concentrates) shipped to animal production sites rather than animals produced near feed production sites.
- Increased use of biotechnology for improved efficiency of production or improved product quality [e.g., recombinant DNA techniques used to produce microbes able to synthesize amino acids such as lysine, tryptophan, and threonine in mass quantities for use in foods and feeds; recombinantly derived bovine somatotropin (growth hormone) administered to dairy cows to increase milk production].
- More extensive integration of animal production (i.e., animal producer contracts with feed manufacturer to provide feed and/or meat packer to slaughter and market

animals). (Integration of the poultry broiler industry became common decades ago; the swine and beef cattle industries are moving in the same direction.)

- Increased emphasis on herd health care by disease prevention through contracted veterinary practitioners and less focus on "fire-fighting" and on treatment of disease in individual animals.

- Greater use of computer technology for farm record keeping, accounting, management decisions, and marketing. (Personal computers, the Internet, and the World Wide Web offer access to educational materials and other information supportive of better management decisions.)

- Movement toward the systems approach to individual segments of an animal production enterprise or to an entire farm enterprise using computer technology (optimization of inputs and outputs to promote a profitable enterprise).

- Greater governmental regulation of individual livestock enterprises (mandated by environmental concerns, e.g., air pollution, water pollution, soil contamination with toxic residues and excesses of nutrients in animal wastes).

- Greater government surveillance (e.g., Food and Drug Administration) of feed ingredients, feed additives, and of animal tissue and milk residues of drugs and other substances administered to animals.

- Greater restrictions on water use and distribution between agricultural and nonagricultural uses (e.g., laws controlling deep-well irrigation). A 1998 report based on a consortium study of projected water needs for agriculture concluded that the agriculture industry can help to mitigate increasing demands for water and adapt to potential climate changes by continuing to improve irrigation and drainage technologies and continuing to conserve and enhance genetic resources to maintain yield growth and allow flexible adaptation of crop types. The focus was on only the next 20 years, and it was emphasized that additional efforts are needed in the longer term. Clearly the future of animal agriculture will be influenced by the water supply available for crops and animals in a world of rapid population growth. Desalinization of ocean water may be the long-term solution in some locations, as already practiced on a small scale in some cultures.

- Continued improvement in efficiency of animal production through new and improved technologies in breeding, feeding, and managements of animals.

- Continued increase in emphasis on higher quality and safety of meat, milk, and other animal food products (e.g., low-fat meat, milk, and marine products, and assurance of freedom from harmful residues and pathogens).

- Continued greater emphasis among animal producers, transporters, and abattoir personnel on animal comfort and well-being.

- Continued increase in total demand for animal products as U.S. population continues to grow and as export market expands.

- Greater use of byproduct feeds and alternative feed resources in all livestock and poultry industries in the United States and throughout the world.

- Introduction of exotic and nontraditional animals in the food supply [e.g., emu, ostrich, and an array of small animal species (micro-livestock)].

- Continued decline in public awareness and appreciation of agriculture in general and animal agriculture in particular [dwindling rural population and increasing disconnection between farm and nonfarm citizens (only a small fraction of today's children have the opportunity to visit grandparents or other relatives who live on farms or are familiar with agriculture)].

- Increasing need for improved communication between those engaged in animal agriculture and consumers (inadequate education of the public about agriculture has resulted in increasingly critical and suspicious attitudes of consumers toward agricultural production practices related to food safety and environmental quality).

- Continued changes in consumer preferences and perceptions of foods.

- Enhanced societal appreciation of and engagement in the notion of the natural interdependence between humans and animals in agriculture as well as in urban society.

OPPORTUNITIES IN ANIMAL AGRICULTURE

The field of animal science is exceedingly broad, as evidenced by the wide range of topics covered in this textbook. Graduates with a Bachelor of Science degree in Animal Science are equipped (if properly prepared with minor specialization in related fields such as economics and business, agronomy, food science, natural resources, vocational agriculture, and others) to enter careers in a variety of areas. In recent years, female graduates are about equal in number to male graduates and available positions exceed available graduates. Examples of career choices are production agriculture (as owner or career track middle manager) and positions in agribusiness, banking, technical positions in private industry and government, secondary education, and state and federal extension service. Students who have interest and strong scientific orientation to pursue graduate degrees (Master of Science or Doctor of Philosophy) often enter government research laboratories, accept university teaching, research, or extension positions, or prefer technical positions in private industry. Approximately 40% of BS degree graduates typically enter agribusiness or business, 20 to 25% pursue study for advanced degrees (MS, PhD., or DVM., and a few MD and DDS), 10% enter farming and ranching, and the remainder embark on education, extension, government, and miscellaneous positions.

A major, perhaps the largest, challenge to society in the twenty-first century will be to provide enough food to meet the needs of 8 to 9 billion people. Those who choose a career related to food and animal production will have an even greater opportunity than those of previous generations to make important and rewarding contributions to meeting this unprecedented food production challenge.

SUMMARY

This final chapter provides an overview of the factors that may govern the future of animals in society. It addresses the prospects for future demand for animal products, the prospects for providing feed resources to support animal agriculture, and projections on the nature of animal agriculture in the twenty-first century. Many opportunities are available for graduates with baccalaureate and advanced degrees (e.g., Master of Science, Doctor of Philosophy, and Doctor of Veterinary Medicine) in animal science and related fields. Those who choose a career in food and animal production will have a great opportunity to contribute significantly to the unprecedented food challenge of the twenty-first century. For those who choose careers outside of animal agriculture, it is hoped that the information covered in this book will have provided a broadened perspective on the role of animals in society and insight into the satisfying human-animal bond that enriches our lives.

REFERENCES

Brown, L. R., Renner, M., and Flavin, C. 1997. *Vital Signs* 1997. W. W. Norton and Company, N.Y.

CAST. 1999. *Animal Agriculture and Global Food Supply*. Council for Agricultural Science and Technology, Ames, IA.

CAST. 1999. *Benefits of Biodiversity*. Council for Agricultural Science and Technology, Ames, IA.

CAST. 1997. *Contribution of Animal Products to Healthful Diets*. Council for Agricultural Science and Technology, Ames, IA.

CAST. 1998. *Food Safety, Sufficiency, and Security*. Council for Agricultural Science and Technology, Ames, IA.

Cheeke, P. R. 1995. *Impacts of Livestock Production on Society, Diet/Health and the Environment*. Interstate Publishers, Danville, IL.

APPENDIX 1
NUTRIENT CONTENT OF SELECTED PLANT AND ANIMAL PRODUCTS

APPENDIX 1-1

BEANS, KIDNEY, MATURE SEEDS, SPROUTED, COOKED, BOILED, DRAINED, WITHOUT SALT

Nutrient	Units	Value per 100 grams of edible portion	Nutrient	Units	Value per 100 grams of edible portion
Proximates			**Lipids**		
Water	g	89.300	Fatty acids, saturated	g	0.083
Energy	kcal	33.000	16:0	g	0.074
Energy	kj	138.000	18:0	g	0.010
Protein	g	4.830	Fatty acids, monounsaturated	g	0.045
Total lipid (fat)	g	0.580			
Carbohydrate, by difference	g	4.720	18:1	g	0.045
			Fatty acids, polyunsaturated	g	0.318
Ash	g	0.580	18:2	g	0.123
Minerals			18:3	g	0.194
Calcium, Ca	mg	19.000	Cholesterol	mg	0.000
Iron, Fe	mg	0.890			
Magnesium, Mg	mg	23.000	**Amino acids**		
Phosphorus, P	mg	38.000	Tryptophan	g	0.050
Potassium, K	mg	194.000	Threonine	g	0.203
Sodium, Na	mg	7.000	Isoleucine	g	0.214
Zinc, Zn	mg	0.440	Leucine	g	0.347
Copper, Cu	mg	0.174	Lysine	g	0.275
Manganese, Mn	mg	0.199	Methionine	g	0.050
Selenium, Se	mcg	0.600	Cystine	g	0.055
			Phenylalanine	g	0.243
Vitamins			Tyrosine	g	0.166
Vitamin C, ascorbic acid	mg	35.600	Valine	g	0.248
			Arginine	g	0.263
Thiamin	mg	0.362	Histidine	g	0.135
Riboflavin	mg	0.273	Alanine	g	0.263
Niacin	mg	3.024	Aspartic acid	g	0.628
Pantothenic acid	mg	0.381	Glutamic acid	g	0.589
Vitamin B-6	mg	0.093	Glycine	g	0.166
Folate	mcg	47.400	Proline	g	0.195
Vitamin B-12	mcg	0.000	Serine	g	0.258
Vitamin A, IU[1]	IU	2.000			
Vitamin A, RE[2]	mcg_RE	0.000			

USDA Nutrient Database for Standard Reference, Release 12 (March 1998)
[1] IU - International Unit
[2] RE - Retinol Equivalent

APPENDIX 1-2

CORN, SWEET, YELLOW, CANNED, VACUUM PACK, NO SALT ADDED

Nutrient	Units	Value per 100 grams of edible portion	Nutrient	Units	Value per 100 grams of edible portion
Proximates			**Lipids**		
Water	g	76.580	Fatty acids, saturated	g	0.077
Energy	kcal	79.000	16:0	g	0.073
Energy	kj	331.000	18:0	g	0.005
Protein	g	2.410	Fatty acids,		
Total lipid (fat)	g	0.500	monounsaturated	g	0.147
Carbohydrate,			18:1	g	0.147
by difference	g	19.440	Fatty acids,		
Fiber, total dietary	g	2.000	polyunsaturated	g	0.237
Ash	g	1.070	18:2	g	0.230
			18:3	g	0.007
Minerals			Cholesterol	mg	0.000
Calcium, CA	mg	5.000			
Iron, Fe	mg	0.420	**Amino acids**		
Magnesium, Mg	mg	23.000	Tryptophan	g	0.017
Phosphorus, P	mg	64.000	Threonine	g	0.097
Potassium, K	mg	186.000	Isoleucine	g	0.097
Sodium, Na	mg	3.000	Leucine	g	0.260
Zinc, Zn	mg	0.460	Lysine	g	0.102
Copper, Cu	mg	0.048	Methionine	g	0.050
Manganese, Mn	mg	0.067	Cystine	g	0.020
Selenium,Se	mcg	0.700	Phenylalanine	g	0.112
			Tyrosine	g	0.092
Vitamins			Valine	g	0.138
Vitamin C,			Arginine	g	0.098
ascorbic acid	mg	8.100	Histidine	g	0.066
Thiamin	mg	0.041	Alanine	g	0.220
Riboflavin	mg	0.073	Aspartic acid	g	0.182
Niacin	mg	1.167	Glutamic acid	g	0.475
Pantothenic acid	mg	0.675	Glycine	g	0.095
Vitamin B-6	mg	0.055	Proline	g	0.218
Folate	mcg	49.300	Serine	g	0.114
Vitamin B-12	mcg	0.000			
Vitamin A, IU	IU[1]	241.000			
Vitamin A, RE	mcg_RE[2]	24.000			
Vitamin E	mg_ATE[3]	0.090			

USDA Nutrient Database for Standard Reference, Release 12 (March 1998)

[1]IU - International Unit
[2]RE - Retinol Equivalent
[3]ATE - Alpha Tocopherol Equivalent

APPENDIX 1-3

BREAD, WHOLE-WHEAT, COMMERCIALLY PREPARED

Nutrient	Units	Value per 100 grams of edible portion	Nutrient	Units	Value per 100 grams of edible portion
Proximates			10:0	g	0.000
Water	g	37.700	12:0	g	0.001
Energy	kcal	246.000	14:0	g	0.016
Energy	kj	1029.000	16:0	g	0.575
Protein	g	9.700	18:0	g	0.318
Total lipid (fat)	g	4.200	Fatty acids, monounsaturated	g	1.680
Carbohydrate, by difference	g	46.100	16:1	g	0.023
Fiber, total dietary	g	6.900	18:1	g	1.658
Ash	g	2.300	20:1	g	0.000
			22:1	g	0.000
Minerals			Fatty acids, polyunsaturated	g	1.003
Calcium, CA	mg	72.000	18:2	g	0.952
Iron, Fe	mg	3.300	18:3	g	0.049
Magnesium, Mg	mg	86.000	18:4	g	0.000
Phosphorus, P	mg	229.000	20:4	g	0.002
Potassium, K	mg	252.000	20:5	g	0.000
Sodium, Na	mg	527.000	22:5	g	0.000
Zinc, Zn	mg	1.940	22:6	g	0.000
Copper, Cu	mg	0.284	Cholesterol	mg	0.000
Manganese, Mn	mg	2.324			
Selenium, Se	mcg	36.600	**Amino acids**		
			Tryptophan	g	0.140
Vitamins			Threonine	g	0.296
Vitamin C, ascorbic acid	mg	0.000	Isoleucine	g	0.376
Thiamin	mg	0.351	Leucine	g	0.670
Riboflavin	mg	0.205	Lysine	g	0.302
Niacin	mg	3.837	Methionine	g	0.155
Pantothenic acid	mg	0.552	Cystine	g	0.214
Vitamin B-6	mg	0.179	Phenylalanine	g	0.463
Folate	mcg	50.000	Tyrosine	g	0.289
Vitamin B-12	mcg	0.010	Valine	g	0.443
Vitamin A, IU	IU	0.000	Arginine	g	0.449
Vitamin A, RE	mcg_RE	0.000	Histidine	g	0.224
Vitamin E	mg_ATE	0.853	Alanine	g	0.358
			Aspartic acid	g	0.536
Lipids			Glutamic acid	g	0.957
Fatty acids, saturated	g	0.917	Glycine	g	0.384
4:0	g	0.000	Proline	g	0.969
6:0	g	0.000	Serine	g	0.463
8:0	g	0.000			

USDA Nutrient Database for Standard Reference, Release 12 (March 1998)

APPENDIX 1-4

BEEF, RIB, WHOLE (RIBS 6–12), SEPARABLE LEAN AND FAT, TRIMMED TO 1/4" FAT, ALL GRADES, RAW

Nutrient	Units	Value per 100 grams of edible portion	Nutrient	Units	Value per 100 grams of edible portion
Proximates			12:0	g	0.070
Water	g	54.540	14:0	g	0.890
Energy	kcal	313.000	16:0	g	6.690
Energy	kj	1310.000	18:0	g	3.390
Protein	g	16.370	Fatty acids,		
Total lipid (fat)	g	26.980	monounsaturated	g	11.630
Carbohydrate,			16:1	g	1.380
by difference	g	0.000	18:1	g	10.210
Fiber, total dietary	g	0.000	20:1	g	0.040
Ash	g	0.770	Fatty acids,		
			polyunsaturated	g	0.970
Minerals			18:2	g	0.620
Calcium, CA	mg	9.000	18:3	g	0.330
Iron, Fe	mg	1.720	20:4	g	0.020
Magnesium, Mg	mg	16.000	Cholesterol	mg	71.000
Phosphorus, P	mg	154.000			
Potassium, K	mg	268.000	**Amino acids**		
Sodium, Na	mg	54.000	Tryptophan	g	0.183
Zinc, Zn	mg	3.670	Threonine	g	0.715
Copper, Cu	mg	0.058	Isoleucine	g	0.736
Manganese, Mn	mg	0.012	Leucine	g	1.294
			Lysine	g	1.362
Vitamins			Methionine	g	0.419
Vitamin C,			Cystine	g	0.183
ascorbic acid	mg	0.000	Phenylalanine	g	0.639
Thiamin	mg	0.080	Tyrosine	g	0.550
Riboflavin	mg	0.130	Valine	g	0.796
Niacin	mg	2.780	Arginine	g	1.034
Pantothenic acid	mg	0.310	Histidine	g	0.560
Vitamin B-6	mg	0.310	Alanine	g	0.987
Folate	mcg	5.000	Aspartic acid	g	1.495
Vitamin B-12	mcg	2.800	Glutamic acid	g	2.459
Vitamin A, IU	IU	0.000	Glycine	g	0.893
Vitamin A, RE	mcg_RE	0.000	Proline	g	0.723
			Serine	g	0.626
Lipids					
Fatty acids,	g	11.130			
saturated					
10:0	g	0.100			

USDA Nutrient Database for Standard Reference, Release 12 (March 1998)

APPENDIX 1-5

LAMB, DOMESTIC, LOIN, SEPARABLE LEAN AND FAT, TRIMMED TO 1/4" FAT, CHOICE, RAW

Nutrient	Units	Value per 100 grams of edible portion	Nutrient	Units	Value per 100 grams of edible portion
Proximates			12:0	g	0.120
Water	g	56.550	14:0	g	1.090
Energy	kcal	310.000	16:0	g	5.890
Energy	kj	1297.000	18:0	g	3.700
Protein	g	16.320	Fatty acids,		
Total lipid (fat)	g	26.630	monounsaturated	g	10.940
Carbohydrate,			16:1	g	0.770
by difference	g	0.000	18:1	g	9.820
Fiber, total dietary	g	0.000	Fatty acids,		
Ash	g	0.840	polyunsaturated	g	2.080
			18:2	g	1.520
Minerals			18:3	g	0.480
Calcium, CA	mg	15.000	20:4	g	0.080
Iron, Fe	mg	1.610	Cholesterol	mg	74.000
Magnesium, Mg	mg	21.000			
Phosphorus, P	mg	152.000	**Amino acids**		
Potassium, K	mg	214.000	Tryptophan	g	0.191
Sodium, Na	mg	56.000	Threonine	g	0.699
Zinc, Zn	mg	2.530	Isoleucine	g	0.787
Copper, Cu	mg	0.105	Leucine	g	1.270
Manganese, Mn	mg	0.018	Lysine	g	1.441
			Methionine	g	0.419
Vitamins			Cystine	g	0.195
Vitamin C,			Phenylalanine	g	0.664
ascorbic acid	mg	0.000	Tyrosine	g	0.549
Thiamin	mg	0.110	Valine	g	0.881
Riboflavin	mg	0.210	Arginine	g	0.970
Niacin	mg	6.470	Histidine	g	0.517
Pantothenic acid	mg	0.630	Alanine	g	0.982
Vitamin B-6	mg	0.130	Aspartic acid	g	1.437
Folate	mcg	17.000	Glutamic acid	g	2.369
Vitamin B-12	mcg	2.040	Glycine	g	0.797
Vitamin A, IU	IU	0.000	Proline	g	0.685
Vitamin A, RE	mcg_RE	0.000	Serine	g	0.607
Vitamin E	mg_ATE	0.180			
Lipids					
Fatty acids, saturated	g	11.760			
10:0	g	0.070			

USDA Nutrient Database for Standard Reference, Release 12 (March 1998)

APPENDIX 1-6

PORK, FRESH, LOIN, WHOLE, SEPARABLE LEAN AND FAT, RAW

Nutrient	Units	Value per 100 grams of edible portion	Nutrient	Units	Value per 100 grams of edible portion
Proximates			10:0	g	0.010
Water	g	66.920	12:0	g	0.010
Energy	kcal	198.000	14:0	g	0.160
Energy	kj	828.000	16:0	g	2.720
Protein	g	19.740	18:0	g	1.420
Total lipid (fat)	g	12.580	Fatty acids, monounsaturated	g	5.610
Carbohydrate, by difference	g	0.000	16:1	g	0.360
Fiber, total dietary	g	0.000	18:1	g	5.140
Ash	g	0.960	20:1	g	0.090
			22:1	g	0.000
Minerals			Fatty acids, polyunsaturated	g	1.340
Calcium, Ca	mg	18.000	18:2	g	1.110
Iron, Fe	mg	0.790	18:3	g	0.090
Magnesium, Mg	mg	21.000	18:4	g	0.000
Phosphorus, P	mg	197.000	20:4	g	0.080
Potassium, K	mg	356.000	20:5	g	0.000
Sodium, Na	mg	50.000	22:5	g	0.000
Zinc, Zn	mg	1.740	22:6	g	0.000
Copper, Cu	mg	0.056	Cholesterol	mg	63.000
Manganese, Mn	mg	0.011			
Selenium, Se	mcg	33.200	**Amino acids**		
			Tryptophan	g	0.244
Vitamins			Threonine	g	0.891
Vitamin C, ascorbic acid	mg	0.600	Isoleucine	g	0.910
Thiamin	mg	0.901	Leucine	g	1.572
Riboflavin	mg	0.248	Lysine	g	1.766
Niacin	mg	4.580	Methionine	g	0.514
Pantothenic acid	mg	0.723	Cystine	g	0.248
Vitamin B-6	mg	0.472	Phenylalanine	g	0.785
Folate	mcg	5.000	Tyrosine	g	0.676
Vitamin B-12	mcg	0.530	Valine	g	1.064
Vitamin A, IU	IU	7.000	Arginine	g	1.245
Vitamin A, RE	mcg_RE	2.000	Histidine	g	0.770
Vitamin E	mg_ATE	0.290	Alanine	g	1.158
			Aspartic acid	g	1.814
Lipids			Glutamic acid	g	3.044
Fatty acids, saturated	g	4.360	Glycine	g	1.019
4:0	g	0.000	Proline	g	0.838
6:0	g	0.000	Serine	g	0.815
8:0	g	0.000			

USDA Nutrient Database for Standard Reference, Release 12 (March 1998)

APPENDIX 1-7

PORK, FRESH, LOIN, TENDERLOIN, SEPARABLE LEAN ONLY, RAW

Nutrient	Units	Value per 100 grams of edible portion	Nutrient	Units	Value per 100 grams of edible portion
Proximates			10:0	g	0.000
Water	g	74.940	12:0	g	0.000
Energy	kcal	120.000	14:0	g	0.040
Energy	kj	502.000	16:0	g	0.750
Protein	g	20.990	18:0	g	0.370
Total lipid (fat)	g	3.410	Fatty acids,		
Carbohydrate,			monounsaturated	g	1.540
by difference	g	0.000	16:1	g	0.110
Fiber, total dietary	g	0.000	18:1	g	1.400
Ash	g	1.760	20:1	g	0.020
			22:1	g	0.000
Minerals			Fatty acids,		
Calcium, Ca	mg	5.000	polyunsaturated	g	0.370
Iron, Fe	mg	1.230	18:2	g	0.300
Magnesium, Mg	mg	26.000	18:3	g	0.010
Phosphorus, P	mg	226.000	18:4	g	0.000
Potassium, K	mg	366.000	20:4	g	0.040
Sodium, Na	mg	50.000	20:5	g	0.000
Zinc, Zn	mg	2.030	22:5	g	0.000
Copper, Cu	mg	0.049	22:6	g	0.000
Manganese, Mn	mg	0.015	Cholesterol	mg	65.000
Selenium, Se	mcg	28.900			
			Amino acids		
Vitamins			Tryptophan	g	0.267
Vitamin C,			Threonine	g	0.958
ascorbic acid	mg	0.900	Isoleucine	g	0.983
Thiamin	mg	0.974	Leucine	g	1.684
Riboflavin	mg	0.281	Lysine	g	1.888
Niacin	mg	4.429	Methionine	g	0.556
Pantothenic acid	mg	0.904	Cystine	g	0.268
Vitamin B-6	mg	0.520	Phenylalanine	g	0.838
Folate	mcg	5.000	Tyrosine	g	0.731
Vitamin B-12	mcg	0.810	Valine	g	1.139
Vitamin A, IU	IU	6.000	Arginine	g	1.305
Vitamin A, RE	mcg_RE	2.000	Histidine	g	0.839
Vitamin E	mg_ATE	0.290	Alanine	g	1.223
			Aspartic acid	g	1.947
Lipids			Glutamic acid	g	3.286
Fatty acids, saturated	g	1.180	Glycine	g	0.997
4:0	g	0.000	Proline	g	0.843
6:0	g	0.000	Serine	g	0.867
8:0	g	0.000			

USDA Nutrient Database for Standard Reference, Release 12 (March 1998)

APPENDIX 1-8

CHICKEN, BROILERS OR FRYERS, MEAT AND SKIN, RAW

Nutrient	Units	Value per 100 grams of edible portion	Nutrient	Units	Value per 100 grams of edible portion
Proximates			12:0	g	0.020
Water	g	65.990	14:0	g	0.120
Energy	kcal	215.000	16:0	g	3.150
Energy	kj	900.000	18:0	g	0.870
Protein	g	18.600	Fatty acids,		
Total lipid (fat)	g	15.060	monounsaturated	g	6.240
Carbohydrate,			16:1	g	0.830
by difference	g	0.000	18:1	g	5.170
Fiber, total dietary	g	0.000	20:1	g	0.150
Ash	g	0.790	22:1	g	0.000
Minerals			Fatty acids,		
Calcium, Ca	mg	11.000	polyunsaturated	g	3.230
Iron, Fe	mg	0.900	18:2	g	2.880
Magnesium, Mg	mg	20.000	18:3	g	0.140
Phosphorus, P	mg	147.000	18:4	g	0.000
Potassium, K	mg	189.000	20:4	g	0.080
Sodium, Na	mg	70.000	20:5	g	0.010
Zinc, Zn	mg	1.310	22:5	g	0.010
Copper, Cu	mg	0.048	22:6	g	0.030
Manganese, Mn	mg	0.019	Cholesterol	mg	75.000
Vitamins			**Amino acids**		
Vitamin C,			Tryptophan	g	0.207
ascorbic acid	mg	1.600	Threonine	g	0.767
Thiamin	mg	0.060	Isoleucine	g	0.924
Riboflavin	mg	0.120	Leucine	g	1.350
Niacin	mg	6.801	Lysine	g	1.509
Pantothenic acid	mg	0.910	Methionine	g	0.493
Vitamin B-6	mg	0.350	Cystine	g	0.249
Folate	mcg	6.000	Phenylalanine	g	0.721
Vitamin B-12	mcg	0.310	Tyrosine	g	0.597
Vitamin A, IU	IU	140.000	Valine	g	0.902
Vitamin A, RE	mcg_RE	41.000	Arginine	g	1.169
Vitamin E	mg_ATE	0.295	Histidine	g	0.544
Lipids			Alanine	g	1.089
Fatty acids, saturated	g	4.310	Aspartic acid	g	1.659
4:0	g	0.000	Glutamic acid	g	2.714
6:0	g	0.000	Glycine	g	1.223
8:0	g	0.000	Proline	g	0.911
10:0	g	0.000	Serine	g	0.657

USDA Nutrient Database for Standard Reference, Release 12 (March 1998)

APPENDIX 1-9

CHICKEN, BROILERS OR FRYERS, MEAT ONLY, RAW

Nutrient	Units	Value per 100 grams of edible portion	Nutrient	Units	Value per 100 grams of edible portion
Proximates			12:0	g	0.010
Water	g	75.460	14:0	g	0.020
Energy	kcal	119.000	16:0	g	0.530
Energy	kj	498.000	18:0	g	0.220
Protein	g	21.390	Fatty acids,		
Total lipid (fat)	g	3.080	monounsaturated	g	0.900
Carbohydrate,			16:1	g	0.120
by difference	g	0.000	18:1	g	0.760
Fiber, total dietary	g	0.000	20:1	g	0.010
Ash	g	0.960	22:1	g	0.000
			Fatty acids,		
Minerals			polyunsaturated	g	0.750
Calcium, Ca	mg	12.000	18:2	g	0.550
Iron, Fe	mg	0.890	18:3	g	0.020
Magnesium, Mg	mg	25.000	18:4	g	0.000
Phosphorus, P	mg	173.000	20:4	g	0.080
Potassium, K	mg	229.000	20:5	g	0.010
Sodium, Na	mg	77.000	22:5	g	0.020
Zinc, Zn	mg	1.540	22:6	g	0.030
Copper, Cu	mg	0.053	Cholesterol	mg	70.000
Manganese, Mn	mg	0.019			
			Amino acids		
Vitamins			Tryptophan	g	0.250
Vitamin C,			Threonine	g	0.904
ascorbic acid	mg	2.300	Isoleucine	g	1.130
Thiamin	mg	0.073	Leucine	g	1.605
Riboflavin	mg	0.142	Lysine	g	1.818
Niacin	mg	8.239	Methionine	g	0.592
Pantothenic acid	mg	1.058	Cystine	g	0.274
Vitamin B-6	mg	0.430	Phenylalanine	g	0.849
Folate	mcg	7.000	Tyrosine	g	0.722
Vitamin B-12	mcg	0.370	Valine	g	1.061
Vitamin A, IU	IU	52.000	Arginine	g	1.290
Vitamin A, RE	mcg_RE	16.000	Histidine	g	0.664
Vitamin E	mg_ATE	0.295	Alanine	g	1.167
			Aspartic acid	g	1.907
Lipids			Glutamic acid	g	3.204
Fatty acids, saturated	g	0.790	Glycine	g	1.051
4:0	g	0.000	Proline	g	0.880
6:0	g	0.000	Serine	g	0.736
8:0	g	0.000			
10:0	g	0.000			

USDA Nutrient Database for Standard Reference, Release 12 (March 1998)

APPENDIX 1-10

FINFISH, CATFISH, CHANNEL, WILD, RAW
Scientific name: Ictalurus punctatus (Rafinesque)

Nutrient	Units	Value per 100 grams of edible portion	Nutrient	Units	Value per 100 grams of edible portion
Proximates			12:0	g	0.000
EWater	g	80.360	14:0	g	0.060
Energy	kcal	95.000	16:0	g	0.440
Energy	kj	397.000	18:0	g	0.150
Protein	g	16.380	Fatty acids,		
Total lipid (fat)	g	2.820	monounsaturated	g	0.844
Carbohydrate,			16:1	g	0.176
by difference	g	0.000	18:1	g	0.594
Fiber, total dietary	g	0.000	20:1	g	0.021
Ash	g	0.960	22:1	g	0.008
			Fatty acids,		
Minerals			polyunsaturated	g	0.865
Calcium, Ca	mg	14.000	18:2	g	0.101
Iron, Fe	mg	0.300	18:3	g	0.071
Magnesium, Mg	mg	23.000	18:4	g	0.013
Phosphorus, P	mg	209.000	20:4	g	0.149
Potassium, K	mg	358.000	20:5	g	0.130
Sodium, Na	mg	43.000	22:5	g	0.100
Zinc, Zn	mg	0.510	22:6	g	0.234
Copper, Cu	mg	0.034	Cholesterol	mg	58.000
Manganese, Mn	mg	0.025			
Selenium, Se	mcg	12.600	**Amino acids**		
			Tryptophan	g	0.183
Vitamins			Threonine	g	0.718
Vitamin C,			Isoleucine	g	0.755
ascorbic acid	mg	0.700	Leucine	g	1.331
Thiamin	mg	0.210	Lysine	g	1.504
Riboflavin	mg	0.072	Methionine	g	0.485
Niacin	mg	1.907	Cystine	g	0.176
Pantothenic acid	mg	0.765	Phenylalanine	g	0.639
Vitamin B-6	mg	0.116	Tyrosine	g	0.553
Folate	mcg	10.000	Valine	g	0.844
Vitamin B-12	mcg	2.230	Arginine	g	0.980
Vitamin A, IU	IU	50.000	Histidine	g	0.482
Vitamin A, RE	mcg_RE	15.000	Alanine	g	0.991
Vitamin E	mg_ATE	0.600	Aspartic acid	g	1.677
			Glutamic acid	g	2.445
Lipids			Glycine	g	0.786
Fatty acids, saturated	g	0.722	Proline	g	0.579
4:0	g	0.000	Serine	g	0.668
6:0	g	0.000			
8:0	g	0.000			
10:0	g	0.000			

USDA Nutrient Database for Standard Reference, Release 12 (March 1998)

APPENDIX 1-11

FINFISH, HALIBUT, ATLANTIC AND PACIFIC, RAW
Scientific name: Hippoglossus hippoglossus (L.) and H. stenolepis Schmidt

Nutrient	Units	Value per 100 grams of edible portion	Nutrient	Units	Value per 100 grams of edible portion
Proximates			12:0	g	0.000
Water	g	77.920	14:0	g	0.056
Energy	kcal	110.000	16:0	g	0.212
Energy	kj	460.000	18:0	g	0.049
Protein	g	20.810	Fatty acids,		
Total lipid (fat)	g	2.290	monounsaturated	g	0.750
Carbohydrate,			16:1	g	0.163
by difference	g	0.000	18:1	g	0.361
Fiber, total dietary	g	0.000	20:1	g	0.124
Ash	g	1.360	22:1	g	0.102
			Fatty acids,		
Minerals			polyunsaturated	g	0.730
Calcium, Ca	mg	47.000	18:2	g	0.030
Iron, Fe	mg	0.840	18:3	g	0.065
Magnesium, Mg	mg	83.000	18:4	g	0.039
Phosphorus, P	mg	222.000	20:4	g	0.139
Potassium, K	mg	450.000	20:5	g	0.071
Sodium, Na	mg	54.000	22:5	g	0.094
Zinc, Zn	mg	0.420	22:6	g	0.292
Copper, Cu	mg	0.027	Cholesterol	mg	32.000
Manganese, Mn	mg	0.015			
Selenium, Se	mcg	36.500	**Amino acids**		
			Tryptophan	g	0.233
Vitamins			Threonine	g	0.912
Vitamin C,			Isoleucine	g	0.959
ascorbic acid	mg	0.000	Leucine	g	1.692
Thiamin	mg	0.060	Lysine	g	1.911
Riboflavin	mg	0.075	Methionine	g	0.616
Niacin	mg	5.848	Cystine	g	0.223
Pantothenic acid	mg	0.329	Phenylalanine	g	0.813
Vitamin B-6	mg	0.344	Tyrosine	g	0.703
Folate	mcg	12.000	Valine	g	1.072
Vitamin B-12	mcg	1.184	Arginine	g	1.245
Vitamin A, IU	IU	155.000	Histidine	g	0.613
Vitamin A, RE	mcg_RE	47.000	Alanine	g	1.259
Vitamin E	mg_ATE	0.850	Aspartic acid	g	2.131
			Glutamic acid	g	3.107
Lipids			Glycine	g	0.999
Fatty acids, saturated	g	0.325	Proline	g	0.736
4:0	g	0.000	Serine	g	0.849
6:0	g	0.000			
8:0	g	0.000			
10:0	g	0.000			

USDA Nutrient Database for Standard Reference, Release 12 (March 1998)

APPENDIX 1-12

FINFISH, SALMON, COHO, WILD, RAW
Scientific name: Oncorhynchus kisutch (Walbaum)

Nutrient	Units	Value per 100 grams of edible portion	Nutrient	Units	Value per 100 grams of edible portion
Proximates			12:0	g	0.000
Water	g	72.660	14:0	g	0.264
Energy	kcal	146.000	16:0	g	0.751
Energy	kj	611.000	18:0	g	0.207
Protein	g	21.620	Fatty acids,		
Total lipid (fat)	g	5.930	monounsaturated	g	2.134
Carbohydrate,			16:1	g	0.506
by difference	g	0.000	18:1	g	1.204
Fiber, total dietary	g	0.000	20:1	g	0.250
Ash	g	1.210	22:1	g	0.146
			Fatty acids,		
Minerals			polyunsaturated	g	1.992
Calcium, Ca	mg	36.000	18:2	g	0.206
Iron, Fe	mg	0.560	18:3	g	0.157
Magnesium, Mg	mg	31.000	18:4	g	0.119
Phosphorus, P	mg	262.000	20:4	g	0.133
Potassium, K	mg	423.000	20:5	g	0.429
Sodium, Na	mg	46.000	22:5	g	0.232
Zinc, Zn	mg	0.410	22:6	g	0.656
Copper, Cu	mg	0.051	Cholesterol	mg	45.000
Manganese, Mn	mg	0.014			
Selenium, Se	mcg	36.500	**Amino acids**		
			Tryptophan	g	0.242
Vitamins			Threonine	g	0.948
Vitamin C,			Isoleucine	g	0.996
ascorbic acid	mg	1.000	Leucine	g	1.757
Thiamin	mg	0.113	Lysine	g	1.985
Riboflavin	mg	0.140	Methionine	g	0.640
Niacin	mg	7.230	Cystine	g	0.232
Pantothenic acid	mg	0.823	Phenylalanine	g	0.844
Vitamin B-6	mg	0.549	Tyrosine	g	0.730
Folate	mcg	9.000	Valine	g	1.114
Vitamin B-12	mcg	4.170	Arginine	g	1.294
Vitamin A, IU	IU	100.000	Histidine	g	0.636
Vitamin A, RE	mcg_RE	30.000	Alanine	g	1.307
Vitamin E	mg_ATE	0.650	Aspartic acid	g	2.214
			Glutamic acid	g	3.227
Lipids			Glycine	g	1.038
Fatty acids, saturated	g	1.260	Proline	g	0.764
4:0	g	0.000	Serine	g	0.882
6:0	g	0.000			
8:0	g	0.000			
10:0	g	0.000			

USDA Nutrient Database for Standard Reference, Release 12 (March 1998)

APPENDIX 1-13

CRUSTACEANS, SHRIMP, MIXED SPECIES, RAW
Scientific name: Penaeidae and Pandalidae

Nutrient	Units	Value per 100 grams of edible portion	Nutrient	Units	Value per 100 grams of edible portion
Proximates			12:0	g	0.005
Water	g	75.860	14:0	g	0.021
Energy	kcal	106.00	16:0	g	0.184
Energy	kj	444.000	18:0	g	0.103
Protein	g	20.310	Fatty acids,		
Total lipid (fat)	g	1.730	monounsaturated	g	0.253
Carbohydrate,			16:1	g	0.083
by difference	g	0.910	18:1	g	0.147
Fiber, total dietary	g	0.000	20:1	g	0.017
Ash	g	1.200	22:1	g	0.005
			Fatty acids,		
Minerals			polyunsaturated	g	0.669
Calcium, Ca	mg	52.000	18:2	g	0.028
Iron, Fe	mg	2.410	18:3	g	0.014
Magnesium, Mg	mg	37.000	18:4	g	0.006
Phosphorus, P	mg	205.000	20:4	g	0.087
Potassium, K	mg	185.000	20:5	g	0.258
Sodium, Na	mg	148.000	22:5	g	0.046
Zinc, Zn	mg	1.110	22:6	g	0.222
Copper, Cu	mg	0.264	Cholesterol	mg	152.000
Manganese, Mn	mg	0.050			
Selenium, Se	mcg	38.000	**Amino acids**		
			Tryptophan	g	0.283
Vitamins			Threonine	g	0.822
Vitamin C,			Isoleucine	g	0.985
ascorbic acid	mg	2.000	Leucine	g	1.612
Thiamin	mg	0.028	Lysine	g	1.768
Riboflavin	mg	0.034	Methionine	g	0.572
Niacin	mg	2.552	Cystine	g	0.228
Pantothenic acid	mg	0.276	Phenylalanine	g	0.858
Vitamin B-6	mg	0.104	Tyrosine	g	0.676
Folate	mcg	3.000	Valine	g	0.956
Vitamin B-12	mcg	1.161	Arginine	g	1.775
Vitamin A, IU	IU	180.000	Histidine	g	0.413
Vitamin A, RE	mcg_RE	54.000	Alanine	g	1.151
Vitamin E	mg_ATE	0.820	Aspartic acid	g	2.100
			Glutamic acid	g	3.465
Lipids			Glycine	g	1.225
Fatty acids, saturated	g	0.328	Proline	g	0.670
4:0	g	0.000	Serine	g	0.800
6:0	g	0.000			
8:0	g	0.000			
10:0	g	0.009			

USDA Nutrient Database for Standard Reference, Release 12 (March 1998)

EGG, WHOLE, RAW, FRESH

Nutrient	Units	Value per 100 grams of edible portion	Nutrient	Units	Value per 100 grams of edible portion
Proximates			16:0	g	2.226
EWater	g	75.330	18:0	g	0.784
Energy	kcal	149.000	20:0	g	0.010
Energy	kj	623.000	22:0	g	0.012
Protein	g	12.490	15:0	g	0.004
Total lipid (fat)	g	10.020	17:0	g	0.017
Carbohydrate,			24:0	g	0.003
by difference	g	1.220	Fatty acids,		
Fiber, total dietary	g	0.000	monounsaturated	g	3.809
Ash	g	0.940	14:1	g	0.008
			16:1	g	0.298
Minerals			18:1	g	3.473
Calcium, Ca	mg	49.000	20:1	g	0.028
Iron, Fe	mg	1.440	22:1	g	0.003
Magnesium, Mg	mg	10.000	Fatty acids,		
Phosphorus, P	mg	178.000	polyunsaturated	g	1.364
Potassium, K	mg	121.000	18:2	g	1.148
Sodium, Na	mg	126.000	18:3	g	0.033
Zinc, Zn	mg	1.100	18:4	g	0.000
Copper, Cu	mg	0.014	20:4	g	0.142
Manganese, Mn	mg	0.024	20:5	g	0.004
Selenium, Se	mcg	30.800	22:5	g	0.000
			22:6	g	0.037
Vitamins			Cholesterol	mg	425.000
Vitamin C,					
ascorbic acid	mg	0.000	**Amino acids**		
Thiamin	mg	0.062	Tryptophan	g	0.152
Riboflavin	mg	0.508	Threonine	g	0.600
Niacin	mg	0.073	Isoleucine	g	0.682
Pantothenic acid	mg	1.255	Leucine	g	1.067
Vitamin B-6	mg	0.139	Lysine	g	0.897
Folate	mcg	47.000	Methionine	g	0.390
Vitamin B-12	mcg	1.000	Cystine	g	0.290
Vitamin A, IU	IU	635.000	Phenylalanine	g	0.664
Vitamin A, RE	mcg_RE	191.000	Tyrosine	g	0.510
Vitamin E	mg_ATE	1.050	Valine	g	0.761
			Arginine	g	0.749
Lipids			Histidine	g	0.296
Fatty acids, saturated	g	3.100	Alanine	g	0.696
4:0	g	0.000	Aspartic acid	g	1.255
6:0	g	0.000	Glutamic acid	g	1.633
8:0	g	0.003	Glycine	g	0.420
10:0	g	0.003	Proline	g	0.498
12:0	g	0.003	Serine	g	0.929
14:0	g	0.034			

USDA Nutrient Database for Standard Reference, Release 12 (March 1998)

100 grams of edible portion = 100 grams

1 cup (4.86 eggs) = 243.000 grams

1 jumbo egg = 65.000 grams

1 extra large = 58.000 grams

1 large = 50.000 grams

1 medium = 44.000 grams

1 small = 37.000 grams

APPENDIX 1-15

EGG, YOLK, RAW, FRESH

Nutrient	Units	Value per 100 grams of edible portion	Nutrient	Units	Value per 100 grams of edible portion
Proximates			16:0	g	6.860
Water	g	48.810	18:0	g	2.417
Energy	kcal	358.000	20:0	g	0.032
Energy	kj	1498.000	22:0	g	0.038
Protein	g	16.760	15:0	g	0.013
Total lipid (fat)	g	30.870	17:0	g	0.051
Carbohydrate,			24:0	g	0.009
by difference	g	1.780	Fatty acids,		
Fiber, total dietary	g	0.000	monounsaturated	g	11.739
Ash	g	1.770	14:1	g	0.024
			16:1	g	0.918
Minerals			18:1	g	10.701
Calcium, Ca	mg	137.000	20:1	g	0.086
Iron, Fe	mg	3.530	22:1	g	0.009
Magnesium, Mg	mg	9.000	Fatty acids,		
Phosphorus, P	mg	448.000	polyunsaturated	g	4.203
Potassium, K	mg	94.000	18:2	g	3.538
Sodium, Na	mg	43.000	18:3	g	0.103
Zinc, Zn	mg	3.110	18:4	g	0.000
Copper, Cu	mg	0.025	20:4	g	0.438
Manganese, Mn	mg	0.069	20:5	g	0.011
Selenium, Se	mcg	45.200	22:5	g	0.000
			22:6	g	0.114
Vitamins			Cholesterol	mg	1281.000
Vitamin C,					
ascorbic acid	mg	0.000	**Amino acids**		
Thiamin	mg	0.170	Tryptophan	g	0.196
Riboflavin	mg	0.639	Threonine	g	0.890
Niacin	mg	0.015	Isoleucine	g	0.848
Pantothenic acid	mg	3.807	Leucine	g	1.472
Vitamin B-6	mg	0.392	Lysine	g	1.330
Folate	mcg	146.000	Methionine	g	0.416
Vitamin B-12	mcg	3.110	Cystine	g	0.300
Vitamin A, IU	IU	1945.000	Phenylalanine	g	0.716
Vitamin A, RE	mcg_RE	584.000	Tyrosine	g	0.746
Vitamin E	mg_ATE	3.160	Valine	g	0.933
			Arginine	g	1.196
Lipids			Histidine	g	0.434
Fatty acids, saturated	g	9.552	Alanine	g	0.861
4:0	g	0.000	Aspartic acid	g	1.255
6:0	g	0.000	Glutamic acid	g	2.124
8:0	g	0.009	Glycine	g	0.518
10:0	g	0.009	Proline	g	0.700
12:0	g	0.009	Serine	g	1.432
14:0	g	0.104			

USDA Nutrient Database for Standard Reference, Release 12 (March 1998)
100 grams of edible portion = 100 grams
1 cup = 243.000 grams
1 large egg yolk = 16.600 grams

APPENDIX 1-16

MILK, FLUID, 3.25% MILKFAT

Nutrient	Units	Value per 100 grams of edible portion	Nutrient	Units	Value per 100 grams of edible portion
Proximates			12:0	g	0.094
Water	g	87.990	14:0	g	0.336
Energy	kcal	61.441	16:0	g	0.879
Energy	kj	257.000	18:0	g	0.405
Protein	g	3.290	Fatty acids,		
Total lipid (fat)	g	3.340	monounsaturated	g	0.965
Carbohydrate,			16:1	g	0.075
by difference	g	4.660	18:1	g	0.840
Fiber, total dietary	g	0.000	20:1	g	0.000
Ash	g	0.720	22:1	g	0.000
			Fatty acids,		
Minerals			polyunsaturated	g	0.124
Calcium, Ca	mg	119.400	18:2	g	0.075
Iron, Fe	mg	0.050	18:3	g	0.049
Magnesium, Mg	mg	13.440	18:4	g	0.000
Phosphorus, P	mg	93.400	20:4	g	0.000
Potassium, K	mg	151.500	20:5	g	0.000
Sodium, Na	mg	49.000	22:5	g	0.000
Zinc, Zn	mg	0.380	22:6	g	0.000
Copper, Cu	mg	0.010	Cholesterol	mg	13.600
Manganese, Mn	mg	0.004	Phytosterols	mg	0.000
Selenium, Se	mcg	2.000			
			Amino acids		
Vitamins			Tryptophan	g	0.046
Vitamin C,			Threonine	g	0.149
ascorbic acid	mg	0.940	Isoleucine	g	0.199
Thiamin	mg	0.038	Leucine	g	0.322
Riboflavin	mg	0.162	Lysine	g	0.261
Niacin	mg	0.084	Methionine	g	0.083
Pantothenic acid	mg	0.314	Cystine	g	0.030
Vitamin B-6	mg	0.042	Phenylalanine	g	0.159
Folate	mcg	5.000	Tyrosine	g	0.159
Vitamin B-12	mcg	0.357	Valine	g	0.220
Vitamin A, IU	IU	126.000	Arginine	g	0.119
Vitamin A, RE	mcg_RE	31.000	Histidine	g	0.089
Vitamin E	mg_ATE	0.100	Alanine	g	0.113
			Aspartic acid	g	0.250
Lipids			Glutamic acid	g	0.689
Fatty acids, saturated	g	2.079	Glycine	g	0.070
4:0	g	0.108	Proline	g	0.319
6:0	g	0.064	Serine	g	0.179
8:0	g	0.037			
10:0	g	0.084			

USDA Nutrient Database for Standard Reference, Release 12 (March 1998)

APPENDIX 1-17

MILK, NONFAT, FLUID, WITH ADDED VITAMIN A (FAT FREE OR SKIM)

Nutrient	Units	Value per 100 grams of edible portion	Nutrient	Units	Value per 100 grams of edible portion
Proximates			10:0	g	0.004
Water	g	90.800	12:0	g	0.003
Energy	kcal	34.912	14:0	g	0.017
Energy	kj	146.000	16:0	g	0.053
Protein	g	3.410	18:0	g	0.019
Total lipid (fat)	g	0.180	Fatty acids,		
Carbohydrate,			monounsaturated	g	0.047
by difference	g	4.850	16:1	g	0.007
Fiber, total dietary	g	0.000	18:1	g	0.038
Ash	g	0.760	20:1	g	0.000
			22:1	g	0.000
Minerals			Fatty acids,		
Calcium, Ca	mg	123.400	polyunsaturated	g	0.007
Iron, Fe	mg	0.040	18:2	g	0.005
Magnesium, Mg	mg	11.360	18:3	g	0.002
Phosphorus, P	mg	100.900	18:4	g	0.000
Potassium, K	mg	165.600	20:4	g	0.000
Sodium, Na	mg	51.500	20:5	g	0.000
Zinc, Zn	mg	0.400	22:5	g	0.000
Copper, Cu	mg	0.011	22:6	g	0.000
Manganese, Mn	mg	0.002	Cholesterol	mg	1.800
Selenium, Se	mcg	2.100			
			Amino acids		
Vitamins			Tryptophan	g	0.048
Vitamin C,			Threonine	g	0.154
ascorbic acid	mg	0.980	Isoleucine	g	0.206
Thiamin	mg	0.036	Leucine	g	0.334
Riboflavin	mg	0.140	Lysine	g	0.270
Niacin	mg	0.088	Methionine	g	0.086
Pantothenic acid	mg	0.329	Cystine	g	0.032
Vitamin B-6	mg	0.040	Phenylalanine	g	0.165
Folate	mcg	5.200	Tyrosine	g	0.165
Vitamin B-12	mcg	0.378	Valine	g	0.228
Vitamin A, IU	IU	204.000	Arginine	g	0.123
Vitamin A, RE	mcg_RE	61.000	Histidine	g	0.092
Vitamin E	mg_ATE	0.040	Alanine	g	0.118
			Aspartic acid	g	0.259
Lipids			Glutamic acid	g	0.714
Fatty acids, saturated	g	0.117	Glycine	g	0.072
4:0	g	0.009	Proline	g	0.330
6:0	g	0.001	Serine	g	0.185
8:0	g	0.002			

USDA Nutrient Database for Standard Reference, Release 12 (March 1998)

APPENDIX 2
CONVERSION TABLES

APPENDIX 2-1

Temperature Conversions

To convert a temperature, in either Celsius (Centigrade) or Fahrenheit, to the other scale, find that temperature in the center column, and then find the equivalent temperature in the other scale either in the Celsius column to the left or in the Fahrenheit column to the right. For example, if a given temperature is 40°F, the equivalent temperature on the Celsius scale will be 4.44°C, (shown in the lefthand column); if the given temperature is 40°C, the corresponding Fahrenheit reading will be 104°F (shown in the righthand column).

On the Celsius scale the temperature of melting ice is 0° and that of boiling water is 100° at normal atmospheric pressure. On the Fahrenheit scale, the equivalent temperatures are 32° and 212° respectively. The formula for converting Fahrenheit to Celsius is $C = 5/9(F - 32)$, and the formula for converting Celsius to Fahrenheit is $F = (9/5C) + 32$.

TEMPERATURE CONVERSIONS

C	F or C reading	F	C	F or C reading	F
−73.33	−100	−148.0	−13.3	8	46.4
−70.56	−95	−139.0	−12.8	9	48.2
−67.78	−90	−130.0	−12.2	10	50.0
−65.00	−85	−121.0	−11.7	11	51.8
−62.22	−80	−112.0	−11.1	12	53.6
−59.45	−75	−103.0	−10.6	13	55.4
−56.67	−70	−94.0	−10.0	14	57.2
−53.89	−65	−85.0	−9.44	15	59.0
−51.11	−60	−76.0	−8.89	16	60.8
−48.34	−55	−67.0	−8.33	17	62.6
−45.56	−50	−58.0	−7.78	18	64.4
−42.78	−45	−49.0	−7.22	19	66.2
−40.0	−40	−40.0	−6.67	20	68.0
−37.23	−35	−31.0	−6.11	21	69.8
−34.44	−30	−22.0	−5.56	22	71.6
−31.67	−25	−13.0	−5.00	23	73.4
−28.89	−20	−4.0	−4.44	24	75.2
−26.12	−15	5.0	−3.89	25	77.0
−23.33	−10	14.0	−3.33	26	78.8
−20.56	−5	23.0	−2.78	27	80.6
−17.8	0	32.0	−2.22	28	82.4
−17.2	1	33.8	−1.67	29	84.2
−16.7	2	35.6	−1.11	30	86.0
−16.1	3	37.4	−0.56	31	87.8
−15.6	4	39.2	0	32	89.6
−15.0	5	41.0	0.56	33	91.4
−14.4	6	42.8	1.11	34	93.2
−13.9	7	44.6	1.67	35	95.0

(continues)

C	F or C reading	F	C	F or C reading	F
2.22	36	96.8	31.7	89	192.2
2.78	37	98.6	32.2	90	194.0
3.33	38	100.4	32.8	91	195.8
3.89	39	102.2	33.3	92	197.6
4.44	40	104.0	33.9	93	199.4
5.00	41	105.8	34.4	94	201.2
5.56	42	107.6	35.0	95	203.0
6.11	43	109.4	35.6	96	204.8
6.67	44	111.2	36.1	97	206.6
7.22	45	113.0	36.7	98	208.4
7.78	46	114.8	37.2	99	210.2
8.33	47	116.6	37.8	100	212.0
8.89	48	118.4	43	110	230
9.44	49	120.2	49	120	248
10.0	50	122.0	54	130	266
10.6	51	123.8	60	140	284
11.1	52	125.6	66	150	302
11.7	53	127.4	71	160	320
12.2	54	129.2	77	170	338
12.8	55	131.0	82	180	356
13.3	56	132.8	88	190	374
13.9	57	134.6	93	200	392
14.4	58	136.4	99	210	410
15.0	59	138.2	100	212	414
15.6	60	140.0	104	220	428
16.1	61	141.8	110	230	446
16.7	62	143.6	116	240	464
17.2	63	145.4	121	250	482
17.8	64	147.2	127	260	500
18.3	65	149.0	132	270	518
18.9	66	150.8	138	280	536
19.4	67	152.6	143	290	554
20.0	68	154.4	149	300	572
20.6	69	156.2	154	310	590
21.1	70	158.0	160	320	608
21.7	71	159.8	166	330	626
22.2	72	161.6	171	340	644
22.8	73	163.4	177	350	662
23.3	74	165.2	182	360	680
23.9	75	167.0	188	370	698
24.4	76	168.8	193	380	716
25.0	77	170.6	199	390	734
25.6	78	172.4	204	400	752
26.1	79	174.2	210	410	770
26.7	80	176.0	216	420	788
27.2	81	177.7	221	430	806
27.8	82	179.6	227	440	824
28.3	83	181.4	232	450	842
28.9	84	183.2	238	460	860
29.4	85	185.0	243	470	878
30.0	86	186.8	249	480	896
30.6	87	188.6	254	490	914
31.1	88	190.4	260	500	932

APPENDIX 2-2

ABBREVIATIONS FOR UNITS OF MEASURE

Units of area and volume		*Units of length*	
liter	L	centimeter	cm
microliter	μL	meter	m
milliliter	mL	micrometer	μm
square centimeter	cm^2	millimeter	mm
square millimeter	mm^2	nanometer	nm
Units of concentration		*Units of mass*	
millimolar (millimoles/liter)	mmol/L	gram	g
micromolar (micromoles/liter)	μmol/L	kilogram	kg
molar (moles/liter)	mol/L	microgram	μg
		milligram	mg

APPENDIX 2-3

WEIGHT-UNIT CONVERSION FACTORS

Units Given	Units Wanted	For Conversion Multiply By
lb	g	453.6
lb	kg	0.4536
oz	g	28.35
kg	lb	2.2046
kg	mg	1,000,000.0
kg	g	1,000.0
g	mg	1,000.0
g	μg	1,000,000.0
mg	μg	1,000.0
mg/g	mg/lb	453.6
mg/kg	mg/lb	0.4536
μg/kg	μg/lb	0.4536
Mcal	kcal	1,000.0
kcal/kg	kcal/lb	0.4536
kcal/lb	kcal/kg	2.2046
ppm	μg/g	1.0
ppm	mg/kg	1.0
ppm	mg/lb	0.4536
mg/kg	%	0.0001
ppm	%	0.0001
mg/g	%	0.1
g/kg	%	0.1

APPENDIX 2-4

AREA CONVERSIONS

Metric

1 square centimeter	=	0.155 sq inch
	=	100 sq millimeters
1 square meter	=	1,550 sq inches
	=	10,764 sq feet
	=	1,196 sq yards
	=	10,000 sq centimeters
1 square kilometer	=	0.3861 sq mile
	=	1,000 sq meters
1 hectare	=	2.471 acres
	=	10,000 sq meters

Imperial

1 square inch	=	6.452 sq centimeters
	=	1/144 sq foot
	=	1/1296 sq yard
1 square foot	=	929.088 sq centimeters
	=	0.0929 sq meter
1 square yard	=	8,361.3 sq centimeters
	=	0.8361 sq meter
	=	1,296 sq inches
	=	9 sq feet
1 square mile	=	2.59 sq kilometers
	=	640 acres
1 acre	=	0.4047 hectare
	=	43,560 sq feet
	=	4,840 sq yards
	=	4,046.87 sq meters
1 kilometer	=	3,281 feet
	=	1,094 yards
	=	0.621 mile
	=	1,000 meters

Imperial

1 inch	=	25.4 millimeters
	=	2.54 centimeters
1 foot	=	30.48 centimeters
	=	0.3048 meter
	=	12 inches
1 yard	=	0.9144 meter
	=	91.44 meter
	=	3 feet
1 mile	=	1,609,347 meters
	=	1,609 kilometers
	=	5,280 feet
	=	1,760 yards

APPENDIX 2-5

VOLUME CONVERSIONS

Metric

1 milliliter	=	1 cubic centimeter (cc)
1 liter	=	1.057 U.S. quarts liquid
	=	0.9081 quart, dry
	=	0.2642 U.S. gallon
	=	0.221 Imperial gallon
	=	1,000 milliliters or cc
	=	0.0353 cubic foot
	=	61.02 cubic inches
	=	0.001 cubic meter
1 cubic meter	=	61,023.38 cubic inches
	=	35,314 cubic feet
	=	1,308 cubic yards
	=	264.17 U.S. gallons
	=	1,000 liters
	=	28.38 U.S. bushels
	=	1,000,000 cu. centimeters
	=	1,000,000,000 cu. millimeters

Imperial

1 fluid ounce	=	1/128 gallon
	=	29.57 cubic centimeters
	=	29.562 milliliters
	=	1.805 cubic inches
	=	0.0625 U.S. pint (liquid)
1 U.S. quart liquid	=	946.3 milliliters
	=	57.75 cubic inches
	=	32 fluid ounces
	=	4 cups
	=	1/4 gallon
	=	2 U.S. pints (liquid)
	=	0.946 liter
1 quart dry	=	1.1012 liters
	=	67.20 cubic inches
	=	2 pints (dry)
	=	0.125 peck
	=	1/32 bushel
1 cubic inch	=	16.387 cubic centimeters
1 cubic foot	=	28,317 cubic centimeters
	=	0.0283 cubic meter
	=	28.316 liters
	=	7.481 U.S. gallons
	=	1,728 cubic inches
1 U.S. gallon	=	16 cups
	=	3.785 liters
	=	231 cubic inches
	=	4 U.S. quarts liquid
	=	8 U.S. pints liquid
	=	8.3453 pounds of water
	=	128 fluid ounces
	=	0.8327 British Imperial gallon

(continues)

VOLUME CONVERSIONS *(continued)*

1 British Imperial gallon	=	4.546	liters
	=	1.201	U.S. gallons
	=	277.42	cubic inches
1 U.S. bushel	=	35.24	liters
	=	2,150.42	cubic inches
	=	1.2444	cubic feet
	=	0.03524	cubic meter
	=	2	pecks
	=	32	quarts (dry)
	=	64	pints (dry)

APPENDIX 2-6

ENERGY CONVERSIONS*

Calorie		Joule
1	=	4.184
1000	=	4184 Joules
1 Calorie	=	4184 Joules
1 kilocalorie	=	4184 Joules
0.239	=	1

*Definition of calorie: The quantity of heat required to raise the temperature of one gram of water by 1 degree Celsius from a standard initial temperature, usually from 4 degrees to 5 degrees Celsius, at 1 atmosphere pressure (sea level).

APPENDIX 2-7

YIELD CONVERSIONS

Metric

1 kilogram per hectare	=	0.89 pound per acre
1 cubic meter per hectare	=	14.2916 cubic feet per acre

Imperial

1 pound per acre	=	1.121 kilograms per hectare
1 ton (2,000 lb) per acre	=	2,242 metric tons per hectare
1 cubic foot per acre	=	0.0699 cubic meter per hectare
1 bushel (60 lb) per acre	=	67.26 kilograms per hectare

NATIONAL RESEARCH COUNCIL PUBLICATIONS ON NUTRIENT REQUIREMENTS OF DOMESTIC ANIMALS AND OTHER ASPECTS OF ANIMAL NUTRITION*

Nutrient Requirements of Beef Cattle, seventh revised edition, 1996
Nutrient Requirements of Dairy Cattle, sixth revised edition, 1989
Nutrient Requirements of Goats; Angora, Dairy, and Meat Goats in Temperate and Tropical Countries, 1981
Nutrient Requirements of Laboratory Animals, fourth revised edition, 1995
Nutrient Requirements of Mink and Foxes, second revised edition, 1982
Nutrient Requirements of Rabbits, revised edition, 1985
Nutrient Requirements of Swine, tenth revised edition, 1998
Nutrient Requirements of Cats, revised edition, 1986
Nutrient Requirements of Dogs, revised edition, 1985
Nutrient Requirements of Horses, fifth revised edition, 1989
Nutrient Requirements of Nonhuman Primates, 1978
Nutrient Requirements of Sheep, sixth revised edition, 1985
Nutrient Requirements of Poultry, ninth revised edition, 1994
Nutrient Requirements of Warm Water Fishes, 1977
Nutrient Requirements of Cold Water Fishes, 1981
Nutrient Requirements of Fish, 1993
Nutritional Energetics of Domestic Animals and Glossary of Energy Terms, 1981
Building a North American Feed Information System, 1995
Predicting Food Intake of Food-Producing Animals, 1987
Mineral Tolerance of Domestic Animals, 1980
Vitamin Tolerance of Animals, 1987
Plant and Animal Products in the U.S. Food System, 1978
Rangeland Health; New Methods to Classify, Inventory, and Monitor Rangelands, 1994
Selenium in Nutrition, revised edition, 1983
Designing Foods: Animal Product Options in the Marketplace, 1988
Metabolic Modifiers: Effects on the Nutrient Requirements of Food-Producing Animals, 1994

*Available from the National Academy Press, 2101 Constitution Avenue NW, Washington, DC 20418

RECENT PUBLICATIONS OF THE BOARD ON AGRICULTURE

Policy and Resources

Forested Landscapes in Perspective: Prospects and Opportunities for Sustainable Management of America's Nonfederal Forests (1997), 264 pp., ISBN 0-309-05641-1

Precision Agriculture in the 21st Century: Geospatial and Information Technologies in Crop Management (1997), 149 pp., ISBN 0-309-05893-7

Wood in Our Future: The Role of Life-Cycle Analysis, (1997) 147 pp., ISBN 0-309-5745-0

Colleges of Agriculture at the Land Grant Universities Public Service and Public Policy, (1996) 120 pp., ISBN 0-309-05433-8

Ecologically Based Pest Management: New Solutions for a New Century (1996), 152 pp., ISBN 0-309-05330-7

Colleges of Agriculture at the Land Grant Universities: A Profile (1995), 146 pp., ISBN 0-309-05295-5

Investing in the National Research Initiative: An Update of the Competitive Grants Program in the U.S. Department of Agriculture (1994), 66 pp., ISBN 0-309-05235-1

Rangeland Health: New Methods to Classify, Inventory, and Monitor Rangelands (1994), 180 pp., ISBN 0-309-04879-6

Soil and Water Quality: An Agenda for Agriculture (1993), 516 pp., ISBN 0-309-04933-4

Managing Global Genetic Resources: Agricultural Crop Issues and Policies (1993), 450 pp., ISBN 0-309-04430-8

Pesticides in the Diets of Infants and Children (1993), 408 pp., ISBN 0-309-04875-3

Managing Global Genetic Resources: Livestock (1993), 294 pp., ISBN 0-309-04394-8

Sustainable Agriculture and the Environment in the Humid Tropics (1993), 720 pp., ISBN 0-309-04749-8

Agriculture and the Undergraduate: Proceedings (1992), 296 pp., ISBN 0-309-04682-3

Water Transfers in the West: Efficiency, Equity, and the Environment (1992), 320 pp., ISBN 0-309-04528-2

Managing Global Genetic Resources: Forest Trees (1991), 244 pp., ISBN 0-309-04034-5

Managing Global Genetic Resources: The U.S. National Plant Germplasm System (1991), 198 pp., ISBN 0-309-04390-5

Sustainable Agriculture Research and Education in the Field: A Proceedings (1991), 448 pp., ISBN 0-309-04578-9

Toward Sustainability: A Plan for Collaborative Research on Agriculture and Natural Resource Management (1991), 164 pp., ISBN 0-309-04540-1

Investing in Research: A Proposal to Strengthen the Agricultural, Food, and Environmental System (1989), 156 pp., ISBN 0-309-04127-9

Alternative Agriculture (1989), 464 pp., ISBN 0-309-03985-1

Understanding Agriculture: New Directions for Education (1988), 80 pp., ISBN 0-309-03936-3

Designing Foods: Animal Product Options in the Marketplace (1988), 394 pp., ISBN 0-309-03798-0; ISBN 0-309-03795-6 (pbk)

Agricultural Biotechnology: Strategies for National Competitiveness (1987), 224 pp., ISBN 0-309-03745-X

Regulating Pesticides in Food: The Delaney Paradox (1987), 288 pp., ISBN 0-309-03746-8

Pesticide Resistance: Strategies and Tactics for Management (1986), 480 pp., ISBN 0-309-03627-5

Pesticides and Groundwater Quality: Issues and Problems in Four States (1986), 136 pp., ISBN 0-309-03676-3

Soil Conservation: Assessing the National Resources Inventory, Volume 1 (1986), 134 pp., ISBN 0-309-03649-9; Volume 2 (1986), 314 pp., ISBN 0-309-03675-5

New Directions for Biosciences Research in Agriculture: High-Reward Opportunities (1985), 122 pp., ISBN 0-309-03542-2

Genetic Engineering of Plants: Agricultural Opportunities and Policy Concerns (1984), 96 pp., ISBN 0-309-03434-5

---

*Available from the National Academy Press, 2101 Constitution Avenue NW, Washington, DC 20418

INDEX

This index is arranged alphabetically by individual chapter subject matter and, in turn, within each chapter. The use of cross-referencing is thereby minimized.